D1247873

Multicomponent
Distillation

PRENTICE-HALL INTERNATIONAL SERIES
IN THE PHYSICAL AND CHEMICAL ENGINEERING SCIENCES

NEAL R. AMUNDSON, EDITOR, *University of Minnesota*

ADVISORY EDITORS

ANDREAS ACRIVOS, *University of California*
MICHEL BOUDART, *University of California*
THOMAS J. HANRATTY, *University of Illinois*
DAVID E. LAMB, *University of Delaware*
JOHN M. PRAUSNITZ, *University of California*
L. E. SCRIVEN, *University of Minnesota*

ARIS   *Vectors, Tensors, and the Basic Equations of Fluid Mechanics*
HOLLAND   *Multicomponent Distillation*
LEVICH   *Physicochemical Hydrodynamics*
LYKOV AND MIKHAYLOV   *Theory of Energy and Mass Transfer*

PRENTICE-HALL, INC.

PRENTICE-HALL INTERNATIONAL, INC., UNITED KINGDOM AND EIRE

PRENTICE-HALL OF CANADA, LTD., CANADA

Multicomponent Distillation

CHARLES D. HOLLAND

Department of Chemical Engineering
Agricultural and Mechanical College of Texas

PRENTICE-HALL, INC.

Englewood Cliffs, New Jersey

1963

PRENTICE-HALL INTERNATIONAL, INC., *London*

PRENTICE-HALL OF AUSTRALIA, PTY., LTD., *Sydney*

PRENTICE-HALL OF CANADA, LTD., *Toronto*

PRENTICE-HALL FRANCE, S.A.R.L., *Paris*

PRENTICE-HALL OF JAPAN, INC., *Tokyo*

PRENTICE-HALL DE MEXICO, S.A., *Mexico City*

© 1963 by
PRENTICE-HALL, INC.
Englewood Cliffs, New Jersey

All rights reserved. No part of this book may be reproduced,
by mimeograph or any other means, without permission in
writing from the publisher.

Much of the material upon which this book is based was
originally presented in *Hydrocarbon Processing & Petroleum
Refiner* and is copyrighted by Gulf Publishing Co., Houston,
Texas.

Library of Congress Catalog Card No. 63-10673
Printed in the United States of America
60476–*C*

To My Wife

Preface

This book is the first of its kind to present several numerical methods for obtaining the steady state solutions of multicomponent distillation problems. In the last decade the availability of high speed computers has changed the approach to solving problems of this type. Instead of seeking exact analytical solutions for models that roughly approximate the actual system, researchers have put a vast amount of effort into the development of iterative procedures in which progressively better initial values of the independent variables are selected for each successive trial. That part of the iterative procedure concerned with the selection of successively improved sets of independent variables is called the "convergence method."

Major emphasis is placed on the convergence method and on the equations that describe the operation of various units rather than on general ideas and philosophies, such as the selection of the particular type of distillation unit to be employed for a given separation. The formulation and testing of convergence methods offer the researcher moments of both exaltation and despair. To the statement of a convergence method "on paper," the normal reaction of the casual observer is "How can it fail?" Many times the first application will give a beautiful demonstration of the answer to this question.

The proposed calculational procedures and the convergence method are based on the solution of a wide variety of problems. The "θ-method" of convergence is used exclusively in Chapters 7 through 15 because no other single method has been extended to include all of these applications.

Other convergence methods, as well as the fundamental concepts of multicomponent distillation, are presented in the first five chapters. In each of the subsequent twelve chapters, a special application is presented, such as complex column, total reflux, minimum reflux, systems of columns with recycle, and the use and determination of plate efficiencies. All of these applications are treated by the same general method, a combination of the Thiele and Geddes calculational procedure and the θ-method of convergence.

The last two Chapters, 16 and 17, are concerned with the correlation of the physical properties of multicomponent mixtures. The thermodynamic principles involved are given in Chapter 16, and the applications of the principles are presented in Chapter 17.

The use of a single approach for the treatment of this wide variety of units and operating conditions represents a unification greatly needed in this field. Certain other contributions to the theory of distillation are presented.

When this book is used as a text, the author recommends that the first seven chapters be covered in the order given. Except where two chapters deal with the same subject, the remaining chapters are independent of one another and may be covered in any order desired without loss of continuity.

The author is deeply indebted to the many co-workers who participated in the development of the calculational procedures presented here. The tenacity and determination demonstrated by graduate students throughout the development of the various extensions of the θ-method of convergence is appreciated. The encouragement, suggestions, and assistance given by Mr. W. M. Harp, Dr. K. K. McMillin, Mr. G. W. Wilson, Mr. W. N. Lyster, and Mr. H. L. Bauni (all of the Humble Oil and Refining Company) promoted the rapid development of the θ-method. Also, the contributions of Mr. R. H. Johnston, Dr. Ralph Cecchetti, Mr. J. T. Kurzeja, and Mr. Joe Niedzwicki (all of the Esso Research and Engineering Company) made possible the successful extension of the θ-method of convergence to the wide variety of units. The valuable advice, encouragement, and assistance given by Dr. J. D. Lindsay made these investigations possible. The projects upon which this book is based received financial support from the Humble Oil and Refining Company, the Esso Research and Engineering Company, and the National Science Foundation. The author is grateful for the assistance given by Mr. R. L. Smith and other members of the Data Processing Center of the A. and M. College of Texas. Helpful suggestions made by other members of the faculty are appreciated—in particular those offered by Professors R. R. Davison, L. D. Durbin, P. T. Eubank, J. K. Gladden, E. C. Klipple, and B. C. Moore. Finally, the author wishes to express his appreciation to *Hydrocarbon Processing & Petroleum Refiner* (formerly published as *Petroleum Refiner*) for publishing many of the articles upon which this book is based.

C.D.H.

Table of Contents

*Multicomponent
Distillation*

Fundamental Concepts Involved in Multicomponent Distillation Calculations

1

The advent of high speed computers has caused a re-examination of the rigorous methods for making multicomponent distillation calculations. Instead of approximate solutions based on a variety of simplifying assumptions, solutions well within the accuracy of the data may be obtained by use of computers. Some of the procedures presently in use for effecting these solutions are presented in this book. These procedures each consists of a prescribed way for making successive approximations until a set of values is found for the variables that satisfy simultaneously all of the equations describing the system.

Common to all of these procedures are certain fundamentals. Each of the procedures presented is concerned with finding the steady state solution. For this case the law of conservation of mass gives

$$\text{Input} - \text{Output} = 0 \tag{1-1}$$

This law is the basis for the material balances used to describe the various distillation systems. Also used in the description of multicomponent systems is the first law of thermodynamics,

$$\Delta H + \Delta \text{K.E.} + \Delta \text{P.E.} = Q - W_s \tag{1-2}$$

Usually the kinetic and potential energy changes as well as the shaft-work may be neglected to give

$$\Delta H = Q \tag{1-3}$$

This equation is the basis for the enthalpy balances used to describe distillation systems. In addition to the law of conservation of mass and the

1

first law of thermodynamics, the condition of physical equilibrium is involved in the description of distillation systems. Henry's law

$$y_i = K_i x_i \qquad (1\text{-}4)$$

may be used to express the condition of equilibrium for component i. Although K is a function of pressure, temperature, and $(c - 1)$ compositions, the effect of composition is neglected in the statement of most of the calculational procedures.

Use of the fundamental concepts represented by Equations (1–1), (1–2), and (1–4) permits the complete description of a system in which a multicomponent distillation is being performed. Unfortunately, the non-linear form of the resulting equations appears to eliminate the possibility of obtaining a general analytical solution. When certain simplifying assumptions are made, analytical solutions may be obtained as shown by several investigators (1, 2, 5).

TRIAL AND ERROR PROCEDURES

Since the equations which describe distillation systems can not be solved explicitly for the unknowns, numerous trial and error procedures have been developed. The procedures have as their objective the selection of a set of values for all of the unknowns that satisfy all of the equations simultaneously. Seldom is the correct set selected for the first trial. After a set of values has been picked and the first trial has been completed and the results have been examined, a better set can generally be selected for making the second trial. In carrying out such a series of calculations manually, the value of each variable for each trial may be selected by a completely unrelated and different type of logic from that employed in any previous trial. Furthermore, the logic to be employed need not be stated in advance and may be changed throughout the course of the solution of the problem. However, in order to perform calculations on a digital computer in an efficient manner, all of the logic to be employed in the solution of a problem must be stated in advance. In general, this rules out the origination of logic during the course of the solution of a problem. Descriptions of some well-known procedures for solving trial and error problems follow.

1. Direct-iteration

In the literature, this procedure is commonly referred to by the name of "iteration." However, since the "number of iterations" and the "number of trials" are frequently used synonymously, the term "direct-iteration" was selected in order to identify the following procedure for making trial calculations. Anyone who has solved a trial and error problem has no doubt employed direct-iteration because it appears to be the natural procedure. However, it does not always converge to the solution. This defect may have gone unnoticed by many who have employed this procedure because, when it gave what appeared to be a poor set of values for the variables for

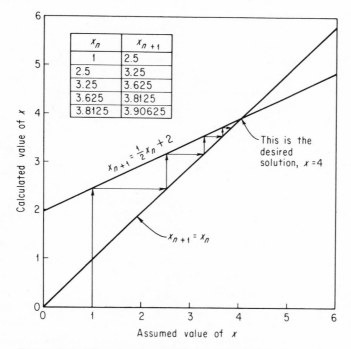

x_n	x_{n+1}
1	2.5
2.5	3.25
3.25	3.625
3.625	3.8125
3.8125	3.90625

Figure 1–1. When the slope of the function is less than unity, the method of direct-iteration converges to the desired solution.

the next trial, it was abandoned and a better set of values was selected by use of some other logic. The properties of the method of direct-iteration are best illustrated by numerical examples. First, suppose it be desired to find the value of x which satisfies the following equation

$$x - \tfrac{1}{2}x - 2 = 0 \qquad (1\text{–}5)$$

Although the answer, $x = 4$, is readily obtained by inspection, it is informative to solve this problem by the method of direct-iteration. Equation (1–5) may be rearranged to the following form.

$$x_{n+1} = \tfrac{1}{2}x_n + 2 \qquad (1\text{–}6)$$

The subscript *"n"* denotes the number of the trial. For the nth trial the assumed value for x (the independent variable) is denoted by x_n and the calculated value of x (the dependent variable) by x_{n+1}. Thus the problem is to find that assumed value of x such that the value of x calculated by Equation (1–6) is equal to it. In the method of direct-iteration the first assumed value for x is selected arbitrarily. Corresponding to the assumed

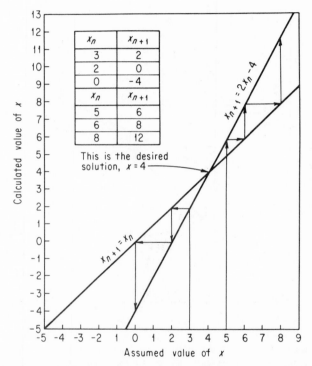

Figure 1–2. When the slope of the function is greater than unity, the method of direct-iteration fails to give the solution.

value for x, the calculated value is obtained by Equation (1–6). In the second trial the assumed value of x is taken equal to the value calculated by the first trial. Continuation of the procedure leads to the correct value of x for some problems. The results obtained by starting with an assumed value of x equal to unity are shown in Figure 1–1. Observe that the slope of the line x_{n+1} versus x_n is less than unity and that the procedure of direct-iteration does converge to the solution $x = 4$.

The fact that convergence was obtained when the x in Equation (1–5) with the coefficient of unity was taken as the dependent variable can not be taken to mean that convergence will be obtained when the other x appearing in Equation (1–5) is selected as the dependent variable. That is, suppose Equation (1–5) to be rearranged to the following form.

$$x_{n+1} = 2x_n - 4 \tag{1–7}$$

As shown in Figure 1–2, when the procedure of direct-iteration is initiated by use of any assumed value of x less than 4, the calculated values of x are progressively further away from the desired solution. Similarly, when calculations are initiated by use of a value of x greater than 4, the calculated values of x are again progressively further away from the solution, $x = 4$. Direct-iteration fails to give the desired solution because the slope of the function is greater than unity at and in the neighborhood of the desired solution.

When the slope is a function of the assumed value of x, the procedure of direct-iteration may or may not lead to a solution depending upon the initial choice for the assumed value of x. This fact is illustrated by the following example. Suppose it be desired to find the roots of the following equation,

$$x^2 - 4x - 4 = 0 \tag{1–8}$$

By use of the familiar quadratic formula, the roots, $x = (2 + 2\sqrt{2})$ and $x = (2 - 2\sqrt{2})$, are readily found. If the x with the coefficient of (-4) is taken to be the dependent variable, Equation (1–8) may be written as follows:

$$x_{n+1} = \tfrac{1}{4}x_n^2 - 1 \tag{1–9}$$

For any initial value of x less than $(2 + 2\sqrt{2})$, the method of direct-iteration converges to the root $x = (2 - 2\sqrt{2})$, as shown in Figure 1–3. For any initial value of x greater than $(2 + 2\sqrt{2})$, direct-iteration fails to give the other root. In the remainder of the argument, the right-hand side of an equation such as Equation (1–9) is represented by the functional notation $f(x)$. Then Equation (1–9) can be stated as

$$x = f(x) \tag{1–10}$$

where it is understood that

$$f(x) = \tfrac{1}{4}x^2 - 1$$

An examination of the results obtained for all of the functions considered shows that a sufficient condition for the method of direct-iteration to converge to the solution is that

$$\left| \frac{df(x)}{dx} \right| < 1 \tag{1–11}$$

at and in the neighborhood of the desired solution. This is not a necessary condition because there is the chance that the correct value of x will be selected as the assumed value of x for the first trial. Also, convergence may be obtained in some instances where the initial value selected for x is such that the absolute value of the slope of the function is equal to or greater

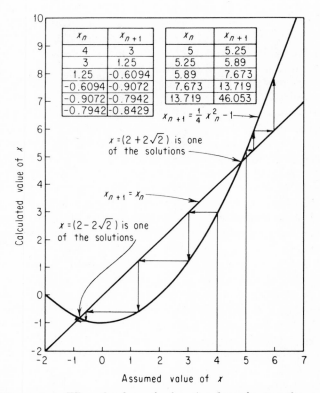

x_n	x_{n+1}
4	3
3	1.25
1.25	-0.6094
-0.6094	-0.9072
-0.9072	-0.7942
-0.7942	-0.8429

x_n	x_{n+1}
5	5.25
5.25	5.89
5.89	7.673
7.673	13.719
13.719	46.053

$x_{n+1} = \frac{1}{4} x_n^2 - 1$

$x = (2 + 2\sqrt{2})$ is one of the solutions

$x_{n+1} = x_n$

$x = (2 - 2\sqrt{2})$ is one of the solutions

Calculated value of x

Assumed value of x

Figure 1-3. When the slope of a function depends upon the assumed value of x, the success or failure of the method of direct-iteration also depends upon the initial value assumed for x.

than unity, such as in the initial choice of $x = 4$ as shown in Figure 1-3. For a system of three independent equations containing the three variables x, y, and z and of the forms

$$x = f_1(x, y, z)$$

$$y = f_2(x, y, z) \tag{1-12}$$

$$z = f_3(x, y, z)$$

a sufficient condition for the method of direct-iteration to converge is that

$$\left| \frac{\partial f_1}{\partial x} \right| + \left| \frac{\partial f_2}{\partial x} \right| + \left| \frac{\partial f_3}{\partial x} \right| < 1$$

$$\left| \frac{\partial f_1}{\partial y} \right| + \left| \frac{\partial f_2}{\partial y} \right| + \left| \frac{\partial f_3}{\partial y} \right| < 1 \tag{1-13}$$

$$\left| \frac{\partial f_1}{\partial z} \right| + \left| \frac{\partial f_2}{\partial z} \right| + \left| \frac{\partial f_3}{\partial z} \right| < 1$$

at and in the neighborhood of the desired solution. This criterion for convergence of the method of direct-iteration has been stated by Nielsen (3). He also points out that unless the sum of these derivatives is in each case substantially less than 1, convergence is very slow.

The method of direct-iteration, as such, is seldom used because for many problems it converges too slowly. After a calculated value has been obtained, a better value than this one for the next assumed value of the variable may be selected by any one of several schemes referred to as convergence methods. However, the complete calculational procedure which includes the convergence method may be regarded as direct-iteration. The criterion for convergence may be applied to the complete calculational procedure.

Unfortunately, for many problems, applying the criterion for convergence is almost as difficult as solving the problem analytically. The usual approach is to check a proposed convergence method by the solution of a wide variety of numerical examples. Although direct-iteration is seldom used throughout a complete problem, it is usually involved in many steps of a complex problem. Hence, the importance of the selection of the best set of dependent variables is not to be minimized.

The properties of direct-iteration that have been demonstrated serve as valuable background information needed for the proper interpretation of the numerical results obtained for complex problems.

2. Newton's method

One systematic procedure for solving a trial and error problem is the method proposed by Newton. Suppose it be desired to find the value of x such that $f(x) = 0$. Newton's method consists of the repeated use of the first two terms of the Taylor series expansion of $f(x)$ about some value of x, say x_n, as follows:

$$f(x) = f(x_n) + f'(x_n)(x - x_n) \tag{1-14}$$

Since only the first two terms of the expansion are used, this is in general an approximation of the function $f(x)$. Now let $x = x_{n+1}$, the value of x that makes $f(x) = 0$. Then Equation (1–14) reduces to

$$x_{n+1} = x_n - \frac{f(x_n)}{f'(x_n)} \tag{1–15}$$

Graphically, Newton's method may be regarded as the linear extension of the function from the point $(x_n, f(x_n))$ to the point $(x_{n+1}, 0)$, as shown

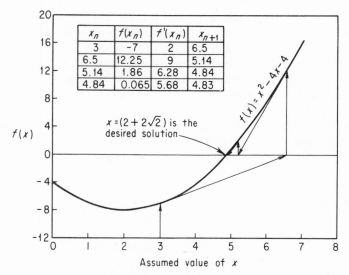

x_n	$f(x_n)$	$f'(x_n)$	x_{n+1}
3	-7	2	6.5
6.5	12.25	9	5.14
5.14	1.86	6.28	4.84
4.84	0.065	5.68	4.83

$x = (2 + 2\sqrt{2})$ is the desired solution

$f(x) = x^2 - 4x - 4$

Assumed value of x

Figure 1–4. According to Newton's method the next best value for the root is given by the straight line extrapolation with the slope $f'(x_n)$ from $[x_n, f(x_n)]$ to $(x_{n+1}, 0)$.

in Figure 1–4. The slope of this line is $f'(x_n)$. If the approximation of the function represented by Equation (1–14) were correct (that is if $f(x)$ is a straight line), the value of x_{n+1} computed by the first trial would be the correct value. In Figure 1–4 the use of Newton's method to solve for the positive root ($x = 2 + 2\sqrt{2}$) which satisfies Equation (1–8) is shown. Although direct-iteration failed for this case, it is seen that Newton's method converges rapidly to the desired solution. Also, it is to be observed that if the first assumed value for x lies to the right of $x = 2$, Newton's method converges to the root $x = (2 + 2\sqrt{2})$. If the first assumed value of x lies to the left of $x = 2$, Newton's method converges to the root $x = (2 - 2\sqrt{2})$. Also, if the value $x = 2$ is selected initially, Newton's method fails because $f'(2) = 0$; and if a point of inflection occurs in the neighborhood of the root, Newton's method may fail to converge as shown by Sokolnikoff (4).

Before Newton's method should be employed, the behavior of the function in the neighborhood of the root should be established and the initial value of x selected accordingly. Certain corrective measures to be taken in the application of Newton's method to functions containing several roots are discussed as the need for them arises in the application of this

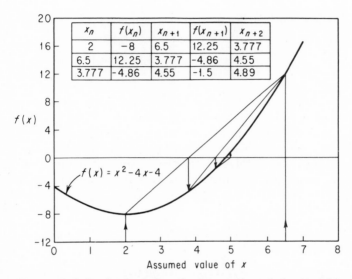

x_n	$f(x_n)$	x_{n+1}	$f(x_{n+1})$	x_{n+2}
2	-8	6.5	12.25	3.777
6.5	12.25	3.777	-4.86	4.55
3.777	-4.86	4.55	-1.5	4.89

$f(x) = x^2 - 4x - 4$

Figure 1–5. By interpolation the intersection of the straight line connecting the points $[x_n, f(x_n)]$ and $[x_{n+1}, f(x_{n+1})]$ with the x-axis gives the next best value for x.

method. Although Newton's method has some shortcomings, it may be successfully applied to solve many of the trial and error problems associated with distillation calculations.

3. Interpolation *(regula falsi)*

Some of the limitations of Newton's method are overcome by the method of interpolation (4), which may be demonstrated by use of the previous example in which it was desired to find the positive root of Equation (1–14). First, for two arbitrarily selected values of x, the corresponding values of the function are calculated. Let these be $x_1 = 2$ and $x_2 = 6.5$, which give, respectively, $f(2) = -8$ and $f(6.5) = 12.25$. Now, let these two points be connected by a straight line as shown in Figure 1–5. This line intersects the x-axis at $x = 3.777$, which is a better value than either $x = 2$ or $x =$

6.5. Corresponding to $x_3 = 3.777, f(x_3) = -4.86$. When the last two points (6.5, 12.25) and (3.777, -4.86) are connected by a straight line, a still better value for x, $x = 4.55$, is obtained. Continuation of this procedure leads to the desired root.

The interpolation formula is readily developed as follows. The equation of the straight line connecting points $(x_n, f(x_n))$ and $(x_{n+1}, f(x_{n+1}))$ is

$$\frac{f(x) - f(x_n)}{x - x_n} = \frac{f(x_n) - f(x_{n+1})}{x_n - x_{n+1}} \tag{1-16}$$

Let the value of x at which $f(x) = 0$ be denoted by x_{n+2}. Then for $x = x_{n+2}$, Equation (1–16) is readily solved for x_{n+2} to give

$$x_{n+2} = \frac{x_n f(x_{n+1}) - x_{n+1} f(x_n)}{f(x_{n+1}) - f(x_n)} \tag{1-17}$$

It is to be observed that this method does not fail as did Newton's method when a value of x is selected for which $f'(x) = 0$. However, like Newton's method, if $f(x)$ is a straight line, the correct value for x is determined by the first trial. Also worthy of note is the fact that the derivative of the function is not involved in the calculation of the next best value of x. However, as in Newton's method, provisions must be made in the treatment of functions having several roots in order to be assured that calculations will be carried out in the interval containing the desired root.

4. Newton-Raphson method

The extension of the method of Newton to functions of several variables is called the Newton-Raphson method (3). It is developed in a manner analogous to that shown for Newton's method. Suppose the set of values of x and y is to be found that makes $f_1(x, y) = 0$ and $f_2(x, y) = 0$, simultaneously. If each function is represented by a Taylor series expansion about the set of values (x_n, y_n), the following result is obtained when all terms which contain derivatives of higher order than the 1st are neglected,

$$f_1(x, y) = f_1(x_n, y_n) + \frac{\partial f_1(x_n, y_n)}{\partial x}(x - x_n)$$

$$+ \frac{\partial f_1(x_n, y_n)}{\partial y}(y - y_n) \tag{1-18}$$

$$f_2(x, y) = f_2(x_n, y_n) + \frac{\partial f_2(x_n, y_n)}{\partial x}(x - x_n)$$

$$+ \frac{\partial f_2(x_n, y_n)}{\partial y}(y - y_n) \tag{1-19}$$

For the set (x_{n+1}, y_{n+1}) of values which give

$$f_1(x_{n+1}, y_{n+1}) = f_2(x_{n+1}, y_{n+1}) = 0,$$

Equations (1–18) and (1–19) reduce to

$$0 = f_1 + \frac{\partial f_1}{\partial x} \Delta x_{n+1} + \frac{\partial f_1}{\partial y} \Delta y_{n+1} \tag{1–20}$$

and

$$0 = f_2 + \frac{\partial f_2}{\partial x} \Delta x_{n+1} + \frac{\partial f_2}{\partial y} \Delta y_{n+1} \tag{1–21}$$

respectively, where

$$\Delta x_{n+1} = x_{n+1} - x_n$$

$$\Delta y_{n+1} = y_{n+1} - y_n$$

Also, it is to be understood that the functions and their derivatives are evaluated at $x = x_n$ and $y = y_n$. The problem then reduces to two equations in the two unknowns, Δx_{n+1} and Δy_{n+1}. The values calculated (x_{n+1} and y_{n+1}) by the nth trial are used as the assumed values for $(n + 1)$st trial. This procedure is repeated until the desired accuracy of the roots is obtained.

The geometrical interpretation is illustrated by Figure 1–6. Equation (1–20) may be represented geometrically by projections in planes that are parallel to the f_1-x and the f_1-y planes. This series of projections begins at the point $f_1(x_n, y_n)$ on the surface of the function $f_1(x, y)$ and terminates at the point (x_{n+1}, y_{n+1}). As shown in Figure 1–6, the first projection has the slope of $\partial f_1/\partial x$, and it begins at $f_1(x_n, y_n)$ and extends a distance Δx_{n+1} as measured along the x-axis. This projection is followed by a second one which has a slope of $\partial f_1/\partial y$ and which extends a distance Δy_{n+1} as measured along the y-axis. This projection lies in a plane parallel to the f_1-y plane, and it terminates in the x-y plane at the point (x_{n+1}, y_{n+1}). The geometrical interpretation of Equation (1–21) is analogous to that of Equation (1–20) as demonstrated by Figure 1–6. However, it is to be emphasized that the same values of Δx_{n+1} and Δy_{n+1} are involved in the projections extending from $f_2(x_n, y_n)$ to the point (x_{n+1}, y_{n+1}) as those used for the projections from $f_1(x_n, y_n)$ to (x_{n+1}, y_{n+1}). It should also be remarked that when both f_1 and f_2 are linear in both x and y, the correct set values for x and y are obtained by the first trial.

With regard to the convergence of the Newton-Raphson method to the desired solution, it is recommended that this phenomenon be investigated by the direct application of the method to a wide variety of problems of the type for which solutions are desired. The use of different initial sets of values for the variables should be investigated. Also, if only the positive roots of the functions are desired, provisions should be made for an alternate selection of variables for the next trial when one or more negative values are computed by an intermediate trial. This direct attack is recommended because it is generally more difficult to produce an analytical proof of either the convergence or divergence of the Newton-Raphson method for a given system of equations than it is to find an example which converges to the desired solution for one or more sets of conditions and diverges for other

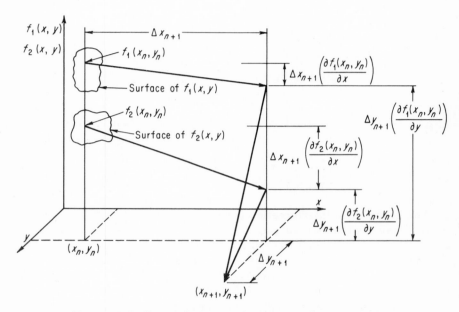

Figure 1-6. Geometrical representation of the Newton-Raphson method.

sets of conditions. As this method is applied, the conditions for which convergence may be expected will be stated.

Although only four methods have been described for solving problems by trial and error process, others such as those described by Nielsen (3) are available. However, the methods presented are the ones most frequently applied in subsequent chapters.

NOTATION

K_i = Multiplier required to relate the mole fractions of component i in the vapor and liquid phases at equilibrium (*i.e.*, $y_i = K_i x_i$)

Q = heat absorbed by the system per lb-mass of material flowing

W_s = shaft work done by the system on the surroundings per lb-mass of material flowing

x_i = mole fraction of component i in the liquid phase

x_n, x_{n+1} = independent and dependent variables for the nth trial for all methods except interpolation (*regula falsi*). In this method the independent variables are denoted by x_n and x_{n+1} and the dependent variable by x_{n+2}

y_i = mole fraction of component i in the vapor phase

ΔH = enthalpy of the output from minus the enthalpy of the input to the system per lb-mass of material flowing

ΔK.E. = kinetic energy of the output from minus the kinetic energy of the input to the system per lb-mass of material flowing

ΔP.E. = potential energy of the output from minus the potential energy of the input to the system per lb-mass of material flowing

LITERATURE CITED

1. Acrivos, Andreas and N. R. Amundson, "On the Steady State Fractionation of Multicomponent and Complex Mixtures in an Ideal Cascade," *Chem. Eng. Science*, **4,** 29 (1949).

2. Murdoch, P. G., "Multicomponent Distillation—Constant Volatility Ratio and Constant Reflux," *Chem. Eng. Progress*, **44,** 855 (1948).

3. Nielsen, K. L., *Methods in Numerical Analysis* (New York: Macmillan Co., 1957), pp. 199–210.

4. Sokolnikoff, I. S. and E. S. Sokolnikoff, *Higher Mathematics for Engineers and Physicists*, 2nd ed. (New York: McGraw–Hill Book Company, Inc., 1941), p. 101.

5. Underwood, A. J. V., "Fractional Distillation of Multicomponent Mixtures," *Chem. Eng. Progress*, **44,** 603 (1948).

Calculational Procedures for Bubble Point and Dew Point Temperatures and Flash Distillations

2

Since each of these calculational procedures is involved in all of the different calculational methods for solving multicomponent distillation problems, they are treated separately. In the introduction of these, it will be assumed that all of the components of the system under consideration are volatile, that is, that they are capable of appearing in both phases. After systems of this type have been considered, the treatment of those systems containing single phase lights and heavies is presented. In the developments that follow, the equilibrium constant, K_i, for each component i is taken to be independent of composition and thus a function of temperature and pressure alone. Also, the enthalpies for the pure components are taken to be independent of pressure and a function of temperature alone. The enthalpy of a mixture at a given temperature T is taken to be the sum of the products of the enthalpies of the pure components (evaluated at the given T) times their respective mole fractions.

CALCULATION OF BUBBLE POINT AND DEW POINT TEMPERATURES FOR SYSTEMS IN WHICH ALL OF THE COMPONENTS ARE VOLATILE

In order for a two-phase, multicomponent system to be at equilibrium, it is necessary that the temperatures as well as the pressures of both phases be the same. Furthermore, if these two phases possess their equilibrium composition, no transfer of material from one phase to the other (or change in composition) will be observed when they are placed in intimate contact. For such a system the vapor is at its dew point temperature and the liquid in equilibrium with it is at its bubble point temperature; these temperatures are of course the same. Hereafter, the names bubble point temperature and dew point temperature are used primarily from a calculational point of view. If the equilibrium temperature is calculated on the basis of the composition of the liquid phase, it is called the bubble point temperature; and if it is calculated on the basis of the vapor composition, it is called the dew point temperature.

1. Calculation of the Bubble Point Temperature

A problem frequently encountered is the determination of the bubble point temperature when the composition of a liquid and the total pressure are specified. If for a system of c components Henry's law ($y_i = K_i x_i$) is applied, c equations are obtained. Since the sum of the y_i's is unity, $(c - 1)$ values of y_i are unknown. Although c values of K_i are unknown, they may all be expressed as a polynomial in the unknown temperature. Since the sum of the y_i's is equal to unity, this system of c equations in c unknowns ($(c - 1)$ values of y_i and the temperature) is reduced to one equation in one unknown by the addition of the expressions, for each component, to give

$$1 = \sum_{i=1}^{c} K_i x_i \tag{2-1}$$

The problem is then to find a value of T such that Equation (2–1) is satisfied. The procedures described in Chapter 1 for solving problems of this type are more readily applied when Equation (2–1) is restated in functional notation as follows:

$$f(T) = \sum_{i=1}^{c} K_i x_i - 1 \tag{2-2}$$

Thus the positive value of T is to be found such that $f(T) = 0$. Since each of the K_i's increases with temperature, $f(T)$ has only one positive root. Newton's method is applied to find the desired root in the following manner. If T_n is the assumed value of T for trial number n, a better value of T (denoted by T_{n+1}) for trial number $(n + 1)$ is given by Newton's formula

$$T_{n+1} = T_n - \frac{f(T_n)}{f'(T_n)} \tag{2-3}$$

The first derivative of $f(T)$ is

$$f'(T) = \sum_{i=1}^{c} x_i \left(\frac{dK_i}{dT}\right)$$

If $K_i = a_i + b_i T + c_i T^2 + d_i T^3$, where a_i, b_i, c_i, and d_i are constants, then

$$f'(T_n) = \sum_{i=1}^{c} x_i(b_i + 2c_i T_n + 3d_i T_n^2)$$

Amundson and Pontinen (1) and Lyster *et al.* (5) were among the first to apply Newton's method for the calculation of bubble point temperatures. They found that this method converges very rapidly to the bubble point temperature. However, certain checks should be included in the calcula-

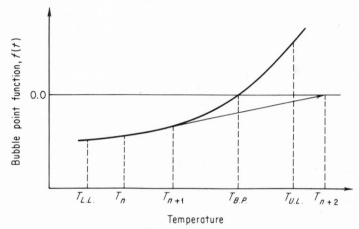

Figure 2–1. If the calculated temperature T_{n+2} is greater than the upper limit $T_{\text{U.L.}}$ of the curve fits, take

$$T_{n+2} = (T_{n+1} + T_{\text{U.L.}})/2.$$

tional procedure in order to prevent the use of temperatures outside the range of values for which the curve-fits for the K-data are applicable. The checks and provisions presented for use with the method of interpolation for the calculation of the bubble point temperature may also be employed with Newton's method.

The method of interpolation (*regula falsi*) is initiated by the selection of two arbitrary values of T within the range of the curve-fits for the K-data. Denoting these values of T by T_n and T_{n+1}, the next best value of T by the method of interpolation is computed as follows:

$$T_{n+2} = \frac{T_n f(T_{n+1}) - T_{n+1} f(T_n)}{f(T_{n+1}) - f(T_n)} \tag{2–4}$$

The next best value of temperature, T_{n+3}, is calculated on the basis of T_{n+1} and T_{n+2}. Each value of T computed in this manner must be checked to determine whether or not it is within the range of the curve-fits. This check is necessary because the roots of the function K lie outside the range of the curve-fits.

The provisions needed are easily seen by consideration of Figures 2–1 and 2–2. If $f(T)$ is concave upward as shown in Figure 2–1, it is possible to compute a value of T greater than the upper limit of the curve-fits.

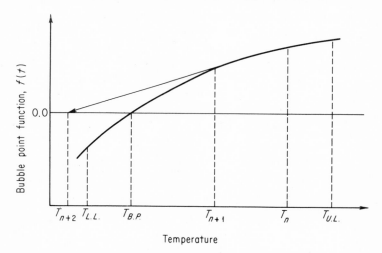

Figure 2–2. If the calculated temperature T_{n+2} is less than the lower limit $T_{\text{L.L.}}$ of the curve fits, take $T_{n+2} + (T_{n+1} + T_{\text{L.L.}})/2$.

Instead of using this value of T, it is suggested that the next best value be computed as follows:

$$T_{n+2} = \frac{T_{n+1} + T_{\text{U.L.}}}{2} \tag{2–5}$$

If a $T > T_{\text{U.L.}}$ is computed several trials in succession, this implies that the bubble point temperature is greater than $T_{\text{U.L.}}$. After this event has occurred a specified number of times, it is suggested that the bubble point temperature be taken equal to $T_{\text{U.L.}}$. If $f(T)$ is concave downward as shown in Figure 2–2, the possibility of computing a $T < T_{\text{L.L.}}$ exists. If this occurs, take the next best value of T to be the one given by

$$T_{n+2} = \frac{T_{n+1} + T_{\text{L.L.}}}{2} \tag{2–6}$$

Again, the calculation of a $T < T_{\text{L.L.}}$ several trials in succession implies that the bubble point temperature is less than the lower limit, $T_{\text{L.L.}}$; and when this event occurs a specified number of times, the bubble point temperature is taken equal to $T_{\text{L.L.}}$.

2. Calculation of the Dew Point Temperature

In the statement of this problem, $(c - 1)$ compositions in the vapor phase and the total pressure are specified and it is required to find the dew point temperature. Although the individual values of the x_i's are unknown, the value of their sum is unity. Since $x_i = y_i/K_i$, it follows that

$$1 = \sum_{i=1}^{c} \frac{y_i}{K_i} \tag{2-7}$$

which fact may be stated in functional notation as follows:

$$F(T) = \sum_{i=1}^{c} \frac{y_i}{K_i} - 1 \tag{2-8}$$

Needed for the application of Newton's method is the first derivative,

$$F'(T) = - \sum_{i=1}^{c} \left(\frac{y_i}{K_i^2}\right)\left(\frac{dK_i}{dT}\right)$$

Dew point temperatures may be determined by using either Newton's method or interpolation in a manner analogous to that shown previously for bubble point temperatures.

3. Calculation of Bubble Point and Dew Point Temperatures by Use of Relative Volatilities

This method is particularly convenient when the relative volatilities are independent of temperature. However, it may also be used to compute the bubble point and dew point temperatures for systems composed of components whose relative volatilities vary with temperature. The relative volatility is defined as follows:

$$\frac{y_i/x_i}{y_b/x_b} = \alpha_i \tag{2-9}$$

and where Henry's law applies

$$\alpha_i = K_i/K_b \tag{2-10}$$

The base component (denoted by the subscript "b") is usually selected as one of the components of the mixture. For the base component $y_b/x_b = K_b$ and $\alpha_b = 1.0$. Expressions needed for the calculation of the bubble point and dew point temperatures are developed in the following manner. For any component i,

$$\frac{y_i}{y_b} = \left(\frac{K_i}{K_b}\right)\left(\frac{x_i}{x_b}\right) \tag{2-11}$$

which may be rearranged to

$$\frac{y_i}{K_b} = \alpha_i x_i \tag{2-12}$$

Summation of both sides of this expression over all components yields

$$\frac{1}{K_b} = \sum_{i=1}^{c} \alpha_i x_i, \quad \text{or} \quad K_b = \frac{1}{\displaystyle\sum_{i=1}^{c} \alpha_i x_i} \tag{2-13}$$

Elimination of K_b from Equations (2–12) and (2–13) gives

$$y_i = \frac{\alpha_i x_i}{\displaystyle\sum_{i=1}^{c} \alpha_i x_i} \tag{2-14}$$

In an analogous manner it is readily shown that

$$K_b = \sum_{i=1}^{c} y_i/\alpha_i \tag{2-15}$$

and that

$$x_i = \frac{y_i/\alpha_i}{\displaystyle\sum_{i=1}^{c} y_i/\alpha_i} \tag{2-16}$$

If the relative volatilities are independent of temperature, the value of K_b corresponding to a given set of either x_i's or y_i's is calculated by use of Equation (2–13) or (2–15), respectively. The temperature required to give the computed value of K_b is readily obtained from a graph of K_b versus temperature or from an algebraic relationship of T as a function of K_b.

When the relative volatilities vary with temperature, Newton's method and interpolation are more readily applied for the calculation of the bubble point temperature when Equation (2–13) is restated in the following form.

$$f(T) = K_b - \frac{1}{\sum_{i=1}^{c} \alpha_i x_i} \qquad (2\text{–}17)$$

In order to apply Newton's method, the first derivative is needed.

$$f'(T) = \frac{dK_b}{dT} + \frac{\sum_{i=1}^{c} x_i(d\alpha_i/dT)}{\left(\sum_{i=1}^{c} \alpha_i x_i\right)^2} \qquad (2\text{–}18)$$

Similarly, the following form of Equation (2–15) is recommended for the calculation of the dew point temperature by use of either Newton's method or interpolation (*regula falsi*).

$$F(T) = K_b - \sum_{i=1}^{c} y_i/\alpha_i \qquad (2\text{–}19)$$

The first derivative of $F(T)$ is

$$F'(T) = \frac{dK_b}{dT} + \sum_{i=1}^{c} \left(\frac{y_i}{\alpha_i^2}\right)\left(\frac{d\alpha_i}{dT}\right) \qquad (2\text{–}20)$$

Calculation of either the bubble point or dew point temperature by use of Equation (2–17) or (2–19), respectively, is performed in the same manner as described previously for Equation (2–2). When relative volatilities are used, the use of interpolation for the calculation of either the bubble point or dew point temperature requires less programming than does Newton's method.

CALCULATION OF BUBBLE POINT AND DEW POINT TEMPERATURES FOR SYSTEMS WHICH CONTAIN SINGLE PHASE COMPONENTS

A single phase light component is defined as one which appears in the gas phase alone; that is, it has a K of infinity. This type of component is identified by the subscript "L." These components are frequently referred to as inert or noncondensible gases. Components which appear in the liquid phase alone are referred to as single phase heavies and denoted by the subscript "H."

When single phase lights and heavies are present in the respective phases of a system at equilibrium, the calculation of the temperature of the system is effected in about the same way as was described previously. The bubble point temperature is calculated by use of Equation (2–22) which is developed as follows. When each side of the expression $y_i = K_i x_i$ is summed over all of the volatile components, the following result is obtained.

$$1 - \sum_L y_L = \sum_{i \neq H, L} K_i x_i \tag{2–21}$$

Since all of the K_H's are zero, it is not necessary to include these components in the sum of the $K_i x_i$'s. The sum of the mole fractions of the single phase lights in the gas phase is denoted by $\sum_L y_L$. For the volatile components, the K_i's are evaluated at the total pressure of the system and at the bubble point temperature. The mole fractions of the volatile components in the liquid phase are computed on the basis of the presence of the single phase heavies in the liquid. Restated in functional notation, Equation (2–21) takes the form

$$f(T) = \sum_{i \neq H, L} K_i x_i - \left(1 - \sum_L y_L\right) \tag{2–22}$$

The bubble point temperature is that positive value of T which makes $f(T) = 0$. Usually the problem to be solved is as follows: Find the corresponding bubble point temperature when the composition of the liquid phase, the total mole fraction of single phase lights ($\sum_L y_L$), and the total pressure of the system are given. This calculation may be carried out by use of either Newton's method or interpolation (*regula falsi*) as described previously.

In an analogous manner to that shown for Equation (2–22), the following expression for the calculation of the dew point temperature is readily developed.

$$F(T) = \sum_{i \neq H, L} \frac{y_i}{K_i} - \left(1 - \sum_H x_H\right) \tag{2–23}$$

A large number of bubble point and dew point temperatures have been determined in which the calculations were performed by use of eight digit arithmetic. Newton's method and interpolation have been used to solve most of the forms of the bubble point and dew point functions, $f(T)$ and $F(T)$, shown here. The lower limit of accuracy which may be required is about 10^{-5}; for example, the trial procedure for the calculation of the bubble point temperature may be continued until a T is found such that

$$|f(T)| \leq 10^{-5} \tag{2–24}$$

Requirement of better accuracy may lead to an excessive number of trials for the calculation of the bubble point or dew point temperatures.

FLASH DISTILLATION CALCULATIONS

The process of flash distillation is the separation of a multicomponent mixture by means of a single equilibrium stage. Mixtures composed primarily of very light and very heavy components are frequently separated into a vapor and a liquid stream by this method. Also, when a feed enters a distillation column, this process may be involved. The results obtained from the following considerations may be applied to the general problem of multicomponent distillation.

Generally, the flash problem to be solved is of the following type. A feed of a given composition is to be flashed at a given temperature and pressure. The determination of the total moles of vapor and liquid formed and the compositions of the respective streams are required. A procedure for solving a problem of this type follows.

1. Calculation of the Moles of Vapor and Liquid Formed by the Flash Process (All Components Volatile)

A feed of a given composition may be divided into two phases provided the specified temperature of the flash, T_F, lies between the bubble point, $T_{\text{B.P.}}$, and dew point, $T_{\text{D.P.}}$, temperatures of the feed, where the latter are evaluated at the specified pressure of the flash. Thus, if T_F satisfies both of the following conditions,

$$f(T_F) > 0 \tag{2-25}$$

$$F(T_F) > 0 \tag{2-26}$$

where the bubble point and dew point functions are defined by

$$f(T_F) = \sum_{i=1}^{c} K_{Fi} X_i - 1 \tag{2-27}$$

and

$$F(T_F) = \sum_{i=1}^{c} \frac{X_i}{K_{Fi}} - 1 \tag{2-28}$$

respectively, it is possible to separate the feed into two phases at the specified conditions of the flash. Alternately, a direct comparison of temperatures may be made. This requires the prior determinations of the bubble point and dew point temperatures of the feed, which are computed by finding the values of T that give $f(T) = 0$ and $F(T) = 0$, respectively.

The following development of the flash equations follows closely that given by Holland and Davison (3). When the flash temperature and pressure are specified such that a two-phase mixture exists, the following material balance for component i applies at steady state,

$$FX_i = V_F y_{Fi} + L_F x_{Fi} \tag{2-29}$$

Since the flash is considered to be an equilibrium process,

$$FX_i = V_F y_{Fi} + \frac{L_F y_{Fi}}{K_{Fi}} \tag{2-30}$$

Then,

$$y_{Fi} = \frac{FX_i}{F - L_F + \dfrac{L_F}{K_{Fi}}} \tag{2-31}$$

since $F = V_F + L_F$. Upon dividing both numerator and denominator of Equation (2–31) by F and rearranging, the following result is obtained.

$$y_{Fi} = \frac{X_i}{1 - \dfrac{L_F}{F}\left(1 - \dfrac{1}{K_{Fi}}\right)} \tag{2-32}$$

The sum over all components of both sides of Equation (2–32) yields

$$1 = \sum_{i=1}^{c} \frac{X_i}{1 - \dfrac{L_F}{F}\left(1 - \dfrac{1}{K_{Fi}}\right)} \tag{2-33}$$

Now for convenience, let L_F/F be denoted by ψ and let the function $p(\psi)$ be defined as follows:

$$p(\psi) = \sum_{i=1}^{c} \frac{X_i}{1 - \psi\left(1 - \dfrac{1}{K_{Fi}}\right)} - 1 \tag{2-34}$$

The desired solution of this equation is obtained when a value of $\psi > 0$ is selected which gives $p(\psi) = 0$. The composition of the vapor, V_F, formed by the flash is given by substitution of this value of ψ (the one which gives $p(\psi) = 0$) into Equation (2–32). For the corresponding liquid phase, L_F, the composition may be computed by use of the equilibrium relationship, $x_{Fi} = y_{Fi}/K_{Fi}$. Needed in the examination of the function $p(\psi)$ and in the application of Newton's method is the first derivative,

$$p'(\psi) = \sum_{i=1}^{c} \frac{X_i\left(1 - \dfrac{1}{K_{Fi}}\right)}{\left[1 - \psi\left(1 - \dfrac{1}{K_{Fi}}\right)\right]^2} \tag{2-35}$$

The function $p(\psi)$ has c roots. Only two of these have physical significance, the value $\psi = 0$ and the desired root $\psi = \psi_r$. Since $p(0) = 0$, $p'(0) < 0$, $p''(0) > 0$, and $p(1) > 0$, the function has a minimum between $\psi = 0$ and $\psi = 1$. Thus the general form of the function is as shown in Figure 2–3. The most important point illustrated by this plot is that the desired root, ψ_r, of the flash equation is greater than the value of ψ at which $p(\psi)$ is a minimum and less than unity. If the value $\psi = 1$ is taken as the initial assumption, Newton's method converges to the desired root ψ_r, since $p(\psi)$,

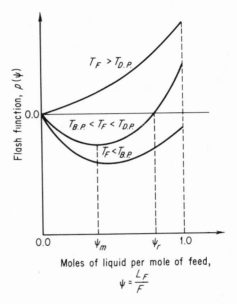

Figure 2–3. Graphical representation of the flash function $p(\psi)$ for a feed composed of volatile components. (Reproduced by permission of *Hydrocarbon Processing & Petroleum Refiner*)

$p'(\psi)$, and $p''(\psi)$ are positive for all values of ψ which satisfy the condition $\psi_r \leqq \psi \leqq 1$. If a value of $\psi < \psi_m$ were taken for the first assumed value of the root, then the application of Newton's method would lead to the root $\psi = 0$, since for $0 \leqq \psi < \psi_m$, $p(\psi) < 0$, and $p'(\psi) < 0$. Traces of the function $p(\psi)$ are also shown for the cases where $T_F > T_{D.P.}$ and $T_F < T_{B.P.}$, where T_F refers to the specified temperature of the flash and $T_{B.P.}$ and $T_{D.P.}$ denote the bubble point and dew point temperatures, respectively, of the feed at the specified pressure of the flash. The determination of ψ_r by use of Newton's method is illustrated by the following numerical example.

Illustrative Example 2–1

This problem is a modification of one used by Brown and Associates (2). Instead of the flash temperature of 110°F employed by these authors, a temperature of 150°F was selected for the purpose of making the problem more difficult to solve by using Equations (2–34) and (2–35). For their problem $\psi_r = L_F/F = 0.93$, whereas for the modified form of the problem, a value of 0.457 was obtained. The statement and solution of this example are shown in Table 2–1. The detail steps are shown for the first trial, and for the remainder of the trials the final results are shown. The rapidity which which the method converges to the root is evident.

Also, the flash expression, Equation (2–34), may be solved for the desired root by use of interpolation (*regula falsi*). Examination of the graph of $p(\psi)$ shows that convergence to the desired root by this method is assured if the first two values of ψ (those used to initiate the interpolation procedure) give positive values for $p(\psi)$. The value of $\psi = 1$ satisfies this condition, and it is taken as the first value of ψ (denoted by ψ_1). The second value of ψ is selected in the following manner. A value of ψ, say ψ_k, lying between $\psi = 0$ and $\psi = 1$ is selected arbitrarily. If $p(\psi_k) < 0$, the value of ψ equal to $(1 + \psi_k)/2$ is investigated. Values of ψ closer and closer to ψ_1 are examined until one that gives $p(\psi) > 0$ is found. This value of ψ is denoted by ψ_2. Use of these two values of ψ (ψ_1 and ψ_2) permit the selection of a better value, ψ_3, by use of the interpolation formula, Equation (1–17).

The process of flash distillation may be described by functions of several different forms. For example, if y_{Fi} is replaced by $K_{Fi}x_{Fi}$ in Equation (2–29) instead of by x_{Fi} by y_{Fi}/K_{Fi}, the following expression is obtained:

$$P(\Psi) = \sum_{i=1}^{c} \frac{X_i}{1 - \Psi(1 - K_{Fi})} - 1 \qquad (2\text{–}36)$$

which has a first derivative of the form

$$P'(\Psi) = \sum_{i=1}^{c} \frac{X_i(1 - K_{Fi})}{[1 - \Psi(1 - K_{Fi})]^2} \qquad (2\text{–}37)$$

The quantity Ψ is used to denote V_F/F. Then the problem reduces to finding the positive value of $\Psi > 0$ that makes $P(\Psi) = 0$. For values of Ψ in the range $0 \leq \Psi \leq 1$, the shape of $P(\Psi)$ is the same as that shown for $p(\psi)$ in Figure 2–3. In the use of Newton's method for solving $P(\Psi) = 0$, convergence to the desired positive root is assured if the initial value of unity is selected for Ψ.

Table 2-1 Statement and Solution of Illustrative Example 2-1

	Statement					Solution		
	$F = 1.0$ mole					First Trial $\psi_1 = 1.0$		
Component	X	K^* at 150°F 50 psia	$1-1/K$	$\psi_1(1-1/K)$	$1-\psi_1(1-1/K)$	$y = \dfrac{X}{1-\psi_1(1-1/K)}$	$\dfrac{X(1-1/K)}{1-\psi_1(1-1/K)}$	$\dfrac{X(1-1/K)}{[1-\psi_1(1-1/K)]^2}$
C_2	0.0079	16.2	0.9383	0.9383	0.0617	0.1280	0.1201	1.9465
C_3	0.1321	5.2	0.8077	0.8077	0.1923	0.6869	0.5548	2.8851
$i\text{-}C_4$	0.0849	2.6	0.6154	0.6154	0.3846	0.2207	0.1358	0.3531
$n\text{-}C_4$	0.2690	1.98	0.4949	0.4949	0.5051	0.5326	0.2636	0.5219
$i\text{-}C_5$	0.0589	0.91	−0.0989	−0.0989	1.0989	0.0536	−0.0054	−0.0049
$n\text{-}C_5$	0.1321	0.72	−0.3889	−0.3889	1.3889	0.0951	−0.0370	−0.0266
C_6	0.3151	0.28	−2.5714	−2.5714	3.5714	0.0882	−0.2268	−0.0635

$$1.8051$$
$$-1.0000$$
$$\overline{}$$
$$p(\psi_1) = 0.8051$$

$$p'(\psi_1) = 5.6116$$

$$\psi_2 = 1.0 - \frac{0.8051}{5.6116} = 0.8565$$

Second Trial: $\psi_2 = 0.8565$

Results: $p(\psi_2) = 0.3671$; $p'(\psi_2) = 1.8370$: $\psi_3 = 0.8565 - \frac{0.3671}{1.8372} = 0.6567$

Third Trial: $\psi_3 = 0.6567$
Results: $p(\psi_3) = 0.1206$; $p'(\psi_3) = 0.8237$; $\psi_4 = 0.5102$
Fourth Trial: $\psi_4 = 0.5102$
Results: $p(\psi_4) = 0.0261$, $p'(\psi_4) = 0.4927$; $\psi_5 = 0.4573$

The value $\psi = 0.4573$ is of sufficient accuracy, since the previous value of $\psi = 0.5102$ gave $p(\psi) = \Sigma y_i - 1 = 0.0261$. Actually a fifth trial based on $\psi = 0.4573$ gave $p(\psi) = \Sigma y_i - 1 = 0.00247$ and the corrected value for ψ was 0.4511.

* The values of the K's were taken from the Fifth Edition of the Technical Manual (1946) prepared by the Natural Gasoline Supply Men's Association, 422 Kennedy Bldg, Tulsa 3, Oklahoma.

Reproduced by permission of *Hydrocarbon Processing & Petroleum Refiner*

2. Calculation of the Moles of Vapor and Liquid Formed by the Flash Process (Single Phase Components Present)

Where the feed contains both single phase lights and heavies and volatile components, the flash function takes the form

$$p(\psi) = \sum_{i \neq H} \frac{X_i}{1 - \psi \left(1 - \dfrac{1}{K_{Fi}} \right)} - 1 \qquad (2\text{--}38)$$

where it is understood that for any single phase light component $(1/K_{FL}) = 0$. For any specified set of flash temperatures and pressures, it is possible to obtain a real solution to Equation (2–38) (one that is physically possible). Also, for any value of T between zero and infinity, the value of ψ that gives $p(\psi) = 0$ is bounded as follows:

$$\sum_{i \neq L} X_i > \psi_r > \sum_{H} X_H \qquad (2\text{--}39)$$

The lower bound represents the formation of a liquid phase composed of the single phase heavies alone, whereas the upper bound corresponds to the formation of a liquid phase consisting of all components except the single phase lights.

For a feed that consists of single phase lights and volatile components, there exists a physically possible ψ that gives $p(\psi) = 0$, provided the specified temperature of the flash is less than the dew point temperature of the feed at the specified pressure. That is if

$$F(T_F) > 0 \qquad (2\text{--}40)$$

where $F(T_F)$ is defined by Equation (2–28), the feed may be separated into two phases. For $0 < T_F < T_{\text{D.P.}}$ (of the feed), the value of $\psi > 0$ that gives $p(\psi) = 0$ is bounded as follows:

$$\sum_{i \neq L} X_i > \psi_r > 0 \qquad (2\text{--}41)$$

Similarly, for a feed composed of single phase heavies and volatile components, there exists a physically possible ψ such that $p(\psi) = 0$, provided the specified temperature of the flash is greater than the bubble point temperature of the feed at the specified pressure. Thus if

$$f(T_F) > 0 \qquad (2\text{--}42)$$

where $f(T_F)$ is defined by Equation (2–27), the feed may be separated into two phases. For $T_{\text{B.P.}} < T_F < \infty$, the quantity ψ_r is bounded as follows:

$$\sum_{H} X_H < \psi_r < 1 \qquad (2\text{--}43)$$

Instead of the theoretical upper and lower limits of temperature of zero and infinity, the practical limits are, of course, $T_{\text{U.L.}}$ and $T_{\text{L.L.}}$.

For a system containing one or more volatile components and both single phase lights and heavies, the function $P(\Psi)$ takes the following form:

$$P(\Psi) = \sum_{i \neq L} \frac{X_i}{1 - \Psi(1 - K_{Fi})} - 1 \qquad (2\text{-}44)$$

For a single phase heavy the value $K_{FH} = 0$ is of course employed in the above expression.

It should be remarked that in solving $p(\psi) = 0$ for the value of $\psi > 0$ by use of either Newton's method or interpolation, the largest value that is physically possible is selected as the first value of ψ. This value, denoted by ψ_1, is calculated as follows:

$$\psi_1 = \frac{\sum\limits_{i \neq L} FX_i}{F} = \sum_{i \neq L} X_i \qquad (2\text{-}45)$$

Similarly, for $P(\Psi)$ the largest value of Ψ which is physically possible is selected; this value is computed in the following manner:

$$\Psi_1 = \frac{\sum\limits_{i \neq H} FX_i}{F} = \sum_{i \neq H} X_i \qquad (2\text{-}46)$$

The application of Equation (2–44) is demonstrated by solution of the following example.

Illustrative Example 2–2

When 0.25 moles of a single phase light component are added to one mole of hydrocarbons having the same composition as shown for Example 2–1, the composition of the feed shown in Table 2–2 for Example 2–2 is obtained. Beginning with a value of

$$\psi_1 = \sum_{i \neq L} FX_i / (F) = 0.8,$$

Newton's method gave $\psi_r = L_F/F = 0.162$ and

$$\sum_{i=1}^{c} y_{Fi} - 1 = 0.0074$$

in five trials.

TABLE 2-2 Statement and Solution of Illustrative Example 2-2

	Statement		Solution					
	$\Sigma FX_i = 1.0$, $F = 1.25$ (i≠L)		Fifth Trial $\psi_5 = 0.1884$					
Component	X	K at 150°F. 50 psia	$1-1/K$	$\psi_5(1-1/K)$	$1-\psi_5(1-1/K)$	$y = \dfrac{X}{1-\psi_5(1-1/K)}$	$\dfrac{X(1-1/K)}{1-\psi_5(1-1/K)}$	$\dfrac{X(1-1/K)}{[1-\psi_5(1-1/K)]^2}$
Single phase light	0.2000		1.0	0.1884	0.8116	0.2464	0.2464	0.3036
C_2	0.0063	16.2	0.9383	0.1768	0.8232	0.0076	0.0071	0.0086
C_3	0.1057	5.2	0.8077	0.1522	0.8478	0.1247	0.1007	0.1188
$i\text{-}C_4$	0.0679	2.6	0.6154	0.1159	0.8841	0.0768	0.0473	0.0535
$n\text{-}C_4$	0.2152	1.98	0.4949	0.0932	0.9068	0.2373	0.1174	0.1295
$i\text{-}C_5$	0.0471	0.91	-0.0989	-0.0186	1.0186	0.0462	-0.0046	-0.0045
$n\text{-}C_5$	0.1057	0.72	-0.3889	-0.0733	1.0733	0.0985	-0.0383	-0.0357
C_6	0.2521	0.28	-2.5714	-0.4845	1.4845	0.1698	-0.4366	-0.2941

$$1.0074$$
$$-1.0000$$
$$\overline{}$$
$$p(\psi_5) = 0.0074$$

$$p'(\psi_5) = 0.2797$$

First Trial: $\psi_1 = \dfrac{\sum\limits_{i \neq L} FX_i}{F} = \dfrac{1}{1.25} = 0.8$

$\psi_6 = 0.1884 - \dfrac{0.0074}{0.2797} = 0.162$

$p(\psi_1) = 1.0208$; $p'(\psi_1) = 6.1336$; $\psi_2 = 0.8 - \dfrac{1.0207}{6.1336} = 0.6336$

Results: $\psi_2 = 0.6336$

Second Trial: $\psi_2 = 0.6336$

Results: $p(\psi_2) = 0.4276$; $p'(\psi_2) = 2.0977$; $\psi_3 = 0.4297$

Third Trial: $\psi_3 = 0.4297$

Results: $p(\psi_3) = 0.1443$; $p'(\psi_3) = 0.9001$; $\psi_4 = 0.2694$

Fourth Trial: $\psi_4 = 0.2694$

Results: $p(\psi_4) = 0.9375$; $p'(\psi_4) = 0.4622$; $\psi_5 = 0.1884$

Fifth Trial: $\psi_5 = 0.1884$

Results: $p(\psi_5) = 0.0074$; $p'(\psi_5) = 0.2797$; $\psi_5 = 0.162$

Reproduced by permission of *Hydrocarbon Processing & Petroleum Refiner*

ENTHALPY REQUIREMENTS FOR FLASH PROCESSES WHICH ARE CARRIED OUT ADIABATICALLY

With regard to the enthalpy requirement the solutions for the two types of problems presented below are the ones most frequently required. In the first of these the temperature and pressure of the flash are specified, and the temperature which the feed must have in order for the process to occur adiabatically at the specified conditions is to be determined. In the second type of problem, both the temperature of the flash and the amount flashed are to be found when the temperature of the feed and the pressure of the flash are specified.

1. Determination of the Temperature of the Feed Required for the Flash to Occur at the Specified Temperature and Pressure

The first step in the solution of a problem of this type is the determination of the moles of vapor formed by the flash process and the corresponding compositions, x_{Fi}'s and y_{Fi}'s. Then the enthalpy of each of the product streams is computed as follows:

$$h_F = \sum_{i=1}^{c} h_{Fi} x_{Fi} \qquad (2\text{--}47)$$

and

$$H_F = \sum_{i=1}^{c} H_{Fi} y_{Fi} \qquad (2\text{--}48)$$

Thus the enthalpy which the feed must possess in order for the flash process to occur adiabatically is given by

$$H = \left(\frac{V_F}{F}\right) H_F + \left(\frac{L_F}{F}\right) h_F \qquad (2\text{--}49)$$

The problem now reduces to finding the temperature of the feed corresponding to this value of H. When all of the components are volatile, the enthalpy of a superheated liquid feed is computed as follows:

$$H = \sum_{i=1}^{c} h_i X_i \qquad (2\text{--}50)$$

For feeds composed of single phase lights, heavies, and volatile components, the enthalpy is calculated in an analogous manner. Let the function $\delta_n(T_n)$ be defined as follows:

$$\delta_n(T_n) = H - H_n \qquad (2\text{--}51)$$

where H denotes the fixed value of the enthalpy as calculated by Equation (2–49) and H_n represents the value of enthalpy given by Equation (2–50) for the assumed temperature T_n. The desired temperature is the one which gives $\delta_n(T_n) = 0$. Either Newton's method or interpolation (*regula falsi*) may be employed to find this particular temperature.

2. Determination of T_F and the Amount of Feed which is Flashed when the Pressure of the Flash and the Enthalpy of the Feed are Specified

In addition to the stipulations above the flash process is to be carried out adiabatically. Two methods for solving this problem are shown here. The first of these makes use of the method of interpolation, which is initiated as follows. For each of two flash temperatures (denoted by T_n and T_{n+1}) that satisfy the necessary conditions for the formation of two phases, either Equation (2–34) or Equation (2–36) is solved for L_F (or V_F) by use of either Newton's method or interpolation (*regula falsi*) as described previously. Then the total enthalpy of the feed corresponding to each of these values of T is computed by use of Equation (2–49). In this procedure let

H = Specified enthalpy of the feed

H_n, H_{n+1} = Enthalpies of the feed given by Equation (2–49) for the flash temperatures T_n and T_{n+1}, respectively.

$\delta_n = H - H_n$

After these quantities have been computed, a better value for the flash temperature is found by use of the interpolation formula,

$$T_{n+2} = \frac{\delta_{n+1} T_n - \delta_n T_{n+1}}{\delta_{n+1} - \delta_n} \tag{2–52}$$

If, for a feed composed of volatile components alone, a value of T_{n+2} is computed by Equation (2–52) that is less than the bubble point or greater than the dew point temperature of the feed at the specified pressure, the value is replaced by

$$T_{n+2} = \frac{T_{n+1} + T_{\text{B.P.}}}{2} \tag{2–53}$$

or

$$T_{n+2} = \frac{T_{n+1} + T_{\text{D.P.}}}{2} \tag{2–54}$$

respectively.

In order to solve this type of problem by the Newton-Raphson method, it is necessary to state the enthalpy balance, Equation (2–49), as a function of only two variables, L_F (or V_F) and T_F. The material balance expressions, Equations (2–34) and (2–36), are already of this form. In the following procedure, Equation (2–36) is selected for use and is identified by the notation $P_1(\Psi, T)$. Equation (2–49) is stated in terms of these variables by the elimination of the x_{Fi}'s and y_{Fi}'s. The y_{Fi}'s are eliminated in the following manner. Consider the function

$$V_F H_F = \sum_{i=1}^{c} H_{Fi} V_F y_{Fi} \tag{2–55}$$

Since $V_F y_{Fi} = FX_i - L_F x_{Fi}$,

$$V_F H_F = FH(X)_F - L_F H(x_F)_F \tag{2–56}$$

where

$$H(X)_F = \sum_{i=1}^{c} H_{Fi} X_i = \text{enthalpy of one mole of vapor evaluated at the composition of the feed and at the temperature of the flash.}$$

$$H(x_F)_F = \sum_{i=1}^{c} H_{Fi} x_{Fi} = \text{enthalpy of one mole of vapor evaluated at the composition of the liquid formed by the flash and at the temperature of the flash.}$$

When $V_F H_F$ in Equation (2–49) is replaced by its equivalent as given by Equation (2–56), the following expression is obtained.

$$FH = FH(X)_F - L_F[H(x_F)_F - h_F] \tag{2–57}$$

Thus

$$H = H(X)_F - (1 - \Psi)[H(x_F)_F - h_F] \tag{2–58}$$

In a manner analogous to that shown for the development of Equation (2–32), it is readily shown that

$$x_{Fi} = \frac{X_i}{1 - \Psi(1 - K_{Fi})} \tag{2–59}$$

By use of this expression the c values of the x_{Fi}'s may be stated in terms of the variables Ψ and T. Thus the desired function representing an enthalpy balance is

$$P_2(\Psi, T) = (1 - \Psi) \left[\sum_{i=1}^{c} \frac{\lambda_{Fi} X_i}{1 - \Psi(1 - K_{Fi})} \right] + H - H(X)_F \tag{2–60}$$

where

$\lambda_{Fi} = H_{Fi} - h_{Fi}$, the latent heat of vaporization for component i at the temperature and pressure of the flash.

A graphical representation of $P_2(\Psi, T)$ is shown in Figure 2–4. It is readily shown that $P_2(0, T) > P_2(1, T)$ and also that $\partial P_2(0, T)/\partial \Psi$ and $\partial P_2(1, T)/\partial \Psi$ are both less than zero. Also, the second derivatives of P_2

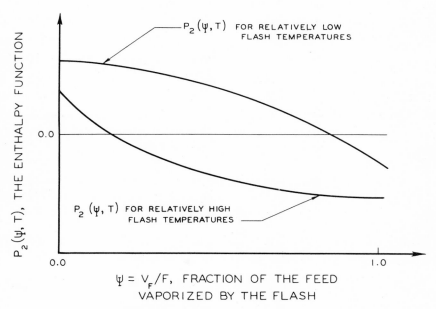

Figure 2–4. Graphical representation of the enthalpy function $P_2(\Psi, T)$.

with respect to Ψ show that at some intermediate temperature the curvature changes from concave upward to concave downward.

In order to find the set of values of Ψ and T which give $P_1 = P_2 = 0$ simultaneously by the Newton-Raphson method, the partial derivatives of P_1 and P_2 with respect to temperature and Ψ are needed. The partial derivative of P_1 with respect to Ψ is given by Equation (2–37), and

$$\frac{\partial P_1(\Psi, T)}{\partial T} = -(\Psi) \left[\sum_{i=1}^{c} \frac{X_i \left(\dfrac{dK_{Fi}}{dT} \right)}{\{1 - \Psi(1 - K_{Fi})\}^2} \right] \qquad (2\text{–}61)$$

The derivatives of the function $P_2(\Psi, T)$ are as follows:

$$\frac{\partial P_2(\Psi, T)}{\partial \Psi} = - \sum_{i=1}^{c} \frac{\lambda_{Fi} X_i K_{Fi}}{[1 - \Psi(1 - K_{Fi})]^2} \tag{2-62}$$

$$\frac{\partial P_2(\Psi, T)}{\partial T} = (1 - \Psi) \left[\sum_{i=1}^{c} \frac{X_i \left(\dfrac{\partial \lambda_{Fi}}{\partial T} \right)}{1 - \Psi(1 - K_{Fi})} \right.$$

$$\left. - (\Psi) \sum_{i=1}^{c} \frac{\lambda_{Fi} X_i \left(\dfrac{\partial K_{Fi}}{\partial T} \right)}{[1 - \Psi(1 - K_{Fi})]^2} \right] - \sum_{i=1}^{c} X_i \left(\frac{\partial H_{Fi}}{\partial T} \right) \tag{2-63}$$

In the Newton-Raphson method, described in Chapter 1, the following linear equations in $\Delta\Psi$ and ΔT are solved simultaneously.

$$0 = P_1 + \left(\frac{\partial P_1}{\partial \Psi} \right) \Delta\Psi + \left(\frac{\partial P_1}{\partial T} \right) \Delta T \tag{2-64}$$

$$0 = P_2 + \left(\frac{\partial P_2}{\partial \Psi} \right) \Delta\Psi + \left(\frac{\partial P_2}{\partial T} \right) \Delta T \tag{2-65}$$

where

$$\Delta\Psi = \Psi_{n+1} - \Psi_n$$

$$\Delta T = T_{n+1} - T_n$$

The subscripts n and $n + 1$ denote respectively the assumed and calculated values of the variables. The functions P_1 and P_2 and their derivatives appearing in Equations (2–64) and (2–65) are evaluated at $\Psi = \Psi_n$ and $T = T_n$. After these equations have been solved for $\Delta\Psi$ and ΔT, the set of values to be assumed for the variables for the next trial are computed as follows:

$$\Psi_{n+1} = \Psi_n + \Delta\Psi$$

$$T_{n+1} = T_n + \Delta T$$

For the problems investigated, it was found that the Newton-Raphson method converged to the desired solution, provided the following calculational procedure was used. The first value of Ψ was taken as unity. (When single phase heavy components are contained in the feed, Ψ_1 is given by Equation (2–46).) If in the calculational procedure a negative value for Ψ_{n+1} is computed, the value is discarded and the following one is used in its place.

$$\Psi_{n+1} = \frac{\Psi_1 + \Psi_n}{2} \qquad (2\text{--}66)$$

Also, for the first value of the temperature, one lying between the bubble point and the dew point of the feed (at the specified pressure) should be used. If in the calculational process a value of T_{n+1} either less than $T_{\text{B.P.}}$ or greater than $T_{\text{D.P.}}$ (for a feed composed of all volatile components) is obtained, the value is discarded and either

$$T_{n+1} = \frac{T_n + T_{\text{B.P.}}}{2} \qquad (2\text{--}67)$$

or

$$T_{n+1} = \frac{T_n + T_{\text{D.P.}}}{2} \qquad (2\text{--}68)$$

is employed.

Illustrative Examples 2–3, 2–4, and 2–5, (stated in Table 2–3) were selected in order to illustrate the solution of the flash problem when enthalpy balances are considered. In effect Examples 2–3, 2–4, and 2–5 represent the same problem solved in different ways. In Example 2–3 the temperature and pressure of the flash are specified, and the problem is to find the moles of vapor formed by the flash and the enthalpy that the feed must possess in order for the flash process to occur adiabatically. Equation (2–36) was solved by Newton's method and the corresponding enthalpy was calculated by use of Equation (2–49). The results are presented in Table 2–4.

In Example 2–4 the pressure of the flash and the enthalpy of the feed are specified, and the problem is to find the moles of vapor formed and the temperature resulting from an adiabatic flash of the feed. Since the enthalpy of the feed obtained by the solution of Example 2–3 was specified as the feed enthalpy for Example 2–4, the same general solution to both examples is to be expected. The desired values of Ψ and T were found by use of Equations (2–36) and (2–52). As pointed out in the development, for each

TABLE 2–3 Statement of Examples

Component	For all examples FX_i	Specifications for examples 2–3, 2–4, 2–5
C_2H_4	2.0	*Example* 2–3: A liquid feed having the composition shown is to be flashed adiabatically at 300 psia and 600°F. Find the moles of vapor formed and the enthalpy of the feed.
C_2H_6	3.0	*Example* 2–4: A liquid feed with an enthalpy of 13,210.0 Btu per lb. mole is to be flashed adiabatically at 300 psia. Find the moles of vapor formed and the temperature of the flash. Solve by interpolation (*regula falsi*).
C_3H_6	5.0	*Example* 2–5: Same as Example 2–4 except solve by use of the Newton-Raphson method.
C_3H_8	10.0	
n-C_4	60.0	
i-C_4	20.0	

Table 2–4 Solution of Examples 2–3, 2–4, and 2–5

Compositions of the Vapor and Liquid Streams Formed by the Flash Process for All Examples

Component	x_{Fi}	y_{Fi}
C_2H_4	0.012427	0.062634
C_2H_6	0.020753	0.082058
C_3H_6	0.044231	0.082478
C_3H_8	0.090999	0.150671
$i\text{-}C_4$	0.203398	0.180872
$n\text{-}C_4$	0.628193	0.442870

Other Results for Example 2–3

Solution: $\Psi = 0.1508$, $V_F = 15.08$, $L_F = 84.92$. Six trials were required by Newton's method to give a Ψ of an accuracy corresponding to

$$\left| \sum_{i=1}^{c} x_{Fi} - 1 \right| < 10^{-4}$$

H (enthalpy of the feed) = 13,210.0 Btu per lb. mole.

Other Results for Example 2–4

Assumed* Flash Temp., °F	Value of Ψ required to give $P_1(\Psi) = 0$ at the assumed temperature.		Corrected Flash Temp., °F
	Ψ	No. of trials required to give $P_1(\Psi) = 0$	
195	0.063812	8	
215	0.68388	4	198.14
198.14	0.11534	7	199.31
199.31	0.13713	7	200.03
200.03	0.15152	7	200.00
200.00	0.15090	7	200.00

* $T_{\text{B.P.}} = 190.12°F$ and $T_{\text{D.P.}} = 219.31°F$.

Other Results for Example 2–5

Assumed Values For Ψ and T		Values of P_1 and P_2		Corrected Values For Ψ and T	
Ψ	T	$P_1(\Psi, T)$	$P_2(\Psi, T)$	Ψ	T
1.0	204.72	0.13011	−519.6	0.27291	198.01
0.27291	198.01	0.01482	−559.9	0.16468	198.36
0.16468	198.36	0.002887	−4.004	0.15178	199.58
0.15178	199.88	0.0001919	0.2852	0.15088	200.00
0.15088	200.00	0.000001	0.00195	0.15087	200.00

value of T found by Equation (2–52), Equation (2–36) is solved for the value of Ψ which gives $P_1(\Psi, T) = 0$. Since either Newton's method or interpolation may be employed for this calculation, Newton's method was used. The results are given in Table 2–4.

Example 2–5 illustrates the application of the Newton-Raphson method to solve the same problem given by the statement of Example 2–4. This method is initiated as follows. On the basis of an assumed set of values for Ψ and T (namely, $\Psi = 1$ and $T = 204.72°F$), the functions P_1, P_2, and their partial derivatives were evaluated by use of Equations (2–36), (2–37), and (2–60) through (2–63). Then the Newton-Raphson equations [Equations (2–64) and (2–65)] were solved simultaneously for $\Delta\Psi$ and ΔT and the next set of values for Ψ and T were computed therefrom. Continuation of this process leads to the results shown for Example 2–5 in Table 2–4. Little advantage of one method over the other was found in comparing of the Newton-Raphson and interpolation (*regula falsi*) methods. The equilibrium and enthalpy data used to solve the illustrative examples were taken from the Appendix.

NOTATION

$$c = \text{total number of components}$$

$f(T), f'(T) =$ a bubble point function and its first derivative

$F(T), F'(T) =$ a dew point function and its first derivative

$F =$ molal flow rate of feed to the flash process

$H =$ enthalpy of one mole of feed

$h_i, H_i =$ enthalpy of one mole of a pure component i in the liquid and vapor states, respectively, at the temperature of the feed

$h_F, H_F =$ enthalpy of one mole of the liquid and one mole of the vapor, respectively, formed by the flash process

$h_{Fi}, H_{Fi} =$ enthalpy of one mole of a pure component i in the liquid and vapor states, respectively, at the temperature of the flash

$H(X)_F =$ enthalpy of one mole calculated on the basis of the composition of the feed, the X_i's, and the vapor emthalpies, H_{Fi}'s (evaluated at the temperature T_F)

$H(x_F)_F =$ enthalpy of one mole calculated on the basis of the composition, x_{Fi}'s, of the liquid formed by the flash process and the vapor enthalpies, H_{Fi}'s (evaluated at the temperature T_F)

H_n = enthalpy of the feed evaluated at the temperature T_n

K_i = multiplier required to relate the mole fractions of component i in the vapor and liquid phases at equilibrium (i.e. $y_i = K_i x_i$)

K_b = base component;

$$\alpha_b = 1;$$

$$K_b = \sum_{i=1}^{c} \frac{y_i}{\alpha_i} = \frac{1}{\sum_{i=1}^{c} \alpha_i x_i}$$

K_{Fi} = value of K for component i at the temperature and pressure of the flash process

L_F = molal flow rate of liquid from the flash process

$T_{\text{U.L.}}, T_{\text{L.L.}}$ = upper and lower limits, respectively, of the curve-fits for the K-data

$T_{\text{B.P.}}, T_{\text{D.P.}}$ = bubble point and dew point temperatures, respectively

V_F = molal flow rate of vapor from the flash process

x_i = mole fraction of component i in the liquid phase

x_{Fi} = mole fraction of component i in the liquid phase leaving the flash process

X_i = total mole fraction of component i in the feed F, regardless of state

y_i = mole fraction of component i in the vapor phase

y_{Fi} = mole fraction of component i in the vapor phase leaving the flash zone

Greek Letters

α_i = relative volatility; defined by Equation (2–9)

$\delta_n(T_n)$ = difference between the known or specified value for the feed enthalpy and the value at the temperature T_n

λ_{Fi} = latent heat of vaporization for component i at the temperature T_F

$\sum_{H}, \sum_{L}$ = sum over all of the single phase heavy and single phase light components, respectively

$\sum_{i \neq H, L}$ = sum over all of the components in the particular system except the single phase heavies and lights

ψ = fraction of the feed leaving the flash process in the liquid phase;

$$\psi = \frac{L_F}{F}$$

Ψ = fraction of the feed leaving the flash process in the vapor phase;

$$\Psi = \frac{V_F}{F}$$

Subscripts

F = a property or quantity evaluated at the temperature and pressure of the flash process

H = single phase heavy component; one which appears in the liquid phase alone

i = a particular component, $i = 1$ through $i = c$

n = number of the trial calculation

PROBLEMS

2–1 Show that for a binary mixture at equilibrium at a given temperature and pressure, the composition of the liquid is given by

$$x_1 = \frac{1 - K_2}{K_1 - K_2}$$

At any given pressure a temperature can be found such that x_1 is either negative or greater than unity. Give the physical interpretations for these values of x.

2–2 For a given binary mixture the relationship between the vapor and liquid phases at a given pressure may be represented by the conventional boiling point diagram (Figure P2–2).

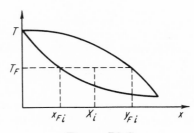

Figure P2–2

Show that if a feed with the composition X_i is flashed at the temperature T_F (and at the pressure consistent with the data given by the boiling point diagram) that the ratio of the length of $\overline{X_i y_{Fi}}$ to the length $\overline{x_{Fi} X_i}$ is equal to L_F/V_F.

2–3 For one mole of feed of a binary mixture, show that the moles of vapor (or liquid) formed by a flash process may be expressed in terms of the K-values of the two components and the composition of the feed as follows:

$$V_F = \frac{1}{1 - K_{F1}} + \frac{X_1(K_{F2} - K_{F1})}{(1 - K_{F2})(1 - K_{F1})}$$

2–4 Frequently equilibrium relationships are represented by Raoult's law,

$$p_i = P_i x_i$$

where

p_i = partial pressure of component i in the gas phase; $p_i = P y_i$, where P is the total pressure.

P_i = vapor pressure of component i at the equilibrium temperature.

Beginning with this equilibrium relationship, develop the expressions corresponding to Equations (2–22) and (2–23).

2–5 Locate the roots of the function $P(\Psi)$, Equation (2–36), with respect to the K_i's.

2–6 (a) Show that the real positive root of $p(\psi)$ for a system which contains volatile components and both single phase lights and heavies is bounded as shown by Equation (2–39).

(b) For a feed which contains volatile components and single phase heavies, show that Equation (2–42) represents a necessary condition for the flash to occur.

(c) Similarly, for a feed consisting of volatile components and single phase lights, show that Equation (2–40) represents a necessary condition for the function $p(\psi)$ to have a real root bounded as indicated by Equation (2–41).

2–7 It is desired to separate three high boiling organic acids from a soluble nonvolatile material by steam-flash distillation. The initial mixture contains 80 moles of the acids and 20 moles of the nonvolatile material. The organic acid mixture contains 30 moles of the low boiler and 25 moles of the other two. The flash distillation is to be carried out at 100°C and at a total pressure of 200 mm of mercury. The vapor pressures of the acids are 20, 14, and 8 mm of mercury at 100°C. Calculate the moles of liquid, L_F, the moles of vapor, V_F, and the moles of steam required if the vapor leaving the flash is to be 95 mole percent steam.

Hint: In the same manner as shown in Reference (4), this type of vaporization may be represented by

$$p(\psi) = \sum_{i \neq L} \frac{x_{fi}}{1 - \psi\left[1 - \dfrac{(1 - y_L)}{K_{Fi}}\right]} - 1$$

when a value of ψ is found such that $p(\psi) = 0$, and where

$\psi = L_F/F$, where F represents the moles of feed exclusive of steam; $V_F + L_F = F$.

$x_{fi} =$ mole fraction of a volatile component i; based on F.

$y_L =$ specified mole fraction of the steam in the total vapor (V_L (steam) + V_F).

Ans. $L_F = 73.14$

2–8 For the case where the nonvolatile components are immiscible in the liquid phase, calculate the moles of steam required to vaporize all of the organic acids in the feed for Problem 2–7. The temperature and pressure of the flash are the same as those stated for Problem 2–7.

Hint: As shown in Reference (4), this process is represented by

$$\frac{V_L}{F^\circ} = \left[\sum_{i \neq H, L} \frac{F_i^\circ/F^\circ}{K_{Fi}}\right] - 1$$

where

$F_i^\circ =$ moles of volatile component i in the volatile part of the feed F° exclusive of steam,

$V_L =$ moles of steam required, and

$H =$ Refers to the non-volatile, immiscible liquid.

Ans. 15.026 moles of steam

LITERATURE CITED

1. Amundson, N. R. and A. J. Pontinen, "Multicomponent Distillation Calculations on a Large Digital Computer," *Ind. Eng. Chem.*, **50, 730** (1958).

2. Brown, G. G. and Associates, *Unit Operations* (New York: John Wiley & Sons, Inc., 1953), p. 389.

3. Holland, C. D. and R. R. Davison, "Simplify Flash Distillation Calculations," *Petroleum Refiner*, **36,** No. 3, 183 (1957).

4. Holland, C. D. and W. B. Hayes, "Steam-Flash Vaporization of Multicomponent Mixtures," *Petroleum Refiner*, **36,** No. 4, 203 (1957).

5. Lyster, W. N., S. L. Sullivan, Jr., D. S. Billingsley and C. D. Holland, "Figure Distillation This New Way: Part 1—New Convergence Method Will Handle Many Cases," *Petroleum Refiner*, **38,** No. 6, 221 (1959).

Solution of the Material Balance and Equilibrium Relationships for Conventional Distillation Columns

3

A conventional distillation column is defined as one in which a single feed is introduced and two streams are withdrawn, the top and bottom products. Because of the highly nonlinear form of the equations which describe the process of distillation of multicomponent mixtures, it is necessary to solve the general problem by use of trial and error procedures. As discussed in Chapter 1, the use of such procedures requires the choice of a set of independent variables. Most all of the proposed calculational procedures stem from two basically different choices of the independent variables. Lewis and Matheson (7) proposed the selection of the terminal rates as the independent variables; whereas Thiele and Geddes (12) selected the temperature of each plate as an independent variable. Until the advent of high speed computers, calculations were carried out by use of these methods combined with rather informal convergence procedures. After a given trial calculation had been performed, the calculated values of the variables were compared with the assumed values employed to make the given trial calculation. In some instances the calculated values were used to make the next trial calculation. Here this procedure is called direct-iteration. In other cases the results obtained by a given trial calculation were used to select the assumed values of the variables for the next trial.

All of the calculational procedures and convergence methods presented in this chapter are based on the use of either the calculational procedure proposed by Lewis and Matheson (7) or that of Thiele and Geddes (12). In order to illustrate these fundamental procedures, a simple problem is solved by each method. Before consideration of this problem, certain principles and conventions used throughout this book are presented.

46

PRINCIPLES, CONVENTION, AND NOTATION

In the statement of the equations describing conventional columns, two types of condensers are considered, total and partial. In the case of a total condenser, all of the vapor leaving the top plate of the column is condensed to the liquid state. Part of the liquid is withdrawn as the top product at a molal flow rate denoted by D. The remainder is returned to the column at the molal flow rate L_0. This stream is sometimes called the external reflux. The term "partial condenser" as used here means that the vapor leaving the top plate of the column is only partially condensed. The vapor formed is withdrawn as the distillate and the liquid produced is returned to the column as reflux. A partial condenser is treated as an equilibrium stage. In order to supply vapor to the column, a reboiler is located at the bottom of the unit. Upon leaving the bottom plate of the column, the liquid enters the reboiler and is partially vaporized. The vapor produced is returned to the bottom plate and passes back up through the column. The liquid withdrawn from the reboiler is called either the bottom product or simply, bottoms. The molal withdrawal rate of bottoms is denoted by B. The reboiler is also treated as an equilibrium stage.

The rectifying section of the column consists of the condenser and all plates above the feed plate; the stripping section consists of the remainder of the column, the feed plate and all plates below it including the reboiler. The plates are numbered consecutively down from the top of the column to the reboiler. The condenser is assigned the number zero, the top plate the number 1, the feed plate the number f, the bottom plate the number N, and the reboiler the number $N + 1$. Each stage is assumed to be perfect; that is, the vapor leaving a plate is assumed to be in physical equilibrium with the liquid leaving.

The total molal rate at which vapor leaves plate j is denoted by V_j, while the rate at which vapor enters plate $j - 1$ is denoted by $\bar{V}_j$. This notation was adopted in order to account for either the introduction or the withdrawal of a stream between plates. Thus V_j is equal to $\bar{V}_j$ provided a stream is neither introduced nor withdrawn between plates $j - 1$ and j. Similarly the molal rate of flow of liquid from plate j is denoted by L_j and the rate of flow of liquid onto plate $j + 1$ by $\bar{L}_j$. The molal rates of flow of the individual components are used almost exclusively. These vapor and liquid rates are denoted by the lower case letters "v" and "l." The subscript i is used to identify the individual rates with respect to component. These rates are related to the total vapor and liquid rates as follows:

$$v_{ji} = V_j y_{ji}, \qquad l_{ji} = L_j x_{ji}$$
$$\bar{v}_{ji} = \bar{V}_j \bar{y}_{ji}, \qquad \bar{l}_{ji} = \bar{L}_j \bar{x}_{ji} \qquad (3\text{-}1)$$
$$d_i = D X_{Di}, \qquad b_i = B x_{Bi}$$

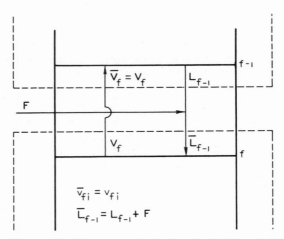

Figure 3-1. Conditions on the feed plate for bubble point liquid feeds.

In the identification of the composition of the distillate, the symbol "X_{Di}" is used to denote the total mole fraction of component i in the distillate regardless of state.

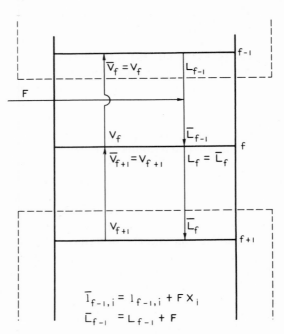

Figure 3-2. Conditions on the feed plate for subcooled feeds.

Since the vapor and liquid streams leaving plate j are assumed to be in equilibrium, the flow rates of the individual components may be related by use of either absorption or stripping factors. This relationship is developed in the following manner. Multiplication of both sides of the equilibrium relationship

$$y_{ji} = K_{ji}x_{ji} \tag{3-2}$$

by V_jL_j yields

$$L_jv_{ji} = K_{ji}V_jl_{ji} \tag{3-3}$$

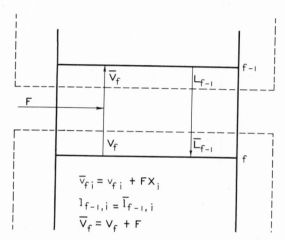

Figure 3–3. Conditions on the feed plate for a dew point vapor feed.

Thus

$$v_{ji} = \left(\frac{K_{ji}V_j}{L_j}\right) l_{ji} = S_{ji}l_{ji} \tag{3-4}$$

Alternately, Equation (3–3) may be solved for l_{ji} to give

$$l_{ji} = \left(\frac{L_j}{K_{ji}V_j}\right) v_{ji} = A_{ji}v_{ji} \tag{3-5}$$

It should be noted that $A_{ji} = 1/S_{ji}$.

Feeds having any one of five general thermal conditions are considered, and the action assumed to occur at the feed plate for each type of feed is represented schematically in Figures 3–1 through 3–5. A boiling point liquid feed is defined as one that enters the column as a liquid at its boiling point at the column pressure. A subcooled feed is defined as one that enters the column as a liquid at a temperature below its bubble point at the column

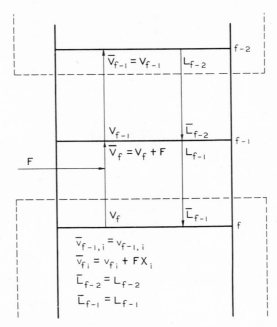

Figure 3–4. Conditions on the feed plate for a superheated feed.

pressure. For boiling point and subcooled feeds assume that upon entering the column, the liquid mixes perfectly with the liquid on the feed plate

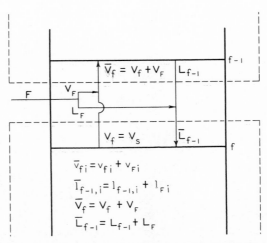

Figure 3–5. Conditions on the feed plate for a partially vaporized feed.

and comes to equilibrium with the vapor immediately above it. A dew point vapor feed is one that enters the column as a vapor at its dew point at the column pressure. A superheated feed enters the column as a vapor at a temperature above its dew point at the column pressure. For dew point and superheated feeds, assume that upon entering the column, the vapor mixes perfectly with the vapor rising from the feed plate and enters the plate above. (Equilibrium between the mixed vapor and the liquid on the feed plate is not assumed.) A partially vaporized feed consists of an equilibrium mixture of liquid and vapor at the flash temperature (T_F) and at the column pressure. As illustrated in Figure 3–5, the liquid part of the feed flows onto the feed plate, mixes perfectly with the liquid on the tray, and comes to equilibrium with the vapor immediately above it. The vapor part of the feed is considered to mix perfectly with the vapor rising from the feed plate and then to enter the plate above the feed plate.

THE CALCULATIONAL PROCEDURE PROPOSED BY THIELE AND GEDDES (12)

The choice of the temperatures throughout the column as the independent variables sets this calculational procedure apart from all others. The following specifications are necessary to apply this calculational procedure to an existing column: the number of plates in each section of the column, the rate of flow as well as the composition and thermal condition of the feed, and two other variables such as the distillate rate, D, and the reflux rate, L_0. In the following statement of the equations for a conventional column, the notation differs from that originally proposed by Thiele and Geddes (12). As in Hummel's notation (6), molal flow rates for the individual components are employed rather than the combination of total rates of flow and mole fractions. Absorption and stripping factors are employed as suggested by Donnell and Turbin (3). In the rectifying section each material balance is written around a given plate and the condenser; in the stripping section each balance includes a given plate and the reboiler. For a conventional column the following expressions represent a combination of the material balances and the equilibrium relationships.

Rectifying Section:

$$v_{1i}/d_i = A_{0i} + 1, \qquad \text{(balance around condenser)} \qquad (3\text{--}6)$$

$$v_{ji}/d_i = A_{j-1,i}(v_{j-1,i}/d_i) + 1, \qquad 2 \leqq j \leqq f - 1 \qquad (3\text{--}7)$$

$$\bar{v}_{fi}/d_i = A_{f-1,i}(v_{f-1,i}/d_i) + 1 \qquad (3\text{--}8)$$

Stripping Section:

$$\bar{l}_{f-1,\, i}/b_i = S_{fi}(l_{fi}/b_i) + 1 \tag{3-9}$$

$$l_{j-1,i}/b_i = S_{ji}(l_{ji}/b_i) + 1, \qquad f + 1 \leqq j \leqq N \tag{3-10}$$

$$l_{Ni}/b_i = S_{N+1,i} + 1, \qquad \text{(balance around reboiler)} \tag{3-11}$$

where

$A_{0i} = L_0/K_{0i}D$ for a partial condenser; for a total condenser $A_{0i} = L_0/D$.

$A_{ji} = $ absorption factor; $A_{ji} = L_j/K_{ji}V_j$.

$\bar{l}_{f-1,i} = $ molal rate at which component i, in the liquid state, flows onto the feed plate f; $\bar{l}_{f-1,i} = l_{f-1,i} + l_{Fi}$.

$l_{Fi} = $ molal rate at which component i enters the column in the liquid part of the feed.

$S_{ji} = $ stripping factor; $S_{ji} = K_{ji}V_j/L_j$ and $S_{N+1,i} = K_{N+1,i}V_{N+1}/B$.

$\bar{v}_{fi} = $ molal rate at which component i, in the vapor state, enters plate $f - 1$; $\bar{v}_{fi} = v_{fi} + v_{Fi}$.

$v_{Fi} = $ molal rate at which component i enters the column in the vapor part of the feed.

Although Equations (3–6) through (3–11) consist of combinations of equilibrium relationships and material balances, hereafter in the interest of simplicity these combinations are referred to as material balances. For the rectifying section Equations (3–6) through (3–8) are developed in the following manner. A material balance around the condenser yields

$$v_{1i} = l_{0i} + d_i \tag{3-12}$$

Upon dividing both sides of this equation by d_i and noting that for a partial condenser,

$$\frac{l_{0i}}{d_i} = \frac{L_0 x_{0i}}{DX_{Di}} = \frac{L_0 x_{0i}}{DK_{0i}x_{0i}} = \frac{L_0}{K_{0i}D} = A_{0i}$$

the desired result, Equation (3–6) is obtained. Since $x_{0i} = X_{Di}$ for a total condenser, $l_{0i}/d_i = L_0/D$, which is also called A_{0i}. A material balance around any plate j and the top of the column yields

$$\frac{v_{ji}}{d_i} = \frac{l_{j-1,i}}{d_i} + 1 \tag{3-13}$$

upon division of both sides of the expression by d_i. Since $l_{j-1,i} = A_{j-1,i}v_{j-1,i}$, it follows that

$$\frac{l_{j-1,i}}{d_i} = A_{j-1,i}\left(\frac{v_{j-1,i}}{d_i}\right) \tag{3-14}$$

Substitution of this expression for $(l_{j-1,i}/d_i)$ into Equation (3–13) gives the desired result, Equation (3–7).

The equations for the stripping section are developed in a manner analogous to that shown for the rectifying section. A material balance around the reboiler may be written as follows:

$$\frac{l_{Ni}}{b_i} = \frac{v_{N+1,i}}{b_i} + 1 \tag{3-15}$$

Since

$$\frac{v_{N+1,i}}{b_i} = \frac{V_{N+1}y_{N+1,i}}{Bx_{Bi}} = \frac{V_{N+1}K_{N+1,i}x_{Bi}}{Bx_{Bi}}$$

$$= \frac{V_{N+1}K_{N+1,i}}{B} = S_{N+1,i}$$

Equation (3–15) reduces to Equation (3–11). A balance around the bottom of the column and any plate j yields

$$\frac{l_{j-1,i}}{b_i} = \frac{v_{ji}}{b_i} + 1 \tag{3-16}$$

Since

$$\frac{v_{ji}}{b_i} = S_{ji}\left(\frac{l_{ji}}{b_i}\right) \tag{3-17}$$

the result given by Equation (3–10) is obtained.

For a given set of L/V's and temperatures, the flow rates of the individual components are determined by use of Equations (3–6) through (3–11). It should be pointed out that with the introduction of enthalpy balances for the calculation of the liquid and vapor rates, the latter may be regarded as dependent variables for all trials after the first one. In the application of Equations (3–6) through (3–11), calculations are commenced at each end of the column and continued to the feed plate. For the case of a boiling point liquid feed, $\bar{v}_{fi} = v_{fi}$. Thus

$$\frac{b_i}{d_i} = \frac{\bar{v}_{fi}/d_i}{v_{fi}/b_i} \tag{3-18}$$

where $\bar{v}_{fi}/d_i$ is calculated by use of the equations for the rectifying section and v_{fi}/b_i by the stripping section equations; that is, $v_{fi}/b_i = S_{fi}(l_{fi}/b_i)$ when l_{fi}/b_i is calculated by Equation (3–10). After b_i/d_i has been determined, d_i is given by

$$d_i = \frac{FX_i}{1 + (b_i/d_i)} \qquad (3\text{–}19)$$

which is obtained by making an over-all material balance. Use of this value of d_i permits the calculation of the individual flow rates throughout the column. The expression for b_i/d_i for a partially vaporized feed is developed as follows. Equation (3–8) may be written in the form

$$\frac{v_{fi}}{d_i} + \frac{v_{Fi}}{d_i} = \frac{l_{f-1,i}}{d_i} + 1 \qquad (3\text{–}20)$$

which may be rearranged to

$$\left(\frac{v_{fi}}{b_i}\right)\left(\frac{b_i}{d_i}\right) + \left(\frac{v_{Fi}}{FX_i}\right)\left(\frac{FX_i}{d_i}\right) = \frac{l_{f-1,i}}{d_i} + 1 \qquad (3\text{–}21)$$

Since

$$\frac{v_{Fi}}{FX_i} = 1 - \frac{l_{Fi}}{FX_i}$$

and

$$\frac{FX_i}{d_i} = 1 + \frac{b_i}{d_i}$$

Equation (3–21) may be solved for b_i/d_i to give

$$\frac{b_i}{d_i} = \frac{(l_{f-1,i}/d_i) + (l_{Fi}/FX_i)}{(v_{fi}/b_i) + (v_{Fi}/FX_i)} \qquad (3\text{–}22)$$

When the appropriate values for l_{Fi} and v_{Fi} are employed, Equation (3–22) may be used to calculate b_i/d_i for a feed of any thermal condition. For bubble point liquid and subcooled feeds, $l_{Fi} = FX_i$ and $v_{Fi} = 0$. For feeds that enter the column as dew point and superheated vapors, $v_{Fi} = FX_i$ and $l_{Fi} = 0$.

Before presentation of further theoretical considerations, the calculational procedure of Thiele and Geddes may be illustrated by solving a relatively simple distillation problem, Example 3–1. The statement of this example is given in Table 3–1. In order to focus attention on the fundamental principles of this method, the total flow rates of the vapor and liquid streams are taken to be constant within each section of the column. As discussed in a later chapter, this condition may be realized for any column by use of intercoolers (or heaters) as required for each plate. Also,

TABLE 3-1 Statement and Specifications for Example 3-1

Comp. No.	FX_i	α_i	Specifications
1	33.3	1	Total condenser, boiling point liquid feed, distillate rate (D) is 50 moles per hour, $N = 3, f = 2,\ V_1 = V_2 = V_3 = V_4 = 100,$
2	33.3	2	$L_0 = L_1 = 50,\ L_2 = L_3 = 150.$
3	33.4	3	On the basis of these specifications, find the product distribution.

the relative volatilities are taken to be constant throughout the column. The specifications are represented schematically by Figure 3–6. The first trial calculation is made on the basis of an assumed temperature profile. Fortunately the calculational procedure is rather insensitive to the profile assumed initially. In view of this insensitivity, the choice of $K_{1b} = K_{2b} = K_{3b} = 1.0$ was made. Calculations were commenced at each end of the column and continued to the feed plate as shown in Table 3–2. Then

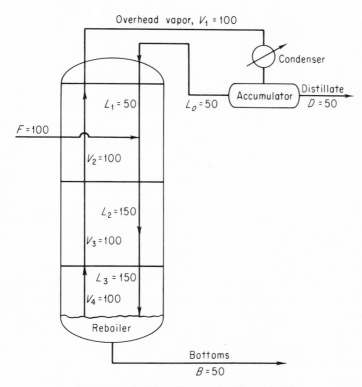

Figure 3–6. Flow diagram for Example 3-1.

TABLE 3-2 Solution of Example 3-1 by the calculational procedure of Thiele and Geddes

TRIAL No. 1: Assume $K_{1b} = K_{2b} = K_{3b} = K_{4b} = 1.0$

1. Calculations for the rectifying Section

Comp. No.	$\dfrac{L_0}{D}$	$\dfrac{v_{1i}}{d_i} = \dfrac{L_0}{D} + 1$	$K_{1i} = K_{1b}\alpha_i$	$A_{1i} = \dfrac{L_1}{K_{1i}V_1}$	$\dfrac{l_{1i}}{d_i} = A_{1i}\left(\dfrac{v_{1i}}{d_i}\right)$	$\dfrac{v_{2i}}{d_i} = \dfrac{l_{1i}}{d_i} + 1$
1	1.0	2.0	1.0	0.5	1.0	2.0
2	1.0	2.0	2.0	0.25	0.5	1.5
3	1.0	2.0	3.0	0.1666667	0.33333334	1.33333333

2. Calculations for the stripping Section

Comp. No.	$K_{4i} = K_{4b}\alpha_i$	$S_{4i} = \dfrac{K_{4i}V_4}{B}$	$\dfrac{l_{3i}}{b_i} = S_{4i} + 1$	$K_{3i} = K_{3b}\alpha_i$	$S_{3i} = \dfrac{K_{3i}V_3}{L_3}$	$\dfrac{v_{3i}}{b_i} = S_{3i}\left(\dfrac{l_{3i}}{b_i}\right)$
1	1.0	2.0	3.0	1.0	0.66666666	1.9999998
2	2.0	4.0	5.0	2.0	1.3333333	6.6666660
3	3.0	6.0	7.0	3.0	1.9999999	13.999999

Table 3-2 (Continued)

Comp. No.	$\dfrac{l_{2i}}{b_i} = \dfrac{v_{3i}}{b_i} + 1$	$K_{2i} = K_{2o}\alpha_i$	$S_{2i} = \dfrac{K_{2i}V_2}{L_2}$	$\dfrac{v_{2i}}{b_i} = S_{2i}\dfrac{l_{2i}}{b_i}$	Product distribution	
					$\dfrac{b_i}{d_i} = \dfrac{v_{2i}/d_i}{v_{2i}/b_i}$	$d_i = \dfrac{FX_i}{1 + b_i/d_i}$
1	2.9999999	1	0.6666666	1.9999999	1.0000000	16.649999
2	7.6666666	2	1.3333333	10.222222	0.14673913	29.038862
3	14.999999	3	1.9999999	29.999995	0.04444444	31.978724
						77.667585

3. Calculation of the compositions and K_b's by direct-iteration

Comp. No.	$\dfrac{d_i}{\Sigma d_i} = X_{Di}$	$\alpha_i X_{Di}$	$\dfrac{b_i}{\Sigma b_i} = x_{Bi}$	$\alpha_i x_{Bi}$	$\left(\dfrac{l_{1i}}{d_i}\right) d_i$	$x_{1i} = \dfrac{(l_{1i}/d_i)\,d_i}{\Sigma (l_{1i}/d_i)\,(d_i)}$
1	0.21437513	0.21437513	0.74555309	0.74555309	16.6499999	0.39804913
2	0.37388651	0.74777302	0.19080507	0.38161014	14.519431	0.34711395
3	0.41173838	1.2352151	0.06364184	0.190925523	10.659575	0.25483692
		2.1973635		1.31808875	41.829005	

$$K_{ob} = \dfrac{1}{\Sigma \alpha_i X_{Di}} \qquad K_{4b} = \dfrac{1}{\Sigma \alpha_i x_{Bi}}$$

$$K_{ob} = 0.45509088 \qquad K_{4b} = 0.75867425$$

TABLE 3-2 (Continued)

Comp. No.	$\alpha_i x_{1i}$	$x_{2i} = \dfrac{(l_{2i}/b_i)b_i}{\Sigma(l_{2i}/b_i)b_i}$	$\alpha_i x_{2i}$	$x_{3i} = \dfrac{(l_{3i}/b_i)b_i}{\Sigma(l_{3i}/b_i)b_i}$	$\alpha_i x_{3i}$
1	0.39804913	0.48057559	0.48057559	0.61511278	0.61511278
2	0.69422790	0.31431014	0.62862028	0.2623704	0.5247308
3	0.76451076	0.20511427	0.61534281	0.12251681	0.3675043
	1.8567878		1.7245387		1.50740401

$$K_{1b} = \frac{1}{\Sigma \alpha_i x_{1i}}$$

$$K_{1b} = 0.53856451$$

$$K_{2b} = \frac{1}{\Sigma \alpha_i x_{2i}}$$

$$K_{2b} = 0.5798652$$

$$K_{3b} = \frac{1}{\Sigma \alpha_i x_{3i}}$$

$$K_{3b} = 0.66339216$$

b_i/d_i for each component was computed after which d_i was obtained by an over-all material balance. The step-by-step calculational procedure used to solve Example 3–1 is sometimes called "nesting."

Direct-Iteration

Inasmuch as the subject of convergence methods is treated in subsequent chapters, it will not be dealt with to any great extent here. However, since the method of direct-iteration appears to be such a logical next step in the solution of a problem, it is presented. Including Thiele and Geddes (12), numerous authors among whom are those given by References (1, 3, 4, 8, 9) have employed either direct-iteration or direct-iteration with modifications in order to obtain solutions to multicomponent distillation problems. As described in Chapter 1, the method of direct-iteration consists of taking the calculated values of the variables as the assumed values for the next trial. In the case of Illustrative Example 3–1, observe that at the end of the first trial the calculated values of the variables are not in agreement with the specified values. For example, the sum of the d_i's is not equal to the specified value of D. Neither do the v_{ji}'s nor l_{ji}'s add to give the specified values of L_j and V_j. By the method of direct-iteration the improved temperature profile is selected on the basis of the calculated values of the variables as follows:

$$y_{ji} = \frac{(v_{ji}/d_i)d_i}{\sum\limits_{i=1}^{c} \left(\frac{v_{ji}}{d_i}\right) d_i} \qquad (3\text{–}23)$$

$$x_{ji} = \frac{(l_{ji}/d_i)d_i}{\sum\limits_{i=1}^{c} \left(\frac{l_{ji}}{d_i}\right) d_i} = \frac{(l_{ji}/b_i)b_i}{\sum\limits_{i=1}^{c} \left(\frac{l_{ji}}{b_i}\right) b_i} \qquad (3\text{–}24)$$

The improved temperatures (or the K_b's) for the next trial are calculated by use of either the y_{ji}'s or x_{ji}'s and either Equation (2–15) or (2–13), respectively. Although the bubble point procedure was used in both sections of the column in the solution of Example 3–1, the dew point procedure could have been used in either section. Since the bubble point procedure is recommended for general use in a subsequent chapter because it leads to a faster rate of convergence for hydrocarbon systems, it is employed here. For the second trial calculation the A_{ji}'s and S_{ji}'s are calculated on the basis of the specified values of L_j, V_j, and D; the K_{ji}'s appearing in these expressions are evaluated on the basis of the improved temperature profile. The results of the second and several successive trials are listed in Table 3–3. For many problems the method of direct-iteration gives rapid convergence to the desired solution. This method is further evaluated in a subsequent chapter.

TABLE 3–3 Solution of Example 3–1 by the Thiele and Geddes Calculational Procedure and Direct-Iteration

Plate No.	Calculated Values of K_b Trial No.			
	1	2	3	4*
0	0.455	0.422	0.416	0.414
1	0.539	0.487	0.470	0.467
2	0.580	0.526	0.515	0.512
3	0.663	0.581	0.561	0.555
4	0.759	0.661	0.639	0.633
D (Calculated)	77.67	57.57	52.14	51.09

* All of the K_b's were correct to eight digits at the end of the 11th trial.

Although as shown in the following section the calculated values of the flow rates of the individual components are in theory independent of the direction of calculation, round-off error is minimized when calculations are made from the top and bottom of a conventional column to the feed plate.

Independence of the Individual Flow Rates of the Direction of Calculation

Although the formula for b_i/d_i, Equation (3–22), was developed on the basis of making calculations up from the bottom and down from the top of the column to the feed plate, equivalent expressions for b_i/d_i may be developed from the equations which represent component-material balances written around either end of the column and any given plate. When balances are written around the bottom of the column and any plate j, Equations (3–9) through (3–11) are applicable for the stripping section. A balance around the bottom of the column and any plate j above the feed plate is represented by

$$\frac{l_{j-1,i}}{b_i} = S_{ji}\left(\frac{l_{ji}}{b_i}\right) + \left(1 - \frac{FX_i}{b_i}\right), \qquad 1 \leq j \leq f - 1 \qquad (3\text{-}25)$$

Before this expression may be applied, it is necessary to evaluate b_i. An outline of the development of the expression for b_i/d_i follows. After b_i/d_i has been determined, b_i and d_i may be calculated by use of the over-all material balance, Equation (3–19). Appearing in the final expression for b_i/d_i is the term v_{fi}/b_i, which is evaluated by making calculations up from the bottom of the column to the feed plate as indicated by Equations (3–10) and (3–11). After l_{fi}/b_i has been computed by Equation (3–10), v_{fi}/b_i is evaluated by use of the equilibrium relationship,

$$v_{fi}/b_i = S_{fi}(l_{fi}/b_i) \qquad (3\text{-}26)$$

where

$$S_{fi} = K_{fi}V_f/L_f$$

The K_{fi}'s are evaluated at the temperature of the feed plate, and V_f and L_f represent the total rates at which the vapor and liquid streams leave the feed plate. The development of the expression for b_i/d_i is initiated by restating Equation (3–9) in the following form,

$$\frac{l_{f-1,i}}{b_i} = \frac{v_{fi}}{b_i} + \left(1 - \frac{l_{Fi}}{b_i}\right) \qquad (3\text{-}27)$$

For plate $f - 1$, Equation (3–25) gives

$$\frac{l_{f-2,i}}{b_i} = S_{f-1,i}\left(\frac{l_{f-1,i}}{b_i}\right) + \left(1 - \frac{FX_i}{b_i}\right) \qquad (3\text{-}28)$$

Elimination of $(l_{f-1,i}/b_i)$ from Equations (3–27) and (3–28) yields

$$\frac{l_{f-2,i}}{b_i} = S_{f-1,i}\left(\frac{v_{fi}}{b_i}\right) + S_{f-1,i}\left(1 - \frac{l_{Fi}}{b_i}\right) + \left(1 - \frac{FX_i}{b_i}\right) \qquad (3\text{-}29)$$

Since an over-all material balance requires that

$$1 - \frac{FX_i}{b_i} = -\frac{d_i}{b_i}$$

and since

$$1 - \frac{l_{Fi}}{b_i} = 1 - \left(\frac{l_{Fi}}{FX_i}\right)\left(\frac{FX_i}{b_i}\right) = 1 - \left(\frac{l_{Fi}}{FX_i}\right)\left(1 + \frac{d_i}{b_i}\right)$$

$$= \frac{v_{Fi}}{FX_i} - \left(\frac{l_{Fi}}{FX_i}\right)\left(\frac{d_i}{b_i}\right)$$

Equation (3–29) reduces to

$$\frac{l_{f-2,i}}{b_i} = S_{f-1,i}\left(\frac{v_{fi}}{b_i}\right) + S_{f-1,i}\left[\frac{v_{Fi}}{FX_i} - \left(\frac{l_{Fi}}{FX_i}\right)\left(\frac{d_i}{b_i}\right)\right] - \left(\frac{d_i}{b_i}\right) \qquad (3–30)$$

Continuation of this substitutional process throughout the remainder of the rectifying section leads to the desired expression,

$$\frac{b_i}{d_i} = \frac{\Phi_i + \phi_i\left(\dfrac{l_{Fi}}{FX_i}\right)}{\phi_i\left(\dfrac{v_{fi}}{b_i} + \dfrac{v_{Fi}}{FX_i}\right)} \qquad (3–31)$$

where

$$\phi_i = S_{0i}S_{1i}\ldots S_{f-2,i}S_{f-1,i}$$

$$\Phi_i = S_{0i}S_{1i}\ldots S_{f-3,i}S_{f-2,i} + S_{0i}S_{1i}\ldots$$

$$\ldots S_{f-4,i}S_{f-3,i} + \ldots + S_{0i}S_{1i} + S_{0i} + 1$$

When component-material balances are written around the top of the column and any plate j, Equations (3–6), (3–7), and (3–8) are applicable for all plates above the feed plate. For the stripping section,

$$\frac{v_{ji}}{d_i} = A_{j-1,i}\left(\frac{v_{j-1,i}}{d_i}\right) + \left(1 - \frac{FX_i}{d_i}\right), \qquad f+1 \leq j \leq N+1 \qquad (3–32)$$

In a manner analogous to that used to develop Equation (3–31), it is readily shown that Equations (3–8), (3–32), and the relationships stated below Equation (3–21) lead to the desired result

$$\frac{b_i}{d_i} = \frac{\omega_i\left[\dfrac{l_{f-1,i}}{d_i} + \dfrac{l_{Fi}}{FX_i}\right]}{\Omega_i + \omega_i\left(\dfrac{v_{Fi}}{FX_i}\right)} \qquad (3–33)$$

where

$$\omega_i = A_{N+1,i}A_{Ni}\ldots A_{f+1,i}A_{fi}$$

$$\Omega_i = 1 + A_{N+1,i} + A_{N+1,i}A_{Ni} + \ldots + A_{N+1,i}A_{Ni}\ldots A_{f+2,i}A_{f+1,i}$$

In order to prove that for a given set of L/V's and K's, the flow rates of the individual components are independent of the direction in which the calculations are made, it will be shown first that all of the expressions for b_i/d_i, Equations (3–22), (3–31), and (3–33) are equivalent. The equivalence of Equations (3–22) and (3–31) is shown by deriving Equation (3–22) from (3–31). First, it is to be noted that $l_{f-1,i}/d_i$ may be represented by the following series, which is obtained by application of the previously described substitutional process to Equations (3–6) and (3–7)

$$l_{f-1,i}/d_i = A_{f-1,i}\ldots A_{0i} + A_{f-1,i}\ldots A_{1i} + \ldots + A_{f-1,i} \qquad (3\text{–}34)$$

Division of the numerator and denominator of Equation (3–31) by ϕ_i gives an expression containing the ratio Φ_i/ϕ_i which may be expressed in terms of the A_{ji}'s as follows:

$$\Phi_i/\phi_i = A_{f-1,i} + A_{f-2,i}A_{f-1,i} + \ldots + A_{0i}\ldots A_{f-1,i}$$

Upon comparison of this expression with Equation (3–34), it is seen that

$$\Phi_i/\phi_i = l_{f-1,i}/d_i \qquad (3\text{–}35)$$

When Φ_i/ϕ_i in Equation (3–31) is replaced by its equivalent as given by Equation (3–35), the desired result, Equation (3–22), is obtained.

In proving the equivalence of Equations (3–22) and (3–33), note that the following formula for v_{fi}/b_i is obtained by combining Equations (3–10) and (3–11).

$$v_{fi}/b_i = S_{fi}\ldots S_{N+1,i} + S_{fi}\ldots S_{Ni} + \ldots + S_{fi} \qquad (3\text{–}36)$$

Division of the numerator and denominator of Equation (3–33) by ω_i gives an expression that contains the ratio Ω_i/ω_i. This ratio may be expressed in terms of the S_{ji}'s as follows:

$$\Omega_i/\omega_i = S_{fi}\ldots S_{N+1,i} + S_{fi}\ldots S_{Ni} + S_{fi} \qquad (3\text{–}37)$$

Comparison of Equations (3–36) and (3–37) shows that the right hand sides are equal. Thus substitution of v_{fi}/b_i for the ratio in the expression obtained by division yields the desired result, Equation (3–22).

When calculations are made from the top of the column down to a particular plate located n plates below the top and k plates above the feed plate, the following expression is obtained by combining Equations (3–6) and (3–7).

$$v_{ni}/d_i = A_{n-1,i}\ldots A_{0i} + A_{n-1,i}\ldots A_{1i} + \ldots + A_{n-1,i} + 1 \qquad (3\text{–}38)$$

This same result is obtained by making calculations from the bottom of the column to plate n as indicated by Equations (3–10), (3–11) and (3–25).

As shown previously, repeated application of Equation (3–25) gives

$$\frac{l_{f-k,i}}{b_i} = (S_{f-k+1,i}\ldots S_{f-1,i})\left[\frac{v_{fi}}{b_i} + \frac{v_{Fi}}{FX_{Fi}} - \left(\frac{l_{Fi}}{FX_{Fi}}\right)\left(\frac{d_i}{b_i}\right)\right]$$

$$- \left[1 + S_{f-k+1,i} + \ldots + S_{f-k+1,i}\ldots S_{f-2,i}\right]\left(\frac{d_i}{b_i}\right) \qquad (3\text{–}39)$$

Multiplication of both sides of Equation (3–39) by $(S_{f-k,i})(b_i/d_i)$ followed by the elimination of b_i/d_i on the right hand side of the resulting expression by use of Equation (3–31) yields

$$\frac{v_{f-k,i}}{d_i} = (S_{f-k,i}\ldots S_{f-1,i})\left[\frac{\Phi_i}{\phi_i} + \frac{l_{Fi}}{FX_{Fi}}\right]$$

$$- (S_{f-k,i}\ldots S_{f-1,i})\left(\frac{l_{Fi}}{FX_{Fi}}\right) - (S_{f-k,i} + S_{f-k+1,i}$$

$$+ \ldots + S_{f-k,i}\ldots S_{f-2,i}) \qquad (3\text{–}40)$$

Since

$$(S_{f-k,i}\ldots S_{f-1,i})\frac{\Phi_i}{\phi_i} = S_{f-k,i}\ldots S_{f-2,i} + S_{f-k,i}\ldots S_{f-3,i}$$

$$+ \ldots + S_{f-k,i} + 1 + A_{n-1,i} + A_{n-1,i}A_{n-2,i}$$

$$+ \ldots + A_{n-1,i}\ldots A_{0i} \qquad (3\text{–}41)$$

Equation (3–40) reduces to the desired result, Equation (3–38).

Although other proofs may be simpler (see Problem 3–6) than the one presented, the particular proof was selected for presentation because it makes use of the same techniques used in the subsequent treatments of complex columns, internal loops, and separated components.

SOLUTION OF THE MATERIAL BALANCE EQUATIONS BY USE OF MATRICES

Many computer programs are available for the solution of a system of linear equations by use of matrix algebra. In order to use such programs, it is necessary to supply only the coefficients of the variables and the constants appearing in the system of equations as input information. Thus the use of such a program eliminates the necessity for writing a program to solve the material balance equations. Amundson and Pontinen (1) were the first to solve multicomponent distillation problems on computers by use of matrices. The following treatment of matrices is not intended to exhaust the subject, but rather to demonstrate the fundamental operations of matrix algebra required to solve a system of linear equations. For more complete treatments see References 2, 5, and 11.

In order to demonstrate the use of matrices to obtain the solution for a system of linear equations, consider the following set of equations

$$v_{1i}/d_i = A_{0i} + 1 \tag{3-42}$$

$$v_{2i}/d_i = A_{1i}(v_{1i}/d_i) + 1 \tag{3-43}$$

$$v_{3i}/d_i = A_{2i}(v_{2i}/d_i) + 1 \tag{3-44}$$

For a column in which the feed enters as a liquid at its boiling point at the column pressure and which contains two plates above the feed plate, Equations (3–42) through (3–44) constitute the material balances for the rectifying section. For any given trial calculation, the A's are regarded as constants. In the interest of simplicity, the subscript i is dropped and the variable (v_j/d) is replaced by Z_j to give

$$Z_1 = A_0 + 1 \tag{3-45}$$

$$Z_2 = A_1Z_1 + 1 \tag{3-46}$$

$$Z_3 = A_2Z_2 + 1 \tag{3-47}$$

Before the consideration of matrices, Equations (3–45) through (3–47) are solved by two algebraic methods. The step-by-step or substitutional process that was used to solve Example 3–1 is represented by

$$Z_1 = A_0 + 1 \tag{3-48}$$

$$Z_2 = A_1(A_0 + 1) + 1 \tag{3-49}$$

$$Z_3 = A_2[A_1(A_0 + 1) + 1] + 1 = A_2A_1A_0 + A_2A_1 + A_2 + 1 \tag{3-50}$$

Since Equations (3–45) through (3–47) represent three equations in three unknowns, a solution may be obtained by algebraic elimination. Equations (3–45) through (3–47) may be restated in the form

$$Z_1 \qquad\qquad\qquad = A_0 + 1 \tag{3-51}$$

$$-A_1Z_1 + \quad Z_2 \qquad = 1 \tag{3-52}$$

$$- A_2Z_2 + Z_3 = 1 \tag{3-53}$$

Performance of the following operations yields the desired solution.

Step 1: Multiply Equation (3–51) by A_1 and add the result to Equation (3–52) to give

$$Z_1 \qquad\qquad = A_0 + 1$$

$$Z_2 \qquad = A_1(A_0 + 1) + 1$$

$$-A_2 Z_2 + Z_3 = 1$$

Step 2: Multiply the second equation by A_2 and add the result to the third equation to give

$$Z_1 \qquad = A_0 + 1$$

$$Z_2 \quad = A_1(A_0 + 1) + 1$$

$$Z_3 = A_2 A_1 (A_0 + 1) + A_2 + 1$$

which is of course identical to the solution given by Equations (3–48), (3–49), and (3–50).

This same solution will now be obtained by use of matrices. In the presentation of this method only the rule (or definition) for the multiplication of two matrices is given. As will be demonstrated, the additional rules of matrix algebra needed here are analogous to the corresponding algebraic operations which may be performed on a system of linear equations. A matrix is defined as an array of numbers arranged in m rows and n columns, which is usually enclosed by brackets as follows:

$$A = \begin{bmatrix} a_{11} & a_{12} & \cdots & a_{1n} \\ a_{21} & a_{22} & \ldots & a_{2n} \\ \vdots & \vdots & \vdots & \vdots \\ a_{m1} & a_{m2} & & a_{mn} \end{bmatrix} \tag{3–54}$$

If $m = n$, the array is called a square matrix of order n. In the applications which follow all of the matrices are square, and this situation corresponds to the case where the number of equations is equal to the number of unknowns. The a's are called the elements of the matrix. Unlike a determinate, a matrix is not equal to any number; however, it may be equal to either another matrix or product of matrices. Two matrices are said to be equal if and only if each of their corresponding elements is equal. The multiplication of matrix A and matrix B is defined only for the case where the number of columns of A is equal to the number of rows of B. Thus the operation of multiplication implied by

$$AB = C \qquad (3\text{--}55)$$

is defined by

$$\begin{bmatrix} a_{11} & a_{12} & a_{13} \\ a_{21} & a_{22} & a_{23} \\ a_{31} & a_{32} & a_{33} \end{bmatrix} \begin{bmatrix} b_{11} & b_{12} \\ b_{21} & b_{22} \\ b_{31} & b_{32} \end{bmatrix} = \begin{bmatrix} c_{11} & c_{12} \\ c_{21} & c_{22} \\ c_{31} & c_{32} \end{bmatrix} \qquad (3\text{--}56)$$

where c_{11} denotes the sum of the products of each element of row 1 of matrix A by the corresponding element of column 1 of matrix B; that is,

$$c_{11} = a_{11}b_{11} + a_{12}b_{21} + a_{13}b_{31}$$

$$c_{21} = a_{21}b_{11} + a_{22}b_{21} + a_{23}b_{31} \qquad (3\text{--}57)$$
$$\vdots \qquad \vdots \qquad \vdots \qquad \vdots$$
$$c_{32} = a_{31}b_{12} + a_{32}b_{22} + a_{33}b_{32}$$

It should be noted that multiplication is not generally commutative; that is, AB is not necessarily equal to BA. The definition for multiplication makes it possible to represent Equations (3–51), (3–52), and (3–53) as follows:

$$\begin{bmatrix} 1 & 0 & 0 \\ -A_1 & 1 & 0 \\ 0 & -A_2 & 1 \end{bmatrix} \begin{bmatrix} Z_1 \\ Z_2 \\ Z_3 \end{bmatrix} = \begin{bmatrix} A_0 + 1 \\ 1 \\ 1 \end{bmatrix} \qquad (3\text{--}58)$$

That these matrices do represent Equations (3–51), (3–52), and (3–53) is readily proved by applying the multiplication rule. For simplicity Equation (3–58) is customarily written

$$AZ = C \qquad (3\text{--}59)$$

In order to solve for Z_1, Z_2, and Z_3, it is necessary to find the inverse matrix of A. This involves the use of a third order identity matrix, which is defined as follows:

$$I = \begin{bmatrix} 1 & 0 & 0 \\ 0 & 1 & 0 \\ 0 & 0 & 1 \end{bmatrix} \qquad (3\text{--}60)$$

Note that $IA = A$, which fact follows from the application of the multiplication rule, Equation (3–56). The inverse matrix of A is defined as that matrix which when multiplied by A gives I; that is,

$$A^{-1}A = I \qquad (3\text{–}61)$$

The matrix A^{-1} may be found by performing the same arithmetic operations on I and A as was performed previously on the system of linear equations. This set of operations transforms the matrix A to the unit matrix I and the unit matrix I to the inverse matrix A^{-1}. In order to demonstrate a further principle, the same operations are performed on the matrix C. Now consider separately the three matrices, A, I, and C.

$$
\overset{A}{\begin{bmatrix} 1 & 0 & 0 \\ -A_1 & 1 & 0 \\ 0 & -A_2 & 1 \end{bmatrix}}
\left|\ \overset{I}{\begin{bmatrix} 1 & 0 & 0 \\ 0 & 1 & 0 \\ 0 & 0 & 1 \end{bmatrix}}\ \right|\
\overset{C}{\begin{bmatrix} A_0 + 1 \\ 1 \\ 1 \end{bmatrix}}
\qquad (3\text{–}62)
$$

The vertical partition lines are used to represent the fact that the matrices are to be considered separately and not as a product. Now perform the following matrix operations, which are analogous to the algebraic operations performed previously in Steps 1 and 2 on Equations (3–51), (3–52), and (3–53).

Step 1: Multiply row 1 of each matrix given by Equation (3–62) by A_1 and add the result to row 2 to give

$$
\begin{bmatrix} 1 & 0 & 0 \\ 0 & 1 & 0 \\ 0 & -A_2 & 1 \end{bmatrix}
\left|\ \begin{bmatrix} 1 & 0 & 0 \\ A_1 & 1 & 0 \\ 0 & 0 & 1 \end{bmatrix}\ \right|\
\begin{bmatrix} A_0 + 1 \\ A_1(A_0 + 1) + 1 \\ 1 \end{bmatrix}
$$

Step 2: Multiply row 2 by A_2 and add the result to row 3

$$
\begin{bmatrix} 1 & 0 & 0 \\ 0 & 1 & 0 \\ 0 & 0 & 1 \end{bmatrix}
\left|\ \begin{bmatrix} 1 & 0 & 0 \\ A_1 & 1 & 0 \\ A_2A_1 & A_2 & 1 \end{bmatrix}\ \right|\
\begin{bmatrix} A_0 + 1 \\ A_1(A_0 + 1) + 1 \\ A_2A_1(A_0 + 1) + A_2 + 1 \end{bmatrix}
$$

$$(3\text{–}63)$$

The operations which transform the matrix A to the identity matrix also transform the identity matrix to the inverse matrix of A. This is proved by multiplication of the transformed matrix of I and A; that is,

$$
\begin{bmatrix} 1 & 0 & 0 \\ A_1 & 1 & 0 \\ A_2A_1 & A_2 & 1 \end{bmatrix}
\begin{bmatrix} 1 & 0 & 0 \\ -A_1 & 1 & 0 \\ 0 & -A_2 & 1 \end{bmatrix} =
\begin{bmatrix} 1 & 0 & 0 \\ 0 & 1 & 0 \\ 0 & 0 & 1 \end{bmatrix}
\tag{3-64}
$$

which result satisfies the definition of the inverse matrix of A, Equation (3–61).

The transformed matrix of C turns out to be $A^{-1}C$, which fact is shown by application of the multiplication rule as follows:

$$
\begin{bmatrix} 1 & 0 & 0 \\ A_1 & 1 & 0 \\ A_2A_1 & A_2 & 1 \end{bmatrix}
\begin{bmatrix} A_0 + 1 \\ 1 \\ 1 \end{bmatrix} =
\begin{bmatrix} A_0 + 1 \\ A_1(A_0 + 1) + 1 \\ A_2A_1(A_0 + 1) + A_2 + 1 \end{bmatrix}
\tag{3-65}
$$

It is to be observed that the matrix $A^{-1}C$ corresponds to the array of numbers on the right hand sides of Equations (3–48), (3–49), and (3–50). Since the multiplication of A^{-1} and C does give the same result as that obtained by operating on C in the manner demonstrated, it is not necessary to include the matrix C in Equation (3–62).

The inverse matrix of A is used to obtain Z_1, Z_2, and Z_3 as follows. Multiplication of both sides of Equation (3–59) by A^{-1} yields

$$
A^{-1}AZ = A^{-1}C
\tag{3-66}
$$

Since $A^{-1}A = I$, Equation (3–66) reduces to

$$
IZ = A^{-1}C
\tag{3-67}
$$

But $IZ = Z$; hence

$$
Z = A^{-1}C
\tag{3-68}
$$

which represents

$$
\begin{bmatrix} Z_1 \\ Z_2 \\ Z_3 \end{bmatrix} =
\begin{bmatrix} A_0 + 1 \\ A_1(A_0 + 1) + 1 \\ A_2A_1(A_0 + 1) + A_2 + 1 \end{bmatrix}
\tag{3-69}
$$

If two matrices are equal, their corresponding elements are equal. Thus the solution given by Equations (3–48), (3–49), and (3–50) is obtained.

THE CALCULATIONAL PROCEDURE PROPOSED BY LEWIS AND MATHESON

This well-known procedure has as its distinguishing feature the selection of the distribution of each component between the top and bottom products as an independent variable. One might ask which procedure is correct—the one proposed by Thiele and Geddes (12) or the one suggested by Lewis and Matheson (7)? The answer is that both procedures are correct because the choice of the independent variables is arbitrary as demonstrated in Chapter 1 in the consideration of Equation (1–5).

If the same set of specifications are made for a conventional column as those stated previously in the Lewis and Matheson procedure, step-by-step calculations are carried out from the top and bottom of the column to the feed plate on the basis of an assumed product distribution. The step-by-step calculational procedure consists of alternately making material balance and bubble point (or dew point) calculations. If the mole fractions of the liquid leaving the feed plate obtained by making calculations down from the top of the column are in agreement component by component with those obtained by making calculations up from the bottom of the column, the correct product distribution was assumed to make the trial calculation. Alternately, the original assumption may be tested by comparison of the mole fractions of the vapor leaving the feed plate.

In order to illustrate the principles of the calculational procedure proposed by Lewis and Matheson (7), Example 3–1 was also solved by this method as shown in Tables 3–4 and 3–5. In order to initiate this calculational procedure, the composition of the distillate at the end of the first trial by the Thiele and Geddes method was taken as the first assumed set of X_{Di}'s as shown in Table 3–4. Then DX_{Di} was computed on the basis of the specified value of D, and the corresponding value of Bx_{Bi} was calculated by use of an over-all material balance. An examination of the results (see Table 3–4) obtained by the first trial calculation shows that the assumed set of distillate compositions was incorrect. Lewis and Matheson (7) and Robinson and Gilliland (10) proposed methods for the selection of a set of corrected X_{Di}'s. Other methods are also presented in a subsequent chapter.

The fundamental principles of the method of direct-iteration for use with the Lewis and Matheson (7) calculational procedure was presented by Lyster *et al* (8). Although this method has not been tested to any appreciable extent, it did converge satisfactorily for Example 3–1. It is presented primarily for the purpose of demonstrating that direct-iteration may be used to carry out successive trial calculations by use of the procedure of Lewis and Matheson as well as the one by Thiele and Geddes. An outline of the combination of the Lewis and Matheson calculation procedure and direct-iteration follows. On the basis of an assumed set of X_{Di}'s, calculations are initiated at the top of the column and continued to the feed

TABLE 3–4 Solution of Example 3–1 by the calculational procedure of Lewis and Matheson

TRIAL No. 1—Assume the distillate has the composition given by the first trial of the Thiele and Geddes procedure.

1. Calculations for the rectifying section

Comp. No.	DX_{Di} (Assumed)	$\dfrac{DX_{Di}}{V}$	$\dfrac{y_{1i}}{\alpha_i}$ (Note: $y_{1i} = X_{Di}$)	$x_{1i} = \dfrac{y_{1i}/\alpha_i}{\Sigma y_{1i}/\alpha_i}$	$\dfrac{Lx_{1i}}{V}$	$y_{2i} = \dfrac{Lx_{1i}}{V} + \dfrac{DX_{Di}}{V}$
1	10.718757	0.10718757	0.21437513	0.39804912	0.19902455	0.30621213
2	18.694326	0.18694326	0.18694326	0.34711395	0.17355697	0.3050023
3	20.586919	0.20586919	0.13724613	0.25483693	0.12741846	0.33328766

$K_{1b} = 0.53856452$

Comp. No.	$\dfrac{y_{2i}}{\alpha_i}$	$x_{2i} = \dfrac{y_{2i}/\alpha_i}{\Sigma y_{2i}/\alpha_i}$	Vy_{2i}	$v_{2i} = \dfrac{Vy_{2i}}{d_i} = \dfrac{Vy_{2i}}{DX_{Di}}$
1	0.30621213	0.5124391	30.621213	2.8567877
2	0.18025012	0.30164449	36.050023	1.9283938
3	0.11109589	0.18591645	33.328766	1.6189293

$K_{2b} = 0.59755814$

TABLE 3-4 (Continued)

2. Calculations for the stripping section

Comp. No.	$Bx_{Bi} = FX_i - DX_{Di}$	x_{Bi}	$\alpha_i x_{Bi}$	$y_{4i} = \dfrac{\alpha_i x_{Bi}}{\Sigma \alpha_i x_{Bi}}$	$\dfrac{Bx_{Bi}}{L}$	$\dfrac{Vy_{4i}}{L}$
1	22.581243	0.45162486	0.45162486	0.25025805	0.15054162	0.16683870
2	14.605674	0.29211348	0.58422696	0.32373661	0.09371160	0.21582441
3	12.813081	0.25626162	0.76876486	0.42600534	0.08542054	0.28400356

$$1.80463668$$
$$K_{4b} = 0.55412816$$

Comp. No.	$x_{3i} = \dfrac{Vy_{4i}}{L} + \dfrac{Bx_{Bi}}{L}$	$\alpha_i x_{3i}$	$y_{3i} = \dfrac{\alpha_i x_{3i}}{\Sigma \alpha_i x_{3i}}$	$\dfrac{Vy_{3i}}{L}$	$x_{2i} = \dfrac{Vy_{3i}}{L} + \dfrac{Bx_{Bi}}{L}$	$\alpha_i x_{2i}$
1	0.31738032	0.31738032	0.15466547	0.10311031	0.25365193	0.25365193
2	0.31319557	0.62639114	0.30525232	0.20350155	0.30087271	0.60174542
3	0.3694241	1.1082723	0.54008219	0.36005480	0.44554534	1.33642602

$$2.0520438 \qquad\qquad 2.19182237$$
$$K_{3b} = 0.48731903 \qquad\qquad K_{2b} = 0.45624114$$

Table 3-4 (Continued)

Comp. No.	$y_{2i} = \dfrac{\alpha_i x_{2i}}{\Sigma \alpha_i x_{2i}}$	$V y_{2i}$	$\dfrac{v_{2i}}{b_i} = \dfrac{V y_{2i}}{B x_{Bi}}$	$\dfrac{b_i}{d_i} = \dfrac{v_{2i}/d_i}{v_{2i}/b_i}$	$d_i = \dfrac{F X_i}{1 + b_i/d_i}$	$X_{Di} = \dfrac{d_i}{\Sigma d_i}$
1	0.11572645	11.572645	0.512489281	5.57433647	5.0651499	0.10910691
2	0.2745410	27.45410	1.8796873	1.02591202	16.437042	0.35406549
3	0.60973254	60.973254	4.7586723	0.34020608	24.921540	0.53682760

Comp. No.	DX_{Di} (Assumed for 2nd Trial)
1	5.4553455
2	17.703275
3	26.841380

TABLE 3–5 Solution of Example 3–1 by the Lewis and Matheson Calculational
Procedure and Direct-Iteration

Plate No.	Calculated Values of K_b Trial No.		
	1	2	3*
0	0.455	0.412	0.414
1	0.539	0.465	0.468
2	0.598	0.509	0.512
3	0.487	0.559	0.553
4	0.554	0.635	0.630
D (Calculated)	46.42	50.30	49.96

* All of the K_b's were correct to eight digits at the end of the 8th
trial.

plate to give a set of $\bar{y}_{fi}$'s. Multiplication of each of these by $\bar{V}_f$ yields $\bar{v}_{fi}$.
Division of $\bar{v}_{fi}$ by the corresponding distillate rate d_i gives a value for
$\bar{v}_{fi}/d_i$. In an analogous manner, a value for v_{fi}/b_i may be calculated on the
basis of the results obtained by making calculations from the bottom of
the column to the feed plate. For the case of a bubble point liquid feed, the
value of b_i/d_i by direct-iteration is

$$\frac{b_i}{d_i} = \frac{\bar{v}_{fi}/d_i}{v_{fi}/b_i} \tag{3–70}$$

and d_i is given by use of Equation (3–19). The composition of the distillate
for the next trial is calculated as follows:

$$X_{Di} = \frac{d_i}{\sum_{i=1}^{c} d_i} \tag{3–71}$$

Then the DX_{Di}'s for the next trial are calculated on the basis of the specified
value of D and the X_{Di}'s given by Equation (3–71), and the corresponding
values of Bx_{Bi} are obtained by use of the over-all material balance,

$$Bx_{Bi} = FX_i - DX_{Di} \tag{3–72}$$

The existence of the possibility of computing a negative value for Bx_{Bi} is to be observed. If such a value is calculated, it is suggested that Bx_{Bi} be taken equal to the value of b_i as calculated by the use of Equations (3–70) and (3–19).

Before concluding this chapter, the reader should be cautioned against drawing premature conclusions concerning either the convergence or the rate of convergence of the calculational procedures of Thiele and Geddes and Lewis and Matheson and direct-iteration. Since it has not been shown analytically that the sufficient conditions stated in Chapter 1 for convergence by direct-iteration have been satisfied, it can not be assumed that these methods will converge for all examples because convergence was obtained for a single example.

NOTATION

A = a matrix

A_{ji} = absorption factor for plate j and component i

b_i = molal withdrawal rate of component i in the bottom product

B = molal withdrawal rate of bottoms

C = a matrix

c = total number of components

d_i = molal withdrawal rate of component i in the distillate

D = molal withdrawal rate of distillate

f = number of the feed plate

F = molal rate of flow of the entering feed

K_{ji} = the Henry law constant $(y = Kx)$ for component i at the temperature of plate j

l_{ji} = molal rate at which component i in the liquid state leaves plate j

$\bar{l}_{f-1,i}$ = molal rate of flow of component i in the liquid state onto plate f

l_{Fi} = molal rate of flow of component i in the liquid part of a partially vaporized feed

L_j = total molal rate of flow of liquid from plate j

$\bar{L}_{f-1}$ = total molal rate of flow of liquid onto the feed plate; $\bar{L}_{f-1} = L_{f-1} + L_F$

L_F = molal rate of flow of the liquid part of the feed. For boiling point liquid and subcooled feeds, $L_F = F$, and for dew point vapor and superheated feeds $L_F = 0$

N = total number of plates in the column. The plates are numbered down from the top with the top being 1, the plate above the reboiler N, and the reboiler $N + 1$

S_{ji} = stripping factor for component i and for plate j

v_{ji} = molal rate at which component i in the vapor state leaves plate j

$\bar{v}_{fi}$ = molal rate at which component i in the vapor state enters plate $f - 1$

v_{Fi} = molal rate of flow of component i in the vapor part of a partially vaporized feed

V_j = total molal rate of flow of vapor from plate j

$\bar{V}_f$ = total molal rate at which vapor enters plate $f - 1$; $\bar{V}_f = V_f + V_F$

V_F = molal rate of flow of the vapor part of the feed. For boiling point liquid and subcooled feeds $V_F = 0$, and for dew point vapor and superheated feeds $V_F = F$

x_{Bi} = mole fraction of component i in the bottoms

x_{Fi} = mole fraction of component i in the liquid part of a partially vaporized feed

x_{ji} = mole fraction of component i in the liquid leaving plate j

X_{Di} = mole fraction of component i in the distillate regardless of state in which it is withdrawn

X_i = total mole fraction of component i in the total feed F

y_{Fi} = mole fraction of component i in the vapor part of a partially vaporized feed

y_{ji} = mole fraction of component i in the vapor leaving plate j

Z = a matrix

α = relative volatility of individual components; $\alpha_i = K_i/K_b$

$\sum$ = denotes a sum; $\displaystyle\sum_{i=1}^{c}$ = sum from $i = 1$ through c

Φ_i, ϕ_i = a product and sum of products of stripping factors; defined immediately following Equation (3–31)

Ω_i, ω_i = a product and sum of products of absorption factors; defined immediately following Equation (3–33)

Subscripts

b = base component; the component for which $\alpha = 1.0$

B = bottom product

D = top product

F = mixture formed by a flash process

f = feed plate

i = component number, $i = 1$ to $i = c$

j = plate number; for the condenser $j = 0$, for the top plate $j = 1$, for the feed plate $j = f$ and for the reboiler $j = N + 1$

PROBLEMS

3–1 Verify the results shown in Table 3–3 for the second trial calculation by use of the calculational procedure of Thiele and Geddes and direct-iteration.

3–2 Verify the results shown in Table 3–5 for the second trial calculation by use of the calculational procedure of Lewis and Matheson and direct-iteration.

3–3 Where the ratios of the K_i's are a function of temperature, demonstrate the modifications which must be made in the calculational procedures shown for Illustrative Example 3–1 by performing the first two trial calculations for the following example by use of both the Thiele and Geddes and the Lewis and Matheson calculational procedures.

Component	FX_i	Specifications
i-C$_4$	33.3	Same as Illustrative Example 3–1. In addition the column is to operate at 50 psia.
n-C$_4$	33.3	
i-C$_5$	33.4	

For purposes of comparison, take each temperature of the first assumed profile for the Thiele and Geddes procedure to be equal to the temperature required to give a K of unity for isobutane at 50 psia. Also use the results of the first trial obtained by the Thiele and Geddes procedure to initiate the calculational procedure of Lewis and Matheson.

3–4 Many authors (1, 9, 10, 12) have stated the material balance equations in terms of mole fractions. Show that for a conventional column

Rectifying Section

$$\frac{y_{1i}}{X_{Di}} = \frac{L_0}{K_{0i}V_1} + \frac{D}{V_1} \qquad \text{(balance around the condenser)}$$

$$\frac{y_{ji}}{X_{Di}} = \left(\frac{L_{j-1}}{K_{j-1,i}V_j}\right)\left(\frac{y_{j-1,i}}{X_{Di}}\right) + \frac{D}{V_j}, \qquad 2 \leq j \leq f - 1$$

$$\frac{\bar{y}_{fi}}{X_{Di}} = \left(\frac{L_{f-1}}{K_{f-1,i}\bar{V}_f}\right)\left(\frac{y_{f-1,i}}{X_{Di}}\right) + \frac{D}{\bar{V}_f}$$

Stripping Section

$$\frac{\bar{x}_{f-1,i}}{x_{Bi}} = \left(\frac{V_f K_{fi}}{\bar{L}_{f-1}}\right)\left(\frac{x_{fi}}{x_{Bi}}\right) + \frac{B}{\bar{L}_{f-1}}$$

$$\frac{x_{ji}}{x_{Bi}} = \left(\frac{V_{j+1} K_{j+1,i}}{L_j}\right)\left(\frac{x_{j+1,i}}{x_{Bi}}\right) + \frac{B}{L_j}, \qquad f - 2 \leq j \leq N + 1$$

$$\frac{x_{Ni}}{x_{Bi}} = \left(\frac{V_{N+1} K_{N+1,i}}{L_N}\right) + \frac{B}{L_N} \qquad \text{(balance around the reboiler)}$$

3-5 (a) Apply the formulas developed in Problem 3–4 to describe the conventional column of Illustrative Example 3–1.

   (b) Show that if y_{2i}/X_{Di} as computed by the material balances of Part (a) is multiplied by V_2/D (where these are the values specified in the statement of the problem), the result is equal to the value of v_{2i}/d_i obtained by use of material balances stated in terms of molal flow rates. Hint: Begin by showing that the equations found in Part (a) may be rearranged to give

$$\frac{y_{2i}}{X_{Di}} = [A_{0i}A_{1i} + A_{1i} + 1]\left(\frac{D}{V_2}\right)$$

   (c) On the basis of the equations found in Part (a), develop the following formula for X_{Di},

$$X_{Di} = \left(\frac{1}{D}\right)\left[\frac{FX_i}{1 + \left(\frac{V_2}{D}\right)\left(\frac{y_{2i}}{X_{Di}}\right)\left(\frac{B}{V_2}\right)\left(\frac{x_{Bi}}{y_{2i}}\right)}\right]$$

The flow rates D, B, and V_2 have the values specified in the statement of the example. Show that the sum of this set of X_{Di}'s is not necessarily equal to unity.

(d) On the basis of the equations found in Part (a), suppose the calculated value of b_i/d_i is defined by

$$\frac{b_i}{d_i} = \frac{\left(\dfrac{V_2}{D}\right)\left(\dfrac{y_{2i}}{X_{Di}}\right)}{\left(\dfrac{V_2}{B}\right)\left(\dfrac{y_{2i}}{x_{Bi}}\right)}$$

After b_i/d_i has been determined, d_i is calculated by Equation (3–19). A set of X_{Di}'s may be computed as follows:

$$X_{Di} = d_i / \sum_{i=1}^{c} d_i$$

Show that this set of X_{Di}'s is equal to the set obtained by normalization of those computed by the formula given in Part (c).

(e) Develop the formulas needed to calculate the set of y_{2i}'s from the y_{2i}/X_{Di}'s and the appropriate set of X_{Di}'s which are equal component by component to those given by Equation (3–23).

3–6 For the Thiele and Geddes procedure, the independence of the flow rates of the individual components of the direction of calculation may be shown in ways other than the one presented in the text.

(a) Beginning with Equations (3–4), (3–5), (3–19), and (3–25), produce Equations (3–6) and (3–7).

(b) State all of the independent material balance equations including an over-all material balance and equilibrium relationships (Equations 3–4 and 3–5) required to describe a conventional distillation column and show that the number of unknowns is equal to the number of equations.

3–7 For the column described by Illustrative Example 3–1, the formulas of Amundson and Pontinen (1) lead to the following set of equations.

$$K_{1i}x_{1i} = X_{Di}$$

$$L_0 X_{Di} - (V_1 K_{1i} + L_1)x_{1i} + V_2 K_{2i}x_{2i} = 0$$

$$L_1 x_{1i} - (L_2 + V_2 K_{2i})x_{2i} + V_3 K_{3i}x_{3i} = -F X_i$$

$$L_2 x_{2i} - (L_3 + V_3 K_{3i})x_{3i} + V_4 K_{4i}x_{4i} = 0$$

$$L_3 x_{3i} - (B + V_4 K_{4i})x_{4i} = 0$$

Show that the normalized mole fractions calculated by these equations are equal component by component to those given by use of Equations (3–4) through (3–11), (3–19), and (3–24).

3–8 State the equations required to describe a conventional column (Equations (3–6) through (3–8) and (3–10) through (3–11)) as a matrix equation. Obtain the inverse of the coefficient matrix (the one which contains the coefficients of the variables v_{ji}/d_i and l_{ji}/b_i).

LITERATURE CITED

1. Amundson, N. R. and A. J. Pontinen, "Multicomponent Distillation Calculations on a Large Digital Computer," *Ind. Eng. Chem.*, **50**, No. 5, 730 (1958).

2. Aitken, A. C., *Determinates and Matrices* (New York: Interscience Publishers, Inc., 1951).

3. Donnell, J. W. and Kenneth Turbin, "Save Time with Systematic Method for Distillation Calculations," *Chem. Eng.* **58**, 112 (July 1951).

4. Edmister, W. C., "Absorption and Stripping-factor Functions for Distillation Calculation by Manual and Digital-Computer Methods," *A.I.Ch.E. Journal*, **3**, No. 2, 165 (1957).

5. Gass, S. I., *Linear Programming* (New York: McGraw–Hill Book Company, Inc., 1958) pp. 12–15, 27–30.

6. Hummel, H. H., "Multicomponent Fractionation: A Simplified Approach to Plate-to-Plate Calculations," *Trans. Am. Inst. Chem. Engrs.*, **40**, 445 (1944).

7. Lewis, W. K. and G. L. Matheson, "Studies in Distillation—Design of Rectifying Columns for Natural and Refinery Gasoline," *Ind. Eng. Chem.*, **24**, 494 (1932).

8. Lyster, W. N., S. L. Sullivan, Jr., D. S. Billingsley and C. D. Holland, "Figure Distillation This New Way: Part 1—New Convergence Method Will Handle Many Cases," *Petroleum Refiner*, **38**, No. 6, 221 (1959).

9. Rea, H. E., Jr. and D. N. Hanson, "Fractionation Calculation for Existing Columns," *Petroleum Refiner*, **31**, No. 11, 139 (1952).

10. Robinson, C. S. and E. R. Gilliland, *Elements of Fractional Distillation* (New York: McGraw–Hill Book Company, Inc., 1952), pp. 219–255.

11. Stoll, R. R., *Linear Algebra and Matrix Theory* (New York: McGraw–Hill Book Company, Inc., 1952).

12. Thiele, E. W. and R. L. Geddes, "Computation of Distillation Apparatus for Hydrocarbon Mixtures," *Ind. Eng. Chem.*, **25**, 289 (1933).

Convergence Methods

4

Most of the basic principles of the various convergence methods may be demonstrated by use of a conventional column operating at a fixed set of vapor and liquid rates. Modifications required when the total flow rates are determined by use of enthalpy balances are presented in the next chapter. Convergence methods involve the adjustment of the calculated values of the variables to give an improved set, which when used as the assumed values of the independent variables for the next trial give a set of calculated values that are closer to the correct set than those obtained by the previous trial. When no adjustment of the calculated values of the variables is made, the resulting procedure is called direct-iteration, which was illustrated in the previous chapter. Observe that the same order is being followed in the treatment of the equations describing multicomponent distillation as that used in the consideration of the simple algebraic equations in Chapter 1. First, the equations were solved by direct-iteration. Next, convergence methods were used to select a better value of the independent variable to be assumed for the next trial than the one obtained by the previous trial calculation.

In this chapter the developments of several of the proposed convergence methods are presented. Application of these methods is demonstrated by the solution of several numerical examples.

THE θ-METHOD OF CONVERGENCE

This convergence method was proposed by Lyster* et al. (6) and shown to give satisfactory results for a conventional distillation column. Sullivan (10) showed that this method could be employed to solve problems in

---

* Presented at a national meeting of the A.I.Ch.E. in Salt Lake City, Utah, September 1958.

which various types of specifications are made. It may be used both with the Thiele and Geddes (11) and the Lewis and Matheson (7) calculational procedures. However, computational and other problems which have been solved in the application of the Thiele and Geddes calculational procedure to complex units have not been solved for the corresponding applications of the Lewis and Matheson procedure. Therefore, the applications shown in subsequent chapters make use of a combination of the Thiele and Geddes calculational procedure and the θ-method of convergence. The solutions to these problems might well represent or lead to suitable solutions of the corresponding problems encountered in the application of other calculational procedures and convergence methods. However, the present chapter is not concerned with these problems, but with the presentation of the fundamentals of the various convergence methods.

DEVELOPMENT OF THE θ-METHOD OF CONVERGENCE FOR USE WITH THE CALCULATIONAL PROCEDURE OF THIELE AND GEDDES

First, the θ-method is developed from an intuitive point of view. This is followed by a development in which the required fundamental postulates are stated and the method developed therefrom. Recall that in the solution of Illustrative Example 3–1 by the calculational procedure of Thiele and Geddes and direct-iteration, the sum of the calculated d_i's did not equal to the specified value of D until convergence was obtained. Now consider the adjustment of the calculated d_i's to give a corrected set that satisfies both an over-all material balance for each component and the specified value of D. Thus it is required that the corrected set of d_i's satisfy

$$FX_i = (d_i)_{co} + (b_i)_{co} \qquad (4\text{–}1)$$

and

$$D = \sum_{i=1}^{c} (d_i)_{co} \qquad (4\text{–}2)$$

simultaneously. Throughout this book the subscript "*co*" is used to denote the corrected value of the variable. Note that there exist infinitely many sets of $(b_i)_{co}$ and $(d_i)_{co}$ which satisfy Equations (4–1) and (4–2) simultaneously. The θ-method consists of one way of selecting one of these sets. For any given set of L/V's and temperatures, a set of b_i/d_i's may be computed, which are henceforth identified by the subscript "*ca*." The quantity $(b_i/d_i)_{ca}$ embodies all of the assumptions made in order to perform a given trial calculation. There is also one set of b_i/d_i's which represent the solution to the problem. They are related to the calculated set as follows:

$$\left(\frac{b_i}{d_i}\right)_{co} = \theta_i \left(\frac{b_i}{d_i}\right)_{ca} \tag{4-3}$$

That is if the final solution is known and the values of $(b_i/d_i)_{ca}$ are available for any trial, certainly the θ_i's may be calculated by Equation (4–3). However, the solution and hence the correct values of b_i/d_i are not generally known. Until the solution has been obtained, insufficient information is available for the determination of the set of θ's defined by Equation (4–3). However, a single value of θ may be found that satisfies simultaneously Equations (4–1) and (4–2). Thus the corrected values of b_i/d_i given by

$$\left(\frac{b_i}{d_i}\right)_{co} = \theta \left(\frac{b_i}{d_i}\right)_{ca} \tag{4-4}$$

may be regarded as the first approximations of the final set. The formula for the calculation of θ is developed in the following manner. Equations (4–1) and (4–4) may be solved for $(d_i)_{co}$ to give

$$(d_i)_{co} = \frac{FX_i}{1 + \theta(b_i/d_i)_{ca}} \tag{4-5}$$

Substitution of this expression into Equation (4–2) followed by rearrangement yields

$$g(\theta) = \sum_{i=1}^{c} \frac{FX_i}{1 + \theta(b_i/d_i)_{ca}} - D \tag{4-6}$$

The desired value of θ is the positive root which gives $g(\theta) = 0$. A graph of the function $g(\theta)$ in the neighborhood of the positive root is shown in Figure 4–1. This positive root may be found by any one of several methods, two of which (Newton's method and interpolation *regula falsi*) were presented in Chapter 1. In the application of Newton's method the first derivative,

$$g'(\theta) = -\sum_{i=1}^{c} \frac{(b_i/d_i)_{ca}FX_i}{[1 + \theta(b_i/d_i)_{ca}]^2} \tag{4-7}$$

with respect to θ is needed. Successive application of Newton's method as described in Chapter 1 leads to the desired value of θ, provided the first assumed value of θ satisfies the inequality $0 \leq \theta \leq \theta_r$. Since $\theta = 0$ represents one value that always satisfies this inequality, it may be taken as the first assumed value of θ. After the positive root, $\theta = \theta_r$, has been found, the corrected values for the d_i's are obtained by substitution of this value of θ into Equation (4–5). The corrected value of b_i is given by

$$(b_i)_{co} = \theta \left(\frac{b_i}{d_i}\right)_{ca} (d_i)_{co} \tag{4–8}$$

Although in theory $(b_i)_{co}$ may be calculated by use of Equation (4–1), in

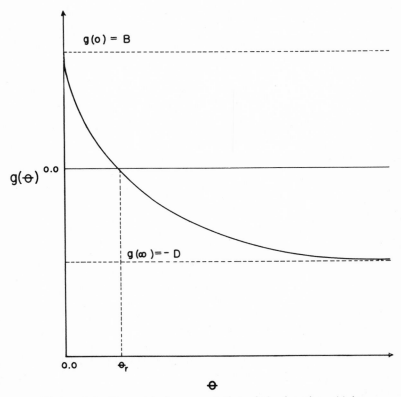

Figure 4–1. Geometrical representation of the function $g(\theta)$ in the neighborhood of the positive root θ_r. (Reproduced by permission of *Hydrocarbon Processing & Petroleum Refiner*)

practice Equation (4–8) is preferred because the range of magnitudes of numbers that may be generated on present-day machines exceeds by far the number of significant figures which may be carried.

When the θ-method of convergence is used with the Thiele and Geddes calculational procedure, the following formulas are employed for the calculation of the corrected mole fractions

$$x_{ji} = \frac{\left(\dfrac{l_{ji}}{b_i}\right)_{ca}(b_i)_{co}}{\sum\limits_{i=1}^{c}\left(\dfrac{l_{ji}}{b_i}\right)_{ca}(b_i)_{co}} = \frac{\left(\dfrac{l_{ji}}{d_i}\right)_{ca}(d_i)_{co}}{\sum\limits_{i=1}^{c}\left(\dfrac{l_{ji}}{d_i}\right)_{ca}(d_i)_{co}} \qquad (4\text{--}9)$$

$$y_{ji} = \frac{\left(\dfrac{v_{ji}}{d_i}\right)_{ca}(d_i)_{co}}{\sum\limits_{i=1}^{c}\left(\dfrac{v_{ji}}{d_i}\right)_{ca}(d_i)_{co}} \qquad (4\text{--}10)$$

Since

$$(b_i)_{ca} = (b_i/d_i)_{ca}(d_i)_{ca} \quad \text{and} \quad (b_i)_{co} = \theta(b_i/d_i)_{ca}(d_i)_{co}$$

it follows that the two expressions given by Equation (4–9) for x_{ji} are equivalent. Because of characteristics of the θ-method which will be discussed in Chapter 6, the corrected temperatures should be calculated by use of the bubble point procedure and the x_{ji}'s. As shown in succeeding paragraphs, Equation (4–9) and (4–10) may be developed from first principles. The combination of the Thiele and Geddes calculational procedure and the θ-method is readily applied as illustrated by the solution of Illustrative Example 3–1 in the previous chapter. The calculated values of b_i/d_i obtained by the first trial calculation (Table 3–2 of Chapter III) were used to compute a θ of 5.6215101 by use of Equation (4–6). Corrected compositions, calculated by use of Equation (4–9), were used to obtain the profile shown in Table 4–1. The final flow rates are also given in Table 4–1. The corrected temperature profile is used to make the next step-by-step calculation through the column in the same manner as shown previously for direct-iteration.

In the previous development the statement of the formulas for x_{ji} and y_{ji} may be regarded as definitions of the mole fractions. However, Equations (4–9) and (4–10) may be developed on the basis of the conventional definition for a mole fraction (moles of a given component in a mixture divided by the total moles of the mixture). In this development it is supposed that the V_j's and L_j's are fixed throughout the column. As mentioned previously, any set of total flow rates may be realized by use of appropriate intercoolers (or heaters). Again the problem is to find a set of terminal flow rates which satisfy both a component-material balance, Equation (4–1), and the specification D. The following postulates lead to the same

TABLE 4-1 Solution of Example 3–1 by use of the θ-method and the Thiele and Geddes calculational procedure

Calculated Values of K_b

Plate No.	Trial No.						
	1	2	3	4	5	6	7
0	0.41086575	0.41362833	0.41372024	0.4137207	0.41372426	0.41372427	0.41372427
1	0.46121292	0.46719933	0.46738321	0.46739097	0.46739133	0.46739136	0.46739136
2	0.48755212	0.51157089	0.51154290	0.51154505	0.51154520	0.51154523	0.51154522
3	0.55069408	0.55398386	0.55401216	0.55401135	0.55401126	0.55401126	0.55401126
4	0.63770834	0.6311654	0.63095157	0.63094266	0.63094222	0.63094220	0.63094220
D (Calculated)	77.667585	49.006364	49.999530	49.999902	49.999993	49.999998	49.999999
θ	5.6215101	0.94749173	0.99997452	0.99999469	0.99999961	0.99999987	0.99999998

TABLE 4–1 (Continued)

Final Flow Rates

Comp. No.	b	d
1	27.764577	5.535423
2	15.224283	18.075717
3	7.011140	26.388860

set of corrected distillate rates that were obtained previously. Now consider the following sum of products,

$$\sum_{i=1}^{c} \left(\frac{v_{ji}}{d_i}\right)_{ca} (d_i)_{co}$$

Certainly this sum is related to the specified flow rate, V_j. However, it is not necessarily equal to V_j, since the two requirements placed on the corrected d_i's did not include this condition. Obviously, if the values of both the sum and V_j are known, the single multiplier required to give an equality may be readily found. These observations lead to the following definitions. Let the multiplier σ_j be defined by

$$(v_{ji})_{co} = \sigma_j \left(\frac{v_{ji}}{d_i}\right)_{ca} (d_i)_{co} \qquad (4\text{–}11)$$

Similarly, let τ_j be defined by

$$(l_{ji})_{co} = \tau_j \left(\frac{l_{ji}}{b_i}\right)_{ca} (b_i)_{co} \qquad (4\text{–}12)$$

These definitions of the multipliers σ_j and τ_j imply that the sums of the corrected vapor and liquid rates of the individual components are equal to V_j and L_j, respectively; that is,

$$V_j = \sigma_j \sum_{i=1}^{c} \left(\frac{v_{ji}}{d_i}\right)_{ca} (d_i)_{co} \qquad (4\text{–}13)$$

$$L_j = \tau_j \sum_{i=1}^{c} \left(\frac{l_{ji}}{b_i}\right)_{ca} (b_i)_{co} \qquad (4\text{–}14)$$

Since $y_{ji} = v_{ji}/V_j$ and $x_{ji} = l_{ji}/L_j$ by the usual definition of the mole fraction, Equations (4–11) through (4–14) are readily combined to give the desired results, Equations (4–9) and (4–10).

The relationship given by Equation (4–4) may also be obtained from the fundamental postulates. For the case of a column with a total condenser, Equation (4–12) gives

$$(l_{0i})_{co} = \tau_0 (l_{0i}/b_i)_{ca} (b_i)_{co}$$

Multiplication of both sides of this equation by D/L_0 followed by rearrangement yields,

$$(b_i)_{co} = (1/\tau_0) (b_i/d_i)_{ca} (d_i)_{co} \qquad (4\text{--}15)$$

The single multiplier $1/\tau_0$ may be replaced by θ to give Equation (4–4). A more general development of this relationship including the case where the column has a partial condenser follows. Suppose a plate $(j = -1)$ to exist (above the condenser) on which the distillate is completely condensed. Then for this plate Equation (4–12) gives

$$(d_i)_{co} = \tau_{-1} (d_i/b_i)_{ca} (b_i)_{co} \qquad (4\text{--}16)$$

Replacing the single multiplier $1/\tau_{-1}$ by θ yields the desired result, Equation (4–4). Alternately, this relationship may be obtained by use of Equation (4–11). In this approach all components are supposed to be completely vaporized on the additional plate $(N + 2)$ located below the reboiler. Also, this treatment leads to the relationship, $\sigma_{N+2} = 1/\tau_{-1} = \theta$. In conclusion, the same basic postulates which lead to expressions for the mole fractions also give the basic relationship between the terminal rates expressed by Equation (4–4). After this relationship has been obtained, the quantity θ which satisfies the two conditions placed on the corrected terminal flow rates is computed as described previously.

Note that the basic postulates, Equations (4–11) and (4–12), could be broadened by taking σ and τ to be functions of each component. Where information is available for the evaluation of multipliers defined in this way, these more general definitions are useful as will be shown in the treatment of other units.

As proposed by Lyster *et al.* (6), the θ-method of convergence may also be used with the calculational procedure of Lewis and Matheson (7). This combination is described in a subsequent section.

CONVERGENCE CHARACTERISTICS OF THE θ-METHOD AND THE THIELE AND GEDDES CALCULATIONAL PROCEDURE

As is shown (Table 4–1) by the solution of Illustrative Example 3–1 by use of the θ-method, the multiplier θ gives corrections in the desired direction. Further insight into the θ-method may be gained by showing why it gives corrections in the right direction. First it will be shown that at a fixed set of L/V's, the calculated values of D follow the same type of fluctuations with respect to temperature as might be expected of an actual column. If on the average the assumed temperature profile is too high, the calculational procedure of Thiele and Geddes gives a value of D that is greater than the specified value; and if the assumed temperature profile is too low, the calculated value of the D is less than the specified value. This is readily shown in a quantitative manner. For the sake of simplicity consider the case where the feed enters the column as a liquid at its boiling point. From Equation (3–34) of Chapter 3 it follows that $\bar{v}_{fi}/d_i$ is a function of the sum of the products of the A_{ji}'s. Since A_{ji} is inversely proportional to K_{ji}, the quantity $\bar{v}_{fi}/d_i$ decreases as the temperature profile in the rectifying section is increased. Similarly, v_{fi}/b_i is a function of the S_{ji}'s that are proportional to the K_{ji}'s. Thus v_{fi}/b_i increases as the temperature profile in the stripping section is increased. This leads to the general result that b_i/d_i decreases with an increase in the temperature in either or both sections of the column. Hence by Equation (3–19), d_i increases as the temperature profile is increased.

Now consider Equation (4–6). If the sum of the calculated values of d_i is greater than the specified value of D, a positive value of θ that is greater than unity is required to satisfy Equation (4–6); and if the sum of the calculated values of d_i is less than the specified value of D, a positive value of θ less than unity is required to satisfy Equation (4–6). Thus if the temperature profile for the previous trial was too low, a value of θ less than unity will be obtained; and if too high, a value of θ greater than unity will be determined.

The use of corrected d_i's based on values of $\theta < 1$ and $\theta > 1$ gives lower and higher temperatures, respectively, than those predicted by the method of direct-iteration. This is readily shown by consideration of the variation of the corrected d_i's with θ for very light and very heavy components. For a very light component b_i/d_i is very small so that Equation (4–5) reduces to

$$(d_i)_{co} \cong FX_i \qquad (4\text{–}17)$$

For a very heavy component, b_i/d_i is very large. Thus

$$(d_i)_{co} \cong \frac{FX_i}{\theta(b_i/d_i)_{ca}} \qquad (4\text{–}18)$$

Now consider the case where the temperature profile of the previous trial was too high. This condition leads to a value of θ greater than unity. In view of Equations (4–17) and (4–18), it is seen that the formulas for the mole fractions for each plate (Equations (4–9) and (4–10)) give sets of compositions with a relatively smaller proportion of heavies than those obtained by direct-iteration. Therefore, the equilibrium temperatures calculated on the basis of the corrected compositions are less than the corresponding temperatures calculated by the method of direct-iteration, since the latter are calculated on the basis of the calculated d_i's.

The conclusions produced by the preceding analysis may be illustrated by comparing the temperature profile calculated by the method of direct-iteration (Table 3–3) with the one calculated by use of the θ-method (Table 4–1) at the end of the first trial calculation. Thus the θ-method is seen to correct in the desired direction. Although a proof that this correction is sufficient to give convergence for all problems has not been presented, this has been the case. Actually, the only problem encountered in the use of this method is that of over-correction. The cause and remedy of this is presented in a subsequent chapter as well as the proof that the θ-method represents a direct solution to a particular problem encountered when a column is operated at total reflux.

COMBINATION OF THE CALCULATIONAL PROCEDURE OF LEWIS AND MATHESON AND THE θ-METHOD OF CONVERGENCE

This combination was proposed first by Lyster *et al.* (6). Later a variation of it was proposed and tested by Peiser (8), who found that it had good convergence characteristics. Calculations are made through the column by use of the calculational procedure of Lewis and Matheson (7) as shown for Example 3–1 in Table 3–4. For the case of a boiling point liquid feed, values for $(b_i/d_i)_{ca}$ may be calculated as shown in Table 3–4 by use of the formula given by Lyster *et al.* (6). In effect, this formula expresses the requirement of a match (or equality) of the vapor rates (as calculated down from the top and up from the bottom of the column) for all components entering the plate above the feed plate. Based on the set of calculated values of b_i/d_i so obtained, a corrected set of b_i/d_i's is calculated by use of Equation (4–6), the θ-method. The corresponding corrected set of b_i's and d_i's are used to initiate the next trial calculation through the column.

In principle, a match (the equality of the flow rates for each component as calculated down from the top and up from the bottom of the column) may be required at any point in the column. However, matches in which subtractions are involved in the step-by-step calculations should be avoided in order to eliminate the possibility of obtaining negative numbers. For the general case of a feed of any thermal condition, the requirement of a match on the vapor entering the plate above the feed plate yields

$$\left(\frac{b_i}{d_i}\right)_{ca} = \frac{\bar{v}_{fDi}/d_i}{\dfrac{v_{fBi}}{b_i} + \dfrac{v_{Fi}}{b_i}} \tag{4-19}$$

For the case of boiling point liquid and subcooled feeds, $v_{Fi} = 0$; and for dew point vapor and superheated feeds, $v_{Fi} = FX_i$. If a match is required on the liquid flowing onto the feed plate, the general formula for b_i/d_i for a feed of any thermal condition is

$$\left(\frac{b_i}{d_i}\right)_{ca} = \frac{\dfrac{l_{f-1,Di}}{d_i} + \dfrac{l_{Fi}}{d_i}}{l_{f-1,Bi}/b_i} \tag{4-20}$$

For boiling point liquid and subcooled feeds, $l_{Fi} = FX_i$; and for dew point vapor and superheated feeds, $v_{Fi} = FX_i$. Until convergence is obtained, each of these formulas gives a different set of values for $(b_i/d_i)_{ca}$. Thus the Lewis and Matheson procedure differs from the one proposed by Thiele and Geddes in that the latter gives the same set of values for b_i/d_i regardless of the plate at which the match is required.

The use of the θ-method for the correction of the calculated values of b_i/d_i obtained by the Lewis and Matheson calculational procedure and Equation (4-19) is shown in Table 4-2 for Example 3-1. The use of Equation (4-20) for the calculation of $(b_i/d_i)_{ca}$ was investigated and found to give a slower rate of convergence for Example 3-1 as shown in Table 4-8.

THE MISMATCH CONVERGENCE METHOD

This method is suitable for use with the calculational procedure proposed by Lewis and Matheson. It was developed in 1953 by Mr. W. M. Harp* and later tested and modified by Bonner (2), who used it in an early computer program. Since many problems have been successfully solved by the use of this convergence method, the development of it is presented and illustrated by a numerical example. As will be recalled in the usual application of the procedure of Lewis and Matheson, calculations are made from the top and from the bottom of the column to the feed plate on the basis of an assumed product distribution. When the correct product distribution is selected to initiate the calculational procedure, a match is obtained at

* Mr. W. M. Harp, Head, Systems Engineering Group, Humble Oil and Refining Company, Baytown, Texas.

TABLE 4–2 Solution of Example 3–1 by use of the calculational procedure of Lewis and Matheson and the θ-method of convergence as proposed by Lyster *et al.* (6)

I. Calculation of a corrected set of b_i's and d_i's by the θ-method

On the basis of the first set of calculated values of b_i/d_i for Example 3–1 obtained by the calculational procedure of Lewis and Matheson (see Trial No. 1, Table 3–4), Equation (4–6) gives $\theta = 0.82776287$.

Comp. No.	$(b_i/d_i)_{ca}$	$(d_i)_{co} = \dfrac{FX_i}{1 + \theta(b_i/d_i)_{ca}}$	$(b_i)_{co} = \theta(b_i/d_i)_{co}(d_i)_{co}$
1	5.57433647	5.931358	27.368642
2	1.025912022	18.007672	15.292328
3	0.34020608	26.060971	7.339029

II. Values of θ used in the solution of Example 3–1

Trial No.	θ	Trial No.	θ
1	0.82776287	5	0.99999514
2	0.98642401	6	0.99999964
3	0.99902780	7	0.99999996
4	0.99993120		

the feed plate. In order to distinguish between the two sets of mole fractions, those obtained by making calculations down from the top of the column are denoted by x_{fDi} and those resulting from making calculations up from the bottom of the column by x_{fBi}. The mismatch convergence method seeks to improve the assumed distillate and bottoms rates on the basis of the corresponding mismatches produced at the feed plate. Equation (3–36) may be used to relate x_{fBi} and the value of x_{Bi} assumed to make the given trial calculation. Division of both sides of Equation (3–36) by S_{fi} yields

$$\frac{l_{fi}}{b_i} = S_{f-1,i} \ldots S_{N+1,i} + S_{f-1,i} \ldots S_{Ni} + \ldots + S_{f-1,i} + 1 \qquad (4\text{--}21)$$

since $S_{fi}(l_{fi}/b_i) = v_{fi}/b_i$. Equation (4–21) may be rearranged to the form

$$x_{fBi} = x_{Bi} \cdot \gamma_i(T_j, V_j, L_j). \qquad (4\text{--}22)$$

where

$$\gamma_i(T_j, V_j, L_j) = \frac{B}{L_f} [S_{f-1,i} \ldots S_{N+1,i} + S_{f-1,i} \ldots S_{Ni}$$

$$+ \ldots + S_{f-1,i} + 1]$$

Thus x_{fBi} may be regarded as a function of the product of x_{Bi} and γ_i. Then the change in x_{fBi} resulting from a change in both x_{Bi} and γ_i is given by

$$dx_{fBi} = (\partial x_{fBi}/\partial x_{Bi}) \, dx_{Bi} + (\partial x_{fBi}/\partial \gamma_i) \, d\gamma_i \qquad (4\text{--}23)$$

From Equation (4–22) it follows that

$$dx_{fBi} = (x_{fBi}/x_{Bi}) \, dx_{Bi} + x_{Bi} \, d\gamma_i \qquad (4\text{--}24)$$

The first term on the right hand side of Equation (4–24) gives the change in the feed plate composition caused by a change in the composition of component i in the bottoms at constant temperature and constant total molal rates of flow. The second term gives the effect of a change in γ_i (the temperature and L/V profiles) at constant composition for component i in the bottoms. The first term is relatively easy to evaluate, whereas the second is more difficult. When the contribution of the second term is disregarded, Equation (4–24) reduces to

$$dx_{fB} = (x_{fB}/x_B) \, dx_B \qquad (4\text{--}25)$$

or

$$\Delta x_{fB} = (x_{fB}/x_B) \, \Delta x_B \qquad (4\text{--}26)$$

where the subscript i has been dropped. Note that the following equations apply to any component present in the mixture. In a similar manner, it is readily shown that by commencing at the top of the column,

$$\Delta x_{fD} = (x_{fD}/X_D)\ \Delta X_D \qquad (4\text{--}27)$$

The error or mismatch at the feed plate for any component is defined by

$$E = x_{fB} - x_{fD} \qquad (4\text{--}28)$$

Now let Equations (4–26) and (4–27) be applied to two successive trials, the one which has just been completed and the next one which is to be performed. These two trials are distinguished by use of the subscripts "I" and "II." Then

$$\Delta x_{fB} = x_{fBII} - x_{fBI} \qquad (4\text{--}29)$$

$$\Delta x_{fD} = x_{fDII} - x_{fDI} \qquad (4\text{--}30)$$

For trials I and II the corresponding mismatches are

$$E_I = x_{fBI} - x_{fDI} \qquad (4\text{--}31)$$

$$E_{II} = x_{fBII} - x_{fDII} \qquad (4\text{--}32)$$

It is to be recalled that the objective of the convergence method is the selection of a set of product rates such that for the next trial a match at the feed plate will be obtained; that is,

$$E_{II} = 0 \qquad (4\text{--}33)$$

When this condition is required, Equation (4–30) may be subtracted from Equation (4–29) to give

$$\Delta x_{fB} - \Delta x_{fD} = x_{fDI} - x_{fBI} \qquad (4\text{--}34)$$

Comparison of Equations (4–31) and (4–34) shows that

$$\Delta x_{fB} - \Delta x_{fD} = -E_I \qquad (4\text{--}35)$$

When Δx_{fB} and Δx_{fD} are replaced by their equivalents as given by Equations (4–26) and (4–27), the following result is obtained

$$(x_{fB}/x_B)\ \Delta x_B - (x_{fD}/X_D)\ \Delta X_D = -E_I \qquad (4\text{--}36)$$

Since

$$\Delta x_B = \Delta b/B \quad \text{and} \quad \Delta X_D = \Delta d/D = -\Delta b/D$$

Equation (4–36) may be solved for Δb to give

$$\Delta b_i = -E_i/R_i \qquad (4\text{--}37)$$

where the subscript I has been dropped and the subscript i has been added in order to emphasize that a correction for each component is to be calculated. The quantity R_i is defined as follows:

$$R_i = (x_{fBi}/b_i) + (x_{fDi}/d_i) \qquad (4\text{--}38)$$

where the symbols b_i and d_i represent the terminal rates assumed to make the given trial calculation. Since the sum of the corrections calculated by Equation (4–37) is not necessarily equal to zero, it is necessary to force this sum to zero in order to obtain a solution to the problem for which D is fixed.

In the application of the mismatch convergence method, Bonner (2) has suggested that the following procedure be employed.

(1) Add the plus and minus corrections separately to obtain

$$\sum \Delta b_i \text{ (plus) and } \sum \Delta b_i \text{ (negative)}$$

(2) Apply the indicated corrections to the components in the order of decreasing values of R until the total plus and minus corrections are equal to $\Sigma \, \Delta b_i$ (plus) or $\Sigma \, \Delta b_i$ (negative), whichever is smaller.

These corrections are used to calculate the corrected terminal rates for the next trial as follows:

$$(\bar{b}_i)_{co} = b_i + \Delta b_i \qquad (4\text{--}39)$$

$$(\bar{d}_i)_{co} = d_i + \Delta d_i \qquad (4\text{--}40)$$

Again b_i and d_i denote the assumed values of the terminal rates used to make the given trial calculation.

The application of the mismatch method of convergence to Example 3–1 is demonstrated in Table 4–3. When the mismatch correction alone is employed, convergence to the specified value of D is not always obtained. Bonner (2) proposed the adjustment of the Δd_i's as required to prevent any change in D from trial to trial. One possible method for making this adjustment was used to solve Example 3–1. The mismatch correction was applied to each component as indicated by Equation (4–40). Then the mole fraction X_{Di} was computed as follows:

$$X_{Di} = (\bar{d}_i)_{co} / \sum_{i=1}^{c} (\bar{d}_i)_{co} \qquad (4\text{--}41)$$

The assumed distillate rate for each component for the next trial was taken to be DX_{Di}, and the corresponding bottoms rate was found by an over-all material balance. In the event of the computation of a negative value of b_i, the assumed value of the bottoms rate used to make the given trial was taken as the assumed rate for the next trial calculation. As shown in Table 4–8, this method gave a satisfactory solution to Example 3–1.

TABLE 4-3 Correction of the terminal rates for Example 3-1 by use of the mismatch convergence method

The first set of calculated values of b_i/d_i (see Trial No. 1 of Table 3-4) obtained by use of the Lewis and Matheson calculational procedure are corrected by use of Equation (4-37) as follows.

Comp. No.	$x_{2D} = \dfrac{y_{2D}/\alpha}{\Sigma y_{2D}/\alpha}$	d	b	x_{2B}	$E = x_{2B} - x_{2D}$
1	0.5124391	10.718757	22.581243	0.25365193	-0.25878717
2	0.30164449	18.694326	14.605674	0.30087271	-0.00077178
3	0.18591645	20.586919	12.813081	0.44547534	0.25955889

Comp. No.	$\dfrac{x_{2B}}{b}$	$\dfrac{x_{2D}}{d}$	$R = \dfrac{x_{2B}}{b} + \dfrac{x_{2D}}{d}$	$\Delta b = -E/R$	Δd
1	0.011232859	0.047807698	0.059040560	4.3832099	-4.3832099
2	0.020599714	0.016135617	0.036735330	0.02100920	-0.02100920
3	0.034767230	0.0090308049	0.04379835	-5.9262679	5.9262679

Comp. No.	$(\bar{d})_{co} = d + \Delta d$	$(\bar{b})_{co} = b + \Delta b$
1	6.335547	26.964453
2	18.673316	14.626683
3	26.513187	6.886813
	51.522050	48.477949

COMBINATION OF THE MISMATCH CORRECTION AND THE θ-METHOD OF CONVERGENCE

In order to further correct the terminal rates calculated by use of the Lewis and Matheson calculational procedure and the mismatch convergence method, Ball (1) suggested the use of the θ-method. Again the θ-method permits the selection of a corrected set of terminal rates which are both in material balance and in agreement with the specification D. The final set of corrected rates are related to those obtained by the mismatch convergence method as follows:

$$(b_i/d_i)_{co} = \theta(\bar{b}_i/\bar{d}_i)_{co} \tag{4-42}$$

The quantity θ is determined in the usual way by use of Equation (4–6). The quantities, $(b_i/d_i)_{ca}$, which appear in this equation are of course replaced by the $(\bar{b}_i/\bar{d}_i)_{co}$'s.

Ball reports that the use of the terminal rates obtained by this application of the θ-method significantly increased the rate of convergence over that obtained by the mismatch correction alone. Example 3–1 was solved by use of this combination of convergence methods as shown in Tables 4–4 and 4–8. In the solution of this example the mismatch correction was applied to each component, as indicated by Equations (4–39) and (4–40), instead of the procedure proposed by Bonner (2).

USE OF THE CALCULATIONAL PROCEDURE OF LEWIS AND MATHESON AND THE θ-METHOD OF CONVERGENCE AS PROPOSED BY PEISER

This method is similar to the combination of the θ-method of convergence and the Lewis and Matheson calculational procedure as proposed by Lyster *et al.* (6). Instead of requiring a match on a single stream at the feed plate as suggested by Lyster, Peiser (8) proposed that a match be required for two streams, the vapor entering the plate above the feed plate and the liquid flowing onto the feed plate. On this basis the calculated value of b_i/d_i is defined as follows:

$$\left(\frac{b_i}{d_i}\right)_{ca} = \sqrt{\frac{\left(\frac{\bar{v}_{fDi}}{d_i}\right)\left(\frac{\bar{l}_{f-1,Di}}{d_i}\right)}{\left(\frac{\bar{v}_{fBi}}{b_i}\right)\left(\frac{\bar{l}_{f-1,Bi}}{b_i}\right)}} \tag{4-43}$$

where again the symbols b_i and d_i denote the values of the terminal rates that were assumed in order to make the given trial calculation. The sub-

TABLE 4-4 Use of the θ-method to correct the terminal rates obtained by the mismatch convergence method

On the basis of the $(\bar{b}_i/\bar{d}_i)_{co}$'s given in Table 4-3, a value of $\theta = 1.841557$ was found by use of Equation (4-42) which gives the following set of corrected rates.

Comp. No.	$(\bar{b}_i/\bar{d}_i)_{co}$	$(d_i)_{co} = \dfrac{FX_i}{1 + \theta(\bar{b}_i/\bar{d}_i)_{co}}$	$(b_i)_{co} = \theta(\bar{b}_i/\bar{d}_i)_{co}(d_i)_{co}$
1	4.2560573	5.9313577	27.368642
2	0.78329325	18.007671	15.292329
3	0.25975047	26.060971	7.3390287

scripts D and B indicate that the values of the variables were obtained by making calculations from the top and bottom of the column, respectively. Peiser employed the θ-method for the calculation of a corrected set of terminal rates. These were used to make the next trial calculation through the column by the calculational procedure of Lewis and Matheson. Example 3–1 was solved by this method as shown in Tables 4–5 and 4–8.

It should be pointed out that in principle Equation (4–43) could be generalized to include the requirement of matches on additional streams located above and below the feed plate. However, because of the possibility of obtaining negative flow rates as well as round-off error, this extension is not recommended.

In the application of the Lewis and Matheson calculational procedure to Example 3–1, a fairly good set of b_i's and d_i's were used for the first assumed set. Peiser (8) states that no particular care needs to be taken in making the original assumptions. However, he does recommend that the amounts of the very light and very heavy components be underestimated in the bottoms and distillate, respectively. He employed arbitrary values of the order of 10^{-24} moles per hour.

THE RELAXATION METHOD

Actually this method makes use of the unsteady state equations for the determination of the steady state solution. It was proposed by Rose, *et al.* (9) who called it the "relaxation method." Ball (1) found that the rate of convergence of this method was too slow to be of practical use and proposed modifications which increase the rate of convergence. Both the original method and the modified one are developed in this chapter. Since the calculational procedure proposed by Rose *et al.* (9) is distinctly different from those of Lewis and Matheson (7) and Thiele and Geddes (11), it might well have been presented in Chapter 3 except for the fact that the calculational procedure and the convergence method are so closely interrelated. When a system is at unsteady state, the law of conservation of mass takes the form

$$\text{Input} - \text{Output} = \text{Accumulation} \qquad (4\text{–}44)$$

When this equation is applied to any component i on any plate j, it is convenient to consider an experiment of length of time Δt. The "Input" and "Output" terms of Equation (4–44) represent the moles of component i respectively entering and leaving plate j during time Δt. "Accumulation" is defined as the moles of component i on plate j at the end of the experiment (at time $t + \Delta t$) minus the moles of component i on plate j at the

Table 4–5 Determination of the calculated values of b_i/d_i at the end of the first trial for Example 3–1 by the formula proposed by Peiser (8) The values for d, b, v_{2D}/d, v_{2B}/b, x_{1D} and V_2y_{2B} are taken directly from Table 3–4 (Solution of Example 3–1 by the calculational procedure of Lewis and Matheson). The terms $\bar{l}_{1D}/d$ and $\bar{l}_{1B}/b$ needed for use of Peiser's formula are evaluated.

Comp. No.	d	b	v_{2D}/d	v_{2B}/b	x_{1D}
1	10.718757	22.581243	2.8567877	0.51248928	0.39804912
2	18.694326	14.605674	1.9283938	1.8796873	0.34711395
3	20.586919	12.813081	1.6189293	4.7586723	0.25483693

Comp. No.	V_2y_{2B}	L_1x_{1D}	$\bar{l}_{1D} = L_1x_{1D} + FX_i$	$\bar{l}_{1D}/d$	$\bar{l}_{1B} = V_2y_{2B} + b$
1	11.572645	19.902456	53.202456	4.9634911	34.153888
2	27.45410	17.3556975	50.6556975	2.7096830	42.0597740
3	60.973254	12.7418465	45.1418465	2.2413186	73.786335

TABLE 4–5 (Continued)

Comp. No.	$\bar{l}_{1B}/b$	$\left(\dfrac{b}{d}\right)_{ca} = \sqrt{\dfrac{(\bar{v}_{fD}/d)}{(\bar{v}_{fB}/b)}\dfrac{(\bar{l}_{f-1,D}/d)}{(\bar{l}_{f-1,B}/b)}}$	$\theta = 0.8865394\,(b/d)_{ca}$	$(d)_{ca}$
1	1.5124893	4.2770473	3.9791833	6.9493235
2	2.8796873	0.98252048	0.87105738	17.7974225
3	5.7586725	0.36388289	0.32260182	25.253254

Comp. No.	$(b)_{ca}$
1	26.3506765
2	15.5025775
3	8.1467460

beginning of the experiment (at time t). The following equations apply for any component i. This being understood, the subscript i is dropped in the interest of simplicity of notation. Also, plate j is selected such that $V_j = \bar{V}_j$ and $L_j = \bar{L}_j$; that is, no stream enters or leaves the column in the vicinity of plate j. Then during time Δt

$$\left.\begin{array}{l}\text{Input of component } i \\ \text{to plate } j \text{ during time} \\ \Delta t\end{array}\right\} = \int_t^{t+\Delta t} L_{j-1}x_{j-1}\, dt + \int_t^{t+\Delta t} V_{j+1}y_{j+1}\, dt \qquad (4\text{--}45)$$

$$\left.\begin{array}{l}\text{Output of component} \\ i \text{ from plate } j \text{ during} \\ \text{time } \Delta t\end{array}\right\} = \int_t^{t+\Delta t} V_j y_j\, dt + \int_t^{t+\Delta t} L_j x_j\, dt \qquad (4\text{--}46)$$

From the definition of accumulation it follows that

$$\left.\begin{array}{l}\text{Accumulation of com-} \\ \text{ponent } i \text{ on plate } j \\ \text{during time } \Delta t\end{array}\right\} = U_j x_j\big|_{t+\Delta t} - U_j x_j\big|_t \qquad (4\text{--}47)$$

where

$$U_j = \text{the moles of liquid holdup on plate } j.$$

The vapor holdup is neglected in the material balance because it is usually small relative to the liquid holdup. In order to obtain the final differential equation, it is necessary to make use of two fundamental theorems of calculus. The first of these is the *mean value theorem of integral calculus* (3).

According to this theorem

$$\int_a^b f(x)\, dx = [f(x)]_m (b - a)$$

$$(4\text{--}48)$$

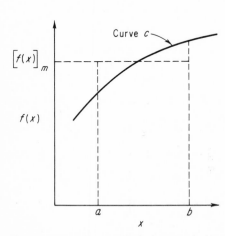

Figure 4–2. Geometrical interpretation of the mean value theorem of integral calculus.

The function $f(x)$ is said to take on its mean value at some value x that is bounded by $x = a$ and $x = b$. Geometrically, the quantities $[f(x)]_m$ and $(b - a)$ form two sides of a rectangle as illustrated in Figure 4–2. As shown by Equation (4–48), the mean ordinate corresponds to that value of $f(x)$ that gives a rectangle having an area equal to the one beneath the curve C from $x = a$ to $x = b$.

The *mean value theorem of differential calculus* (3) relates the value of a function at $x + \Delta x$ to its value at x as follows:

$$f(x) \big|_{x+\Delta x} = f(x) \big|_x + \Delta x f'(x) \big|_{x+\epsilon\Delta x} \qquad (4\text{-}49)$$

where $0 < \epsilon < 1$. This theorem has the geometrical interpretation that between x and $x + \Delta x$ there exists a point on curve C (at $x + \epsilon\,\Delta x$) at which the tangent line is parallel to the chord AB as shown in Figure

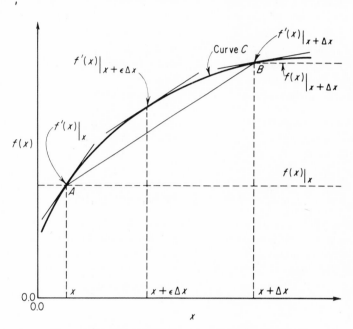

Figure 4–3. Graphical interpretation of the mean value theorem of differential calculus.

4–3. Then by Equation (4–48), Equations (4–45) and (4–46) reduce to

$$\text{Input} = (L_{j-1}x_{j-1})_m \,\Delta t + (V_{j+1}y_{j+1})_m \,\Delta t \qquad (4\text{-}50)$$

$$\text{Output} = (V_j y_j)_m \,\Delta t + (L_j x_j)_m \,\Delta t \qquad (4\text{-}51)$$

and by the *mean value theorem of differential calculus*, Equation (4–47) reduces to

$$\text{Accumulation} = U_j x_j \big|_t + \Delta t \frac{d(U_j x_j)}{dt} \bigg|_{t+\epsilon\Delta t} - U_j x_j \big|_t \qquad (4\text{-}52)$$

Note that Equations (4–50) through (4–52) hold for any value of Δt, since the theorems given by Equations (4–48) and (4–49) are valid for any value of Δt. Substitution of Equations (4–50), (4–51), and (4–52) into Equation (4–44) yields

$$(L_{j-1}x_{j-1})_m + (V_{j+1}y_{j+1})_m - (V_j y_j)_m - (L_j x_j)_m$$

$$= U_j \frac{dx_j}{dt}\bigg|_{t+\epsilon\Delta t} + x_j \frac{dU_j}{dt}\bigg|_{t+\epsilon\Delta t} \quad (4\text{–}53)$$

where Δt has been eliminated by division. The differential equation is obtained by taking the limit of each term of Equation (4–53) as Δt approaches zero. In the limit each term approaches its instantaneous value. Rose *et al.* (9) assumed that the holdup on each plate remained constant with respect to time to give

$$L_{j-1}x_{j-1} + V_{j+1}y_{j+1} - V_j y_j - L_j x_j = U_j(dx_j/dt) \quad (4\text{–}54)$$

If all of the compositions and flow rates are known on the plates throughout the column at any time t, Equation (4–54) may be used to compute the value of the derivative at time t. Rose and his co-workers used this value of the derivative in the calculation of the composition on plate j at time $t + \Delta t$. In general, the mole fraction on plate j at time $t + \Delta t$ as given by the *mean value theorem of differential calculus* is

$$x_j\big|_{t+\Delta t} = x_j\big|_t + \Delta t \frac{dx_j}{dt}\bigg|_{t+\epsilon\Delta t} \quad (4\text{–}55)$$

As implied above, Rose assumed that

$$\frac{dx_j}{dt}\bigg|_{t+\epsilon\Delta t} = \frac{dx_j}{dt}\bigg|_t \quad (4\text{–}56)$$

As may be seen from Figure 4–3, this amounts to the assumption that x_j varies linearly from time t to time $t + \Delta t$. Combining Equations (4–55) and (4–56) produces

$$x_{j,t+1} = x_{j,t} + \Delta t(dx_{j,t}/dt) \quad (4\text{–}57)$$

where for convenience the times t and $t + \Delta t$ have been included in the subscripts as t and $t + 1$, respectively. Equations (4–54) and (4–57) constitute the working equations of the procedure proposed by Rose *et al.* (9). On the basis of an initial set of compositions on each plate, such as that of the feed, Equation (4–54) may be applied to give a value of $dx_{j,t}/dt$ for each component on each plate. (Actually, for the feed plate, the condenser, and the reboiler, the appropriate equations differ slightly from Equation (4–54)). Based on these derivatives and a preselected time interval Δt, the compositions at time $t + \Delta t$ are computed by use of Equation (4–57). These compositions are used to compute the temperature of each plate at time $t + \Delta t$ by use of the conventional bubble point calculational procedure. This procedure also yields the vapor compositions at time $t + \Delta t$. These values of the vapor and liquid compositions are used as the initial values for the second increment of time. This procedure is continued until there is no change in the composition on each plate with respect to time. When the total flow rates are allowed to vary, a set of rates may be calculated at the end of each trial by use of enthalpy balances as shown in the next chapter.

Ball (1) reported that the rate of convergence of the basic relaxation method of Rose *et al.* (9) is generally too slow to be of practical value. In order to increase the rate of convergence, he proposed several modifications. Instead of taking the slope at time $(t + \epsilon \Delta t)$ to be equal to the one at time t, Ball proposed the use of one lying between those at time t and $t + \Delta t$; namely,

$$\frac{dx_j}{dt}\bigg|_{t+\epsilon\Delta t} = \frac{dx_j}{dt}\bigg|_t + \beta\left[\frac{dx_j}{dt}\bigg|_{t+\Delta t} - \frac{dx_j}{dt}\bigg|_t\right] \tag{4–58}$$

where, $0 \leq \beta \leq 1$. Examination of Figure 4–3 shows that such a β can be found. Ball (1) reports that for $\beta > \frac{1}{2}$, any value of Δt may be employed and the equation will remain stable. In general, he employed $\beta = 1$. Because of the simplifications which result, this value of β is employed in the development of the equations proposed by Ball. For other values of β the development is analogous. For $\beta = 1$, Equation (4–58) reduces to

$$\frac{dx_j}{dt}\bigg|_{t+\epsilon\Delta t} = \frac{dx_j}{dt}\bigg|_{t+\Delta t} \tag{4–59}$$

which is the value of the slope at the end of the increment of time Δt. Substitution of this result into Equation (4–55) yields

$$x_{j,t+1} = x_{j,t} + \Delta t\,\frac{dx_{j,t+1}}{dt} \tag{4–60}$$

When the value of dx_j/dt at $(t + \Delta t)$ as given by Equation (4–54) is substituted into Equation (4–60), the following result is obtained upon rearrangement

$$\left(\frac{-\Delta t L_{j-1}}{U_j}\right)x_{j-1,t+1} + \left(\frac{\Delta t V_j K_{j,t+1}}{U_j} + 1 + \frac{\Delta t L_j}{U_j}\right)x_{j,t+1}$$

$$+ \left(\frac{-\Delta t V_{j+1}K_{j+1,t+1}}{U_j}\right)x_{j+1,t+1} = x_{j,t} \tag{4–61}$$

If the approximation that

$$K_{j,t+1} = K_{j,t} \tag{4–62}$$

is made, the coefficient of each x in Equation (4–61) may be evaluated to give one equation in the unknowns, $x_{j-1,t+1}$, $x_{j,t+1}$, and $x_{j+1,t+1}$. In an analogous manner the corresponding equations are developed for each equilibrium stage of the column to give the following array of equations for each component.

$$
\left.\begin{aligned}
A_0 x_0 + B_0 x_1 \hspace{4.5cm} &= D_0 \\[6pt]
A_1 x_0 + B_1 x_1 + C_1 x_2 \hspace{2.5cm} &= D_1 \\[6pt]
A_2 x_1 + B_2 x_2 + C_2 x_3 \hspace{1.5cm} &= D_2 \\[4pt]
\cdots\cdots\cdots\cdots\cdots\cdots\cdots\cdots\cdots \\[4pt]
A_N x_{N-1} + B_N x_N + C_N x_{N+1} &= D_N \\[6pt]
A_{N+1} x_N + B_{N+1} x_{N+1} &= D_{N+1}
\end{aligned}\right\} \quad (4\text{–}63)
$$

where the A's, B's, C's and D's represent coefficients and constants, respectively, of the form of those appearing in Equation (4–61). For a column with N plates, a condenser, and a reboiler a system of $N + 2$ equations in $N + 2$ unknowns is obtained. As discussed previously in Chapter 3, these equations may be solved by use of matrices. For equations such as these which are tridiagonal in form, Grabbe *et al.* (4) have presented a procedure for the determination of the solution. In the application of this method let

$$ f_0 = C_0/B_0, \qquad g_0 = D_0/B_0 \qquad\qquad (4\text{–}64) $$

then compute:

$$ f_k = \frac{C_k}{B_k - A_k f_{k-1}}, \qquad g_k = \frac{D_k - A_k g_{k-1}}{B_k - A_k f_{k-1}} \qquad (4\text{–}65) $$

for $k = 1, 2, \ldots, N + 1$. The values of x are then given by

$$ x_{N+1} = g_{N+1} \qquad\qquad (4\text{–}66) $$

and

$$ x_k = g_k - f_k x_{k+1} $$

for $k = N, N - 1, N - 2, \ldots, 0$.

This procedure is illustrated by carrying out the first trial calculation for Example 3–1. The equations and formulas for the coefficients and constants for this example are given in Table 4–6. The solution of the equations by use of the procedure of Grabbe *et al.* (4) is presented in Table 4–7. The values employed for the time period, Δt, and the holdup, U_j, are of

TABLE 4-6 Unsteady state equations as modified
by Ball (1) for the solution of Example 3-1

I. *Equations*:

$$B_0 x_0 + C_0 x_1 = D_0$$

$$A_1 x_0 + B_1 x_1 + C_1 x_2 = D_1$$

$$A_2 x_1 + B_2 x_2 + C_2 x_3 = D_2$$

$$A_3 x_2 + B_3 x_3 + C_3 x_4 = D_3$$

$$A_4 x_3 + B_4 x_4 = D_4$$

$$B_0 = \frac{\Delta t L_0}{U^*} + 1 + \frac{\Delta t D}{U} \qquad\qquad B_1 = \frac{\Delta t L_1}{U} + 1 + \frac{\Delta t V_1 K_{1,t}}{U}$$

$$C_0 = \frac{-\Delta t V_1 K_{1,t}}{U} \qquad\qquad C_1 = \frac{-\Delta t V_2 K_{2,t}}{U}$$

$$D_0 = x_{0,t} \qquad\qquad D_1 = x_{1,t}$$

$$A_2 = \frac{-\Delta t L_1}{U}$$

$$A_1 = \frac{-\Delta t L_0}{U} \qquad\qquad B_2 = \frac{\Delta t V_2 K_{2,t}}{U} + 1 + \frac{\Delta t L_2}{U}$$

$$C_2 = \frac{-\Delta t V_3 K_{3,t}}{U} \qquad\qquad C_3 = \frac{-\Delta t V_4 K_{4,t}}{U}$$

$$D_2 = x_{2,t} + \frac{\Delta t F X}{U} \qquad\qquad D_3 = x_{3,t}$$

$$A_4 = \frac{-\Delta t L_3}{U}$$

$$A_3 = \frac{-\Delta t L_2}{U} \qquad\qquad B_4 = \frac{\Delta t V_4 K_{4,t}}{U} + 1 + \frac{\Delta t B}{U}$$

$$B_3 = \frac{\Delta t L_3}{U} + 1 + \frac{\Delta t V_3 K_{3,t}}{U} \qquad D_4 = x_{4,t}$$

* The holdup is taken equal for all stages.

the same order of magnitude as those suggested by Rose *et al.* (9). A trial
calculation yields a calculated set of d_i's and b_i's. Based on these calculated
values, a corrected set of terminal rates which are both in material balance
and in agreement with the specified value of D may be found by use of the

TABLE 4–7 First trial calculation for Example 3–1 by use of the relaxation method as modified by Ball (1)

I. *Evaluation of the constants*

Basis for the first trial calculation is liquid feed at its bubble point on each plate. Also, the values of Δt and U_j are fixed at 0.5 hrs. and 500 moles, respectively.

Comp. No.	X_i	α_i	α_iX_i	$K_i = \alpha_iK_b$	B_0	C_0	D_0	A_1	B_1
1	0.333	1	0.333	0.4997012	1.10	−0.049975012	0.333	−0.05	1.0999750
2	0.333	2	0.666	0.99950024	1.10	−0.099950024	0.333	−0.05	1.1499500
3	0.334	3	1.002	1.4992504	1.10	−0.14992504	0.334	−0.05	1.1999250

2.002

$K_b = 0.49975012$

Comp.	C_1	D_1	A_2	B_2	C_2	D_2	A_3	B_3
1	−0.04997012	0.333	−0.05	1.1999750	−0.49975012	0.3663	−0.15	1.0999750
2	−0.099950024	0.333	−0.05	1.2499500	−0.099950024	0.3663	−0.15	1.1499500
3	−0.14992504	0.334	−0.05	1.2999250	−0.14992504	0.3674	−0.15	1.1999250

TABLE 4–7 (Continued)

Comp.	C_3	D_3	A_4	B_4	D_4
1	−0.049975012	0.333	−0.15	1.0999750	0.333
2	−0.099950024	0.333	−0.15	1.1499500	0.333
3	−0.14992504	0.334	−0.15	1.1999250	0.334

II. *Calculation of the compositions by use of the procedure proposed by Grabbe et al.* (4)

Comp. No.	$f_0 = \dfrac{C_0}{B_0}$	$g_0 = \dfrac{D_0}{B_0}$	$f_1 = \dfrac{C_1}{B_1 - A_1 f_0}$	$g_1 = \dfrac{D_1 - A_1 g_0}{B_1 - A_1 f_0}$
1	−0.045431829	0.30272727	−0.04552688	0.31714974
2	−0.090863658	0.30272727	−0.08726159	0.30394123
3	−0.013629549	0.30363636	−0.01256590	0.29266517

Table 4-7 (Continued)

Comp. No.	$f_2 = \dfrac{C_2}{B_2 - A_2 f_1}$	$g_2 = \dfrac{D_2 - A_2 g_1}{B_2 - A_2 f_1}$	$f_3 = \dfrac{C_3}{B_3 - A_3 f_2}$	$g_3 = \dfrac{D_3 - A_3 g_2}{B_3 - A_3 f_2}$	$g_3 = \dfrac{D_4 - A_4 g_3}{B_4 - A_4 f_3}$ $\quad g_4 = x_4 = x_B$
1	−0.04172586	0.31907649	−0.04186507	0.31905531	0.34823073
2	−0.08024331	0.30627895	−0.08074071	0.30611334	0.33301462
3	−0.11589375	0.29531603	−0.11689688	0.29495931	0.31989761
					1.00114296

Comp. No.	$f_3 x_4$	$x_3 = g_3 - f_3 g_4$	$f_2 x_3$	$x_2 = g_2 - f_2 x_3$	$f_1 x_2$	$x_1 = g_1 - f_1 x_2$
1	−0.014578704	0.33634014	−0.013921166	0.33299765	−0.015160344	0.33231008
2	−0.026887837	0.33300118	−0.026719691	0.33299864	−0.029057994	0.33299922
3	−0.037395033	0.33235434	−0.038517791	0.33383382	−0.041949224	0.33461439
		0.99898953		0.99983011		0.99992369

TABLE 4-7 (Continued)

Comp. No.	$f_0 x_1$	$x_0 = g_0 - f_0 x_1$	$D x_0 = (d)_{ca}$	$B x_4 = (b)_{ca}$	$(b/d)_{ca}$
1	−0.015097455	0.31782472	15.891236	17.411536	1.0956691
2	−0.030257527	0.33298480	16.649240	16.650731	1.0000896
3	−0.045606432	0.34924279	17.462139	15.994880	0.91597484

1.0000523

θ-method of convergence. Ball (1) reported that the θ-method appreciably increased the rate of convergence of the modified relaxation method. It is to be noted that the x_j's do not add to give unity. In principle, two methods may be used to obtain a set whose sum is unity. First, they may be normalized, each mole fraction being weighted equally; this method amounts to direct-iteration for all stages except the condenser and the reboiler. Secondly, the θ-method may be employed, each composition being weighted differently. The calculated value of l_{ji} is given by multiplication of the calculated value of x_{ji} by the specified value of L_j. The corrected set of compositions are then computed by use of Equation (4–9). This process should further increase the rate of convergence of this method.

USE OF THE NEWTON-RAPHSON METHOD IN THE CALCULATIONAL PROCEDURE AND CONVERGENCE METHOD

This novel calculational procedure and convergence method was proposed by Greenstadt *et al.* (5). In that the calculational procedure is initiated on the basis of an assumed product distribution, it is like the one proposed by Lewis and Matheson (7). It differs from the latter procedure in that instead of making alternate bubble point (or dew point) and material balance calculations, Greenstadt and his co-workers solved the corresponding simultaneous equations for each plate by use of the Newton-Raphson method. For a system containing c components and for any plate j in the stripping section, the condition of equilibrium on plate j gives c equations of the form

$$K_{ji}x_{ji} - y_{ji} = 0 \qquad (4\text{--}67)$$

There are also c material balances which may be represented by

$$L_j x_{ji} - V_{j+1}y_{j+1,i} - b_i = 0 \qquad (4\text{--}68)$$

and one defining equation for the mole fraction,

$$\sum_{i=1}^{c} y_{ji} - 1 = 0 \qquad (4\text{--}69)$$

Equations (4–67) through (4–69) represent $(2c + 1)$ equations in $(2c + 1)$ unknowns, c values of y_j, c values of x_j, and the temperature of plate j. In principle, these equations may be solved by use of the Newton-Raphson method as described in Chapter 1. The resulting y_j's obtained by solving these equations are used in the solution of the corresponding set of equations for plate $j - 1$. This calculational procedure is carried out from the bottom of the column to the plate above the feed plate and from the top of the column to the feed plate.

When the total vapor and liquid rates are calculated by enthalpy balances, two additional unknowns (V_j and L_j) are involved, and two additional equations may be stated; one of these represents the requirement that the total flow rates be in material balance, and the other one requires that all streams be in enthalpy balance. These equations may be solved simultaneously with those represented by Equations (4–67) through (4–69) by use of the Newton-Raphson method.

If the flow rates for each component obtained by making calculations up from the bottom and down from the top of the column are in agreement at the plate above the feed plate, the correct set of d_i's (and b_i's) were assumed to make the given trial calculation. If not, the Newton-Raphson method is employed to find a corrected set of d_i's that satisfies simultaneously the matching equations and the specification D. These requirements may be stated as ($2c + 1$) unknowns as follows:

$$\bar{v}_{fDi} - \bar{v}_{fBi} = 0 \tag{4-70}$$

$$\bar{l}_{f-1,Di} - \bar{l}_{f-1,Bi} = 0 \tag{4-71}$$

$$\sum_{i=1}^{c} (d_i)_{co} - D = 0 \tag{4-72}$$

The corrected set of d_i's (and b_i's) are used to initiate the next trial calculation.

COMPARISON OF THE CONVERGENCE METHODS

At the outset it should be remarked that Example 3–1 was selected for illustrative purposes, and that it is not considered to be an appropriate problem to adequately test the various convergence methods. However, in the process of demonstrating the principles of the various convergence methods, the solution to this problem was obtained by several methods. The number of trials required to give convergence for those methods that could be placed on about the same basis are given in Table 4–8. Actually, the relaxation method as modified by Ball (1) was not necessarily placed on the same basis as the others. Its rate of convergence for Example 3–1 could very likely be markedly increased by making choices for Δt and U_j other than those that were employed (see Table 4–7).

As shown in Table 4–8, all applications of the θ-method require about the same number of trials for convergence. For this particular example more trials are required by the Lewis and Matheson calculational procedure when the rates of flow of each component in the liquid onto the feed plate are included in the formula for the computation of $(b_i/d_i)_{ca}$.

Even though the combination of the Thiele and Geddes calculational procedure and the θ-method converge rapidly for the constant-α and constant-L/V example, the tendency of this combination toward convergence is even more pronounced for variable-α and variable-L/V problems. In fact the problem of providing suitable damping arises and is solved in the manner explained in subsequent chapters.

In theory the calculational procedure of Thiele and Geddes and the relaxation method of Rose and Ball are independent of the direction of calculation. In subsequent applications of the Thiele and Geddes procedure, this independence is seen to be particularly advantageous. On the other hand, more computer storage space is generally required by these procedures than by the one proposed by Lewis and Matheson.

TABLE 4–8 Comparison of the number of trials required by the various convergence methods to give a solution to Example 3–1 in which the calculated and corrected values of the variables for successive trials agreed to within seven or eight digits

Calculational procedure	Convergence method	Number of trials required
Thiele and Geddes	Direct-iteration	11
Lewis and Matheson	Direct-iteration $[(b_i/d_i)_{ca}$ based on the vapor entering the plate above the feed plate].	9*
Thiele and Geddes	θ-method	7
Lewis and Matheson	θ-method $[(b_i/d_i)_{ca}$ based on the vapor entering the feed plate].	8
Lewis and Matheson	Mismatch	Converged to $D =$ 51.66 in 7 trials
Lewis and Matheson	Mismatch plus normalization	9
Lewis and Matheson	Mismatch and θ-method $[(b_i/d_i)_{ca}$ based on the vapor entering the plate above the feed plate]	8

TABLE 4–8 (Continued)

Calculational procedure	Convergence method	Number of trials required
Lewis and Matheson	θ-method $[(b_i/d_i)_{ca}$ calculated by the formula proposed by Peiser.]	14
Lewis and Matheson	θ-method $[(b_i/d_i)_{ca}$ based on the liquid flowing onto the feed plate.]	21
Relaxation method as modified by Ball (1)	Direct-iteration plus normalization of all compositions	At the end of 50 trials, the first two digits of all of the K_b's were correct except for one which was correct to one digit
Relaxation method as modified by Ball (1)	Direct-iteration plus normalization of all compositions except D and B. These were determined by the θ-method	At the end of 40 trials, K_b's of the same accuracy as stated for the previous case were obtained.

* Since the results of the first trial by the Thiele and Geddes procedure were used as the initial values for the Lewis and Matheson calculational procedure, the trial numbers shown contain one additional trial to account for this.

The solution of the illustrative examples presented in this chapter were obtained by Mr. D. L. Taylor. This assistance is gratefully acknowledged.

NOTATION

(See also Chapter 3)

$a = $ a constant used in the statement of the *mean value theorem of integral calculus*

$A_0, \ldots, A_{N+1} = $ coefficients in Equation (4–63)

$b = $ a constant used in the statement of the *mean value theorem of integral calculus*

$b_i = $ molal flow rate of component i in the bottoms. Used to denote the assumed flow rate in equations pertaining to the Lewis and Matheson calculational procedure

$(b_i)_{ca}$ = calculated value of the flow rate of component i in the bottoms

$(b_i)_{co}$ = corrected value of the flow rate obtained by the θ-method of convergence

$(\bar{b}_i)_{co}$ = corrected value of the flow rate obtained by the mismatch convergence method

Δb_i = correction of the bottoms rate as calculated by the mismatch convergence method

$B_0, \ldots, B_{N+1}$ = coefficients in Equation (4–63)

$C_1, \ldots, C_N$ = coefficients in Equation (4–63)

d_i = molal flow rate of component i in the distillate. Used to denote the assumed flow rate in the equations pertaining to the Lewis and Matheson calculational procedure

$(d_i)_{ca}$ = calculated value of the flow rate of component i in the distillate

$(d_i)_{co}$ = corrected value of the flow rate obtained by the θ-method of convergence

$(\bar{d}_i)_{co}$ = corrected value of the flow rate obtained by the mismatch convergence method

$D_0, \ldots, D_{N+1}$ = constants in Equation (4–63)

f_0, f_k = used to denote combinations of constants which arise in the solution of the system of equations represented by Equation (4–63)

$f(x), [f(x)]_m$ = the function $f(x)$ and the mean value of the function, respectively

$f'(x)$ = the first derivative of the function $f(x)$ with respect to x

$f(x)\,|_{x+\Delta x}$ = the value of the function $f(x)$ at $x + \Delta x$

g_0, g_k = used to denote combinations of constants which arise in the solution of the system of equations represented by Equation (4–63)

$t, \Delta t$ = time and an increment of time, respectively

U_j = the total liquid holdup in moles on plate j

$\bar{v}_{fBi}$ = molal rate of flow at which component i in the vapor enters the plate above the feed plate as calculated up from the bottom of the column by the Lewis and Matheson calculational procedure

$\bar{v}_{fDi}$ = same as $\bar{v}_{fBi}$ except it is obtained by making calculations down from the top of the column

x_{fBi} = mole fraction of component i in the liquid leaving the feed plate; it is obtained by making calculations up from the bottom of the column to the feed plate by the procedure of Lewis and Matheson

x_{fDi} = same as x_{fBi} except it is obtained by making calculations down from the top of the column

$g(\theta)$ = the function used to compute the positive value θ required to satisfy both a component-material balance and the specified distillate rate, D

E = the mismatch obtained at the feed plate by the Lewis and Matheson calculational procedure; defined by Equation (4–28)

$\bar{l}_{f-1,\,Bi}$ = molal rate of flow of component i (in the liquid phase) onto the feed plate as calculated up from the bottom of the column by the Lewis and Matheson calculational procedure

$\bar{l}_{f-1,\,Di}$ = same as $\bar{l}_{f-1,\,Bi}$ except it is obtained by making calculations down from the top of the column

R_i = used to denote several terms involved in the calculation of the mismatch correction; defined by Equation (4–38)

Greek Letters

β = a number bounded by zero and one

γ = a function of the temperatures and L/V profiles

ϵ = a number bounded by zero and one

θ = a multiplier; defined by Equation (4–4)

σ_j = a multiplier for the vapor rates for plate j; defined by Equation (4–11)

τ_j = a multiplier for the liquid rates for plate j; defined by Equation (4–12)

Subscripts

B = the bottoms or a quantity of obtained by making calculations up from the bottom of the column

ca = calculated value of a variable

co = corrected value of a variable

D = the distillate, or a quantity obtained by making calculations down from the top of the column

f = feed plate

I, II = trials one and two

k = an integer used for counting

PROBLEMS

4–1 Show that the expressions given for x_{ji} in Equation (4–9) are equivalent.

4–2 (a) Using the values of $(b_i/d_i)_{ca}$ given in Table 3–2 for the first trail calculation for Example 3–1, show that the value of θ obtained by use of Equation (4–6) is $\theta = 5.6215101$.

   (b) Using the corrected distillate rates, compute the x_{ji}'s by Equation (4–9).
   Then calculate the K_b's and compare them with those given in Table 4–1.

   (c) Repeat Part (b) except base the K_b's on the y_{ji}'s given by Equation
   (4–10) instead of the x_{ji}'s.

   (d) Give an analytical proof of the equality of the K_b's obtained in Parts (b)
   and (c). Also, show that if the α's are independent of temperature, then
   the temperatures obtained by use of the bubble point and dew point
   procedures (wherein the x_{ji}'s and y_{ji}'s obtained by Equations (4–9) and
   (4–10) are employed) are equal. Using the K_b's obtained in Part (b) or
   (c), make a step-by-step calculation through the column by use of the
   procedure of Thiele and Geddes and show that a calculated value of
   49.006364 is obtained for D.

4–3 Develop Equation (4–4) by use of Equation (4–11). State any additional
postulates required in the application of Equation (4–11) to the bottoms.

4–4 On the basis of the corrected terminal rates given in Table 4–2, carry out the
next trial calculation through the column by the calculational procedure of
Lewis and Matheson and verify the second value of θ given in Table 4–2.

4–5 Beginning with first principles, verify the formulas given in Table 4–6.

LITERATURE CITED

1. Ball, W. E., "Computer Programs for Distillation," paper presented at the
Machine Computation Special Workshop Session on Multicomponent Distillation at the 44th National Meeting of the A.I.Ch.E. in New Orleans, February 27, 1961.

2. Bonner, J. S., "Solution of Multicomponent Distillation Problems on a Stored-
program Computer," American *Petroleum Institute Quarterly*, Division of
Refining, **36**, No. 3, 238 (1956).

3. Courant, R., *Differential and Integral Calculus*, 2 ed. (New York: Interscience
Publishers, Inc., 1957), Vol. 1, pp. 102 and 126.

4. Grabbe, E. M., S. Ramo, D. E. Wooldridge, *Handbook of Automation, Computation, and Control* (New York: John Wiley & Sons, Inc., 1958), Vol. 1,
Chap. 14, p. 34.

5. Greenstadt, John, Yonathan Bard, and Burt Morse, "Multicomponent Distillation Calculation on the IBM 704," *Ind. Eng. Chem.*, **50,** 1644 (1958).

6. Lyster, W. N., S. L. Sullivan, Jr., D. S. Billingsley, and C. D. Holland, "Figure Distillation This New Way: Part 1—New Convergence Method Will Handle Many Cases," *Petroleum Refiner*, **38,** No. 6, 221 (1959).

7. Lewis, W. K., and G. L. Matheson, "Studies in Distillation-Design of Rectifying Columns for Natural and Refinery Gasoline," *Ind. Eng. Chem.*, **24,** 494 (1932).

8. Peiser, A. M., "Better Computer Solution of Multicomponent Systems," *Chemical Engineering*, **67,** 129 (July 1960).

9. Rose, Arthur, R. F. Sweeny, and V. N. Schrodt, "Continuous Distillation Calculations by Relaxation Method," *Ind. Eng. Chem.*, **50,** 737 (1958).

10. Sullivan, S. L., Jr., "Use of Computers for Multicomponent Distillation Calculations," M.S. thesis, A. and M. College of Texas, College Station, Texas, (January 1959).

11. Thiele, E. W. and R. L. Geddes, "Computation of Distillation Apparatus for Hydrocarbon Mixtures," *Ind. Eng. Chem.* **25,** 289 (1933).

Enthalpy Balances for Conventional Columns

5

The total flow rates throughout the column are determined by use of the approximate form of the first law of thermodynamics, $\Delta H = Q$, Equation (1–3). Procedures are presented for the calculation of the total enthalpy of a stream in two different ways—the conventional method, which has been used for a number of years, and the constant-composition method, was only recently set forth (3, 6, 10). In addition, the Q-method for making enthalpy balances is presented. This method is directed toward finding the adiabatic solution for each plate if one exists within the specified range of flow rates; otherwise, intercoolers (or heaters) are employed as required to maintain the flow rates within the specified limits. These methods are applied to a conventional column for illustration.

The primary purpose of this chapter is to introduce these general enthalpy procedures and to show how they are used with the calculational procedures of Thiele and Geddes and Lewis and Matheson. The superiority of the constant-composition method over the conventional method for the calculation of enthalpies is most pronounced in the treatment of absorbers, illustrated in Chapter 8. The combination of the calculational procedure of Thiele and Geddes with each of the enthalpy procedures follows.

CONVENTIONAL METHOD FOR MAKING ENTHALPY BALANCES

In the use of this method, it is generally assumed that each plate of a conventional column is to be operated adiabatically except for the partial condenser and the reboiler. For the case where the vapor and liquid streams leaving plate j are ideal solutions, the enthalpies are computed by

$$H_j = \sum_{i=1}^{c} H_{ji} y_{ji} \qquad \text{(vapor)} \qquad (5\text{–}1)$$

$$h_j = \sum_{i=1}^{c} h_{ji} x_{ji} \qquad \text{(liquid)} \qquad (5\text{–}2)$$

where H_{ji} and h_{ji} are the enthalpies of the pure component i in the vapor and liquid streams, respectively, at the temperature of plate j. The quantities H_j and h_j are also referred to here as stream enthalpies.

In the rectifying section the enthalpy balances are written around the condenser and any given plate; and in the stripping section, the reboiler and any particular plate. After the rate of flow of the liquid or vapor stream has been calculated by an enthalpy balance, the second stream is calculated by a material balance.

Rectifying Section

$$V_1 H_1 = L_0 h_0 + D H_D + Q_c \text{ (enthalpy balance around the condenser)}$$

$$(5\text{--}3a)$$

or,

$$L_0 = \left[\frac{M_D - H_1}{H_1 - h_0} \right] [D] \qquad (5\text{--}3b)$$

since $V_1 = L_0 + D$. Alternately, Equation (5–3a) may be solved for Q_c. Similarly for a balance enclosing the condenser and any plate j,

$$V_{j+1} H_{j+1} = L_j h_j + D H_D + Q_c \qquad (5\text{--}3c)$$

Elimination of V_{j+1} by use of the material balance

$$V_{j+1} = L_j + D, \qquad 0 \le j \le f - 2 \qquad (5\text{--}3d)$$

yields an expression of the form:

$$L_{j-1} = \left[\frac{M_D - H_j}{H_j - h_{j-1}} \right] [D], \qquad 1 \le j \le f - 1 \qquad (5\text{--}3e)$$

Similarly

$$L_{f-1} = \left[\frac{(M_D - H_f) - \dfrac{V_F}{D} (H_F - H_f)}{H_f - h_{f-1}} \right] [D] \qquad (5\text{--}3f)$$

$$\bar{V}_f = L_{f-1} + D \qquad (5\text{--}3g)$$

where

H_F, h_F = Enthalpies of one mole of the vapor and liquid parts of the feed, respectively.

$M_D = H_D + Q_c/D$; H_D represents the enthalpy per mole of distillate withdrawn, regardless of state, and Q_c is the condenser duty, the net heat removed by the condenser per unit time.

For the stripping section, the corresponding equations are as follows:

Stripping Section

$$V_j = \left[\frac{h_{j-1} - M_B}{H_j - h_{j-1}} \right] [B], \qquad f + 1 \leq j \leq N + 1 \qquad (5\text{-}4a)$$

$$V_f = \left[\frac{(h_{f-1} - M_B) - \dfrac{L_F}{B}(h_{f-1} - h_F)}{H_f - h_{f-1}} \right] [B] \qquad (5\text{-}4b)$$

$$L_{j-1} = V_j + B, \qquad f + 1 \leq j \leq N + 1 \qquad (5\text{-}4c)$$

$$\bar{L}_{f-1} = V_f + B \qquad (5\text{-}4d)$$

where

$M_B = h_B - Q_R/B$; Q_R is the reboiler duty, the net heat put into the system by the reboiler per unit time. Also, according to the numbering system, $h_B = h_{N+1}$. The condenser and reboiler duties are related by the over-all enthalpy balance

$$Q_R = DH_D + Bh_B + Q_c - FH \qquad (5\text{-}5)$$

The symbol H represents the total enthalpy per mole of feed entering the column.

$$H = \frac{V_F}{F} \sum_{i=1}^{c} H_{Fi} y_{Fi} + \frac{L_F}{F} \sum_{i=1}^{c} h_{Fi} x_{Fi} \qquad (5\text{-}6)$$

General Calculational Procedure for the Combination of the Thiele and Geddes Method and the Conventional Method for Enthalpy Balances

In general, enthalpy balances are employed in order to determine the total rates of flow throughout the column. When enthalpy balances are combined with the Thiele and Geddes calculational procedure, any given trial calculation is carried out on the basis of L/V and temperature profiles in the same manner as described in Chapter 4 to give corrected sets of compositions and temperatures. These are used in the calculation of a set of flow rates by enthalpy balances as indicated by Equations (5–3) and (5–4). The flow rates so obtained are used in the computation of the absorption and stripping factors for the next trial.

In the process of solving a wide variety of numerical examples, it became evident that the change in the temperatures and the flow rates between successive trials should be limited. The methods by which these are limited are referred to as forcing procedures. Those presented here were proposed by Lyster *et al.* (7). These authors determined the corrected temperature profiles by use of the bubble point procedure. (The results obtained by use of the bubble point and dew point procedures are compared in a subsequent chapter.) When actual K-values are employed instead of constant relative volatilities and the corrected temperature profile is computed by use of the bubble point procedure, the tendency toward convergence is much more pronounced. In fact over-corrections which led to the first forcing procedure are common. For numerous examples in which the molal rates of flow were taken to be constant, the calculated values of D were alternately smaller and larger than the specified value for D. Similarly, the calculated temperature profiles were alternately too high and too low. Reasoning that the best profile to be employed for the next trial calculation lay somewhere between these two led to the development of the averaging procedure.

In this procedure each calculated profile after the first one is averaged plate by plate with the profile used to make the particular trial calculation. In general, it was found that for systems in which the boiling range of the feeds was relatively narrow, convergence to the desired value of D was so rapid that the averaging of the profiles neither reduced nor increased to any appreciable extent the number of trials required, whereas for systems in which the boiling range of the feeds was relatively wide, the number of trials required to obtain a D of the desired accuracy was noticeably reduced by the averaging procedure. As shown in a subsequent chapter, when the feed consists almost entirely of a very light component whose K-value is nearly independent of temperature, further restrictions must be placed on the change in the temperatures employed for successive trials.

The second forcing procedure is used in order to provide stability when the molal flow rates are calculated by use of enthalpy balances. In general, it was found that the deviation of the calculated values of D from the specified value was ar. plified by the introduction of the enthalpy balances. This was due in part to the comparatively small differences between large numbers involved in the expressions for flow rates.

Since all problems in which the flow rates were assumed constant could be solved, it appeared plausible to limit the variation in the rates of flow between successive trials in the solution of problems in which these rates were varied. The following procedure, which is not necessarily the optimum, was finally adopted.

(1) The first two trial calculations are carried out at the liquid and vapor rates assumed initially. This procedure allows the temperature profile to attain some degree of stability before making enthalpy balances.

(2) The maximum value of any vapor rate calculated at the end of the second through the sixth trials is limited to 1.2 times the corresponding value used to make the particular trial calculation. For the minimum rate, the corresponding factor is $1/1.2$.

(3) At the end of the seventh and twelfth trials, the limits are further reduced to 1.1 and $1/1.1$ and to 1.025 and $1/1.025$, respectively.

(4) The vapor rates that are within the above limits and calculated at the end of the third and each successive trial are averaged plate by plate with those employed to make the particular trial calculation.

This procedure recognizes to some extent that problems which are easily solved do not need a restriction on either the temperatures or the vapor rates, whereas for the more difficult problems either the 10% (1.1 and $1/1.1$) or the 2.5% (1.025 and $1/1.025$) restriction as well as the averaging of the temperature profiles are needed in order to obtain the desired solution. Most of the problems encountered were solved within seven trials, and in many instances where more than seven trials were required the changes in the vapor rates between successive trials were less than the limitations imposed. Whenever this occurred, all of the vapor rates were of course averaged.

In the application of the first forcing procedure (the averaging of the temperature profiles) to problems in which the rates of flow varied, the enthalpies of the pure components in Equations (5–1) and (5–2) were evaluated at the temperature profile obtained by averaging. The liquid-stream enthalpies, Equation (5–2) were evaluated on the basis of the x_{ji}'s obtained by use of the θ-method as indicated by Equation (4–9). These x_{ji}'s together with the K_{ji}'s (evaluated at the bubble point temperature) give rise to a set of y_{ji}'s that are used in the evaluation of the vapor-stream enthalpies, Equation (5–1). There exists the possibility of evaluating the vapor-stream enthalpies on the basis of the vapor compositions given by the θ-method as indicated by Equation (4–10). This approach was investigated and found to give no significant improvements.

The equilibrium constants, K's, employed in the calculation of the absorption and stripping factors for the next trial are evaluated on the basis of the temperature profile obtained by averaging. Also, the vapor and liquid rates to be used in the absorption and stripping factors for the next trial are those given by the forcing procedures.

Instead of limiting the vapor rates, a forcing procedure may be devised whereby the variation in the value of L/V for each plate is limited for successive trials. In the application of such a procedure, it is of course necessary to maintain the vapor and liquid rates in material balance.

In the illustrative examples which follow, calculations were made up

TABLE 5–1 Feed compositions for Examples 5–1 through 5–6

Component	Example 5–1	Examples 5–2, 5–3, 5–4, 5–5, 5–6
	FX	FX
CH_4	0.0	2.0
C_2H_6	0.0	10.0
C_3H_6	0.0	6.0
C_3H_8	5.0	12.5
$i\text{-}C_4$	15.0	3.5
$n\text{-}C_4$	25.0	15.0
$i\text{-}C_5$	20.0	0.0
$n\text{-}C_5$	35.0	15.2
$n\text{-}C_6$	0.0	11.3
$n\text{-}C_7$	0.0	9.0
$n\text{-}C_8$	0.0	8.5
360*	0.0	7.0
Total	100.0	100.0

* Commonly referred to as the 360°F—normal boiling fraction.

Reproduced by permission of *Hydrocarbon Processing & Petroleum Refiner*

from the bottom and down from the top of the column as described in Chapter 4. As demonstrated in the next chapter, this approach minimizes round-off error.

The conventional method for making enthalpy balances and the use of the forcing procedures are illustrated by the solution of the examples which are stated in Tables 5–1 and 5–2. The equilibrium data used to obtain the solutions are given in Tables A–2 and A–3, and the enthalpy data are

TABLE 5-2 Specifications for Examples 5-1 through 5-6

Example	Initial temperature profile	Feed condition	Distillate rate	Reflux ratio L_0/D	No. of stages	No. of feed plate*	Type of condenser	Column pressure (psia)
5-1	Linear (130°-250°F)	Boiling point liquid	48.9	2.58	10	5	Total	120
5-2	Linear (50°-450°F)	Boiling point liquid	31.6	2.0	13	4	Partial	264.7
5-3	Constant at 150°F	Boiling point liquid	31.6	2.0	13	4	Partial	264.7
5-4	Constant at 300°F	Boiling point liquid	31.6	2.0	13	4	Partial	264.7
5-5	Linear (50°-450°F)	50 percent vapor	31.6	2.0	13	4	Partial	264.7
5-6	Linear (50°-450°F)	Boiling point liquid	31.6	2.0	51	13	Partial	264.7

* The plates were numbered down from the top of the column with the partial condenser being designated zero and the top plate being numbered one.

Reproduced by permission of *Hydrocarbon Processing & Petroleum Refiner*

presented in Tables A–6 and A–7 of the Appendix. These examples were taken from Reference (7). The solutions of the first two of these are given in detail, whereas for the remaining examples only the final results are shown.

This series of illustrative examples was selected in order to demonstrate the effect of boiling range, the thermal condition of the feed, the number of plates, and the temperature profile initially assumed on the number of trials required for convergence. Example 5–1 consists of components having a relatively narrow boiling range compared with those of Example 5–2. The latter is a slight modification of the gasoline-stabilization example solved by Robinson and Gilliland (8).

The temperature profiles obtained by use of the θ-method without employing either one of the forcing procedures are shown in Table 5–3. Although rapid convergence is obtained for Example 5–1 without using the forcing procedures, it was necessary to apply both of the forcing procedures in order to obtain a solution for Example 5–2. The temperature profiles obtained for this example are presented in Table 5–4. The effect of the second forcing procedure on Examples 5–1 and 5–2 is shown in Table 5–5. For systems such as Example 5–1, the limits of the second forcing procedure were never applied because all of the calculated rates fell within the permissible range of values. The final product distributions which were obtained for these two examples are presented in Table 5–6.

As shown in Table 5–7, the number of trials required to obtain a solution of the desired accuracy is almost independent of the temperature profile assumed initially, the number of plates, and the thermal condition of the feed. A comparison of Tables 5–3 and 5–7 shows that the use of forcing procedures in the solution of Example 5–1 increased the number of trials required to obtain D's of a given accuracy.

Although some speed is sacrificed in the solution of the relatively easy problems, the use of forcing procedures made it possible to solve most problems. A few problems were encountered which could not be solved by this method because of either the calculation of a permanent inverse in the temperature profile or the continued calculation of negative vapor rates. Such problems led to the development of the following procedure described by Weisenfelder *et al.* (10).

CONSTANT-COMPOSITION METHOD FOR MAKING ENTHALPY BALANCES

Instability of the conventional method for making enthalpy balances was most pronounced in systems composed almost entirely of very light and heavy components. (Most absorber systems are of this type.) For such systems the denominators of the expressions for L_{j-1} and V_j (Equations (5–3e) and (5–4a)) are extremely sensitive to small changes in

TABLE 5–3 Temperature profiles and distillate rates obtained with enthalpy balances (conventional method) and without forcing procedures for Example 5–1

Plate No.	Temperature profiles (°F) Trial number						
	Initial	1	2	3	4	5	6
0 (Distillate)	130.00	146.34	147.55	147.60	147.63	147.63	147.63
1	130.00	164.44	165.57	165.64	165.71	165.71	165.71
2	143.33	180.08	179.30	179.34	179.41	179.40	179.40
3	156.67	195.19	189.80	189.88	189.91	189.89	189.90
4 (Feed)	170.00	208.10	196.82	197.50	197.38	197.37	197.38
5	183.33	217.46	200.51	202.78	202.22	202.31	202.30
6	196.67	223.20	211.05	211.89	211.51	211.56	211.56
7	210.00	228.14	219.41	219.56	219.29	219.32	219.32
8	223.33	231.93	225.86	225.75	225.59	225.60	225.60
9	236.67	234.65	230.69	230.54	230.43	230.45	230.45
10 (Bottoms)	250.00	236.56	234.25	234.14	234.08	234.09	234.09
D (Calculated by θ-method)	—	41.82	52.40	48.65	49.01	48.93	48.94
D (Calculated by direct-iteration)	—	41.82	43.68	44.86	46.04	47.04	47.67

(Note: Nineteen trials were required to obtain a D of 48.94 by direct-iteration.)

Reproduced by permission of *Hydrocarbon Processing & Petroleum Refiner*

TABLE 5-4 Temperature profiles and distillate rates obtained with the forcing procedures and enthalpy balances (conventional method) for Example 5-2

Temperature profiles (°F)
Trial number

Plate No.	1	2	3	4	5	6	7	8	12
0 (Distillate)	90.34	93.01	92.74	92.32	92.17	92.14	92.13	92.13	92.13
1	119.45	119.50	118.49	117.36	116.60	116.13	115.84	115.66	115.41
2	148.15	145.19	141.39	138.15	136.20	135.08	134.44	134.08	133.65
3	178.50	172.84	165.81	160.18	157.28	155.87	155.19	154.86	154.53
4 (Feed)	223.05	217.87	206.13	197.25	194.45	193.91	193.88	193.90	193.86
5	226.59	229.91	224.99	219.32	217.19	216.63	216.54	216.56	216.56
6	230.95	238.23	237.21	233.86	232.37	231.88	231.77	231.76	231.77
7	236.32	245.31	246.56	244.87	243.91	243.51	243.38	243.35	243.35
8	243.57	252.50	254.71	254.03	253.40	253.07	252.92	252.87	252.85
9	254.26	261.36	263.29	262.99	262.51	262.20	262.04	261.97	261.94
10	270.47	274.04	274.65	274.24	273.79	273.50	273.35	273.29	273.26
11	294.98	294.25	293.25	292.73	292.44	292.29	292.22	292.19	292.19
12 (Bottoms)	334.09	333.09	332.95	333.04	333.10	333.13	333.15	333.16	333.16
D (Calculated by θ-method)	30.61	31.71	32.16	32.10	31.79	31.67	31.62	31.611	31.601
D (Calculated by direct-iteration)	30.61	29.41	29.99	30.42	30.53	30.61	30.75	30.79	31.08

(Note: By direct iteration a D = 31.47 was obtained at the end of 23 trials with distillate and bottoms temperaures of 90.84°F and 332.7°F, respectively.)

Reproduced by permission of *Hydrocarbon Processing & Petroleum Refiner*

TABLE 5-5 Vapor rates obtained with enthalpy balances (conventional method) and forcing procedures for Examples 5-1 and 5-2

Plate No.	Vapor rates for example 5-1 Trial number				Vapor rates for example 5-2 Trial number				
	2*	3	4	8	2†	3	4	5	7
1	175.0	175.0	175.0	175.0	94.8	94.8	94.8	94.8	94.8
2	172.8	171.5	170.9	170.6	95.3	94.0	93.5	93.3	93.0
3	170.7	168.6	167.7	167.4	92.9	91.0	90.5	90.1	89.4
4	169.8	167.3	166.2	165.6	86.9	83.8	83.2	82.2	80.5
5	170.1	167.4	166.1	164.8	113.8	117.9	112.0	110.1	110.2
6	172.8	170.1	168.2	165.7	113.8	128.4	125.9	124.4	124.0
7	172.8	170.4	168.7	166.6	113.8	133.3	133.6	132.7	132.2
8	172.9	170.8	169.4	167.5	113.8	135.3	138.0	138.0	137.7
9	173.0	171.2	169.9	168.4	113.8	135.2	139.7	140.6	140.7
10	173.1	171.4	170.3	169.1	113.8	133.4	138.9	140.4	140.8
11	—	—	—	—	113.8	129.6	134.7	136.2	136.4
12	—	—	—	—	113.8	120.4	122.4	122.9	122.7

* Vapor rate assumed constant at 175.0 for the first two trials.
† Vapor rate assumed constant at 94.8 for the first two trials.

Reproduced by permission of *Hydrocarbon Processing & Petroleum Refiner*

TABLE 5–6 Final product distributions for Examples 5–1 and 5–2 obtained by use of enthalpy balances (conventional method) and forcing procedures

Component	Product distributions			
	Example 5–1		Example 5–2	
	d^*	b	d	b
CH_4	—	—	2.00000	0.0
C_2H_6	—	—	9.99994	0.00005
C_3H_6	—	—	5.96602	0.03397
C_3H_8	4.997387	0.0026130	12.27752	0.22247
$i\text{-}C_4$	14.66936	0.3306400	0.66940	2.83059
$n\text{-}C_4$	23.10224	1.897760	0.68200	14.31799
$i\text{-}C_5$	3.56211	16.43789	0.00504	0.0
$n\text{-}C_5$	2.608903	32.391097	0.00005	15.19495
$n\text{-}C_6$	—	—	0.0	11.29994
$n\text{-}C_7$	—	—	0.0	8.99999
$n\text{-}C_8$	—	—	0.0	8.49999
360	—	—	0.0	6.99999

* In the statement of the final results, all rates less than 10^{-7} were taken equal to zero.

composition and temperature because H_j is approximately equal to h_{j-1}. The constant-composition method virtually eliminates this problem. In this method, it is recognized that the vapor leaving plate $(j + 1)$ of the rectifying section of a column consists of the distillate and the liquid entering plate $(j + 1)$ from plate j. Thus the term $V_{j+1}H_{j+1}$ may be expressed in the following form:

$$V_{j+1}H_{j+1} = \sum_{i=1}^{c} H_{j+1,i}v_{j+1,i} = \sum_{i=1}^{c} H_{j+1,i}(l_{ji} + d_i) \qquad (5\text{–}7)$$

TABLE 5-7 Final results obtained for Examples 5–1 through 5–6 by use of the enthalpy balances (conventional method) and forcing procedures

Example	Trials required for $\dfrac{\Delta D}{D} = \pm 0.01$	Temperature, °F		Trials required for $\Delta D = \pm 0.001$	Temperature, °F	
		Distillate	Bottoms		Distillate	Bottoms
5–1	5	147.59	234.28	8	147.62	234.09
5–2	5	92.17	333.10	7	92.13	333.15
5–3	5	92.20	332.83	7	92.14	333.09
5–4	5	92.17	332.99	6	92.16	333.07
5–5	7	114.56	320.72	12	114.21	320.55
5–6	5	89.57	334.34	8	89.52	334.37

Reproduced by permission of *Hydrocarbon Processing & Petroleum Refiner*

or

$$V_{j+1}H_{j+1} = L_j H(x_j)_{j+1} + DH(X_D)_{j+1} \qquad (5\text{--}8)$$

where

$$H(x_j)_{j+1} = \sum_{i=1}^{c} H_{j+1,i}x_{ji}$$

$$H(X_D)_{j+1} = \sum_{i=1}^{c} H_{j+1,i}X_{Di}$$

When the expression for $V_{j+1}H_{j+1}$ as given by Equation (5–8) is substituted into Equation (5–3c) and solved for L_j, the following result is obtained.

$$L_j = \frac{D[H_D - H(X_D)_{j+1}] + Q_c}{[H(x_j)_{j+1} - h_j]}, \qquad 0 \leqq j \leqq f - 2 \qquad (5\text{--}9a)$$

In a similar manner, the following expression for the calculation of the condenser duty is developed

$$Q_c = L_0[H(x_0)_1 - h_0] + D[H(X_D)_1 - H_D] \qquad (5\text{-}9\text{b})$$

and

$$L_{f-1} = \frac{D[H_D - H(X_D)_f] + Q_c + V_F[H(y_F)_f - H_F]}{[H(x_{f-1})_f - h_f]} \qquad (5\text{-}9\text{c})$$

$$V_{j+1} = \frac{B[h(x_B)_j - h_B] + Q_R}{[H_{j+1} - h(y_{j+1})_j]}, \qquad f \leqq j \leqq N \qquad (5\text{-}9\text{d})$$

where

$$h(y_{j+1})_j = \sum_{i=1}^{c} h_{ji} y_{j+1,i}$$

$$h(x_B)_j = \sum_{i=1}^{c} h_{ji} x_{Bi}$$

The corresponding vapor and liquid rates for the rectifying and stripping sections are computed by use of the material balance expressions given by Equations (5-3) and (5-4), respectively. The reboiler duty is calculated by use of an over-all enthalpy balance, Equation (5-5).

The name of this method reflects the interpretation which may be given to the enthalpy differences appearing in Equation (5-9). For example, the term $[H(x_j)_{j+1} - h_j]$ represents the difference between the enthalpy of one mole of vapor at the temperature T_{j+1} and the enthalpy of one mole of liquid with the same composition as the vapor and at the temperature T_j. All of the enthalpy differences appearing in Equation (5-9) may be interpreted in terms of thermodynamic processes which occur at constant composition.

When H_{j+1} of Equation (5-8) is calculated by use of Equation (5-1), the identity given by Equation (5-8) holds only when convergence is obtained because it is only then that the corrected flow rates for the individual components are in material balance. The improved convergence tendency of the constant-composition method over the conventional method may be attributed in part to the fact that the former places on the system the additional requirement that each component be in material balance. Also, the constant-composition method gives more stability in the calculational process because the denominators of Equation (5-9) are always of the order of magnitude of the latent heat of vaporization, whereas the denominators of the corresponding expressions for the conventional method take on a wide range of values including positive and negative numbers.

USE OF THE Q-METHOD IN MAKING ENTHALPY BALANCES

This method makes use of intercoolers (or heaters) as required to maintain the flow rates throughout the column within specified limits. It is directed toward finding the adiabatic solution for each plate if such a solution exists. Any imbalance in enthalpy resulting from the second forcing procedure is eliminated by the Q-method. This method may be used with either the conventional or the constant-composition methods for making enthalpy balances. However, it should be recognized that once it is agreed to employ an array of intercoolers (or heaters), infinitely many solutions exist, and different calculational procedures might be expected to lead to different arrays of intercoolers and heaters. The desired solution is of course the one in which the flow rates throughout the column are maintained within the specified limits with a minimum number of intercoolers and heaters. It was found that the combination of the Q-method and the constant-composition method was far superior to the Q-method and the conventional method because the former gave adiabatic solutions to many problems for which an array of intercoolers and heaters were required by the latter combination.

A development of the equations for a combination of the Q-method and the constant-composition method for conventional columns follows. When two of the specifications are taken to be V_1 (or L_0) and D, calculations are begun at the top of the column and continued to the bottom. Let the minimum and maximum allowable liquid rates be denoted by L_{min} and L_{max}. Suppose the variation of the liquid rates between successive trials is restricted in a manner similar to that required in step (1) through (3) of the second forcing procedure. The condenser duty is given by a balance around the condenser as stated previously in Equation (5–9b). For an enthalpy balance around the top plate, Equation (5–9a) reduces to

$$L_1 = \frac{D[H_D - H(X_D)_2] + Q_c}{[H(x_1)_2 - h_1]} \tag{5–10}$$

This value of L_1 is compared with $L_{1,1}$ (the rate used in making the last trial calculation through the column). Suppose a "10 per cent variation" per trial is permitted; that is, if L_1 satisfies the inequality

$$L_{min} \leqq \frac{L_{1,1}}{1 + p} \leqq L_1 \leqq (1 + p)L_{1,1} \leqq L_{max}$$

(where $p = 0.1$ for the 10 per cent variation), it is used in making the next trial through the column. The corresponding vapor rate to be employed for the next trial is calculated by material balance.

If the value of L_1 computed by use of Equation (5–10) is less than

$L_{1,1}/(1 + p)$ and greater than $L_{\min}$, then the value of L_1 to be employed for the next trial calculation through the column is taken equal to $L_{1,1}/(1 + p)$.

In order to keep the column in enthalpy balance at this liquid rate, an intercooler (or heater) is used on plate 1. The duty of the intercooler is calculated by an enthalpy balance as follows:

$$Q_1 = \left(\frac{L_{1,1}}{1 + p}\right) [H(x_1)_2 - h_1] - D[H_D - H(X_D)_2] - Q_c \qquad (5\text{–}11)$$

For the case where $L_1 \leqq (1 + p) L_{1,1}$ and $(1 + p) L_{1,1}$ is equal to or less than $L_{\max}$, the calculational procedure is analogous to that described above. If either

$$L_1 \leqq \frac{L_{1,1}}{1 + p} \leqq L_{\min}$$

or

$$L_1 \geqq (1 + p) L_{1,1} \geqq L_{\max}$$

L_1 is taken equal to either $L_{\min}$ or $L_{\max}$, respectively, and the corresponding intercooler (or heater) duty is computed as indicated by Equation (5–11), where $(L_{1,1}/(1 + p))$ is replaced by either $L_{\min}$ or $L_{\max}$. The value of Q_1 is included in the enthalpy balance for the calculation of L_2. For adiabatic operation of plate 2,

$$L_2 = \frac{D[H_D - H(X_D)_3] + Q_c + Q_1}{[H(x_2)_3 - h_2]} \qquad (5\text{–}12)$$

If this value of L_2 corresponding to $Q_2 = 0$ lies within the prescribed limits, it is used in the next trial calculation through the column. If not, the appropriate limit is used and the corresponding value of Q_2 is computed in a manner analogous to that described for Q_1. This procedure is continued throughout the column until L_N and Q_N have been determined. Then the reboiler duty $Q_R = -Q_{N+1}$ is given by the following over-all enthalpy balance.

$$Q_{N+1} = FH - Bh_B - DH_D - Q_c - \sum_{j=1}^{N} Q_j \qquad (5\text{–}13)$$

After each trial calculation through the column, the entire procedure is repeated; and if adiabatic operation of each and every plate is possible, this type of operation is selected. If not, the required intercoolers (or heaters) are employed. It should also be noted that only minor modifications of the Q-method are required to permit the specification of an intercooler (or heater) duty for any given plate.

TABLE 5-8 Statement of Example 5-7

Component	FX	Specifications
CH$_4$	2.0	$D = 31.6$, $V_1 = 94.8$, boiling point liquid feed, partial condenser, column pressure = 300 psia, three rectifying plates, and eight stripping plates plus a reboiler. Equilibrium and enthalpy data for all components except the enthalpy data for the 400-normal boiling component were taken from Tables A-4 and A-8 of the Appendix. For the 400 component, the following enthalpy data were used.
C$_2$H$_6$	10.0	
C$_3$H$_6$	6.0	
C$_3$H$_8$	12.5	
i-C$_4$	3.5	$*h^{\frac{1}{2}} = -203.32192 + 63.932857T - 21.611909 \times 10^5 T^2$, $(T^\circ R)$
n-C$_4$	15.0	
n-C$_5$	15.2	$*H^{\frac{1}{2}} = 72.328160 + 18.933822 \times 10^6 T - 59.003314 \times 10^6 T^2$, $(T^\circ R)$
n-C$_6$	11.3	The initial temperature profile is to be taken linear from 50° to 450°F with plate number. Each vapor rate for the first two trials is to be taken equal to 94.8.
n-C$_7$	9.0	
n-C$_?$	8.5	
400	7.0	

* From J. B. Maxwell, *Data Book on Hydrocarbons* (New York: D. Van Nostrand Company, Inc., New York 1955).

The combination of the constant-composition and Q-method is demonstrated by the solution of Example 5-7. A statement of this example is presented in Table 5-8 and the solution is given in Tables 5-9, 5-10, and 5-11. Sullivan (9) solved this problem in about the same number of trials by use of the conventional method for making enthalpy balances. Actually, the restrictions placed on the variation of the liquid rates by the second forcing procedure is more severe than is generally needed when the combination of the constant-composition and Q-methods is employed for conventional columns.

COMBINATION OF ENTHALPY BALANCES AND THE LEWIS AND MATHESON CALCULATIONAL PROCEDURE

When these methods are combined, a solution of all the equations describing each plate may be found in the process of making a given trial calculation through the column. The equations representing the conventional and constant-composition methods are applicable. However, it

TABLE 5–9 Temperature profiles and distillate rates obtained with the forcing procedures and enthalpy balances (constant-composition and Q-methods) for Example 5–7

Plate No.	Temperature profiles (°F) Trial number					
	1	2	3	4	11	12
0 (Distillate)	117.59	112.84	110.24	108.74	107.58	107.58
1	148.88	142.29	138.44	136.07	134.39	134.39
2	175.46	163.72	157.29	153.71	151.95	151.95
3	201.53	184.56	175.44	170.92	170.30	170.30
4 (Feed)	249.06	224.61	209.49	204.03	207.51	207.49
5	249.26	239.79	232.35	228.33	228.76	228.76
6	251.42	249.85	246.83	244.06	243.34	243.35
7	255.67	258.13	257.57	255.77	254.19	254.20
8	262.46	266.22	266.60	265.21	262.96	262.97
9	272.85	275.75	275.93	274.46	271.77	271.78
10	288.59	289.21	288.49	286.87	284.21	284.21
11	313.70	311.96	310.99	309.80	308.03	308.02
12 (Bottoms)	367.25	366.36	366.23	366.36	366.57	366.57
D (Calculated)	30.48	32.86	32.29	31.91	31.600	31.600
θ	0.1871	1.8962	1.5267	1.2488	1.0001	1.0001

should be noted that if a solution is obtained for each plate, these equations are identical since Equation (5–8) is satisfied by the solution for each plate.

Various methods exist for solving the material and enthalpy-balance equations simultaneously. These may be divided into two categories. In the first is included those methods in which a solution of all the equations

TABLE 5-10 Vapor rates obtained with enthalpy balances (constant-composition and Q-method) and with forcing procedures for Example 5-7

Vapor rates and intercooler (or heater) duties

Plate No.	Trial No. 2 V'_j	Q_j	Trial No. 3 V_j	Q_j	Trial No. 4 V_j	Q_j	Trial No. 11 V_j	Q_j	Trial No. 12 V_j	Q_j
0	—	$Q_c = 40.1 \times 10^4$	—	$Q_c = 39.8 \times 10^4$	—	$Q_c = 39.6 \times 10^4$	—	$Q_c = 39.6 \times 10^4$	—	$Q_c = 39.6 \times 10^4$
1	94.8	0.0	94.8	0.0	94.8	0.0	94.8	0.0	94.8	0.0
2	92.8	0.0	93.3	0.0	93.5	0.0	93.3	0.0	93.3	0.0
3	89.5	0.0	90.1	0.0	90.2	0.0	89.4	0.0	89.4	0.0
4	79.8	86.4×10^3	81.6	0.0	81.8	0.0	80.1	0.0	80.1	0.0
5	113.8	27.2×10^3	118.0	0.0	113.5	0.0	110.7	0.0	110.7	0.0
6	113.8	22.0×10^3	128.2	0.0	128.6	0.0	126.0	0.0	126.0	0.0
7	113.8	25.1×10^3	134.8	26.8×10^3	138.2	0.0	136.5	0.0	136.5	0.0
8	113.8	26.5×10^3	136.5	28.9×10^3	144.7	0.0	144.0	0.0	144.0	0.0
9	113.8	22.6×10^3	136.5	14.1×10^3	148.6	0.0	148.4	0.0	148.4	0.0
10	113.8	40.9×10^2	136.5	0.0	149.5	0.0	149.0	0.0	149.0	0.0
11	113.8	0.0	133.9	0.0	144.6	0.0	143.3	0.0	143.3	0.0
12	103.3	$Q_R = 11.1 \times 10^5$	117.7	$Q_R = 12.5 \times 10^5$	124.9	$Q_R = 13.2 \times 10^5$	123.3	$Q_R = 13.2 \times 10^5$	123.3	$Q_R = 13.2 \times 10^5$

TABLE 5–11 Product distribution for Example 5–7

Component	d	X_D
CH_4	2.00000	$0.63291 \cdot 10^{-1}$
C_2H_6	9.99988	0.31645
C_3H_6	5.97234	0.18900
C_3H_8	$1.23464 \cdot 10$	0.39071
$i\text{-}C_4$	0.74224	$0.23489 \cdot 10^{-1}$
$n\text{-}C_4$	0.53708	$0.16996 \cdot 10^{-1}$
$n\text{-}C_5$	$0.20157 \cdot 10^{-2}$	$0.63787 \cdot 10^{-4}$
$n\text{-}C_6$	$0.940469 \cdot 10^{-5}$	$0.29762 \cdot 10^{-6}$
$n\text{-}C_7$	$0.63453 \cdot 10^{-7}$	$0.20080 \cdot 10^{-8}$
$n\text{-}C_8$	$0.44408 \cdot 10^{-9}$	$0.14053 \cdot 10^{-10}$
400	$0.65181 \cdot 10^{-12}$	$0.20627 \cdot 10^{-13}$

for each plate is obtained each time a trial calculation through the column is made.

As described briefly in Chapter 4, the Newton-Raphson method may be employed to solve all of the equations describing each plate as proposed by Greenstadt (5).

Another procedure of the first category was proposed by Davis and Sobel (4) and found by Ball (1) to give good results. In order to focus attention on the procedure as it is applied, let it be supposed that, on the basis of an assumed product distribution, the condenser and reboiler duties have been determined. Now consider plate ($j - 1$) in the stripping section where it is further supposed that calculations for all plates below plate ($j - 1$) have been carried out in the same way as that to be described for plate ($j - 1$) to give the temperature (T_j) and composition (y_{ji}'s) of the vapor leaving plate j and entering plate $(j-1)$. The method of Davis and Sobel consists of the following steps.

(a)   Assume $V_{j,1} = V_{j+1}$, where $V_{j,1}$ denotes the first assumed value of the variable V_j.

(b)   Compute L_{j-1} and the $x_{j-1,i}$'s by use of material balances as follows:

$$l_{j-1,i} = V_j y_{ji} + b_i \tag{5-14}$$

$$L_{j-1} = \sum_{i=1}^{c} l_{j-1,i} \tag{5-15}$$

$$x_{j-1,i} = l_{j-1,i}/L_{j-1} \tag{5-16}$$

(c)   On the basis of the $x_{j-1,i}$'s so obtained, determine the temperature T_{j-1} by making a bubble point calculation.

(d)   On the basis of the compositions and temperatures obtained, calculate H_j and h_{j-1} as indicated by Equations (5–1) and (5–2), respectively.

(e)   Calculate V_j by enthalpy and material balances as follows:

$$L_{j-1}h_{j-1} = V_j H_j + B h_B - Q_R \tag{5-17}$$

Since $L_{j-1} = V_j + B$, Equation (5–17) may be solved for V_j to give Equation (5–4a).

(f)   If V_j obtained in (e) is equal to $V_{j,1}$ assumed in (a), proceed to the next plate. If not, steps (a) through (e) are repeated on the basis of the assumed vapor rate $V_{j,2}$, which is computed as follows:

$$V_{j,2} = m V_{j,1} + (1 - m) V_j \tag{5-18}$$

Initially m is taken equal to 0.5. If there is a tendency toward divergence, m is reduced as required to obtain convergence.

In the second category is included those methods in which a solution is obtained for certain of the equations, and the remaining variables are determined by direct-iteration by use of the remaining equations. An example of this approach is the procedure proposed by Bonner (2), which consists of the following steps. On the basis of an assumed set of flow rates and product distribution, calculations throughout the column are performed by the Lewis and Matheson procedure. The temperatures and compositions so obtained are used to compute the stream enthalpies by use of Equations (5–1) and (5–2). The total flow rates to be assumed for the next trial are calculated by the conventional method for making enthalpy balances, Equations (5–3) through (5–6).

NOTATION

(See also Chapters 2 through 4)

H_j, h_j = enthalpy of one mole of the vapor and of one mole of the liquid leaving plate j, respectively

H_{ji}, h_{ji} = enthalpy of one mole of a pure component i in the vapor and liquid states, respectively, at the temperature of plate j

h_B = enthalpy of one mole of the bottoms (B) leaving the column

$h(x_B)_j$ = enthalpy of one mole calculated on the basis of the x_{Bi}'s and the liquid enthalpies $(h_{ji}$'s) evaluated at the temperature of plate j

$h(y_{j+1})_j$ = enthalpy of one mole calculated on the basis of the $y_{j+1, i}$'s and the h_{ji}'s

$H(x_j)_{j+1}$ = enthalpy of one mole calculated on the basis of the x_{ji}'s and the $H_{j+1, i}$'s

H_D = enthalpy of one mole of distillate withdrawn, regardless of state

$H(X_D)_{j+1}$ = enthalpy of one mole calculated on the basis of the X_{Di}'s and the $H_{j+1, i}$'s

L_{min} and L_{max} = minimum and maximum allowable liquid rates

m = a multiplier; defined below Equation (5–18)

M_D, M_B = quantities appearing in the enthalpy balance (conventional method) for the rectifying and stripping sections, respectively; defined below Equation (5–3) and (5–4)

p = a number used to express the permitted change per trial of the liquid rates; see the discussion following Equation (5–10)

Q_c = condenser duty; net rate of heat removal by the overhead condenser

Q_R = reboiler duty; net rate of heat input by the reboiler

Q_j = intercooler duty for plate j

PROBLEMS

5–1 Beginning with first principles, develop the expressions for the conventional method (Equations 5–3 through 5–6) for making enthalpy balances for conventional columns.

5-2 (a) Show that the combination of the constant-composition and Q-methods for conventional columns are represented by the following set of equations, where the Q's are evaluated as described in the text.

$$Q_c = L_0[H(x_0)_1 - h_0] + D[H(X_D)_1 - H_D]$$

$$L_1 = \frac{D[H_D - H(X_D)_2] + Q_c}{[H(x_1)_2 - h_1]}$$

$$L_j = \frac{D[H_D - H(X_D)_{j+1}] + Q_c + \sum_{k=1}^{j-1} Q_k}{[H(x_j)_{j+1} - h_j]}, \qquad 2 \leq j \leq f - 2$$

$$L_{f-1} = \frac{D[H_D - H(X_D)_f] + Q_c + V_F[H(y_F)_f - H_F] + \sum_{k-1}^{f-2} Q_k}{[H(x_{f-1})_f - h_{f-1}]}$$

$$L_j = \frac{D[H_D - H(X_D)_{j+1}] + Q_c - F[H - H(X)_{j+1}] + \sum_{k=1}^{j-1} Q_k}{[H(x_j)_{j+1} - h_j]},$$

$$f \leq j \leq N$$

(b) Devise a thermodynamic process for each enthalpy difference appearing in the expression for L_j for the rectifying section.

5-3 Show that when the combination of the Thiele and Geddes calculational procedure and the θ-method converges (the temperatures and compositions do not change from trial to trial and $\theta = 1$), the total vapor and liquid rates calculated by material balances are in agreement with those calculated by enthalpy balances.

5-4 (a) For the combination of the Thiele and Geddes calculational procedure, the θ-method, and the conventional method for making enthalpy balances show that the results of each intermediate trial are dependent upon the base (or datum) selected for the enthalpies of each component. Also, show that when convergence is obtained, the total flow rates are independent of the base (or datum) selected for the enthalpy of each component.

(b) When the constant-composition method is employed instead of the conventional method for making enthalpy balances, show that the results for any intermediate trial are independent of the base selected for the enthalpies of each component.

LITERATURE CITED

1. Ball, W. E., "Computer Programs for Distillation," paper presented at the Machine Computation Special Workshop Session on Multicomponent Distillation at the 44th National Meeting of the A.I.Ch.E. in New Orleans, February 27, 1961.

2. Bonner, J. S., "Solution of Multicomponent Distillation Problems on a Stored-program Computer," *American Petroleum Institute Quarterly*, Division of Refining, **36,** No. 3, 23 (1956).

3. Canik, L. J., B. W. Hardy, and C. D. Holland, "Figure Separations This New Way: Part 7—Absorbers with Reboilers," *Petroleum Refiner*, **40,** No. 12, 161 (1961).

4. Davis, P. C. and B. A. Sobel, "Absorber-stripper Calculations with a Digital Computer," paper presented at the National Meeting of the A.I.Ch.E. in Tulsa, Oklahoma, in September 1960.

5. Greenstadt, John, Yonathan Bard, and Burt Morse, "Multicomponent Distillation Calculation on the IBM 704," *Ind. Eng. Chem.*, **50,** 1644 (1958).

6. Hardy, B. W., S. L. Sullivan, Jr., and C. D. Holland, "Figure Separations This New Way: Part 5—A Convergence Method for Absorbers," *Petroleum Refiner*, **40,** No. 9, 237 (1961).

7. Lyster, W. N., S. L. Sullivan, Jr., D. S. Billingsley, and C. D. Holland, "Figure Distillation This New Way: Part 1—New Convergence Method Will Handle Many Cases," *Petroleum Refiner*, **38,** No. 6, 221 (1959).

8. Robinson, C. S. and E. R. Gilliland, *Elements of Fractional Distillation*, (New York: McGraw–Hill Book Company, Inc., 1950), p. 261.

9. Sullivan, S. L., Jr., "Use of Computers for Multicomponent Distillation Calculations," M.S. thesis, A. and M. College of Texas, College Station (January 1959).

10. Weisenfelder, A. J., C. D. Holland and R. H. Johnston, "Figure Separations This New Way: Part 6—Minimization of Round-Off Errors and Other Developments," *Petroleum Refiner*, **40,** No. 10, 175 (1961).

Further Refinements for Conventional Columns* 6

As additional problems were solved by use of the combination of the Thiele and Geddes calculational procedure and the θ-method, certain weaknesses became apparent. The rectification of these led to the refinements presented in this chapter. Some of these are closely related while others are independent of each other. The topics considered are as follows: minimization of round-off error, treatment of separated components, treatment of single phase components, effect of bubble points and dew points on the rate of convergence, and other specifications for conventional columns.

MINIMIZATION OF ROUND-OFF ERROR IN CONVENTIONAL DISTILLATION COLUMNS

As indicated in previous chapters, round-off error is minimized in a conventional distillation column when calculations are made down from the top and up from the bottom of the column to the feed plate. This result is explained by the analysis presented in this section.

The ability to detect round-off error and to minimize it wherever it exists depends upon an important property of the Thiele and Geddes calculational procedure. This property gives this procedure a significant advantage over that of Lewis and Matheson. As shown in Chapter 3 for any given set of L/V's and temperatures, the Thiele and Geddes calculational procedure gives the same set of flow rates for each component at each plate regardless of whether calculations are made from the top of the column down or from the bottom up. Thus any difference found in the rates obtained by making calculations in different directions may be at-

---

* A summary of this work was presented in a paper by S. L. Sullivan, Jr., A. J. Weisenfelder, and C. D. Holland at the Technical Meeting of the South Texas Section of the A.I.Ch.E. in Houston, Texas, October 28, 1960.

tributed to round-off error. Use of the Thiele and Geddes procedure permits calculations to be made down from the top for one component and up from the bottom for another as required to minimize round-off error. In the application of the Lewis and Matheson calculational procedure, calculations must be made in the same direction for each component because all of the mole fractions are required for each plate in order to make the equilibrium calculations (bubble point and dew point) for each plate as calculations are carried through the column.

It might be thought that with as many as eight digits available, the possibility of obtaining round-off error is nil. The following illustration, Example 6–1, shows this notion to be naive. Consider the following system of equations.

$$Z_2 = AZ_1 - B$$

$$Z_3 = AZ_2 - B$$

$$Z_4 = AZ_3 - B$$

$$\vdots \qquad \vdots \qquad \vdots$$

$$Z_j = AZ_{j-1} - B$$

Suppose that $A = B = 10$, $Z_1 = \frac{10}{9}$ and that it is required to find Z_{11}. A computer using eight digit arithmetic takes the following value for Z_1, namely,

$$Z_1 = 1.1111111$$

then

$$Z_2 = (10)\ (1.1111111) - 10 = 1.1111110$$

$$Z_3 = (10)\ (1.1111110) - 10 = 1.1111100$$

$$Z_4 = (10)\ (1.1111100) - 10 = 1.1111000$$

$$Z_5 = (10)\ (1.1111000) - 10 = 1.1110000$$

$$Z_6 = (10)\ (1.1110000) - 10 = 1.1100000$$

$$Z_7 = (10)\ (1.1100000) - 10 = 1.1000000$$

$$Z_8 = (10)\ (1.1000000) - 10 = 1.0000000$$

$$Z_9 = (10)\ (1.0000000) - 10 = 0.0000000$$

$$Z_{10} = (10)\ (0.0000000) - 10 = -10.000000$$

$$Z_{11} = (10)\ (-10.000000) - 10 = -110.00000$$

The correct answer for Z_{11} is of course

$$Z_{11} = 1.1111111$$

Round-off error of this type may be involved in distillation systems, depending upon the direction in which calculations are carried out.

In order to show that round-off error is minimized in conventional columns by making calculations down from the top and up from the bottom to the feed plate (called "matching at the feed plate"), other possible calculational procedures must be considered. In Chapter 3 are presented the formulas for making calculations from the top to the bottom of the column [Equations (3–6) through (3–8) and (3–32)] as well as those for making calculations from the bottom of the column to the top [Equations (3–9) through (3–11) and (3–25)]. These two step-by-step calculational procedures are respectively referred to as "matching at the bottom" and "matching at the top." If it were not for round-off error, all of the calculational procedures would give the same sets of flow rates throughout the column. A test that recognizes the rates which possess the least amount of round-off error remains to be developed. Fortunately, the formulas for b_i/d_i [Equations (3–22), (3–31), and (3–33)] are not only equivalent theoretically, but they are also nearly independent of round-off error. They were found to give values of b_i/d_i that agreed to within seven out of a possible eight digits. When all of the step-by-step calculations throughout the column are to be made in the same direction, values of b_i/d_i must be computed before crossing the feed plate. These ratios are computed by use of any one of the formulas given by Equations (3–22), (3–31), and (3–33); and the values so obtained are labeled as follows:

$$(b_i/d_i)_{\text{formula}}$$

A value for b_i/d_i may also be computed as the end result of any one of the step-by-step calculational procedures. For example, suppose calculations are made from the top down as indicated by Equations (3–6) through (3–8) and (3–32). At the bottom of the column, a value for $v_{N+1,i}/d_i$ is obtained as an end result. The corresponding value of b_i/d_i is calculated as follows:

$$(b_i/d_i)_{\text{step-by-step}} = A_{N+1,i}(v_{N+1,i}/d_i) \tag{6-1}$$

Similarly, when calculations are made from the bottom to the top of the column, the value of b_i/d_i is obtained as the last step of Equation (3–25). The corresponding step-by-step value for b_i/d_i is computed in the following manner.

$$(b_i/d_i)_{\text{step-by-step}} = \frac{1}{S_{0i}(l_{0i}/b_i)} \tag{6-2}$$

As shown by the previous numerical example, the terminal values resulting from a step-by-step calculation are affected more than are any of the intermediate quantities by round-off error. Thus in testing for round-off error, the terminal ratio (or the ratio b_i/d_i that can be calculated therefrom) was selected for consideration.

The test consists of noting that the deviation of the ratio,

$$\frac{(b_i/d_i)_{\text{step-by-step}}}{(b_i/d_i)_{\text{formula}}}$$

from unity gives a measure of the round-off error incurred in the particular calculational procedure. Since the evaluation of b_i/d_i by the formula given by Equation (3–22) requires that calculations be made down from the top and up from the bottom of the column to the feed plate, it is evident for this case that $(b_i/d_i)_{\text{formula}}$ and $(b_i/d_i)_{\text{step-by-step}}$ are one and the same number and that the ratio of the two is of course equal to unity. Thus for matching at the feed plate, no round-off error is detectable by the test.

Weisenfelder *et al.* (4) and Weisenfelder (5) investigated the effect of round-off error in conventional columns by solving several relatively simple examples. These results are given in Table 6–1 and show that large errors were encountered when the flow rates in the stripping section for a very heavy component were calculated by material balances written around the top of the column, case 4. Similarly, when the flow rates for a very light component in the rectifying section were calculated by material balances that included the bottom of the column and the given plate, large errors resulted also, case 2. The round-off error results from the negative terms, $(1 - FX_i/d_i)$ and $(1 - FX_i/b_i)$, which appear on the right-hand sides of Equations (3–32) and (3–25), respectively. Generally the round-off error is small when calculations past the feed plate to the top and bottom of the column are made for very heavy or light components, respectively, as shown by cases 3 and 5. In each instance the negative term mentioned previously is relatively small, numerically, compared with the other terms in the equations. In the cases where round-off error was most pronounced, the equations were of the same form as that of the Example 6–1. These results are represented schematically in Figure 6–1.

The step-by-step calculational procedures described for conventional columns in Chapter 3 make use of a numerical process sometimes referred to as "nesting." Instead of using nesting, a general formula for v_{ji}/d_i may be employed. It is developed by the substitutional process whereby the expression for v_{ji}/d_i is substituted successively into the one for $v_{j+1,i}/d_i$ and the term $(1 - FX_i/d_i)$ is replaced by its equivalent $(-b_i/d_i)$. By application of the formula so obtained, round-off error of the type shown may be eliminated in some instances for conventional columns. However, this procedure does not completely eliminate round-off error as may be shown by reconsideration of Example 6–1. Continued substitution of the

TABLE 6-1 Round-off error given by different calculational procedures for conventional columns

(For all cases shown $N = 10$, the column has a partial condenser and a reboiler, thermal condition of the feed is boiling point liquid and the absorption factor, A, remains constant throughout the column.)

Case No.	Location of Feed Plate	Absorption Factor A	Matched at the bottom $\dfrac{(b/d)_{\text{step-by-step}}}{(b/d)_{\text{formula}}}$	Matched at the top $\dfrac{(b/d)_{\text{step-by-step}}}{(b/d)_{\text{formula}}}$
1	11	1.0000000	1.0000	1.0000
2	11	0.095555555	1.0000	0.9044
3	11	9.5555555	1.0000	1.0000
4	1	9.5555555	-4.0388×10^2	1.0000
5	1	0.095555555	1.0000	1.0000
6	1	1.00000000	1.0000	1.0000

Reproduced by permission of *Hydrocarbon Processing & Petroleum Refiner*

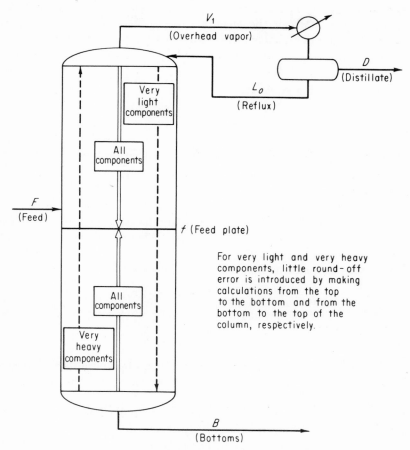

V_1
(Overhead vapor)

D
(Distillate)

L_o
(Reflux)

Very
light
components

All
components

F
(Feed)

f (Feed plate)

For very light and very heavy
components, little round-off
error is introduced by making
calculations from the top
to the bottom and from the
bottom to the top of the
column, respectively.

All
components

Very
heavy
components

B
(Bottoms)

Figure 6–1. Round-off error in conventional columns is minimized by matching at the feed plate.

type suggested above leads to

$$Z_{11} = A^{10}Z_1 - (A^9 + A^8 + \cdots + A + 1)B$$

Since

$$Z_1 = \frac{10}{9}, \quad B = 10, \quad \text{and} \quad A^9 + A^8 + \cdots + A + 1 = \frac{A^{10} - 1}{A - 1}$$

the formula for Z_{11} reduces to

$$Z_{11} = \frac{10^{11}}{9} - \left(\frac{10^{10} - 1}{10 - 1}\right)10$$

When eight digit arithmetic is employed, the value of Z_{11} is seen to depend upon the order in which the algebraic operations are performed. If the value for the sum of the geometric series is computed first, then

$$Z_{11} = 0$$

because the following equality

$$\frac{10^{10} - 1}{10 - 1} = \frac{10^{10}}{9}$$

holds for eight digit arithmetic. If the multiplication is carried out first,

$$Z_{11} = \frac{10^{11}}{9} - \frac{10^{11}}{9} + \frac{10}{9} = \frac{10}{9}$$

the correct result is obtained. However, in the equations for distillation columns, the A's are seldom equal and the value of the sum of the series must be computed directly. The order of accuracy of the value of the sum so obtained is the same as that shown for the case where the value $Z_{11} = 0$ was found.

The formulas for v_{ji}/d_i in terms of the A_{ji}'s (top-down) and v_{ji}/b_i in terms of the S_{ji}'s (bottom-up) may be employed to compute the values of

$$(b_i/d_i)_{\text{step−by−step}}$$

for use in the ratio test. Application of the ratio test permits the selection of the best combination of formulas (v_{ji}/d_i or v_{ji}/b_i) for the computation of the rates throughout the column.

In columns with a large number of plates, round-off error could become appreciable in the addition process, say in the calculation of $l_{f-1,i}/d_i$ by the nesting procedure. This may be partially rectified by ordering the addition of the terms of the series [see Equation (3–34)] according to size, the smallest term being first.

SINGLE PHASE COMPONENTS

The following treatment follows that given in References (1, 2, 4). A component that is present in the gas phase alone is referred to as a "single phase light." (Such a component is frequently called an inert gas.) Similarly, if a component appears only in the liquid phase, it is called a "single phase heavy" component. Certain gases such as helium are generally considered to be genuine single phase components. Others are sometimes treated in this manner because of the lack of data. The single phase lights are denoted by the subscript "L" and the single phase heavy components are identified by the subscript "H." The total rates of flow of all of the single phase light components and all of the single phase heavies are denoted by

$$\sum_{L} v_{jL} \quad \text{and} \quad \sum_{H} l_{jH},$$

respectively. In a conventional column the $\sum_{L} v_{jL}$ is equal to the sum of the FX's for these components for all of the plates above the feed plate, and $\sum_{L} v_{jL} = 0$ for each plate below the feed plate. Similarly, $\sum_{H} l_{jH}$ is equal to the sum of the corresponding FX_i's for the feed plate and all plates below it, and $\sum_{H} l_{jH} = 0$ for all plates above the feed plate. The statements and development of the formulas for both the calculation of the compositions and the convergence method follow.

Calculation of Compositions

$$y_{ji} = \left(\frac{V_j - \sum_{L} v_{jL}}{V_j} \right) \frac{\left(\frac{v_{ji}}{d_i}\right)_{ca} (d_i)_{co}}{\sum_{i \neq H, L} \left(\frac{v_{ji}}{d_i}\right)_{ca} (d_i)_{co}}, \qquad i \neq H, L \qquad (6\text{-}3)$$

$$x_{ji} = \left(\frac{L_j - \sum_{H} l_{jH}}{L_j} \right) \frac{\left(\frac{l_{ji}}{b_i}\right)_{ca} (b_i)_{co}}{\sum_{i \neq H, L} \left(\frac{l_{ji}}{b_i}\right)_{ca} (b_i)_{co}}, \qquad i \neq H, L \qquad (6\text{-}4)$$

$$y_{jL} = \frac{v_{jL}}{V_j} \qquad \text{and} \qquad x_{jH} = \frac{l_{jH}}{L_j} \tag{6-5}$$

Unless intercoolers (or heaters) are employed, L_j and V_j are not generally known. Except where they are specified (for example, the specifications of L_0 and V_1), the following formulas are recommended for use

$$V_j = \sum_{i \neq H, L} \left(\frac{v_{ji}}{d_i}\right)_{ca} (d_i)_{co} + \sum_{L} v_{jL} \tag{6-6}$$

$$L_j = \sum_{i \neq H, L} \left(\frac{l_{ji}}{b_i}\right)_{ca} (b_i)_{co} + \sum_{H} l_{jH} \tag{6-7}$$

Method of Convergence

For a conventional column, where the values of the flow rates V_1 (or L_0) and D are included in the specifications, the following formulas are applicable

$$(d_i)_{co} = \frac{FX_i}{1 + \theta(b_i/d_i)_{ca}}, \quad i \neq H, L \tag{6-8}$$

The quantity θ is the positive root which gives $g(\theta) = 0$, where the function g is defined as follows:

$$g(\theta) = \sum_{i \neq H, L} (d_i)_{co} - (D - \sum_L FX_L) \tag{6-9}$$

The positive root is found by use of either Newton's method or interpolation (*regula falsi*) as described in Chapters 1 and 4. After $(d_i)_{co}$ has been computed by Equation (6-8), $(b_i)_{co}$ is calculated in the following manner.

$$(b_i)_{co} = \theta \left(\frac{b_i}{d_i}\right)_{ca} (d_i)_{co} \tag{6-10}$$

For a single phase heavy, $(b_H)_{co}$ is of course equal to FX_H. Equations (6-3) through (6-10) are employed with the calculational procedure of Thiele and Geddes in an analogous manner to that described in Chapters 3 and 4.

Development of the Expressions for the g-Function and the Compositions

The development of Equations (6-3) through (6-10) from first principles follows closely the same approach as that presented previously in Chapter 4. In view of this, many of the steps are omitted. In the following arguments, suppose that the V_j's and L_j's be fixed throughout the column by use of appropriate intercoolers (or heaters). The feed is supposed to consist of both "distributed" components and single phase lights and heavies. Those components which appear in both phases throughout the column as well as the distillate and bottoms are called distributed components. The problem is to find a set of corrected values for d_i and b_i which are both in component balance,

$$FX_i = (d_i)_{co} + (b_i)_{co} \tag{6-11}$$

and which satisfy the specification D; that is

$$D - \sum_L v_{0,L} = \sum_{i \neq H, L} (d_i)_{co} \tag{6-12}$$

where the sum of the $v_{0,L}$'s is equal to the corresponding sum of FX_L's.

Following the same arguments given in Chapter 4, it is postulated that for all of the distributed components,

$$(v_{ji})_{co} = \sigma_j \left(\frac{v_{ji}}{d_i}\right)_{ca} (d_i)_{co}, \qquad i \neq H, L \qquad (6\text{--}13)$$

$$(l_{ji})_{co} = \tau_j \left(\frac{l_{ji}}{b_i}\right)_{ca} (b_i)_{co}, \qquad i \neq H, L \qquad (6\text{--}14)$$

The development of the formula for $(b_i/d_i)_{co}$, Equation (6–10), is precisely the same as that shown in Chapter 4. After this formula has been obtained, Equation (6–11) is readily solved for $(d_i)_{co}$ to give Equation (6–8). In view of this formula, observe that the expression for the function $g(\theta)$ is obtained by a rearrangement of Equation (6–12).

The formulas for the calculation of the compositions are developed in the following manner. By the postulates represented by Equations (6–13) and (6–14), it follows that

$$V_j = \sum_{i \neq H, L} \sigma_j \left(\frac{v_{ji}}{d_i}\right)_{ca} (d_i)_{co} + \sum_L v_{jL} \qquad (6\text{--}15)$$

$$L_j = \sum_{i \neq H, L} \tau_j \left(\frac{l_{ji}}{b_i}\right)_{ca} (b_i)_{co} + \sum_H l_{jH} \qquad (6\text{--}16)$$

According to the definition of the mole fraction, Equations (6–13) and (6–15) may be combined to give

$$y_{ji} = \frac{\sigma_j (v_{ji}/d_i)_{ca} (d_i)_{co}}{\displaystyle\sum_{i \neq H, L} \sigma_j (v_{ji}/d_i)_{ca} (d_i)_{co} + \sum_L v_{jL}} \qquad (6\text{--}17)$$

Elimination of σ_j from this expression by use of Equation (6–15) followed by rearrangement leads to the desired result, Equation (6–3). Equations (6–4) and (6–5) are developed in an analogous manner.

When convergence is obtained, $\sigma_j = \tau_j = 1$ for all j. When τ_j and σ_j are taken equal to unity for each plate and for each trial, Equations (6–15) and (6–16) reduce to the approximate expressions for V_j and L_j, Equations (6–6) and (6–7). Satisfactory results have been obtained by use of these formulas in solving a wide variety of problems.

Calculation of Temperatures

The temperatures throughout the column are calculated by use of the bubble point procedure. As discussed in Chapter 2, the bubble point temperature is that positive value of T which makes $f(T) = 0$ where

$$f(T) = \sum_{i \neq H, L} K_{ji} x_{ji} - (1 - \sum_L y_{jL}) \qquad (6\text{-}18)$$

Similarly, the dew point temperature is defined as that positive value of T which gives $F(T) = 0$ where

$$F(T) = \sum_{i \neq H, L} \frac{y_{ji}}{K_{ji}} - (1 - \sum_H x_{jH}) \qquad (6\text{-}19)$$

Since $f(T)$ contains mole fractions of both the liquid and the vapor phases, all of the compositions must be computed as indicated by Equations (6–3) through (6–5), whereas only the x_{ji}'s were needed when all of the components were distributed.

The treatment of systems containing single phase components is illustrated by the solution of Example 6–2. The statement of this example is given in Tables 6–2 and 6–3; and its solution is presented in Table 6–4. This example as well as the others given in Tables 6–2 and 6–3 were taken from the work of Weisenfelder *et al.* (4).

SEPARATED COMPONENTS

Although certain components appear in both phases in the neighborhood of the feed plate, they are separated for all practical purposes in either the rectifying or stripping section and leave the column in only one product stream. These components are called "separated components," and they are detected in several ways. If b_i/d_i is less than some small pre-assigned number (the order of magnitude of the lower limit of the computing machine), the component is called a "separated light" component. For such a component $b_i = 0$ and $d_i = FX_i$, which hold for both the calculated and corrected values of b_i and d_i. Similarly, if b_i/d_i is equal to or greater than some large number of the same order of magnitude as the upper limit of the computing machine, the component is said to be a "separated heavy" component. For such a component, the calculated and corrected d_i's and b_i's have the following values: $d_i = 0$ and $b_i = FX_i$. For a separated light component, the flow rates above the feed plate are calculated by use of Equations (3–6) through (3–8) in the usual manner. The flow rates below the feed plate are also computed by use of balances written around the top of the column, Equation (3–32). Observe that a simplification is obtained because the term $(1 - FX_i/d_i)$ is equal to zero. A high degree of accuracy may be expected, since the negative term $(1 - FX_i/d_i)$ that gave the round-off error for the examples shown in Table 6–1 is equal to zero. Similarly, for a separated heavy component, the flow rates below

TABLE 6-2 Statement of Examples 6-2 through 6-11

Component	Composition of Feed, FX Example Number								
	6-2	6-3	6-4	6-5	6-6	6-7	6-8	6-9	6-10
Single Phase Light	50								
*$C_{K=10}$									
CH_4			50.0	50.0	60.0	60.0	70	80.0	85
C_2H_6		0.54							
C_3H_8	3	28.03							
i-C_4	10	15.40							
n-C_4	15	7.52	33.4	33.4	26.7	26.7	20	13.34	10
i-C_5	7	20.24	16.6	16.6	13.3	13.3	10	6.66	5
n-C_5	5	11.80							
n-C_6	10	4.82							
n-C_8		7.20							
500		4.45							

* A fictitious component that has a $K = 10$ at all temperatures at a pressure of 300 psia.

Reproduced by permission of *Hydrocarbon Processing & Petroleum Refiner*

TABLE 6-3 Specifications for Examples 6-2 through 6-11

Example	Specifications
6-2	$N = 10$, $f = 4$, $V_1 = 225$, $D = 75$ (vapor), partial condenser, and the feed enters partially vaporized at 140°F at the column pressure of 300 psia. The equilibrium and enthalpy data were taken from Tables A-4 and A-8, respectively, of the Appendix. The enthalpy of the single phase light component was taken equal to that of methane.
6-3	$N = 38$, $f = 19$, $V_1 = 140$, $D = 40$ (vapor), partial condenser, and the feed enters partially vaporized at 240°F at the column pressure of 300 psia. The equilibrium and enthalpy data were taken from Tables A-4 and A-8, respectively, of the Appendix. The initial temperature profile was taken to be linear with plate number between 140 and 335°F. Initial vapor rates were 140 and 130 in the rectifying and stripping sections, respectively.
6-4 through 6-10	$N = 18$, $f = 17$, $V_1 = 108$, $D = 90$ (vapor), partial condenser, and the feed enters as a vapor at its dew point at the column pressure of 300 psia. Vapor and liquid rates are as follows: in the rectifying section, $V = 108$ and $L = 18$; in the stripping section, $V = 8$ and $L = 18$. Equilibrium data taken from Table A-4 of the Appendix.

Reproduced by permission of *Hydrocarbon Processing & Petroleum Refiner*

TABLE 6-4 Solution of Example 6-2 which contained a single phase light component

Plate No.	Temperature (°F) Trial No.			Vapor rates Trial No.			Component	Final flow rates (Trial No. 12)	
	Initial profile	6	12	Initial profile	6	12	Single phase light	d	b
								50.000	0
0	160	116.33	116.32	75	75.0	75.0	C_3H_8	2.999	9.880×10^{-4}
1	175	199.41	199.68	225	225.0	225.0	$i\text{-}C_4$	9.717	2.835×10^{-1}
2	190	207.52	210.09	225	294.6	288.3	$n\text{-}C_4$	12.210	2.790
3	205	211.69	214.34	225	294.6	295.5	$i\text{-}C_5$	6.335×10^{-2}	6.937
4	220	217.50	219.54	225	294.6	292.4	$n\text{-}C_5$	1.059×10^{-2}	4.989
5	235	253.31	252.46	175	204.8	210.9	$n\text{-}C_6$	5.750×10^{-6}	9.99994
6	250	260.30	259.56	175	235.5	237.4			
7	265	269.63	269.01	175	233.0	232.9			
8	280	282.07	281.74	175	223.6	226.5			
9	295	298.57	298.47	175	217.6	219.0			
10	310	319.72	319.72	175	211.2	211.0			
11	325	335.14	335.18	175	203.2	204.8			
D (Calculated)		74.961	74.999						
θ_0		0.9852	0.9998						

Reproduced by permission of *Hydrocarbon Processing & Petroleum Refiner*

the feed plate are given by application of Equations (3–9) through (3–11). Above the feed plate calculations are continued by use of Equation (3–25). Again simplification results, since $(1 - FX_i/b_i) = 0$. Separated light components may be detected also in making calculations from the bottom of the column toward the feed plate. If in this process, a j is found such that l_{ji}/b_i is greater than some large preassigned number, the component is considered as a separated light component and treated as described previously. This procedure amounts to taking $b_i/d_i = 0$ and results in little error. As is shown in the next section, if a j exists such that

$$\frac{l_{ji}}{b_i} \geqq \rho$$

then for a component having S_{ji}'s greater than unity

$$\frac{b_i}{d_i} < \frac{f + 1}{\rho} \tag{6-20}$$

where

ρ = a large number of the order of magnitude of the upper limit of the computer.

Since the right hand side of Equation (6–20) is approximately the same order of magnitude as the lower limit $(1/\rho)$ of the computer, it may be taken equal to zero. The l_{ji}/b_i's found by making calculations up from the bottom are discarded, and all of the flow rates are found by making calculations down from the top of the column by use of Equations (3–6) through (3–8) and (3–32).

Similarly, if in making calculations down from the top of the column a j is found such that

$$\frac{v_{ji}}{d_i} \geqq \rho$$

then it may be shown that b_i/d_i is approximately the same order of magnitude as ρ, implying that d_i is zero. The v_{ji}/d_i's found by making calculations down from the top are discarded and the flow rates for the separated heavy component found by use of Equations (3–9) through (3–11) and Equation (3–25). The proposed procedure is represented schematically in Figure 6–2.

Development of the Inequality Given by Equation (6-20)

In order for l_{ji}/b_i to be equal to or greater than ρ, one or more of the S_{ji}'s must be greater than unity. Generally, they are all large numbers for relatively light components. Thus consider a light component for which $S_{ji} > 1$ for all j. Suppose that in making calculations up from the bottom

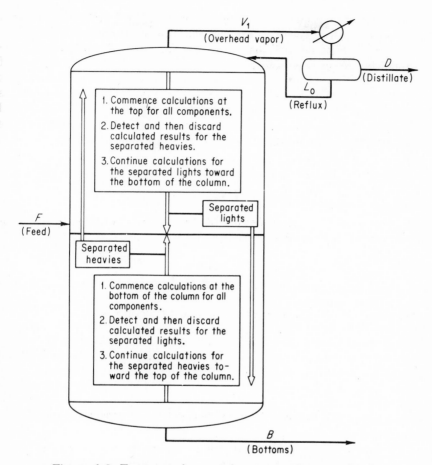

Figure 6–2. Treatment of separated components in conventional columns.

of the column a j (denoted by m) is found such that $l_{mi}/b_i \geqq \rho$ (a large number of the order of magnitude of say, 10^{38}). Since all of the S's are taken to be greater than unity

$$\frac{v_{mi}}{b_i} > \frac{l_{mi}}{b_i}$$

Continued application of Equation (3–10) gives larger and larger numbers. Thus

$$\frac{v_{fi}}{b_i} > \frac{v_{mi}}{b_i}$$

Now consider Equation (3–34). Since all of the S's are greater than unity, it follows that all of the A_{ji}'s are less than unity. Therefore, if the value $A_{ji} = 1$ is substituted in Equation (3–34) for $j = 0$ through $j = f - 1$, the following result is obtained

$$\frac{l_{f-1,i}}{d_i} < f$$

where f is the number of the feed plate. Also in Equation (3–22),

$$\frac{l_{Fi}}{FX_i} \leqq 1$$

Thus, the numerator of Equation (3–22) is less than $f + 1$. Also, the denominator is greater than ρ; that is

$$\frac{v_{fi}}{b_i} + \frac{v_{Fi}}{FX_i} > \rho$$

Substitution of these results into Equation (3–22) gives

$$\frac{b_i}{d_i} < \frac{f + 1}{\rho} \tag{6–21}$$

Modifications of the Formulas to Include Separated Components

The formulas developed for distributed components are applicable for separated components if the terms that are indeterminate for the separated components are replaced by their equivalents. In the expression for y_{ji} [Equation (6–3)], the term $(v_{ji}/d_i)_{ca}(d_i)_{co}$ is indeterminate for a separated heavy component, since

$$\lim_{(d_i)_{ca} \to 0} \frac{(d_i)_{co}}{(d_i)_{ca}} = \frac{0}{0} \tag{6–22}$$

The limit of the indeterminate is found by restating the original expression as follows:

$$\cdot \left(\frac{v_{ji}}{d_i}\right)_{ca} (d_i)_{co} = \left(\frac{v_{ji}}{b_i}\right)_{ca} \left(\frac{b_i}{d_i}\right)_{ca} (d_i)_{co} \tag{6–23}$$

Replacing $(d_i)_{co}$ by its equivalent as given by Equation (6–10) yields

$$\left(\frac{v_{ji}}{d_i}\right)_{ca} (d_i)_{co} = \left[\left(\frac{v_{ji}}{b_i}\right)_{ca} \left(\frac{b_i}{d_i}\right)_{ca}\right]\left[\frac{1}{\theta}\left(\frac{d_i}{b_i}\right)_{ca} (b_i)_{co}\right]$$

Thus

$$\left(\frac{v_{ji}}{d_i}\right)_{ca} (d_i)_{co} = \frac{1}{\theta}\left(\frac{v_{ji}}{b_i}\right)_{ca} (b_i)_{co} = \frac{(v_{ji})_{ca}}{\theta} \qquad (6\text{–}24)$$

since $(b_i)_{ca} = (b_i)_{co} = FX_i$ for a separated heavy component.

Similarly, in Equation (6–4), the term $(l_{ji}/b_i)_{ca}(b_i)_{co}$ for a separated light component is indeterminate. By an approach analogous to that used for separated heavy components, it is readily shown that for a separated light component

$$\left(\frac{l_{ji}}{b_i}\right)_{ca} (b_i)_{co} = \theta \left(\frac{l_{ji}}{d_i}\right)_{ca} (d_i)_{co} = \theta (l_{ji})_{ca} \qquad (6\text{–}25)$$

In the application of the g-function, Equation (6–9), to systems containing separated components, $(d_i)_{co}$ has the following values. For a separated light, $(d_i)_{co} = FX_i$; and for a separated heavy component, $(d_i)_{co} = 0$.

The occurrence and treatment of separated components is demonstrated by Example 6–3 (see Tables 6–2, 6–3, and 6–5).

USE OF BUBBLE POINTS VERSUS DEW POINTS

As shown in Chapter 4, the combination of the θ-method of convergence and the Thiele and Geddes calculational procedure gives rise to corrected sets of compositions for both the vapor and the liquid phases. The dew point and bubble point temperatures corresponding to these respective, compositions become equal when convergence to the problem is obtained; otherwise, they may be widely divergent.

The following discussion pertains to hydrocarbon systems and is based on the results of several investigations (3, 4, 5). In general, bubble points are found to give satisfactory results for all systems except those containing a large percentage of a relatively light component. For a system composed almost entirely of lights, bubble points tended to give an overcorrection; and for a system consisting mostly of heavies, dew points tended to give a slow rate of convergence. In order to obtain the effect of dew points and bubble points alone on the rate of convergence, a variety of examples

TABLE 6-5 Solution of Example 6-3 illustrates separated components

Plate No.	Temp., (°F) (Trial No. 10)	Vapor rates (Trial No. 10)	Compositions (y) (Trial No. 10)		Final flow rates (Trial No. 10)		
			Component		Component	d	b
			$n\text{-}C_8$	500-Comp.			
0	165.1	40.0	0*	0*	C_2H_6	54.00×10^{-2}	31.75×10^{-13}
1	175.6	140.0	1.08×10^{-31}	0	C_3H_8	28.03	46.36×10^{-5}
2	182.8	139.2	5.01×10^{-30}	0	$i\text{-}C_4$	10.91	44.93×10^{-1}
10	195.6	138.7	8.69×10^{-18}	0	$n\text{-}C_4$	52.30×10^{-2}	69.97×10^{-1}
18	208.2	132.6	4.75×10^{-6}	1.13×10^{-10}	$i\text{-}C_5$	10.73×10^{-7}	20.24
19	216.8	128.4	1.13×10^{-4}	8.14×10^{-8}	$n\text{-}C_5$	14.47×10^{-9}	11.80
20	237.0	109.1	2.05×10^{-3}	4.38×10^{-5}	$n\text{-}C_6$	69.86×10^{-18}	48.20×10^{-1}
21	243.8	111.8	2.24×10^{-3}	4.87×10^{-5}	$n\text{-}C_8$	0.0	72.00×10^{-1}
22	249.2	116.0	2.39×10^{-3}	5.27×10^{-5}	500	0.0	44.50×10^{-1}
30	262.7	128.0	2.80×10^{-3}	6.42×10^{-5}			
37	288.3	126.9	4.22×10^{-3}	1.01×10^{-4}			
38	301.6	125.7	6.29×10^{-3}	1.34×10^{-4}			
39	335.6	115.2	2.03×10^{-2}	6.47×10^{-4}			
D (Calculated)	39.999						
θ_0	0.9998						

* A heavy component was taken to be separated when $v_{ji}/d_i < 10^{30}$.

Reproduced by permission of *Hydrocarbon Processing & Petroleum Refiner*

was solved in which the vapor and liquid rates were held fixed throughout the column. The following analysis was suggested by these results.

An examination of hydrocarbon systems shows that the rate of change with temperature of the equilibrium constant, K, increases as the molecular weight of the hydrocarbon is increased. For a light component such as methane, this slope is of the order zero over a fairly wide range of temperatures and pressures. On the other hand, the change of K with respect to temperature for a heavy component is very large. Consider a system in which methane (or any light component for which K is essentially independent of temperature) is the primary constituent of the gas phase. For any plate the bubble point equation reduces approximately to $y = Kx = 1.0$. Since the K for methane is almost independent of temperature, it follows that for small changes in the composition of the liquid, larger changes in temperature are required to satisfy the bubble point equation. Because of this factor, the θ-method frequently gives overcorrections for such systems.

Consider next a system with a liquid phase that consists almost entirely of a heavy component, and suppose the corrected temperature is to be calculated by use of dew points. For any plate the dew point equation reduces approximately to $y/K = x \cong 1.0$. Thus for large changes in y for the heavy component the dew point equation is satisfied by small changes in T. Use of dew points for such systems gives a slow rate of convergence.

Since it is perhaps easier to dampen than to speed up a convergence procedure, the possibility of the use of the θ-method and bubble points for all systems was investigated. Examples 6–4 through 6–10 (see Tables 6–2, 6–3, and 6–6) show that bubble points may be used for systems composed of very light components provided additional restrictions are placed on the variation of the temperature profiles between successive trials as indicated in Table 6–6. Note that for these problems solutions were obtained by use of dew points (with no restrictions other than the averaging of the temperature profiles) in about the same number of trials as those shown for bubble points.

OTHER TYPES OF SPECIFICATIONS FOR CONVENTIONAL COLUMNS

Instead of the specification of the total moles of distillate, D, any one of several other types of specifications may be imposed on the system as shown by Lyster *et al.* (3). However, it is to be noted that the solution to a problem of this type may be found by solving a series of problems for which each of several different values of D is specified. A more direct approach consists of choosing θ (at the end of each trial) such that the

Table 6-6 Results of θ-method and bubble points for feeds containing large percentages of light components

Example	CH$_4$ in feed (FX)	C$_{K=10}$ in feed (FX)	Number of Trials		Restriction of Temp. Profile μ*
			$\left\lvert\dfrac{\Delta D}{D}\right\rvert \leq 0.01$	$\left\lvert\dfrac{\Delta D}{D}\right\rvert \leq 0.001$	
6-4	50		5	7	1/2
6-5		50	5	7	1/2
6-6	60		6	9	1/2
6-7		60	8	11	1/2
6-8	70		5	6	1/4
6-9	80		3	5	1/4
6-10	85		7	10	1/8

* Defined by: T (Assumed for next trial) = T (Assumed for previous trial) + $\mu[T$ (calculated) − T (Assumed for previous trial)$]$.

Reproduced by permission of *Hydrocarbon Processing & Petroleum Refiner*

particular specification is satisfied. Thus the problem reduces to finding the g-function for each of the various types of specifications. In the interest of simplicity these developments are given for systems composed entirely of distributed components; that is, neither single phase lights nor separated components are supposed to be present. In addition to the specification D (or its substitute) assume that the following specifications have been made: the number of plates in each section; the quantity, composition and thermal condition of the feed; the column pressure; and the reflux ratio (or V_1 or L_0).

1. Specifications: $\sum_{i=1}^{k} d_i$ or $\sum_{i=1}^{k} b_i$ where $1 \leq k \leq c$, and V_1 or L_0 or L_0/D

When the sum of either the d_i's or b_i's and one of the flow rates, either V_1 or L_0, are specified, the system is fixed in the sense that no further specifications may be made. Consider first specification $\sum_{i=1}^{k} d_i$, where none of the d_i's are known individually unless $k = 1$. By numbering the components in any arbitrary order, this specification is generalized to include any arbitrary set of d_i's (or b_i's). The relationships given by Equation (6–10) and

$$(d_i)_{co} = \frac{FX_i}{1 + \theta(b_i/d_i)_{ca}} \tag{6-26}$$

are developed in the same manner as shown in Chapter 4. The desired value of θ is the positive root which makes $g(\theta) = 0$, where

$$g(\theta) = \sum_{i=1}^{k} (d_i)_{co} - \sum_{i=1}^{k} d_i \tag{6-27}$$

The second summation on the right hand side of Equation (6–27) is the specification. Equation (6–27) is solved for the desired value of θ as described in Chapter 4.

After the desired value of θ has been determined, the corrected value for each of the d_i's is obtained by use of Equation (6–26). Thus the corrected distillate rate to be employed in the next trial calculation is obtained by summing both sides of Equation (6–26) from $i = 1$ through $i = c$, which process gives

$$D_{co} = \sum_{i=1}^{c} \frac{FX_i}{1 + \theta(b_i/d_i)_{ca}} \tag{6-28}$$

After both θ and the corrected d_i's have been obtained, the corresponding corrected b_i's are calculated by use of Equation (6–10).

When the second specification is taken to be V_1, the reflux rate is obtained by the material balance, $L_0 = V_1 - D_{co}$. Similarly, when L_0 is specified, V_1 is computed by use of the same equation. When the second specification is taken to be L_0/D, V_1 is calculated from $V_1 = (L_0/D + 1)D_{co}$.

The special case of the first specification where $k = c$ (the total distillate rate D is specified) has been discussed in detail in Chapters 4 and 5. Note also that when the first specification is the $\sum_{i=1}^{k} b_i$, it may be restated, if desired, in terms of the d_i's, since

$$\sum_{i=1}^{k} d_i = \sum_{i=1}^{k} FX_i - \sum_{i=1}^{k} b_i.$$

For this type of specification as well as "Specification 2" and "Specification 3" which follow, the specified sum of d's must be less than the corresponding sum of FX's.

Observe also that, when the second specification is taken as V_1, solutions are possible provided that a value of V_1 is specified such that the final corrected value for D will give a positive value for L_0, where $L_0 = V_1 - D_{co}$. The limiting value for D is F.

2. Specifications: d_1 or b_1 and V_1 or L_0 or L_0/D

This set of specifications is a special case of "Specification 1," $k = 1$, where the components may be numbered in any arbitrary manner. Since Equation (6–27) reduces to

$$d_1 = \frac{FX_1}{1 + \theta(b_1/d_1)_{ca}} \tag{6–29}$$

the desired value of θ may be calculated directly. The corrected d_i's are calculated by use of Equation (6–26), and the total distillate rate to be employed for the next trial calculation is obtained by use of Equation (6–28).

3. Specifications: b_1/d_1 and V_1 or L_0 or L_0/D

This set of specifications may be transformed to "Specification 2," since

$$d_1 = \frac{FX_1}{1 + (b_1/d_1)}$$

4. Specifications: (a) Temperature of Distillate and V_1 or L_0 or (b) Temperature of Bottoms and V_{N+1} or L_N

For illustrative purposes assume that the first specification is taken to be the dew point of the distillate at the column pressure. The expression for $g(\theta)$ for this set of specifications is developed in the following manner. The corrected d_i's must satisfy not only a material balance but also the dew point relationship

$$1 = \frac{\sum\limits_{i=1}^{c} (d_i)_{co}/K_i}{D_{co}} \tag{6-30}$$

where the K_i's are evaluated at the specified temperature. Upon substitution of the relationships for $(d_i)_{co}$ and D_{co} as given by Equations (6–26) and (6–28), respectively, the equation $g(\theta) = 0$, is obtained where

$$g(\theta) = \sum_{i=1}^{c} \frac{FX_i(1 - (1/K_i))}{1 + \theta(b_i/d_i)_{ca}} \tag{6-31}$$

After the desired value of θ has been found by use of Equation (6–31), the remainder of the calculational procedure is the same as that given in "Specification 1."

When the first specification is the temperature of the bubble point of the distillate, $g(\theta)$ takes the form

$$g(\theta) = \sum_{i=1}^{c} \frac{FX_i(1 - K_i)}{1 + \theta(b_i/d_i)_{ca}} \tag{6-32}$$

This expression is developed in a manner analogous to that shown for Equation (6–31).

The function defined by Equation (6–31) has $(c - 2)$, real, negative roots and one, real, positive root provided that the specified temperature is greater than the boiling point of the most volatile component and less than the dew point of the feed at the column pressure. Similarly, when the temperature of the bubble point of the distillate is specified, the function defined by Equation (6–32) has $(c - 2)$, real, negative roots and one, real, positive root provided that the specified temperature is less than the bubble point of the feed and greater than the boiling point of the most volatile component.

For each type of specification successive trials lead to the solution for a particular problem provided that the specified temperature is not only within the above limits but also greater than that of the condenser at the condition of total reflux in the rectifying section. The upper temperature

TABLE 6–7 Solution of Example 5–7 when the specifications are taken to be

$$\sum_{i=1}^{3} d_i = 17.9723$$

$$V_1 = 94.8$$

Temperature profiles (°F)
Trial number

Plate No.	1*	2	3	4	5	6	7	10	11
0 (Distillate)	108.47	111.06	113.07	111.34	109.26	108.13	107.71	107.60	107.60
1	142.53	146.00	145.35	140.86	137.02	135.14	134.52	134.42	134.42
2	170.93	173.35	167.94	159.89	154.48	152.35	151.89	151.99	152.00
3	206.86	204.66	190.34	177.57	171.39	170.01	170.13	170.38	170.35
4 (Feed)	296.20	270.35	231.34	209.30	204.86	206.93	208.11	207.54	207.47
5	291.37	277.75	252.12	234.77	228.73	228.34	228.83	228.82	228.77
6	286.99	281.75	264.35	251.01	244.97	243.48	243.39	243.38	243.36
7	286.78	284.81	272.68	262.37	256.79	254.83	254.35	254.21	254.19
8	288.00	288.15	279.39	271.15	266.09	263.97	263.25	262.95	262.94

9	292.16	292.93	286.37	279.60	275.10	272.99	272.16	271.75	271.74
10	300.42	301.01	296.15	290.75	287.14	285.34	284.58	284.17	284.17
11	316.56	317.35	314.76	311.79	309.78	308.74	308.28	308.03	308.02
12 (Reboiler)	366.01	367.45	368.71	368.30	367.52	367.00	366.75	366.61	366.60
$\sum_{i=1}^{3} d_i$	17.601	17.959	17.990	17.988	17.980	17.974	17.9721	17.97241	17.97235
D_{ca}	27.92†	31.62	35.11	33.58	32.12	31.630	31.571	31.610	31.607
θ	0.065	0.676	2.893	2.367	1.398	1.045	0.991	1.004	1.002

* This profile was calculated on the basis of a distillate temperature of 100°F with an increase of 10°F per plate. All profiles other than the first one are averaged.

† A value of D of 17.9723 was assumed to make the first trial calculation.

Reproduced by permission of *Hydrocarbon Processing & Petroleum Refiner*

limit prohibits the making of a specification in which no rectification of the feed is to occur.

In order to obtain a solution when the temperature of the bubble point of the bottoms is specified, this temperature must be greater than the bubble point of the feed and not only less than the boiling point of the least volatile component of the feed but also less than the temperature of the reboiler at the conditions of total reflux in the stripping section.

The specification of a sum of d_i's instead of D is illustrated by the example shown in Table 6–7. In the formulation of this problem, the sum of the d_i's for the first three components obtained previously (see Example 5–7, Table 5–11) were taken as the specification for the distillate. In obtaining the solution shown, Sullivan (3) used the conventional method for making enthalpy balances.

NOTATION

(See also Chapters 2 through 5)

$k =$ an integer used for counting

$m =$ an integer used for counting

$\rho =$ a large number of the order of magnitude of the upper limit of a computing machine

Problems

6–1 Following the outline given in the text, develop Equations (6–3) through (6–10).

6–2 Show that the use of Equations (6–6) and (6–7) for the approximation of V_j and L_j (where they are unknown) in Equations (6–3) and (6–4) yields

$$y_{ji} = \frac{(v_{ji}/d_i)_{ca}(d_i)_{co}}{V_j}, \quad i \neq H, L$$

$$x_{ji} = \frac{(l_{ji}/b_i)_{ca}(b_i)_{co}}{L_j}, \quad i \neq H, L$$

6–3 (a) When V_j and L_j are fixed, Equations (6–3) and (6–4) take this information into account by means of two multipliers that were eliminated in the development process. State the expressions for these multipliers and describe a procedure by which the mole fractions could be calculated by making direct use of the multipliers.

(b) Show that the corresponding v_{ji}'s and l_{ji}'s given by Equations (6–3) through (6–5) are not necessarily in component-material balance.

6–4 Show that if in the process of making calculations down from the top of a conventional distillation column, a v_{ji}/d_i is found which is greater than some large preassigned number ρ, this implies that

$$\frac{d_i}{b_i} \cong 0$$

6–5 Verify the result given by Equation (6–25).

6–6 Show that if the conditions stated after Equation (6–32) are realized, the function $g(\theta)$, as given by Equation (6–31) has $(c - 2)$ real, negative roots and one, real positive root.

6–7 Show that if the bubble point of the bottoms is taken as one of the specifications, the following expression for the g-function is obtained

$$g(\theta) = \sum_{i=1}^{c} \frac{\theta(h_i/d_i)_{ca} FX_i(1 - K_i)}{1 + \theta(b_i/d_i)_{ca}}$$

6–8 (a) Show that when the sum of the first k values of the X_{Di}'s and V_1 (or L_0) are specified, the following expression is obtained for the g-function.

$$g(\theta) = \sum_{i=1}^{k} \frac{FX_i}{1 + \theta(b_i/d_i)_{ca}} - \left(\frac{\sum\limits_{i=1}^{k} X_{Di}}{1 - \sum\limits_{i=1}^{k} X_{Di}} \right) \left[\sum_{i=k+1}^{c} \frac{FX_i}{1 + \theta(b_i/d_i)_{ca}} \right]$$

(b) Discuss the possibility of making impossible specifications (Hint: see Reference (3)).

6–9 Verify the results given in Table 6–1 for Cases 1, 2, and 4.

LITERATURE CITED

1. Canik, L. J., B. W. Hardy, C. D. Holland, and H. L. Bauni, "Figure Separations This New Way: Part 7—Absorbers with Reboilers," *Petroleum Refiner*, **40**, No. 12, 161 (1961).

2. Hardy, B. W., S. L. Sullivan, Jr., C. D. Holland, and H. L. Bauni, "Figure Separations This New Way: Part 5—A Convergence Method for Absorbers," *Petroleum Refiner*, **40**, No. 9, 237 (1961).

3. Lyster, W. N., S. L. Sullivan, Jr., D. S. Billingsley, and C. D. Holland, "Figure Distillation This New Way: Part 2—Product Purity Can Set Conditions for Column," *Petroleum Refiner*, **38,** No. 7, 151 (1959).

4. Weisenfelder, A. J., C. D. Holland, and R. H. Johnston, "Figure Separations This New Way: Part 6—Minimization of Round-Off Errors and Other Developments," *Petroleum Refiner*, **40,** No. 10, 175 (1961).

5. Weisenfelder, A. J., "Minimization of Round-Off Error and Treatment of Single Phase and Separated Components in Conventional and Complex Columns," M.S. thesis, A. and M. College of Texas, College Station, Texas, (May 1961).

Complex Columns   7

The combination of the Thiele and Geddes calculational procedure and the θ-method of convergence is readily extended to include complex columns.

A complex column is defined as one which has either more feed plates or streams withdrawn or a combination of these than does a conventional column. In order to illustrate the combined procedure, a column having two feed plates and two side-streams (in addition to the top and bottom products) is treated in detail.

In the application of the method of Thiele and Geddes to complex columns, one specifies the column pressure, the number of plates, the rate, composition and thermal condition of each feed as well as the locations of the feed plates and side-streams. The number of additional specifications that may be made is equal to the total number of streams withdrawn (the distillate, bottoms and side-streams). For a column containing two side-streams, the additional specifications V_1 (or L_0), D, W_1 and W_2 may be made. These in turn fix the dependent variable B.

In order to make the first trial, temperature and L/V profiles for the column are assumed. This allows one to carry out calculations down from the top and up from the bottom of the column. After the convergence method has been applied, the compositions and corresponding temperatures as well as the total molal rates of flow of all streams are calculated. This combined procedure is repeated until satisfactory agreement between the assumed and calculated temperature profiles is obtained.

CONVERGENCE METHOD

The convergence method for complex columns is developed as shown by Canik et al. (1) in a manner analogous to that employed in the consideration of conventional columns in Chapters 4 and 6. For systems composed of distributed, separated, and single phase components the following expressions constitute the θ-method of convergence. However, before they can be applied to systems containing separated components, certain terms which become indeterminate for these components must be replaced by their equivalents. These equivalent forms follow the statement of the general equations which constitute the θ-method for complex columns.

Each side-stream withdrawn from a column gives an additional degree of freedom, which permits one specification to be made on the side-stream such as the total withdrawal rate of the side-stream. Each such specification gives rise to an additional θ multiplier. In order to distinguish between the θ's, they are assigned subscripts as shown in Equations (7–1), (7–2), and (7–3).

Beginning with the same set of basic postulates stated in Chapter 4, note that

$$\left(\frac{b_i}{d_i}\right)_{co} = \theta_0 \left(\frac{b_i}{d_i}\right)_{ca}, \quad i \neq H, L \tag{7–1}$$

$$\left(\frac{w_{1i}}{d_i}\right)_{co} = \theta_1 \left(\frac{w_{1i}}{d_i}\right)_{ca}, \quad i \neq H, L \tag{7–2}$$

$$\left(\frac{w_{2i}}{d_i}\right)_{co} = \theta_2 \left(\frac{w_{2i}}{d_i}\right)_{ca}, \quad i \neq H, L \tag{7–3}$$

Again the corrected rates are those which satisfy simultaneously, the specifications D, W_1, and W_2 (where B is taken to be the dependent variable) and the over-all material balance

$$FX_i = (d_i)_{co} + (w_{1i})_{co} + (w_{2i})_{co} + (b_i)_{co}, \quad i \neq H, L \tag{7–4}$$

where

$$FX_i = F_1X_{1i} + F_2X_{2i}$$

Combination of Equations (7–1) through (7–4) yields the following expression for the corrected distillate rate,

$$(d_i)_{co} = \frac{FX_i}{1 + \theta_0(b_i/d_i)_{ca} + \theta_1(w_{1i}/d_i)_{ca} + \theta_2(w_{2i}/d_i)_{ca}}, \quad i \neq H, L \tag{7–5}$$

When this expression for $(d_i)_{co}$ is substituted into Equations (7–1) through (7–3), formulas for $(b_i)_{co}$, $(w_{1i})_{co}$, and $(w_{2i})_{co}$ are obtained. The requirement that the corrected rates satisfy the specifications D, W_1, and W_2 leads to the g-functions

$$g_0(\theta_0, \theta_1, \theta_2) = \sum_{i \neq H, L} (d_i)_{co} - (D - \sum_L d_L) \tag{7-6}$$

$$g_1(\theta_0, \theta_1, \theta_2) = \sum_{i \neq H, L} (w_{1i})_{co} - (W_1 - \sum_H w_{1H}) \tag{7-7}$$

$$g_2(\theta_0, \theta_1, \theta_2) = \sum_{i \neq H, L} (w_{2i})_{co} - (W_2 - \sum_H w_{2H}) \tag{7-8}$$

that represent three equations in the three unknowns, θ_0, θ_1, and θ_2. The desired solution is the set of positive values of θ_0, θ_1, and θ_2 that gives $g_0 = g_1 = g_2 = 0$, simultaneously. These formulas apply for the case where the distillate is withdrawn as a vapor and the side-streams as liquids. When W_1 is withdrawn above the feed plate at which the single phase heavy components enter, observe that in Equation (7-7), $\sum_H w_{1H} = 0$. If W_1 and W_2 are withdrawn from plates p and q below the lowest feed plate, the flow rates of the single phase components are computed as follows:

$$\sum_H w_{1H} = \left(\frac{W_1}{L_p}\right) \sum_H FX_H \tag{7-9}$$

$$\sum_H w_{2H} = \left(\frac{W_2}{L_q}\right) \sum_H (FX_H - w_{1,H}) \tag{7-10}$$

When the distillate is withdrawn as a vapor and the side-streams as vapors, Equations (7-7) and (7-8) are modified as follows:

$$(W_1 - \sum_H w_{1H}) \text{ is replaced by } (W_1 - \sum_L w_{1L})$$

$$(W_2 - \sum_H w_{2H}) \text{ is replaced by } (W_2 - \sum_L w_{2L})$$

In the event separated components are present, certain terms in Equations (7-6) through (7-8) become indeterminate. For the separated heavy components, $(d_i)_{co} = 0$, and

$$(w_{1i})_{co} = \theta_1 \left(\frac{w_{1i}}{d_i}\right)_{ca} (d_i)_{co}$$

$$= \frac{FX_i}{1 + (\theta_0/\theta_1)(b_i/w_{1i})_{ca} + (\theta_2/\theta_1)(w_{2i}/w_{1i})_{ca}} \tag{7-11}$$

The expression for $(w_{2i})_{co}$ for a separated heavy is

$$(w_{2i})_{co} = \theta_2 \left(\frac{w_{2i}}{d_i}\right)_{ca} (d_i)_{co} = \frac{FX_i}{1 + (\theta_0/\theta_2)(b_i/w_{2i})_{ca} + (\theta_1/\theta_2)(w_{1i}/w_{2i})_{ca}}$$

(7–12)

Also, for a separated heavy component,

$$(b_i)_{co} = \theta_0 \left(\frac{b_i}{d_i}\right)_{ca} (d_i)_{co} = \frac{FX_i}{1 + (\theta_1/\theta_0)(w_{1i}/b_i)_{ca} + (\theta_2/\theta_0)(w_{2i}/b_i)_{ca}}$$

(7–13)

If the component is separated below plate p (the location of the withdrawal of W_1), then $(w_{1i})_{ca} = 0$ and $(w_{1i})_{co} = 0$ and Equations (7–12) and (7–13) are modified accordingly. Equations (7–11) through (7–13) are developed as shown in a subsequent section concerned with the treatment of separated components.

CALCULATION OF THE θ's

For a system composed of distributed components alone and for a column with one side-stream withdrawn, graphs of the functions g_0 and g_1 in the neighborhood of the positive roots are shown in Figures 7–1 and 7–2.

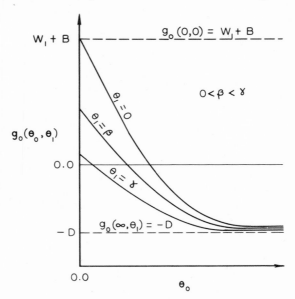

Figure 7–1. Graphic representation of the function $g_0(\theta_0, \theta_1)$ for the case of one side-stream. (Reproduced by permission of *Hydrocarbon Processing & Petroleum Refiner*)

The object is to find the positive set of θ's that makes all functions equal to zero simultaneously. Of the methods which have been investigated (3, 5), either the method of Newton-Raphson or this method with modifications was found to be the most satisfactory. Since the basic method was described in Chapter 1, only the details of application and the modifications are presented here. In the application of the Newton-Raphson method, the best results were obtained by taking the first assumed value for each θ

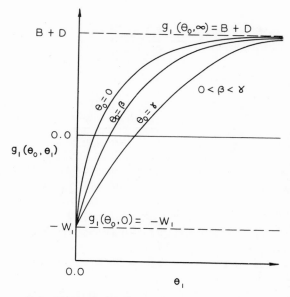

Figure 7–2. Graphic representation of the function $g_1(\theta_0, \theta_1)$ for the case of one side-stream. (Reproduced by permission of *Hydrocarbon Processing & Petroleum Refiner*)

equal to unity; that is, $\theta_{0,1} = \theta_{1,1} = \theta_{2,1} = 1.0$. The second subscript is used to denote the trial number with respect to the application of the Newton-Raphson method. Calculations are initiated by evaluation of the functions g_0, g_1, and g_2 and their partial derivatives on the basis of the first assumed set of θ's. Then as described in Chapter 1, the Newton-Raphson equations are solved to give the second set of θ's, namely, $\theta_{0,2}$, $\theta_{1,2}$, and $\theta_{2,2}$, which are used to make the next trial calculation. If in a given trial calculation (for the correct set of θ's) a negative value for a θ is obtained, a value equal to one half of the previously assumed value should be employed (3).

In the statement of the Newton-Raphson method in Chapter 1, the use of the analytical expressions for the partial derivatives was implied. A modification which consists of an alternate method for evaluation of the derivatives was investigated by Tomme (5) and found to give satisfactory results. This method is initiated by the choice of a set of positive values for the θ's, denoted by $\theta_{0,1}$, $\theta_{1,1}$, $\theta_{2,1}$. The functions appearing in the Newton-Raphson equations are evaluated at this set of θ's. In order to compute the value of the partial derivative, $\partial g_0 / \partial \theta_0$, in the neighborhood of the first set of θ's all of the θ's are held fixed save for θ_0 which is allowed to take on the value of $(\theta_{0,1} + p)$. Then by the definition of the partial derivative, it follows that

$$\frac{\partial g_0}{\partial \theta_0} = \frac{g_0[(\theta_{0,1} + p), \theta_{1,1}, \theta_{2,1}] - g_0[\theta_{0,1}, \theta_{1,1}, \theta_{2,1}]}{(\theta_{0,1} + p) - \theta_{0,1}}$$

Similarly,

$$\frac{\partial g_0}{\partial \theta_1} = \frac{g_0[\theta_{0,1}, (\theta_{1,1} + p), \theta_{2,1}] - g_0[\theta_{0,1}, \theta_{1,1}, \theta_{2,1}]}{p}$$

The other partials are evaluated in a manner analogous to that shown. The selection of a value for p is rather arbitrary, provided that a number considerably less than unity is picked (5). When p was taken equal to 0.001, satisfactory results were obtained. Of course, if either $\theta_{0,1}$ (or $\theta_{1,1}$) become so large that because of the number of digits available $\theta_{0,1} + p = \theta_{0,1}$, the value of p must be increased. When the Newton-Raphson equations are solved on the basis of this set of values for the functions and their derivatives, the next set of θ's is obtained. This set of θ's is used (in the same way as that described for the first set) to carry out the next trial calculation for the determination of the third set of θ's. Again, a negative value obtained for any θ is replaced by one half of the value of the particular θ which was used to make the given trial calculation.

Another method worthy of mention is that of interpolation (*regula falsi*). When it was extended to include functions of several variables as described by Lyster *et al.* (3), satisfactory results were obtained. However, it was found to be considerably slower than the Newton-Raphson method.

MATERIAL BALANCE EQUATIONS

The following material balances apply for the distributed components in a column such as that shown in Figure 7–3. The numbers of the plates from which the two side-streams (liquid phase) are withdrawn are designated, for convenience, "*p*" and "*q*." The number of the upper feed plate (the one nearest the top of the column) is denoted by "*f*" and the number of the lower feed plate is denoted by "*t*." For all plates above the lower feed plate *t*, the flow rates are determined by use of material balances which

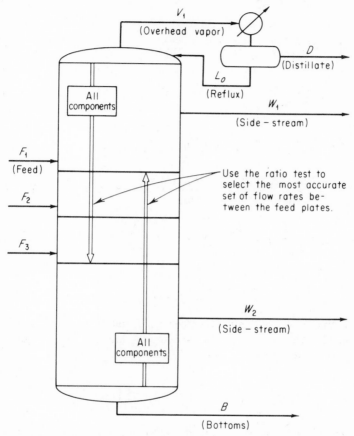

Figure 7–3. Complex column with two feed plates and two side-streams. (Reproduced by permission of *Hydrocarbon Processing & Petroleum Refiner*)

enclose the top of the column and any plate *j*. Similarly, for all plates below the upper feed plate *f*, the balances include the bottom of the column and any plate *j*. Thus, two possible sets of equations exist for the calculation of the flow rates of each component between the two feed plates. As proposed in a subsequent section, the flow rates in this section are computed by each set of equations and that set of flow rates is selected which possesses the least amount of round-off error. For any plate above the feed plate t, the material balances are represented by the following equations.

$$\frac{v_{1i}}{d_i} = A_{0i} + 1, \text{ (balance around the condenser)} \tag{7-14a}$$

$$\frac{v_{ji}}{d_i} = A_{j-1,i}\left(\frac{v_{j-1,i}}{d_i}\right) + 1, \quad 2 \le j \le p + 1 \tag{7-14b}$$

$$\frac{v_{ji}}{d_i} = A_{j-1,i}\left(\frac{v_{j-1,i}}{d_i}\right) + C_{1i}, \quad p + 2 \le j \le f - 1 \tag{7-14c}$$

$$\frac{v_{fi}}{d_i} = A_{f-1,i}\left(\frac{v_{f-1,i}}{d_i}\right) + \frac{l_{F_1 i}}{d_i} + \left(C_{1i} - \frac{F_1 X_{1i}}{d_i}\right) \tag{7-14d}$$

$$\frac{v_{ji}}{d_i} = A_{j-1,i}\left(\frac{v_{j-1,i}}{d_i}\right) + \left(C_{1i} - \frac{F_1 X_{1i}}{d_i}\right), \quad f + 1 \le j \le t - 1 \tag{7-14e}$$

$$\frac{v_{ti}}{d_i} = A_{t-1,i}\left(\frac{v_{t-1,i}}{d_i}\right) + \frac{l_{F_2 i}}{d_i} + \left(C_{1i} - \frac{F X_i}{d_i}\right) \tag{7-14f}$$

where

$$C_{1i} = 1 + w_{1i}/d_i$$

The quantity w_{1i}/d_i is evaluated after v_{pi}/d_i has been computed by use of Equation (7-14b). Since the side-stream W_1 has the same composition as the liquid leaving plate p, it follows that

$$\frac{w_{1i}}{d_i} = \left(\frac{W_1}{L_p}\right)\left(\frac{l_{pi}}{d_i}\right) = \left(\frac{W_1}{L_p}\right)\left(A_{pi}\frac{v_{pi}}{d_i}\right) \tag{7-15}$$

For any plate below the top feed plate f, the material balances are represented by the following equations.

$$\frac{l_{Ni}}{b_i} = S_{N+1,i} + 1, \text{ (balance around the reboiler)} \tag{7-16a}$$

$$\frac{l_{j-1,i}}{b_i} = S_{ji}\left(\frac{l_{ji}}{b_i}\right) + 1, \quad q + 2 \le j \le N \tag{7-16b}$$

$$\frac{l_{j-1,i}}{b_i} = S_{ji}\left(\frac{l_{ji}}{b_i}\right) + C_{2i}, \quad t + 1 \le j \le q + 1 \tag{7-16c}$$

$$\frac{l_{t-1,i}}{b_i} = S_{ti}\left(\frac{l_{ti}}{b_i}\right) - \frac{l_{F_2 i}}{b_i} + C_{2i} \tag{7-16d}$$

$$\frac{l_{j-1,i}}{b_i} = S_{ji}\left(\frac{l_{ji}}{b_i}\right) + \left(C_{2i} - \frac{F_2 X_{2i}}{b_i}\right), \quad t-1 \leq j \leq f+1 \tag{7-16e}$$

where,

$$C_{2i} = 1 + w_{2i}/b_i$$

Calculations are made up from the bottom of the column in the usual way until $l_{q+1,i}/b_i$ has been computed. Before the step-by-step procedure can be continued, it is necessary to compute w_{2i}/d_i. For $j = q + 1$, Equation (7–16c) gives

$$\frac{l_{qi}}{b_i} = S_{q+1,i}\left(\frac{l_{q+1,i}}{b_i}\right) + 1 + \frac{w_{2i}}{b_i} \tag{7-17}$$

Since

$$\frac{l_{qi}}{b_i} = \left(\frac{L_q}{W_2}\right)\left(\frac{w_{2i}}{b_i}\right) \tag{7-18}$$

Equation (7–17) is readily solved for w_{2i}/b_i to give

$$\frac{w_{2i}}{b_i} = \left(\frac{W_2}{L_q - W_2}\right)\left[S_{q+1,i}\left(\frac{l_{q+1,i}}{b_i}\right) + 1\right] \tag{7-19}$$

When the side-streams are withdrawn as vapors, Equation (7–14) and (7–16) are modified accordingly. In the application of these equations, calculations are made down from the top and up from the bottom of the column to feed plates f and t, respectively, in the same general manner as described in Chapter 3 and 4. Before the flow rates between the feed plates may be calculated by Equations (7–14) and (7–16), b_i/d_i must be computed. The following equivalent formulas for b_i/d_i are readily developed in a manner analogous to that shown for Equation (3–31).

$$\frac{b_i}{d_i} = \frac{\omega_i(l_{f-1,i}/d_i) + (1 + \Omega_i - Z_i)C_{1i}}{(v_{ti}/b_i) + Z_i C_{2i}} \tag{7-20}$$

where

$$Z_i = \frac{(\Omega_i + 1)F_1 X_{1i} - \omega_i l_{F_1 i} + v_{F_2 i}}{FX_i}$$

$$\omega_i = A_{t-1,i}\, A_{t-2,i} \ldots A_{f+1,i}\, A_{fi}$$

$$\Omega_i = A_{t-1,i} + A_{t-1,i}\, A_{t-2,i} + \ldots + A_{t-1,i}\, A_{t-2,i} \ldots A_{f+1,i}\, A_{fi}$$

and

$$\frac{b_i}{d_i} = \frac{(l_{f-1,i}/d_i) + C_{1i}z_i}{\phi_i(v_{ti}/b_i) + C_{2i}(\Phi_i - z_i)} \tag{7-21}$$

where

$$z_i = \frac{\Phi_i F_2 X_{2i} - \phi_i v_{F_2 i} + l_{F_1 i}}{FX_i}$$

$$\phi_i = S_{fi} \, S_{f+1,i} \, \ldots \, S_{t-2,i} \, S_{t-1,i}$$

$$\Phi_i = 1 + S_{fi} + S_{fi} \, S_{f+1,i} + \ldots + S_{fi} S_{f+1,i} \ldots S_{t-2,i} \, S_{t-1,i}$$

After b_i/d_i has been computed, the distillate rate for each component is obtained by the over-all material balance,

$$d_i = \frac{FX_i}{C_{1i} + \dfrac{w_{2i}}{d_i} + \dfrac{b_i}{d_i}} \tag{7-22}$$

Then the flow rates between the two feed plates may be calculated as indicated by Equations (7–14) and (7–16). The formulas for b_i/d_i (Equations (7–20) and (7–21)) are like those for conventional columns in that they are almost independent of round-off error (8).

MINIMIZATION OF ROUND-OFF ERROR

The round-off error given by various calculational procedures for a complex column with two feed plates was examined in a manner analogous to that shown for conventional columns. As in the case of conventional columns, the most accurate flow rates above the top and below the bottom feed plate are obtained by making calculations down from the top and up from the bottom of the column, respectively. Thus for complex columns the problem to be resolved is whether the flow rates between the top and bottom feed plates should be computed by use of material balances that include the top or the bottom of the column. Any difference between the values for a particular flow rate obtained by different calculational procedures may be attributed to round-off error because it can be shown in a manner analogous to that given in Chapter 3 for conventional columns that the expressions for a given flow rate (obtained by writing material balances around the top and the bottom of the column) are equivalent. Similarly, all of the various expressions which may be developed for b_i/d_i are equivalent. Several simple examples were solved by Weisenfelder *et al.* (7) and Weisenfelder (8) and the results obtained are given in Table 7–1.

TABLE 7-1 Round-off error given by different calculational procedures for complex columns

(For all cases shown, $N = 10$, the column has a partial condenser and reboiler, thermal condition of each feed is boiling point liquid, the absorption factor A, remains constant throughout the column, and no streams are withdrawn other than the distillate and bottoms. Feed F_1 enters on plate no. 1 and Feed F_2 enters the column on plate no. 11 for all cases.)

Case No.	F_1X_1 and F_2X_2	Absorption factor A	Match at top feed plate $\dfrac{(b/d)_{\text{step-by-step}}}{(b/d)_{\text{formula}}}$	Match at bottom feed plate $\dfrac{(b/d)_{\text{step-by-step}}}{(b/d)_{\text{formula}}}$
1	$F_1X_1 = F_2X_2$	9.5555555	1.0000	0.5554
2	$F_1X_1 = 2F_2X_2$	9.5555555	1.0000	8.6634×10^6
3	$F_1X_1 = \dfrac{F_2X_2}{2}$	9.5555555	1.0000	0.7991
4	$F_2X_2 = 0$	9.5555555	1.0000	-4.0388×10^2
5	$F_1X_1 = 0$	0.095555555	0.9044	1.0000
6	$F_1X_1 = F_2X_2$	0.095555555	-1.0180×10^{-8}	1.0000
7	$F_1X_1 = 2F_2X_2$	0.095555555	-9.1285×10^{-5}	1.0000
8	$F_1X_1 = \dfrac{F_2X_2}{2}$	0.095555555	3.1819	1.0000
9	$F_1X_1 = F_2X_2$	1.0000000	1.0000	1.0000

Reproduced by permission of *Hydrocarbon Processing & Petroleum Refiner*

These results show that if a component enters the column in only one feed, the most accurate calculational procedure consists of making calculations down from the top and up from the bottom of the column to the given feed

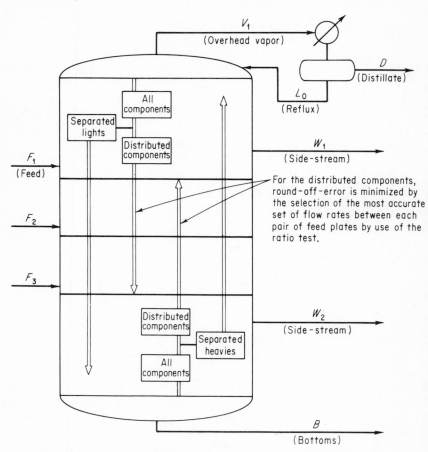

Figure 7–4. Minimize round-off error by making calculations from the top of the column to the lowermost feed plate and from the bottom to the uppermost feed plate, and select the most accurate set of flow rates between each pair of feed plates by use of the ratio test.

plate at which the given component enters. When a component enters the column in each of several feeds, the most accurate calculational procedure is found by carrying out the ratio test for each feed plate as shown in Table 7–1. A schematic representation of the proposed calculational procedure is shown in Figure 7–4.

Since the formulas for the calculation of b_i/d_i (Equations (7–20) and and (7–21)) are almost independent of round-off error, only one of the expressions is needed. In carrying out the ratio test for a component at plate f, the following procedure is employed. After the formula value for b_i/d_i has been obtained by use of either Equation (7–20) or (7–21), the calculations implied by Equations (7–14) and (7–16) are performed. The value of v_{fi}/d_i is obtained by use of Equation (7–14d) and l_{fi}/b_i by Equation (7–16e). The value of the latter is used to compute v_{fi}/b_i as follows:

$$\frac{v_{fi}}{b_i} = A_{fi}\left(\frac{l_{fi}}{b_i}\right)$$

On the basis of the values so obtained, the step-by-step value of b_i/d_i is computed in the following manner.

$$\left(\frac{b_i}{d_i}\right)_{\text{step−by−step}} = \frac{(v_{fi}/d_i)}{(v_{fi}/b_i)}$$

The ratio test for plate f consists of the evaluation of the ratio

$$\frac{(b_i/d_i)_{\text{step−by−step}}}{(b_i/d_i)_{\text{formula}}}$$

For the feed plate t, the ratio test is carried out in the same manner to that shown for plate f.

TREATMENT OF SEPARATED COMPONENTS

The definitions of the separated light and heavy components stated in Chapter 6 are retained for complex columns. That is, a separated light is a component for which $(b_i)_{ca} = 0$; and a separated heavy is one for which $(d_i)_{ca} = 0$. The possibility of either $(w_{1i})_{ca}$ or $(w_{2i})_{ca}$ being equal to zero exists and must be considered in the calculational procedure.

In the treatment of separated components in complex columns, it is convenient to classify all complex columns as one of two types. The first type consists of those columns with multiple feeds and only two streams withdrawn, the distillate and bottoms. In the second type are included those columns with multiple feeds and one or more side-streams withdrawn other than the distillate and bottoms. The treatment of separated components in columns of the first type follows very closely that described for conventional columns. Suppose, for example, a separated light component is detected below the lower feed plate. Then for this component the distillate rate is known, since

$$d_i = F_1 X_{1i} + F_2 X_{2i} = FX_i \qquad (7\text{–}23)$$

Calculations are made from the top of the column past the lower feed plate and toward the bottom by use of equations similar in form to Equation (7–14).

For columns of the second type, calculations are carried out in the

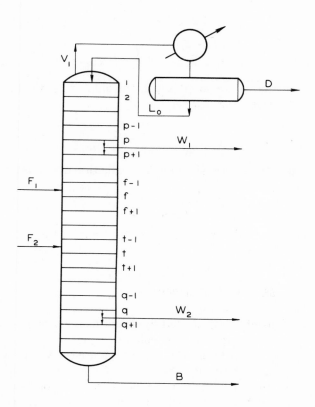

Figure 7–5. Directions for making calculations for separated and distributed components in complex columns.

directions indicated in Figure 7–5. For the distributed components, round-off error is minimized between the feed plates by use of the ratio test as described previously. However, the detection of a separated component does not lead to the simplifications found for columns of the first type. Although $b_i = 0$ for a separated light component, the value of d_i does not follow immediately as it did for complex columns of the first type. Further calculations must be performed before d_i can be evaluated. For purposes of illustration, consider the column shown in Figure 7–3. Component i enters at both plates f and t at the rates $F_1 X_{1i}$ and $F_2 X_{2i}$, respectively.

The calculational procedure to be followed for a separated light component in a complex column such as the one shown in Figure 7–3 follows. A separated component in a complex column may be detected as described previously for conventional columns. Suppose a separated light component is detected in the process of making calculations up from the bottom of the column toward the lower feed plate t; that is, a j is found such that $l_{ji}/b_i > \rho$. As in the case of conventional columns, it can be shown that b_i/d_i is near the lower limit, $1/\rho$, and may be taken equal to zero. All ratios of the flow rates (l_{ji}/b_i) obtained for the given component by making calculations up from the bottom of the column are discarded. For such a component the material balances are written around the top of the column and any given plate. Calculations are carried out in the usual way to the feed plate f to give values for w_{1i}/d_i and $l_{f-1,i}/d_i$. For plates f through $t - 1$ the flow rates are given by Equations (7–14d) and (7–14e); and for j equal to or greater than t, the following equations are applicable:

$$\frac{v_{ti}}{d_i} = \frac{l_{t-1,i}}{d_i} + \frac{l_{F_2 i}}{d_i} - \frac{w_{2i}}{d_i} \tag{7–24a}$$

$$\frac{v_{ji}}{d_i} = A_{j-1,i}\left(\frac{v_{j-1,i}}{d_i}\right) - \frac{w_{2i}}{d_i}, \quad t + 1 \leq j \leq q \tag{7–24b}$$

$$\frac{v_{q+1,i}}{d_i} = \left(\frac{L_q - W_2}{L_q}\right)\left(\frac{l_{qi}}{d_i}\right) \tag{7–24c}$$

$$\frac{v_{ji}}{d_i} = A_{j-1,i}\left(\frac{v_{j-1,i}}{d_i}\right), \quad q + 2 \leq j \leq N + 1 \tag{7–24d}$$

After $l_{f-1,i}/d_i$ has been determined by use of Equation (7–14), it is necessary to evaluate w_{2i}/d_i and d_i before further calculations may be performed.

From the upper feed plate, f, to the lower one, t, a substitutional procedure is followed whereby the expression for v_{ji}/d_i is substituted successively into the one for $v_{j+1,i}/d_i$. This procedure gives

$$\frac{l_{t-1,i}}{d_i} = \omega_i\left(\frac{l_{f-1,i}}{d_i} + \frac{l_{F_1 i}}{d_i}\right) + \Omega_i\left(C_{1i} - \frac{F_1 X_{1i}}{d_i}\right) \tag{7–25}$$

where ω_i and Ω_i have the same definitions as those given after Equation

(7–20). Between plates t and q, the substitutional procedure leads to

$$\frac{l_{qi}}{d_i} = \omega_{qi} \left(\frac{l_{t-1,i}}{d_i} + \frac{l_{F_2 i}}{d_i} \right) - \Omega_{qi} \left(\frac{w_{2i}}{d_i} \right) \tag{7–26}$$

where

$$\omega_{qi} = A_{qi} \ldots A_{ti}$$

$$\Omega_{qi} = A_{qi} + A_{qi} A_{q-1,i} + \ldots + A_{qi} \ldots A_{ti}$$

The unknown d_i may be eliminated from Equations (7–25) and (7–26) by use of the result obtained by an over-all material balance,

$$d_i = \frac{F X_i}{C_{1i} + (w_{2i}/d_i)} \tag{7–27}$$

Since $l_{qi}/d_i = (L_q/W_2)(w_{2i}/d_i)$, Equations (7–25), (7–26), and (7–27) may be solved for w_{2i}/d_i to give

$$\frac{w_{2i}}{d_i} = \frac{\omega_{qi}[\omega_i(l_{f-1,i}/d_i) + \Omega_i C_{1i}] - Z_i C_{1i}}{[(L_q/W_2) + \Omega_{qi} + Z_i]} \tag{7–28}$$

where

$$Z_i = \frac{\omega_{qi}[\Omega_i F_1 X_{1i} - \omega_i l_{F_1 i} - l_{F_2 i}]}{F X_i}$$

After w_{2i}/d_i has been computed by use of Equation (7–28), d_i is evaluated by use of Equation (7–27). Then calculations may be carried out toward the bottom of the column by use of Equation (7–24) until a j is found such that $v_{ji}/d_i \leq 1/\rho$.

The calculational procedure described is readily extended to include columns from which any number of side-streams are withdrawn. Also, the treatment of separated heavy components is analogous to that described for separated light components.

EVALUATION OF TERMS WHICH BECOME INDETERMINATE FOR SEPARATED COMPONENTS

The formulas given in Chapter 6 for the calculation of the compositions for conventional columns are applicable to complex columns. In the same manner as shown there, the term $[(v_{ji}/d_i)_{ca}](d_i)_{co}$ becomes indeterminate for a separated heavy, and is replaced by its equivalent,

$$\left(\frac{v_{ji}}{d_i} \right)_{ca} (d_i)_{co} = \left(\frac{1}{\theta_0} \right) \left(\frac{v_{ji}}{b_i} \right)_{ca} (b_i)_{co} \tag{7–29}$$

where $(b_i)_{co}$ is given by Equation (7–13). Similarly for a separated light component, the term $[(l_{ji}/b_i)_{ca}](b_i)_{co}$ is replaced by its equivalent, which follows:

$$\left(\frac{l_{ji}}{b_i}\right)_{ca} (b_i)_{co} = \theta_0 \left(\frac{l_{ji}}{d_i}\right)_{ca} (d_i)_{co} \tag{7–30}$$

where $(d_i)_{co}$ is given by Equation (7–5).

When a heavy component is separated above plate p (the withdrawal location of W_1) the formula for $(w_{1i})_{co}$ for the separated heavy component is developed in the following manner. Division of Equation (7–2) by Equation (7–1) yields

$$\left(\frac{b_i}{w_{1i}}\right)_{co} = \left(\frac{\theta_0}{\theta_1}\right) \left(\frac{b_i}{w_{1i}}\right)_{ca} \tag{7–31}$$

Similarly, Equations (7–2) and (7–3) are readily solved to give

$$\left(\frac{w_{2i}}{w_{1i}}\right)_{co} = \left(\frac{\theta_2}{\theta_1}\right) \left(\frac{w_{2i}}{w_{1i}}\right)_{ca} \tag{7–32}$$

Since $(d_i)_{co} = 0$ for a separated heavy component, it is required that the corrected rates satisfy the over-all material balance, Equation (7–4). This expression is readily solved for $(w_{1i})_{co}$ to give

$$(w_{1i})_{co} = \frac{FX_i}{1 + (b_i/w_{1i})_{co} + (w_{2i}/w_{1i})_{co}} \tag{7–33}$$

The desired formula for $(w_{1i})_{co}$, Equation (7–11), is obtained by replacing the two ratios in the denominator of Equation (7–33) by their equivalents as given by Equation (7–31) and (7–32). The formulas for $(w_{2i})_{co}$ and $(b_i)_{co}$ (Equations (7–12) and (7–13)) for a separated heavy component are developed in a manner analogous to that shown for Equation (7–11).

OTHER RELATIONSHIPS

Single phase lights and heavies are treated in the same manner as described for conventional columns in Chapter 6. The conventional, the constant-composition, and the Q-methods for making enthalpy balances are also applied in the same manner as described in the previous chapter. The temperatures are calculated by use of the bubble point procedure, Equation (6–19). Variations between the temperatures and flow rates between successive trials are also restricted as described previously.

TABLE 7-2 Statement of Examples 7-1, 7-2, and 7-3

Component	F_1X_1	F_2X_2
CH₄	2.0	0.0
C₂H₆	10.0	0.0
C₃H₆	6.0	1.0
C₃H₈	12.0	7.0
i-C₄	1.0	4.0
n-C₄	3.0	17.0
n-C₅	0.5	15.2
n-C₆	0.0	9.0
n-C₇	0.0	4.5
n-C₈	0.0	4.3
360	0.0	3.5
Total	34.5	65.5

Specifications

Example No.	Distillate D	Vapor V_1	Side-stream W_1	Side-stream W_2
7-1	38.0	94.8	0.0	0.0
7-2	23.0	94.8	15.0	0.0
7-3	23.0	94.8	15.0	25.0

Side-stream W_1 withdrawn as liquid from plate No. 3.
Side-stream W_2 withdrawn as vapor from plate No. 15.
Thermal condition of feed F_1 = dew point vapor.
Thermal condition of feed F_2 = bubble point liquid.
Feed F_1 to enter on plate No. 7.
Feed F_2 to enter on plate No. 12.
Total number of plates = 19.
Operating pressure = 264.7 psia.
Type of condenser = partial.
Equilibrium and enthalpy data to be taken from Tables A–3 and A–7 of the Appendix.

Reproduced by permission of *Hydrocarbon Processing & Petroleum Refiner*

TABLE 7-3 Solution of Example 7-1

Trial number	θ_0	Temp. of D, °F	Temp. of B, °F	Calculated value of D
1	275.56	92.12	295.94	54.7
2	0.14	92.59	295.38	33.4
3	0.38	93.12	294.89	36.0
4	0.53	93.69	294.42	36.6
5	0.91	93.89	294.34	37.8
10	1.009	94.47	294.05	38.019
11	0.990	94.50	294.04	37.979
12	1.005	94.53	294.03	38.010

Reproduced by permission of *Hydrocarbon Processing & Petroleum Refiner*

TABLE 7–4 Solution of Example 7–2

Trial number	θ_0	θ_1	Temp. of D, °F	Temp. of W_1, °F	Temp. of B, °F	Calculated value of D	Calculated value of W_1
1	489.45	1.54	77.31	101.78	295.26	27.48	31.80
2	0.16	0.94	77.17	103.84	293.99	20.18	11.49
3	0.36	0.96	77.08	105.03	293.49	21.80	13.36
4	0.50	0.97	77.03	105.89	293.13	22.22	13.87
5	0.788	0.991	77.01	106.18	293.17	22.78	14.34
6	0.846	0.993	76.99	106.41	293.14	22.84	14.75
7	0.951	0.997	77.00	106.51	293.17	22.95	14.93
8	0.943	0.996	76.99	106.62	293.13	22.94	14.92
9	0.983	0.998	76.98	106.69	293.11	22.97	14.99
10	0.976	0.997	76.98	106.75	293.08	22.97	14.97
11	0.992	0.999	76.98	106.79	293.06	22.99	14.998

Reproduced by permission of *Hydrocarbon Processing & Petroleum Refiner*

TABLE 7-5 Solution of Example 7-3

Trial number	θ_0	θ_1	θ_2	Temp. of D, °F	Temp. of W_1, °F	Temp. of W_2, °F	Temp. of B, °F	Calculated value of D	Calculated value of W_1	Calculated value of W_2
1	156.78	1.30	7.84	77.64	114.40	238.07	354.72	26.78	23.39	31.96
2	0.47	1.08	0.61	77.46	112.48	253.54	350.39	22.88	13.00	24.69
3	0.64	1.04	0.76	77.34	111.52	262.87	347.12	22.94	13.84	24.54
4	0.78	1.02	0.85	77.27	111.06	267.20	345.45	22.95	14.31	24.84
5	0.93	1.01	0.96	77.22	110.74	268.56	344.96	23.04	14.73	23.42
6	0.94	1.01	0.96	77.19	110.60	269.16	344.73	23.00	14.81	24.04
7	0.980	1.004	0.988	77.17	110.52	269.34	344.67	23.01	14.93	25.01
8	0.984	1.002	0.986	77.16	110.50	269.41	344.63	23.00	15.22	25.04
9	1.000	1.000	1.000	77.15	110.48	269.40	344.60	23.00	14.98	25.01

Reproduced by permission of *Hydrocarbon Processing & Petroleum Refiner*

TABLE 7-6 Final flow rates for Examples 7-1, 7-2, and 7-3

Component	Example 7-1	Example 7-2		Example 7-3		
	d	d	w_1	d	w_1	w_2
CH_4	0.2000×10	0.1973×10	0.2653×10^{-1}	0.1974×10	0.2612×10^{-1}	0.1950×10^{-10}
C_2H_6	0.1000×10^2	0.9079×10	0.9207	0.9106×10	0.8947	0.2136×10^{-4}
C_3H_6	0.6930×10	0.3758×10	0.3150×10	0.3782×10	0.3000×10	0.2163
C_3H_8	0.1795×10^2	0.8135×10	0.9554×10	0.8048×10	0.8931×10	0.1994×10
$i\text{-}C_4$	0.7398	0.3961×10^{-1}	0.6545	0.6284×10^{-1}	0.9640	0.3333×10
$n\text{-}C_4$	0.3810	0.1478×10^{-1}	0.6917	0.2687×10^{-1}	0.1159×10	0.1354×10^{-2}
$n\text{-}C_5$	0.4181×10^{-4}	0.1152×10^{-5}	0.3168×10^{-2}	0.2083×10^{-5}	0.5130×10^{-2}	0.4365×10
$n\text{-}C_6$	0.1025×10^{-9}	0.9654×10^{-12}	0.1248×10^{-6}	0.3728×10^{-11}	0.4194×10^{-6}	0.1121×10
$n\text{-}C_7$	0.2126×10^{-14}	0.1021×10^{-16}	0.7047×10^{-10}	0.5243×10^{-16}	0.3049×10^{-9}	0.2826
$n\text{-}C_8$	0.1983×10^{-19}	0.1283×10^{-21}	0.6586×10^{-13}	0.2865×10^{-20}	0.1200×10^{-11}	0.1350
360	0.3311×10^{-25}	0.4096×10^{-28}	0.1956×10^{-15}	0.1274×10^{-26}	0.4476×10^{-14}	0.2989×10^{-1}

Reproduced by permission of *Hydrocarbon Processing & Petroleum Refiner*

Illustrative Examples

The statements and solutions of three illustrative examples taken from the work of Lyster *et al.* (3) are given in Tables 7–2 through 7–6. Example 7–1 has two feeds while Example 7–2 has in addition a side-stream withdrawn above the upper feed plate. Example 7–3 has two feeds and two side-streams. The side-stream W_1 is withdrawn above the upper feed plate and the side-stream W_2 is withdrawn below the lower feed plate. The temperatures were determined by use of the bubble point procedure and the vapor rates were calculated by use of the conventional method for making enthalpy balances. Both of the forcing procedures stated in Chapter 5 were applied. The temperatures shown in Tables 7–3 through 7–6 were obtained by averaging.

It should be mentioned that no particular effort was made to select good initial values for the temperatures and vapor rates. For all examples a linear variation of the temperature profile (80 and 450°F) was assumed in order to make the first trial. An overhead vapor rate of $V_1 = 94.8$ was specified for all examples. For the first two trials the remaining vapor rates throughout the column were held constant either at this value or at the appropriate one obtained by taking into account the thermal condition of each feed and the specified flow rate of each side-stream. Corresponding to these vapor rates, the liquid rates employed were those required for material balance. After the first two trials, the vapor and liquid rates were calculated by enthalpy balances (conventional method).

In general it appears that the rate of convergence increases as the number of side-streams is increased.

ABSORBERS WITH REBOILERS

A diagram of the particular unit considered by Canik *et al.* (1) and Canik (2) is shown in Figure 7–6. Applications of columns of this type have been discussed by Treybal (6). Recently McNeese (4) used the θ-method of convergence in the treatment of a stripper-stabilizer problem in which both W and F were equal to zero. The unit shown in Figure 7–6 is a special case of a complex column which has two feeds, F and L_0, and three withdrawals, B, W_1, and V_1. This unit may be considered as a complex column without a rectifying section; that is, one without any plates above the top feed plate.

For the reboiler-absorber shown in Figure 7–6, Canik (2) found that round-off error is minimized by the same general procedure which was proposed for complex columns. Below the lower feed plate f, the flow rates for the distributed components are computed by use of material balances that include the bottom of the column and any given plate j. Between the feed plates 1 and f, the rates are calculated both by material balances that include the top of the column as well as by balances that enclose the bottom of the column. That set of rates is retained which possesses the minimum round-off error as determined by the ratio test.

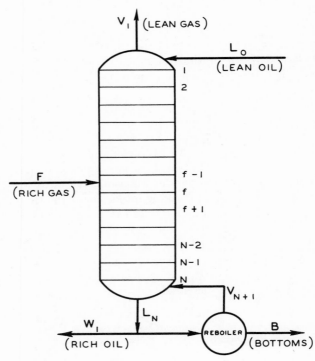

Figure 7–6. Absorber with a reboiler and a side-stream. (Reproduced by permission of *Hydrocarbon Processing & Petroleum Refiner*)

When the feed F contains a large percentage of lights and the feed L_0 contains a large percentage of heavies, the system becomes very sensitive to the procedures employed for the determination temperatures as well as the method employed for making enthalpy balances. Canik *et al.* (1) showed that the bubble point procedure could be used for all problems, provided the change in the temperature between successive trials is restricted as shown previously for complex columns. The possibility of using direct-iteration and bubble points was investigated. However, for one of the problems treated in this way, convergence could not be obtained unless the thermal condition of the feed plate f was fixed so that large amounts of the lightest component appeared below this plate. It was concluded that, qualitatively, the tendency of a system to converge is promoted by the presence of very light components, provided they are distributed throughout the system. The latter condition is seldom realized for any column with a feed plate located at an intermediate position between the top and the bottom of a column. However, the combination of the θ-method and the bubble point procedure (with suitable restrictions on the change in the temperatures between successive trials) gave a solution to these problems, and it is recommended for the treatment of reboiler-absorbers.

Many problems were found that diverged when the conventional method for making enthalpy balances was employed. Solutions to these problems could be obtained by use of a combination of the conventional and the Q-methods. Unfortunately, these solutions were not the ones desired because they required the use of a large number of intercoolers and heaters for problems which had adiabatic solutions. The adiabatic solutions were obtained by application of the constant-composition and Q-methods. In fact, this combination appeared to always give either the adiabatic solution or the one with the minimum number of intercoolers and heaters. The results obtained by each of the methods are illustrated by the solution of Examples 7–4 and 7–5 (see Tables 7–7 through 7–9) which were taken from the work of Canik *et al.* (1). In the solution of Example 7–4, a combination of the conventional and Q-methods was employed, whereas for Example 7–5 the combination of the constant-composition and Q-methods was used. These examples differ only in the specifications for the maximum and minimum allowable vapor rates. A smaller variation was required for Example 7–4 in order to obtain a final temperature profile within the range of the curve-fits. Even so, the temperature of one of the plates is seen to be at the lower limit.

TABLE 7-7 Statements and specifications for Examples 7–4 and 7–5

Component	FX	$L_0 x_0$	Specifications
CH_4	80.000000	0.0	$N = 9$, $f = 6$, $V_1 = 95$, $W_1 = 15$, and column pressure $= 400$ psia. The feed F enters as a dew point vapor and the oil L_0 as a liquid at 90°F. For Example 7–4 calculate the total flow rates by use of a combination of enthalpy balances subject to the following restrictions: for $j < f$, $V_{min} = 95 \leq V_j \leq 100 = V_{max}$, and for $j \geq f$, $V_{min} = 45 \leq V_j \leq 55 = V_{max}$. In Example 7–5 the constant-composition and θ-methods are to be employed with the following restrictions: for $1 < j < f$, $V_{min} = 80 \leq V_j \leq 200 = V_{max}$, and for $j \geq f$, $V_{min} = 10 \leq V_j \geq 100 = V_{max}$. Use the equilibrium and enthalpy data given in Tables A–5 and A–8 of the Appendix.
C_2H_6	6.6666666	0.0	
C_3H_8	6.6666666	0.0	
$n\text{-}C_4$	6.6666666	0.0	
$n\text{-}C_8$	6.6666666	30.0	

Reproduced by permission of *Hydrocarbon Processing & Petroleum Refiner*

TABLE 7–8 Solution of Example 7–4 by use of a combination of the conventional and Q-methods for making enthalpy balances

Plate No.	Temp. °F Trial No.		Vapor rates Trial No.			Q_j Trial No.		Final flow rates (Trial No. 27)		
	7*	27	Initial profile	7	27	7	27	Component	v_i	w_i
1	204.4	218.4	95.0	95.0	95.0	-1.5×10^5	-3.6×10^5	CH_4	78.998	1.32×10^{-4}
2	148.1	119.7	97.5	95.0	95.0	1.8×10^4	2.9×10^5	C_2H_6	6.62	3.44×10^{-2}
3	157.4	194.1	97.5	100.0	100.0	7.3×10^3	-6.4×10^4	C_3H_8	4.81	1.26
4	184.0	196.9	97.5	100.0	96.8	-7.3×10^4	-2.5×10^5	$n\text{-}C_4$	0.38	3.75
5	40.0	40.0	97.5	95.0	95.0	3.8×10^5	6.8×10^5	$n\text{-}C_8$	3.18	9.94
6	232.3	202.4	50.0	47.6	45.0	-2.0×10^5	-3.1×10^5			
7	291.8	270.0	50.0	47.6	55.0	-1.9×10^5	-1.4×10^5			
8	352.9	327.1	50.0	55.0	55.0	-2.4×10^5	0.0			
9	428.0	407.8	50.0	55.0	53.6	-2.6×10^5	-8.2×10^4			
10	483.4	475.5	50.0	55.0	55.0	-2.2×10^5	-7.6×10^5			

V_1 (Calculated)   95.57   95.29

W_1 (Calculated)   14.67   14.87

θ_0 1.158   1.067

θ_1 1.163   1.064

* Initial temperature profile was linear between 240 and 465°F with plate number. The variation of the temperatures employed for successive trials (exclusive of the first) was restricted to $\frac{1}{4}$.

Reproduced by permission of *Hydrocarbon Processing & Petroleum Refiner*

TABLE 7-9 Solution of Example 7-9 by use of a combination of the constant-composition and Q-methods

| | Temperatures, vapor rates and intercooler (or heater) duties | | | | | | | | Final flow rates (Trial No. 27) | |
| | Temp. °F Trial No. | | | Vapor rates Trial No. | | | | | | |
Plate No.	7*	17	27	Initial profile	7	17	27	Component	v_1	w_1
1	148.1	131.0	139.4	95.0	95.0	95.0	95.0	CH$_4$	79.999	8.270×10^{-4}
2	158.6	148.3	147.2	97.5	108.4	107.2	106.8	C$_2$H$_6$	6.655	8.777×10^{-3}
3	159.7	157.4	157.2	97.5	113.6	110.9	110.5	C$_3$H$_8$	6.267	0.2817
4	152.1	160.8	161.1	97.5	115.8	113.3	113.1	n-C$_4$	1.511	3.203
5	146.6	156.3	156.3	97.5	117.4	115.6	115.6	n-C$_8$	0.5667	11.506
6	270.4	267.3	268.3	50.0	20.0	21.1	21.4			
7	316.2	329.8	331.3	50.0	46.2	56.0	57.0			
8	377.3	392.4	394.2	50.0	60.4	66.2	67.0			
9	446.5	454.4	455.5	50.0	64.4	68.7	70.0			
10	492.5	494.9	495.3	50.0	79.1	83.3	84.6			
V_1 (Calculated)	94.79	94.97	94.996	94.996						
W_1 (Calculated)	14.94	14.98	14.996	14.996						
θ_0	0.914	0.984	0.998							
θ_1	0.933	0.989	0.990							

All intercoolers (or heater) duties were zero except the reboiler duty which was 9.84×10^5 Btu's per hour for Trial No. 27.

* Initial temperature profile was linear between 240 and 465°F with plate number. The variation of the temperatures employed for successive trials (exclusive of the first) was restricted to $\frac{1}{4}$.

Reproduced by permission of *Hydrocarbon Processing & Petroleum Refiner*

NOTATION

(See Chapters 2 through 6)

PROBLEMS

7–1 (a) Beginning with the same basic postulates stated in Chapter 4 and the requirement that the specifications, D, W_1, and W_2 are to be satisfied, develop Equations (7–1), (7–2), and (7–3).

(b) On the basis of the same postulates and requirements, obtain the results given by Equations (7–5), and (7–6) through (7–8).

7–2 Show that for the case where a side-stream W_1 is withdrawn in addition to the distillate and bottoms, the partial derivatives of the g-functions have the following values.

(a)
$$\frac{\partial g_0}{\partial \theta_0} = - \sum_{i \neq H,L} \frac{(b_i/d_i)_{ca}(d_i)^2_{co}}{FX_i}$$

(b)
$$\frac{\partial g_0}{\partial \theta_1} = - \sum_{i \neq H,L} \frac{(w_{1i}/d_i)_{ca}(d_i)^2_{co}}{FX_i}$$

(c)
$$\frac{\partial g_1}{\partial \theta_0} = - \sum_{i \neq H,L} \frac{\theta_1(w_{1i}/d_i)_{ca}(b_i/d_i)_{ca}(d_i)^2_{co}}{FX_i}$$

(d)
$$\frac{\partial g_1}{\partial \theta_1} = \sum_{i \neq H,L} \frac{(w_{1i}/d_i)_{ca}[1 + \theta_0(b_i/d_i)_{ca}](d_i)^2_{co}}{FX_i}$$

7–3 Develop Equations (7–12) and (7–13).

7–4 Develop Equations (7–14) and (7–16).

7–5 Verify the formulas given by Equations (7–20) and (7–21).

7–6 Verify the result given by Equation (7–28).

7–7 (a) Develop the material balances for the reboiler-absorber shown in Figure 7–6.

(b) Show that the set of component-material balances which enclose the bottom of the reboiler-absorber and every plate j may be solved to give

$$\frac{b_i}{v_{1i}} = \frac{Z_i}{\phi_i(v_{fi}/b_i) + C_{1i}(\Phi_i - Z_i)}$$

where

$$\phi_i = S_{1i}S_{2i}\ldots S_{f-2,i}S_{f-1,i}$$

$$\Phi_i = 1 + S_{1i} + S_{1i}S_{2i} + \ldots + S_{1i}S_{2i}\ldots S_{f-2,i}S_{f-1,i}$$

$$Z_i = \frac{\Phi_i FX_i + l_{0i} - \phi_i v_{Fi}}{FX_i + l_{0i}}$$

(c) Show that the set of material balances corresponding to matching at the feed plate f may be combined with an over-all material balance to yield.

$$\frac{b_i}{v_{1i}} = \frac{\omega_i + z_i}{(v_{fi}/b_i) + C_{1i}(\Omega_i - z_i)}$$

where

$$\omega_i = A_{1i}A_{2i}\ldots A_{f-2,i}A_{f-1,i}$$

$$\Omega_i = 1 + A_{f-2,i} + A_{f-2,i}A_{f-3,i} + \ldots + A_{f-2i}\ldots A_{1i}$$

$$z_i = \frac{\Omega_i FX_{Fi} - v_{Fi}}{FX_i + l_{0i}}$$

(d) The formulas given in parts (b) and (c) were found by Canik (2) to be almost independent of round-off error. In view of this and the fact that the reboiler-absorber may be regarded as a complex column with two feeds (F, L_0), how should the equations obtained in parts (a), (b), and (c) be applied in order to minimize round-off error?

7-8 Tomme (5) has shown that it is always possible to find a positive set of θ's that make all of the functions go to zero for a column having one side-stream. By use of the following outline, construct the proof of the existence of a positive set of θ's such that $g_0 = g_1 = 0$, simultaneously, for a column with one side-stream. It is also to be understood that D and W_1 are specified positive numbers such that $D + W_1 < F$; that is, $F = D + W_1 + B$, where $B > 0$.

Step (1): Construct the graphs for g_0 and g_1 in the neighborhood where both θ_0 and θ_1 are positive. Let the values of g_0 and g_1 be represented by the vertical direction. From these graphs, show that the traces of g_0 and g_1 in the $\theta_1\theta_0$ plane are of the following general form.

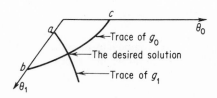

Figure P7-8

The curve formed by the intersection of the surfaces g_0 and g_1 with the $\overline{\theta_1\theta_0}$ plane are called traces. In order for a point of intersection to always exist, it is necessary for the traces to exist.

Step (2): In order to prove that g_0 always has a trace, the following approach may be employed. First, show that a θ_0 namely, $\theta_0 = c$ exists such that

$$g_0(\theta_0, 0) = 0$$

and a θ_1 (denoted by $\theta_1 = b$) exists such that

$$g_0(0, \theta_1) = 0$$

Begin each of these proofs by showing that

$$g_0(0, 0) = F - D = B + W_1 > 0$$

and then make use of the values obtained for g_0 as θ_0 and θ_1 are allowed to increase without bound. Then show that for any positive value of $\theta_0 < c$, the value of θ_1 required to make $g_0 = 0$ is less than b.

Step (3): In order to prove that g_1 always has a trace, show that for any value of $\theta_0 > 0$,

$$g_1(\theta_0, 0) = -W_1$$

Then show that for any fixed, finite value of $\theta_0 > 0$,

$$\lim_{\theta_1 \to \infty} g_1(\theta_0, \theta_1) = F - W_1 = D + B$$

Step (4): In order to prove that a point of intersection exists for every pair of functions, it is sufficient to show that

$$a < b$$

In order to prove this, verify the following relationships and then employ them as required.

$$|\, g_0(0, 0) \,| = B + W_1$$

$$|\, g_1(0, 0) \,| = W_1$$

$$\left|\frac{\partial g_0(0, \theta_1)}{\partial \theta_1}\right| = \left|\frac{\partial g_1(0, \theta_1)}{\partial \theta_1}\right|$$

LITERATURE CITED

1. Canik, L. J., B. W. Hardy, C. D. Holland, and H. L. Bauni, "Figure Separations This New Way: Part 7—Absorbers With Reboilers," *Petroleum Refiner*, **40**, No. 12, 161 (1961).

2. Canik, L. J., "Use of Computers for Making Multicomponent Distillation Calculations for Reboiler-Absorbers," M.S. thesis, A. and M. College of Texas, College Station, Texas, 1961.

3. Lyster, W. N., S. L. Sullivan, Jr., D. S. Billingsley, and C. D. Holland, "Figure Distillation This New Way: Part 3—Consider Multi-Feed Columns with Side-Streams," *Petroleum Refiner*, **38,** No. 10, 139 (1959).

4. McNeese, C. R., "The Solution of Stripper-Stabilizer Problems by Use of Digital Computers," presented at the 38th Annual Convention of the N.G.A.A. at Dallas, Texas, April 1959.

5. Tomme, W. J., "A Convergence Method for Distillation Systems," Ph.D. dissertation, A. and M. College of Texas, College Station, Texas, 1963.

6. Treybal, R. E., *Mass Transfer Operations* (New York: McGraw-Hill Book Company, Inc., 1955), p. 250.

7. Weisenfelder, A. J., C. D. Holland, and R. H. Johnston, "Figure Separations This New Way: Part 6—Minimization of Round-Off Errors and Other Developments," *Petroleum Refiner*, **40,** No. 10, 175 (1961).

8. Weisenfelder, A. J., "Minimization of Round-Off Error and Treatment of Single Phase and Separated Components in Conventional and Complex Columns," M.S. thesis, A. and M. College of Texas, College Station, Texas, 1961.

Absorbers* and Strippers

8

Although these units constitute special cases of complex columns, a chapter is devoted to them because most of the problems occasionally met in the solution of complex units are generally encountered in the solution of absorber and stripper problems. These units are like complex columns in that they may be regarded as that section of a complex column enclosed by two feed plates.

The procedures proposed for the treatment of absorbers and strippers is about the same as that recommended for complex columns. Round-off error is minimized by use of the ratio test, whereas flow rates are determined by a combination of the constant-composition and Q-methods and temperatures are calculated by use of the bubble point procedure. Details of the application of these procedures follow first for absorbers and then for strippers.

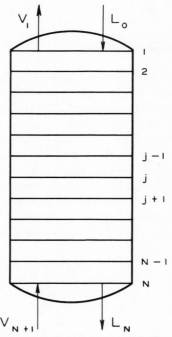

Figure 8–1. Absorber (or stripper).

ABSORBERS

The material balance equations are similar to those given by Franklin and Horton (1), Kremser (5), Souders and Brown (7), and Thiele and Geddes. A diagram of the particular unit considered here is shown in Figure 8–1. A calcula-

* A summary of this work was presented in a paper by H. L. Bauni (Humble Oil & Refining Co.) at the Machine Computation Special Workshop Session on Multicomponent Distillation at the 44th National Meeting of the A.I.Ch.E. in New Orleans, February 27, 1961.

tional procedure and convergence method differing in some respects from the one proposed here was recently suggested by McNeese (6).

In the basic calculational procedure proposed for absorbers, it is supposed that the following specifications have been made: the number of plates, the compositions and rates of flow of the lean oil and rich gas, the column pressure, the lean gas rate V_1 (or the rich oil rate L_N), and the enthalpy of either the lean oil or the rich gas. On the basis of these specifications, the product distribution and the enthalpy of the rich gas (or lean oil) is to be determined. In the extension of the θ-method, the constant-composition, and the Q-methods to absorbers, Hardy (2, 3) used this set of specifications because it corresponds closely to those used for conventional and complex columns. The specifications of V_1 for the absorber corresponds to the specification of D for the column, and the determination of the enthalpy of L_0 for the absorber corresponds to the determination of the overhead condenser duty for the distillation column. Other types of specifications, some of which are presented here, have been investigated by Wetherold (8).

Material Balances

As shown in Figure 8–1, the plates of the absorbers are numbered down from the top; the top plate is assigned the number "1" and the bottom plate the number "N." The lean oil entering the top plate is identified by the subscript "zero," and the rich gas entering the N'th plate by the subscript "$N + 1$." The components are numbered in the order of decreasing volatility; the most volatile is given the number 1 and the least volatile the number c, where c is also equal to the total number of components. Material balances may enclose either the top or the bottom of the column and any given plate. For any component i that appears in both the vapor and liquid phases, a material balance around the top of the absorber and plate $(j - 1)$ is represented by

$$\frac{v_{ji}}{v_{1i}} = A_{j-1,i}\left(\frac{v_{j-1,i}}{v_{1i}}\right) + \left(1 - \frac{l_{0i}}{v_{1i}}\right), \quad 2 \leqq j \leqq N + 1 \qquad (8\text{--}1)$$

Before this equation may be applied, it is necessary to evaluate the quantity $(1 - l_{0i}/v_{1i})$. After l_{Ni}/v_{1i} and v_{1i} have been determined, the value of $(1 - l_{0i}/v_{1i})$ is obtained by means of an over-all material balance. Repeated substitution of the expression for v_{ji}/v_{1i} into the one for $v_{j+1,i}/v_{1i}$ as given by Equation (8–1) yields

$$\frac{v_{N+1,i}}{v_{1i}} = \omega_i + \Omega_i\left(1 - \frac{l_{0i}}{v_{1i}}\right) \qquad (8\text{--}2)$$

where

$$\omega_i = A_{Ni}A_{N-1,i}\ldots A_{2i}A_{1i}$$

$$\Omega_i = 1 + A_{Ni} + A_{Ni}A_{N-1,i} + \ldots + A_{Ni}A_{N-1,i}\ldots A_{3i}A_{2i}$$

An over-all balance is represented as follows:

$$1 + \frac{l_{Ni}}{v_{1i}} = \frac{l_{0i}}{v_{1i}} + \frac{v_{N+1,i}}{v_{1i}} \tag{8-3}$$

When Equations (8–2) and (8–3) are solved for l_{Ni}/v_{1i}, the desired result,

$$\frac{l_{Ni}}{v_{1i}} = \frac{\omega_i l_{0i} + (\Omega_i + \omega_i - 1)v_{N+1,i}}{\Omega_i l_{0i} + v_{N+1,i}} \tag{8-4}$$

is obtained. The corresponding value of v_{1i} is obtained by rearranging Equation (8–3) to the following form.

$$v_{1i} = \frac{l_{0i} + v_{N+1,i}}{1 + (l_{Ni}/v_{1i})} \tag{8-5}$$

When the material balances enclose the bottom of the column and any given plate, the following equations are obtained:

$$\frac{l_{j-1,i}}{l_{Ni}} = S_{ji}\left(\frac{l_{ji}}{l_{Ni}}\right) + \left(1 - \frac{v_{N+1,i}}{l_{Ni}}\right), \quad 1 \leq j \leq N \tag{8-6}$$

and

$$\frac{l_{Ni}}{v_{1i}} = \frac{l_{0i} + \Phi_i v_{N+1,i}}{(\Phi_i + \phi_i - 1)l_{0i} + \phi_i v_{N+1,i}} \tag{8-7}$$

where

$$\phi_i = S_{1i}S_{2i}\ldots S_{N-1,i}S_{Ni}$$

$$\Phi_i = 1 + S_{1i} + S_{1i}S_{2i} + S_{1i}S_{2i}S_{3i} + \ldots + S_{1i}S_{2i}\ldots S_{N-2,i}S_{N-1,i}$$

Equations (8–1) through (8–7) imply that V_{N+1} enters the column as a vapor either at its dew point at the column pressure or at some higher temperature and that L_0 enters either at its bubble point at the column pressure or at some lower temperature. If either of these streams is a two-phase mixture, it may be handled in the same manner as that shown in Chapters 3 and 7 for partially vaporized feeds.

In the same manner as shown in Chapter 3 for b_i/d_i, the two expressions for l_{Ni}/v_{1i} are shown to be equivalent. Also, the flow rates given by Equations (8–1) and (8–6) are equivalent. In practice the material balances (Equations (8–1) and (8–6)) are subject to round-off error, whereas Equations (8–4) and (8–7) are almost independent of this source of error.

Round-Off Error

In order to demonstrate the effect of round-off error, Hardy *et al.* (3) solved several simple examples which are presented in Table 8–1. For all cases considered, it was found that Equations (8–4) and (8–7) gave values of l_{Ni}/v_{1i} to within seven or eight digits out of a possible eight. The value of l_{Ni}/v_{1i} obtained by use of either Equations (8–4) or (8–7) is denoted by the subscript "formula." Values of l_{Ni}/v_{1i} were also found by the step-by-step application of Equations (8–1) and (8–6), and denoted by the subscript "step-by-step." The results given in Table 8–1 are seen to support the use of the procedure by which the flow rates are determined by both Equations (8–1) and (8–6) and the best set selected by use of the ratio test.

Convergence Method

For a system containing any number of single phase lights and single phase heavies, denoted by the subscripts "L" and "H," respectively, the θ-method of convergence consists of the application of the following set of equations. The development of these equations, which is similar to that shown in Chapter 6 has been presented by Hardy *et al.* (3). The compositions are calculated as follows:

$$y_{ji} = \left(\frac{V_j - \sum_L v_{jL}}{V_j} \right) \frac{(v_{ji}/v_{1i})_{ca}(v_{1i})_{co}}{\sum_{i \neq H,L} (v_{ji}/v_{1i})_{ca}(v_{1i})_{co}}, \quad i \neq H, L \qquad (8\text{–}8a)$$

$$y_j = \frac{v_{jL}}{V_j} \qquad (8\text{–}8b)$$

$$x_{ji} = \left(\frac{L_j - \sum_H l_{j,H}}{L_j} \right) \frac{(l_{ji}/l_{Ni})_{ca}(l_{Ni})_{co}}{\sum_{i \neq H,L} (l_{ji}/l_{Ni})_{ca}(l_{Ni})_{co}}, \quad i \neq H, L \qquad (8\text{–}8c)$$

$$x_{jH} = \frac{l_{jH}}{L_j} \qquad (8\text{–}8d)$$

Although the rates of flow of the single phase components are constant throughout the column (for columns in which streams are introduced and withdrawn only at the ends), the subscript j was retained in Equation (8–8) for the sake of generality. When the V_j's and L_j's are all unknown except for the specified values of the terminal flow rates, V_1, V_{N+1}, L_0 and

TABLE 8-1 Round-off error given by different calculational procedures for absorbers

(For all cases shown $N = 10$ and A remains constant throughout the column.)

Case No.	l_0 and v_{N+1}	Absorption factor A	$\dfrac{(l_N/v_1)_{\text{step-by-step}} \text{ by Eq. (8-1)}}{(l_N/v_1)_{\text{formula}}}$ *	$\dfrac{(l_N/v_1)_{\text{step-by-step}} \text{ by Eq. (8-6)}}{(l_N/v_1)_{\text{formula}}}$
1	$l_0 = 0$†	0.1	1.0000	0.9000
2	$l_0 = 0$	10.0	1.0000	0.9000
3	$v_{N+1} = l_0/2$	0.1	1.0000	2.9000
4	$v_{N+1} = l_0$	0.1	1.0000	1.9000
5	$v_{N+1} = 2l_0$	0.1	1.0000	1.4000
6	$v_{N+1} = 0$	0.1	1.1111	1.0000
7	$v_{N+1} = 0$	10.0	1.1111	1.0000
8	$v_{N+1} = l_0/2$	10.0	0.7143	1.0000
9	$v_{N+1} = l_0$	10.0	0.5263	1.0000
10	$v_{N+1} = 2l_0$	10.0	0.3448	1.0000
11	$v_{N+1} = 0$	9.9999999	−109.999	1.0000
12	$v_{N+1} = l_0$	1.0	1.0000	1.0000

* Value of (l_N/v_1) given by Equation (8-4) [or Equation (8-7)].
† Component enters the column only in v_{N+1}.

Reproduced by permission of *Hydrocarbon Processing & Petroleum Refiner*

L_N, the unknown rates in the expressions for the mole fractions should be estimated by use of the following formulas.

$$V_j = \sum_{i \neq H, L} \left(\frac{v_{ji}}{v_{1i}}\right)_{ca} (v_{1i})_{co} + \sum_{L} v_{jL} \tag{8-9}$$

$$L_j = \sum_{i \neq H, L} \left(\frac{l_{ji}}{l_{Ni}}\right)_{ca} (l_{Ni})_{co} + \sum_{H} l_{jH} \tag{8-10}$$

However, except when they are specified, the values of V_j and L_j to be employed in the calculation of the A_j's and S_j's are those obtained from the enthalpy balances.

Again for any volatile component

$$\left(\frac{l_{Ni}}{v_{1i}}\right)_{co} = \theta \left(\frac{l_{Ni}}{v_{1i}}\right)_{ca}, \quad i \neq H, L \tag{8-11}$$

where it is required that the corrected rates satisfy the specification V_1 and the over-all material balance

$$(v_{1i})_{co} + (l_{Ni})_{co} = l_{0i} + v_{N+1,i}, \quad i \neq H, L \tag{8-12}$$

Equations (8–11) and (8–12) are readily combined to give the expression for $(v_{1i})_{co}$; namely,

$$(v_{1i})_{co} = \frac{l_{0i} + v_{N+1,i}}{1 + \theta(l_{Ni}/v_{1i})_{ca}}, \quad i \neq H, L \tag{8-13}$$

The quantity θ is the positive root of the function $g(\theta)$ where

$$g(\theta) = \sum_{i \neq H, L} (v_{1i})_{co} - \left(V_1 - \sum_{L} v_{1,L}\right) \tag{8-14}$$

Because of the correspondence between the specification of V_1 for an absorber and the specification of D for a distillation column, the former was selected for the statement of the convergence method. Other specifications are considered in a subsequent section.

Outline of the Development of the Equations Representing the Convergence Method

Except for a more general set of postulates, the development is analogous to that shown previously for conventional columns. Again suppose that the V_j's and L_j's be fixed for each plate by use of appropriate intercoolers (or heaters), and find sets of corrected rates that satisfy the specified values of all of the V_j's and L_j's. In addition the terminal set of corrected rates must be in component-material balance. Let σ_j and τ_j be defined by

$$(v_{ji})_{co} = \sigma_j \left(\frac{v_{ji}}{v_{1i}}\right)_{ca} (v_{1i})_{co}, \qquad i \neq H, L, \tag{8-15}$$

$$1 \leq j \leq N$$

$$(l_{ji})_{co} = \tau_j \left(\frac{l_{ji}}{l_{Ni}}\right)_{ca} (l_{Ni})_{co}, \qquad i \neq H, L, \tag{8-16}$$

$$1 \leq j \leq N$$

For $j = 0$ and $j = N + 1$, more general definitions are permitted for σ and τ in that only the ratio of $(\sigma_{N+1,i}/\tau_{0i})$ need be taken independent of i; that is,

$$(v_{N+1,i})_{co} = \sigma_{N+1,i} \left(\frac{v_{N+1,i}}{v_{1i}}\right)_{ca} (v_{1i})_{co}, \quad i \neq H, L \tag{8-17}$$

$$(l_{0i})_{co} = \tau_{0i} \left(\frac{l_{0i}}{l_{Ni}}\right)_{ca} (l_{Ni})_{co}, \quad i \neq H, L \tag{8-18}$$

The corrected component rates are defined as the sets whose sums are in agreement with the specifications:

$$V_j - \sum_L v_{jL} \quad \text{and} \quad L_j - \sum_H l_{jH}$$

These conditions are satisfied when σ_j and τ_j are selected so that

$$V_j = \sum_{i \neq H, L} \sigma_j \left(\frac{v_{ji}}{b_{1i}}\right)_{ca} (v_{1i})_{co} + \sum_L v_{jL}, \quad 1 \leq j \leq N \tag{8-19}$$

$$L_j = \sum_{i \neq H, L} \tau_j \left(\frac{l_{ji}}{l_{Ni}}\right)_{ca} (l_{Ni})_{co} + \sum_H l_{jH}, \quad 1 \leq j \leq N \tag{8-20}$$

The remainder of the development of the formulas for the convergence method follows closely that described in Chapters 4 and 7.

Calculational Procedure for Absorbers

The proposed procedure is based on the solution of a wide variety of numerical examples (2, 3). Because the change of K with temperature for a heavy oil is almost infinite, the use of dew points leads to a slow rate of convergence for most problems (2). On the other hand because the change of K with temperature for many relatively light components is almost zero, the use of bubble points and the θ-method tends to give overcorrections. However, since it is generally easier to dampen than it is to speed-up a convergence procedure, the use of the latter combination is recommended where it is applied as described in the following discussion

For systems with feeds containing up to about 50 or 60 per cent of a very light component, a combination of the θ-method and bubble points (with averaging) gives satisfactory results. Above 50 or 60 per cent lights, this combination tends to give corrections that are characterized by the calculation of temperature profiles and values of V_1 which are alternately too large and too small. The range of operation for the combination of the θ-method and bubble points may be extended by placing more severe restrictions than that represented by averaging on the variation of the temperature profiles for successive trials. For example, only one fourth of the calculated correction for the profile may be used.

Unlike the situation described for a reboiler-absorber, the light components always appear in significant amounts throughout an absorber. Hence the combination of direct-iteration ($\theta = 1$) and bubble points (with averaging) should be expected to give convergence for absorbers which contain a large percentage of lights. Hardy *et al.* (3) obtained very satisfactory results for such systems by use of this combination. However, for systems containing relatively smaller amounts of lights, this combination led to a slow rate of convergence, whereas the combination of the θ-method and bubble points (with averaging) gave rapid convergence. Thus the combination of direct-iteration and bubble points should be used only after it has been found that the combination of the θ-method and bubble points (with averaging or quartering) leads to bouncing as a result of an overcorrection. Of passing interest is the fact that the treatment of a light component as a single phase component reduces the convergence tendency exhibited by the system when the component is considered to be distributed between two phases.

For the calculation of the total flow rates throughout an absorber, a combination of the constant-composition and Q-methods is recommended. Very few solutions could be obtained by use of the conventional method for making enthalpy balances. Although solutions could be obtained by use of a combination of the conventional and Q-methods, they were seldom adiabatic. For the same problem, the combination of the constant-composition and Q-methods gave either adiabatic solutions or ones which appeared to possess a minimum of intercoolers or heaters. These methods are illustrated by Examples 8–1 and 8–2 (see Tables 8–2, 8–3, 8–4). In the statement of Example 8–2, a wide range of flow rates were permitted in order to increase the chances of obtaining an adiabatic solution by the combination of the constant-composition and Q-methods. However, when a combination of the conventional and Q-methods was used, the range of allow-

TABLE 8–2 Statements and specifications of absorber Examples 8–1 and 8–2

Component	v_{N+1}	l_0	Specifications
CH_4	70	0.0	For both examples: column pressure = 300 psia, $V_1 = 85$ and $N = 8$. Lean oil enters at 90°F. Use the equilibrium and enthalpy data given in Tables A–4 and A–8 of the Appendix. Use a combination of the conventional and Q-methods in the solution of Example 8–1 where the vapor rates are bounded as follows: $88 \leq V_j \leq 93$ $(1 < j < N + 1)$. Use a combination of the constant-composition and Q-methods in the solution of Example 8–2 where the vapor rates are bounded as follows: $$50 = V_{\min} \leq V_j \leq V_{\max} = 150, \ 2 \leq j \leq N.$$
C_2H_6	15	0.0	
C_3H_8	10	0.0	
n-C_4	4	0.0	
n-C_5	1	0.0	
n-C_8	0.0	20	

Reproduced by permission of *Hydrocarbon Processing & Petroleum Refiner*

Table 8–3 Solution of absorber Example 8–1 by use of a combination of the conventional and Q-methods for making enthalpy balances

	Temperatures, vapor rates and intercooler (or heater) duties						Q_j Trial No.		Final flow rates (Trial No. 28)		
	Temperature °F Trial No.			Vapor rates Trial No.		28		Component	v_1	l_N
Plate No.	Initial profile	7	28	Initial profile	28					
1	240	147.7	146.7	85.0	85	-1.4×10^5		CH_4	67.929	2.071
2	230	44.8	63.2	86.8	88	1.9×10^5		C_2H_6	12.132	2.868
3	220	40.0	118.9	88.7	93	3.0×10^4		C_3H_8	42.429×10^{-1}	5.757
4	210	134.8	195.6	90.6	93	-2.5×10^5		$n\text{-}C_4$	13.815×10^{-2}	3.862
5	200	69.2	93.6	92.5	88	2.8×10^5		$n\text{-}C_5$	19.887×10^{-6}	99.998×10^{-2}
6	190	133.3	191.9	94.3	93	-3.0×10^5		$n\text{-}C_8$	56.226×10^{-2}	19.438
7	180	76.6	70.0	96.2	88	1.8×10^5				
8	170	74.3	68.4	98.1	93	0.0				
V_1 (Calculated)		84.49	85.004							

Reproduced by permission of *Hydrocarbon Processing & Petroleum Refiner*

TABLE 8–4 Solution of absorber Example 8–2 by use of a combination of the constant-composition and Q-methods for making enthalpy balances

Plate No.	Temperature profiles Trial No.			Vapor rates Trial No.		Final flow rates (Trial No. 25)		
	Initial profile	7	25*	Initial profile	25	Component	V_1	l_N
1	240	105.2	107.6	85.0	85.0	CH_4	67.950	2.049
2	230	102.7	111.4	86.8	89.8	C_2H_6	12.282	2.717
3	220	101.2	112.4	88.7	90.5	C_3H_8	45.084×10^{-1}	5.491
4	210	99.8	112.1	90.6	90.7	$n\text{-}C_4$	83.566×10^{-3}	3.916
5	200	100.2	110.2	92.5	90.9	$n\text{-}C_5$	66.002×10^{-7}	1.000
6	190	101.4	105.8	94.3	91.2	$n\text{-}C_8$	17.451×10^{-2}	19.825
7	180	97.1	96.4	96.2	91.8			
8	170	74.3	74.3	98.1	93.1			
V_1 (Calculated)		84.42	84.9996					

* Profiles between successive trials agreed to within 4 digits.

Reproduced by permission of *Hydrocarbon Processing & Petroleum Refiner*

able vapor rates (Table 8–2) had to be reduced in order to obtain temperatures within the range of the curve fits. Also, in the examples shown, the variation of the vapor rates between successive trials was limited in the following manner. The first two trials were made on the basis of the same set of L/V's. For the next six trials, the vapor rates were restricted to 1.1 and $1/1.1$ times the value used to make the given trial calculation. For the next six trials the restrictions were 1.025 and $1/1.025$ and for all subsequent trials, the restrictions were 1.01 and $1/1.01$.

STRIPPERS

Formulas stated previously for absorbers are applicable to strippers provided the symbols are reinterpreted to have the following meanings. The stripping medium (usually steam) enters at the molal rate V_{N+1} at plate N (as shown in Figure 8–1) and leaves the top of the column with the rate V_1. The rich oil enters the top of the column at plate 1 at the molal rate L_0 and leaves plate N at the rate L_N.

The material balances are generally written around the bottom of the stripper and any given plate, Equation (8–6). As discussed previously, this minimizes round-off error provided all of the two-phase components enter only in L_0 and provided the stripping medium consists of a single phase light component. When the stripping medium contains two-phase components which also enter in L_0, round-off error is minimized by use of the ratio test as described for absorbers. Also, for the specification of V_1, the formulas for the convergence method are the same as those stated previously.

However, several significant differences between absorbers and strippers were found by Wetherold (8). Unlike absorbers, most of the stripper examples considered did not have adiabatic solutions provided the vapor rates were required to lie within reasonable limits. In all of the examples considered by Wetherold (8), he supposed that all of the entering steam remained in the vapor phase throughout the column. It might appear that the required heating duty could be introduced in the rich oil, L_0. However, as the value of T_0 was increased, the necessity of employing an intercooler on the top plate in order to obtain a liquid rate L_1 of sufficient magnitude to give a V_2 within the specified limits became apparent. In order to avoid the requirement of an intercooler, the temperature of the steam should be specified instead of the temperature of the lean oil. When this temperature (T_{N+1}) is specified, the requirement of an intercooler at the bottom of the column will generally be avoided because the enthalpy of the steam is usually much smaller over a given range of temperatures than the corresponding enthalpy of the rich oil, L_0. When T_{N+1} and V_1 are specified, the enthalpy balances are written around the bottom of the stripper and any given plate.

In the extension of the procedures for absorbers to strippers, certain modifications were required because of the relatively large percentage of steam in the vapor phase near the bottom of the column. The oscillation of the temperatures and vapor rates with trial number was attributed to the presence of steam because of the uncertainties it created. For the bottom plate the value of the quantity $(1 - y_{N,1})$ of the bubble point function is not only small but also uncertain until convergence is obtained. (In the following development, steam is assigned the component number 1, which is considered to be the only single phase component present in the column.) The quantity $y_{N,1} = V_{N+1}/V_N$ represents an approximation because the correct value of V_N is not known until convergence is obtained.

These oscillations were reduced to within the desired limits by finding a set of values for T_N and V_N which were in agreement with the equilibrium relationship as well as the material and enthalpy balances for the bottom plates. In these calculations, the temperature T_{N-1} of plate $N - 1$ is held fixed at the one obtained by use of the convergence method. Also, it is supposed that the temperature, T_{N+1}, and flow rate V_{N+1}, of the entering steam are specified and that L_N is known from the specifications. The corrected terminal rates, $(l_{Ni})_{co}$'s, are also held fixed at the values obtained by the convergence method for the last trial. Prior to the investigation of Wetherold (8), Johnston and co-workers (4) had used a procedure similar to the one presented here in the successful treatment of pipe stills and other units in which steam stripping was involved.

Two independent relationships are required in order to determine T_N and V_N. The first of these is the bubble point function, Equation (2–22), which may be regarded as a function of T_N and V_N and stated in the following form:

$$f(T_N, V_N) = \sum_{i\neq1} K_{Ni}x_{Ni} - \left(1 - \frac{V_{N+1}}{V_N}\right) \tag{8-21}$$

where for simplicity, the system was assumed to contain no single phase heavy components. The compositions (x_{Ni}'s) are those found by use of the convergence method; that is, $x_{Ni} = (l_{Ni})_{co}/L_N$. The second function is developed by commencing with an enthalpy balance for the bottom plate,

$$V_N H_N + L_n h_N = L_{N-1}h_{N-1} + V_{N+1}H_{N+1} \tag{8-22}$$

Since

$$V_N H_N = \sum_{i=1}^{c} v_{Ni}H_{Ni} = \sum_{i\neq1} H_{Ni}(l_{N-1,i} - l_{Ni}) + V_{N+1}H_{N,1}$$

$$= L_{N-1}H(x_{N-1})_N - L_N H(x_N)_N + V_{N+1}H_{N,1}$$

Equation (8–22) may be rearranged to the following form:

$$L_{N-1} = \frac{L_N[H(x_N)_N - h_N] + V_{N+1}[H_{N+1,1} - H_{N,1}]}{[H(x_{N-1})_N - h_{N-1}]} \qquad (8\text{–}23)$$

In view of the material balance,

$$V_N = L_{N-1} + V_{N+1} - L_N \qquad (8\text{–}24)$$

the unknown L_{N-1} is readily eliminated from Equation (8–23) to give upon rearrangement,

$$p(T_N, V_N) = \frac{L_N[H(x_N)_N - h_N] + V_{N+1}[H_{N+1,1} - H_{N,1}]}{[H(x_{N-1})_N - h_{N-1}]}$$
$$+ V_{N+1} - L_N - V_N \qquad (8\text{–}25)$$

Actually, the right-hand side of Equation (8–25) is a function of T_N and V_N alone only if $x_{N-1,i}$ is eliminated by use of the component-material balance for the bottom plate,

$$\left(\frac{l_{N-1,i}}{l_{Ni}}\right)_{ca} = S_{Ni} + 1$$

When this expression is combined with the definition of the mole fraction,

$$x_{N-1,i} = \frac{(l_{N-1,i}/l_{Ni})_{ca}(l_{Ni})_{co}}{\sum_{i \neq 1} (l_{N-1,i}/l_{Ni})_{ca}(l_{Ni})_{co}}$$

the following expression for $x_{N-1,i}$ as a function of T_N and V_N is obtained.

$$x_{N-1,i} = \frac{[(K_{Ni}V_N/L_N) + 1](l_{Ni})_{co}}{\sum_{i \neq 1} [(K_{Ni}V_N/L_N) + 1](l_{Ni})_{co}} \qquad (8\text{–}26)$$

Thus the problem reduces to finding the positive set of values for T_N and V_N that make $f(T_N, V_N) = p(T_N, V_N) = 0$, simultaneously. These values may be found by use of any one of several methods, two of which are Newton-Raphson and interpolation (*regula falsi*). Of these only the method of interpolation was applied to Equations (8–21) and (8–25). This method may be initiated by the selection of an arbitrary value of V_N denoted by $V_{N,1}$. Then the corresponding value of T_N that makes $f = 0$ is found. On the basis of this set of values for V_N and T_N, the value of the function p is determined and denoted by p_1. This procedure is repeated for another value of V_N denoted by $V_{N,2}$ to give p_2. The next best value of V_N is computed by the interpolation formula

$$V_{N,3} = \frac{p_2 V_{N,1} - p_1 V_{N,2}}{p_2 - p_1} \tag{8-27}$$

Using this value of V_N, the procedure described previously is repeated to give p_3. The next best value of V_N is found by interpolating between $(V_{N,2}, p_2)$ and $(V_{N,3}, p_3)$. This process is continued until values of V_N and T_N of the desired accuracy are found.

The determination of T_N and V_N was ordered in the calculational procedure as follows. After a given trial had been performed on the basis of an assumed set of L/V's and T's and the θ-method had been applied to give a corrected set of terminal rates, the temperatures throughout the column were determined by use of the bubble point procedure. Then a better set of values for T_N and V_N for the bottom plate were determined by the method described. Values of V_N as determined by Equation (8-27) were used to make the next trial calculation provided they satisfied the following inequality

$$V_{N+1} < V_N < V_{N-1} \tag{8-28}$$

For this comparison, the value of V_{N-1} used to make the previous trial calculation through the column was used. When values of V_N were calculated by Equation (8-27), which did not satisfy this inequality, the appropriate limiting value (V_{N+1} or V_{N-1}) was used for V_N and the corresponding temperature was computed by use of Equation (8-21). Then the required intercooler (or heater) duty was determined by enthalpy balance.

After the conditions at the bottom of the column had been determined, enthalpy balances were continued to the top of the column. In order to avoid solutions involving internal reflux, the vapor rates were limited as follows

$$(V_j)_{\min} = V_{N+1} + (N + 1 - j) \left[\frac{V_1 - V_{N+1}}{N} \right] \tag{8-29}$$

$$(V_j)_{\max} = V_1, \quad j < N \tag{8-30}$$

The usual forcing procedures were also employed. Except for the temperature T_N, each calculated temperature was averaged with the corresponding one employed to make the given trial calculation. This procedure was commenced at the end of the second trial. With regard to the variation of the vapor rates between successive trials, the following limits were employed for all plates except the bottom one. The first four trials were made on the basis of a fixed set of L/V's for all plates. For the next two trials the rates were restricted to 1.1 and 1/1.1 times the rate used to make the

TABLE 8-5 Statements of Examples 8-3 and 8-4

Component	l_0	Specifications
C_1	0.01	*Example 8-3:* Column pressure is 50 psia. The steam rate is 13.47, and it enters the column at 50 psia and 500°F. Also, V_1 is 23.67, and $N = 8$. Enthalpy balances are to be made by use of the constant-composition and Q-methods. T_N and V_N are to be determined each trial by use of Equations (8–21) and (8–25). The maximum and minimum vapor rates are as follows:
C_2	0.17	
C_3	1.30	
$n\text{-}C_4$	2.83	
$n\text{-}C_5$	1.75	$$23.67 \geq V_j \geq V_{N+1} + (N + 1 - j)\left[\frac{V_1 - V_{N+1}}{N}\right]$$
$n\text{-}C_6$	2.35	
$n\text{-}C_7$	2.55	*Example 8-4:* For this example $\sum_{i=1}^{7} v_{1i} = 21.44570$.
500	82.24	All other specifications are the same as those for example 8-3. The enthalpy and equilibrium data for both examples are to be taken from Tables A–1 and A–8 of Appendix. For steam: $H^{1/2} = -40.48668 + 0.48685187 T - 3.112164 T^2 \times 10^{-4}$, ($T$°R). Data for the curve fit were taken from page 279 of *Chemical Engineers Handbook,* 3d ed., J. H. Perry, Editor, (New York: McGraw-Hill Book Company, Inc., 1950).
Total (L_0)	93.20	

given trial calculation. For the next six trials the limits were 1.05 and 1/1.05, and for all subsequent trials limits of 1.005 and 1/1.005 were employed. The procedure for the determination of T_N and V_N was initiated at the end of the fourth trial.

The statement of Example 8–3 is given in Table 8–5, which illustrates the solution of a problem in which the total vapor rate V_1 is specified. The final solution of this example is presented in Table 8–6. The determination of T_N and V_N for this example at the end of the 11th trial is shown in Table 8–7.

Although the determination of T_N and V_N by use of Equations (8–21) and (8–25) at the end of each trial reduced the amplitude of the oscillations, it did not completely eliminate it. When trials in addition to those shown in Table 8–6 were carried out, the value of V_N changed from 16.3 to 16.2 about every 10 trials. Corresponding to these values of V_N the temperature T_N changed from 418.5 to 420.0. This oscillation can be attributed, perhaps, to the limitations imposed by the use of eight-digit arithmetic, which are reflected by the fact that during the sequence of trials the value of θ changed from 0.999 to 1.0008.

OTHER SPECIFICATIONS FOR STRIPPERS AND ABSORBERS

In addition to the specifications stated below, it is supposed that the number of plates, the compositions and flow rates of the streams L_0 and V_{N+1}, and the limiting set of flow rates for the remaining plates have been specified. Instead of the specification of V_1 a sum of v_{1i}'s may be specified as indicated by the following set of specifications.

Specifications

$$(1) \quad T_{N+1} \text{ (or } T_0\text{)} \quad \text{and} \quad (2) \quad \sum_{i=2}^{s} v_{1i} \text{ (or } \sum_{i=2}^{s} l_{Ni}\text{)}, \quad 2 \leqq s \leqq c$$

This specification may be employed for either an absorber or a stripper. First the treatment of a steam-stripper is given and then the application to absorbers is presented. This set of specifications includes others such as the fraction of a group of components to be stripped from the rich oil, L_0, since this fraction may be stated in terms of a sum of v_{1i}'s. Also, the values (or value) of v_1 are to be specified for components other than single phase components. The values of the latter are fixed at $v_{1,1} = V_{N+1}$ and $v_{1,H} = 0$. The equations stated previously for the θ-method are all applicable ex-

TABLE 8-6 Solution of Example 8-3

Temperatures, vapor rates, and intercooler (or heater) duties

Plate No.	Temp. (°F) Trial No.			Vapor rates Trial No.		Q_j Trial No.	Final flow rates Trial 17		
	Initial profile	11	17	Initial profile	17	17	Component	v_1	l_N
1	340	355.84	355.09	23.67	23.67	0.0	Steam	13.4700	0.0
2	345	397.56	399.66	22.40	22.40	-4.8×10^5	CH_4	0.0100	4.0871×10^{-13}
3	350	413.55	417.24	21.12	21.12	-2.0×10^5	C_2H_6	0.1700	1.1581×10^{-8}
4	355	420.61	423.03	19.85	19.85	-8.0×10^4	C_3H_8	1.3000	1.3303×10^{-6}
5	360	424.88	421.80	18.57	18.57	-1.0×10^4	$n\text{-}C_4$	2.8285	1.4963×10^{-3}
6	365	430.55	422.00	17.30	17.30	-3.2×10^3	$n\text{-}C_5$	1.7112	3.8804×10^{-2}
7	370	435.94	426.52	16.02	16.89	0.0	$n\text{-}C_6$	1.9497	4.0028×10^{-1}
8	375	426.00	418.50	14.75	16.33	0.0	$n\text{-}C_7$	1.3682	1.1818
V_1 (Calculated)		23.6516	23.6682				500	0.8606	81.379
θ		0.9901	0.9990						

TABLE 8-7 Solution of Equations (8–21) and (8–25) for T_N and V_N at the end of trial 11 for Example 8–3

Trial No.	V_N (assumed)	T_N (by Eq. (8–21))	$p(V_N, T_N)$	V_N (by interpolation, Eq. (8–27))
1	16.4592	422.600	-2.4050	—
2	18.8642	470.873	25.8000	16.6643
3	16.6643	427.734	1.1914	16.5578
4	16.5578	415.103	-6.2875×10^{-1}	16.5946
5	16.5946	416.020	1.1145×10^{-2}	16.59393
6	16.59393	416.004	2.8729×10^{-4}	16.59392
7	16.59392	416.003	1.1730×10^{-4}	16.5940

cept Equation (8–14). The value of θ to be employed in Equations (8–8) and (8–13) is the positive root which gives $g(\theta) = 0$ where

$$g(\theta) = \sum_{i=2}^{s} \frac{v_{N+1,i} + l_{0i}}{1 + \theta(l_{Ni}/v_{1i})_{ca}} - \sum_{i=2}^{s} v_{1i} \qquad (8\text{–}31)$$

Note that the second summation on the right-hand side of Equation (8–31) is one of the specifications. When the numbering of all components except 1 is taken to be arbitrary, generalization of the above specification to include any component or group of components is obtained. The corrected terminal rates for each of the two phase components are calculated by use of Equations (8–11) and (8–13). The corrected vapor rate for any trial is taken to be the one given by

$$(V_1)_{co} = \sum_{i \neq 1, H} \frac{v_{N+1,i} + l_{0i}}{1 + \theta(l_{Ni}/v_{1i})_{ca}} + V_{N+1} \qquad (8\text{–}32)$$

The total flow rates of the vapor and liquid throughout the column are determined by use of the constant-composition and Q-methods for making enthalpy balances. The upper limit of the vapor rate [see Equation (8–30)] is taken equal to the corrected value of V_1 as given by Equation (8–32). The values for T_N and V_N are determined by use of Equations (8–21) and (8–25) in a manner analogous to that described previously.

The use of this set of specifications is illustrated by the solution of Example 8–4, which is stated in Table 8–5. Since the specified sum of v_{1i}'s was selected on the basis of the solution of Example 8–3, the final solutions are identical (within the limits of accuracy) as shown in Tables 8–6 and 8–8.

When T_0 (or T_{N+1}) and a sum of v_{1i}'s (or l_{Ni}'s) are specified for an absorber, either the θ-method or direct-iteration ($\theta = 1$) may be employed, as described in the previous treatment of absorbers. When the θ-method is used, Equation (8–31) may be used to determine the quantity θ. When the procedure of direct-iteration is employed, the compositions are calculated on the basis of the calculated values of v_{1i} and l_{Ni}; that is, $(v_{1i})_{co}$ and $(l_{Ni})_{co}$, are replaced by $(v_{1i})_{ca}$ and $(l_{Ni})_{ca}$, respectively, in Equations. (8–8) through (8–10). In order to carry out the enthalpy balances, a value of V_1 (denoted by $(V_1)_{co}$) is selected which is related to the specified sum of v_{1i}'s as follows:

$$(V_1)_{co} = \sum_{i=1}^{s} v_{1i} + \sum_{i=s+1}^{c} (v_{1i})_{ca} \qquad (8\text{–}33)$$

The first summation on the right-hand side of Equation (8–33) is of course recognized as one of the specifications. This value of V_1 and the correspond-

TABLE 8–8 Solution of Example 8–4

$$\sum_{i=1}^{7} v_{li} = 21.4457$$

Plate No.	Temperature, °F at trial number given				
	5	10	15	20	24
1	358.02	354.75	354.40	354.36	354.28
2	395.74	397.20	298.99	399.65	399.92
3	406.76	417.35	417.42	418.26	418.68
4	407.06	429.98	424.73	424.35	423.92
5	402.24	438.43	427.07	423.01	423.54
6	394.44	442.72	425.45	423.83	422.31
7	384.69	443.56	429.23	427.63	425.18
8	380.51	423.29	425.17	420.92	419.35
$\sum_{i=1}^{7} v_{li}$	21.4908	21.3998	21.4431	21.4451	21.4461
V_1 (Calculated)	24.0088	23.2318	23.6930	23.6589	23.6690
θ	1.1372	0.8865	0.9929	0.9983	1.0011

ing values of V_j and L_j are used in the absorption and stripping factors for the next trial.

For other sets of specifications for absorbers and strippers such as T_{N+1} and T_0, the following indirect approach would probably prove to be among the easiest procedures to apply. Solutions may be obtained for each of several values of V_1 and the specified value of T_{N+1} (or T_0). For each V_1, a value of T_0 (or T_{N+1}) is given by the respective solution. The value of V_1 that should be specified in order to satisfy the given set of specifications (T_0 and T_{N+1}) may be obtained by making successive interpolations.

NOTATION

(See Chapters 2 through 7)

PROBLEMS

8–1 Develop the expressions given by Equations (8–1), (8–4), (8–6), and (8–7).

8–2 Show that Equations (8–4) and (8–7) are theoretically equivalent.

8–3 Since l_{0i} and $v_{N-1,i}$ are known feed rates, the calculated and corrected values are equal. On the basis of this information, Equations (8–17), (8–18), and the postulate concerning the ratio of $\sigma_{N+1,i}$ to τ_{0i}, show that

$$\left(\frac{l_{Ni}}{v_{1i}}\right)_{co} = \theta \left(\frac{l_{Ni}}{v_{1i}}\right)_{ca}$$

8–4 On the basis of the postulates represented by Equations (8–15), (8–16), (8–19), (8–20), and the definition of a mole fraction, show that the expressions for the calculation of the compositions are those given by Equations (8–8a) through (8–8d).

8–5 (a) For the case where the temperature of L_0 is specified (in addition to the others mentioned in the text), develop the following expressions which constitute a combination of the constant-composition and Q-methods.

$$L_1 = \frac{V_1[H_1 - H(y_1)_2] + L_0[H(x_0)_2 - h_0]}{[H(x_1)_2 - h_1]}$$

$$L_j = \frac{V_1[H_1 - H(y_1)_{j+1}] + L_0[H(x_0)_{j+1} - h_0] + \sum_{k=1}^{j-1} Q_k}{[H(x_j)_{j+1} - h_j]},$$

$$2 \leqq j \leqq N - 1$$

$$H_{N+1} = \cfrac{V_1 H_1 + L_N h_N + \sum_{k=1}^{N-1} Q_k - L_0 h_0}{V_{N+1}}$$

(b) For the case where the temperature of V_{N+1} is specified instead of the temperature of L_0, develop the corresponding expressions for the combination of the constant-composition and Q-methods.

8-6 The following absorber may be solved manually fairly rapidly.

Component	Component No.	v_{N+1}	l_0	Specifications
Single phase light	1	70	0.0	$V_1 = 85, \quad P = 400$ psia
C_3H_8	2	30	0.0	$T_0 = 90°F, \quad$ and $N = 3$
Single phase heavy	3	0.0	15	

(a) Show that $(v_{1,2})_{co} = 15$ for all trials.

(b) Show that $\theta = (v_{1,2}/l_{N,2})_{ca}$.

(c) In which direction should the material balances for propane be made in order to minimize round-off error.

(d) Show that the K's corresponding to the bubble point temperatures may be solved for directly without trial and error.

(e) Make two or three trials using combinations of (1) the conventional and Q-methods and (2) the constant-composition and Q-methods. Use the enthalpy data of methane and normal octane for the single phase light and heavy components, respectively.

8-7 Verify the results given in Table 8-1 for Cases 3, 7, and 11.

LITERATURE CITED

1. Franklin, W. B. and George Horton, "Calculation of Absorber Performance and Design," *Ind. Engr. Chem.*, **32**, 1384 (1940).

2. Hardy, B. W., "A Convergence Method for Absorbers," M.S. thesis, A. and M. College of Texas, College Station, Texas, May 1961.

3. Hardy, B. W., S. L. Sullivan, Jr., C. D. Holland, and H. L. Bauni, "Figure Separations This New Way: Part 5—A Convergence Method for Absorbers," *Petroleum Refiner*, **40**, No. 9, 237 (1961).

4. Johnston, R. H., personal communication.

5. Kremser, A., "Theoretical Analysis of Absorption Process," *Nat. Pet. News*, **22,** No. 21, 42 (May 21, 1930).

6. McNeese, C. R., "Small Digital Computer Can Solve Rigorous Absorber Calculation," paper presented at the 44th National Meeting of the A.I.Ch.E. in New Orleans, February 27, 1961.

7. Souders, M. and G. G. Brown, "Fundamental Design of Absorbing and Stripping Columns for Complex Vapors," *Ind. Eng. Chem.* **24,** 519 (1932).

8. Wetherold, R. G., "A Convergence Method Used for Various Types of Specifications for Strippers and Absorbers," M.S. thesis, A. and M. College of Texas, College Station, Texas, 1962.

Conventional and Complex Columns at Total Reflux, Total Reboil, and Total Recycle

9

In this chapter the θ-method of convergence is extended to include conventional columns operating at total reflux in the rectifying and/or total reboil in the stripping section. In addition, the method is further extended to include complex columns. These procedures and the ones for columns operating at a finite reflux provide a means for the examination of a given column over a wide range of operating conditions. Numerous examples were solved by Lyster *et al.* (2) to show that only one point of operation for a distillation column with a fixed number of plates and a given reflux rate is suitable to yield the maximum concentration of a given component in the distillate (or bottoms) product. The calculational procedures and convergence methods presented in this chapter are the same as those proposed by Lyster *et al.* (2).

CONVENTIONAL COLUMNS

Three cases are considered—total reflux in the rectifying section, total reboil in the stripping section, and total recycle. The proposed treatments make use of a combination of the Thiele and Geddes calculational procedure and the θ-method of convergence. The equations apply of course only for those systems that do not contain any single phase components.

Total Reflux in the Rectifying Section

When the specifications $D = 0$ and $L_0 =$ finite number are made, the condition of total reflux in the rectifying section arises. For this case $B = F$, $V_j = L_{j-1}$ (where $1 \leq j \leq f - 1$), and $\bar{V}_f = L_{f-1}$. Also material balances

229

show that $y_{ji} = x_{j-1,i}$ (where $1 \leqq j \leqq f - 1$). When this relationship is combined with the equilibrium relationship, $y = Kx$, the following equations are obtained for the rectifying section.

$$\frac{y_{1i}}{x_{0i}} = 1$$

$$\frac{x_{1i}}{x_{0i}} = \frac{1}{K_{1i}}$$

$$\frac{x_{2i}}{x_{0i}} = \frac{1}{K_{2i}K_{1i}}$$

$$\vdots$$

$$\frac{x_{ji}}{x_{0i}} = \frac{1}{K_{ji}K_{j-1,i}\cdots K_{2i}K_{1i}}, \quad j \leqq f - 1 \qquad (9\text{--}1a)$$

Since $\bar{y}_{fi} = x_{f-1,i}$

$$\frac{\bar{y}_{fi}}{x_{0i}} = \frac{1}{K_{f-1,i}K_{f-2,i}\cdots K_{2i}K_{1i}} \qquad (9\text{--}1b)$$

The match at the feed plate for the case of total reflux in the rectifying section is effected in the following manner. The quantity $(v_{fi}/b_i)_{ca}$ is computed by the conventional stripping section equations (stated in Chapter 3). Multiplication of both sides of Equation (9–1b) by $\bar{V}_f/L_0$ gives $(\bar{v}_{fi}/l_{0i})_{ca}$. Since $\bar{v}_{fi} = v_{fi} + v_{Fi}$, the general matching equation for a feed of any thermal condition is

$$\left(\frac{l_{0i}}{b_i}\right)_{ca} = \frac{(v_{fi}/b_i)_{ca} + (v_{Fi}/FX_i)}{(\bar{v}_{fi}/l_{0i})_{ca}} \qquad (9\text{--}2)$$

The corrected b_i's are given by

$$(b_i)_{co} = FX_i \qquad (9\text{--}3)$$

since $D = 0$ and $B = F$. The corrected values of the l_{0i}'s may be represented by

$$(l_{0i})_{co} = \theta_0 (l_{0i}/b_i)_{ca}(b_i)_{co} \qquad (9\text{--}4)$$

which follows immediately from the basic postulate (Equation 4–12) by taking

$$\tau_0 = \theta_0$$

When both sides of Equation (9–4) are summed over all components the following result is obtained

$$L_0 = \sum_{i=1}^{c} \theta_0 (l_{0i}/b_i)_{ca} (b_i)_{co} \tag{9–5}$$

which may be used for the calculation of θ_0. However, as is evident from the equations that follow, θ_0 need not be evaluated. The corrected compositions to be employed for the calculation of the bubble point temperatures are obtained by use of the following equations:

$$x_{ji} = \frac{(l_{ji}/b_i)_{ca}(b_i)_{co}}{\displaystyle\sum_{i=1}^{c}(l_{ji}/b_i)_{ca}(b_i)_{co}} = \frac{(x_{ji}/x_{0i})_{ca}(x_{0i})_{co}}{\displaystyle\sum_{i=1}^{c}(x_{ji}/x_{0i})_{ca}(x_{0i})_{co}}, \quad 1 \leq j \leq f - 1 \tag{9–6}$$

and

$$x_{ji} = \frac{(l_{ji}/b_i)_{ca}(b_i)_{co}}{\displaystyle\sum_{i=1}^{c}(l_{ji}/b_i)_{ca}(b_i)_{co}}, \quad f \leq j \leq N + 1 \tag{9–7}$$

The calculated values appearing in Equations (9–6) and (9–7) are computed on the basis of assumed temperature and L/V profies. Equation (9–1) is used for the rectifying section, and the appropriate equations of Chapter 3 are used for the stripping section. Corrected values of the b's are given by Equation (9–3). For the calculation of the corrected values of the x_0's, the desired expression is obtained by division of each member of Equation (9–4) by the corresponding member of Equation (9–5) to give

$$(x_{0i})_{co} = \frac{(l_{0i}/b_i)_{ca}(b_i)_{co}}{\displaystyle\sum_{i=1}^{c}(l_{0i}/b_i)_{ca}(b_i)_{co}} \tag{9–8}$$

When partial condensers are specified, the composition of the distillate (vapor) is also of interest at $D = 0$. It is computed in the following manner. After the temperature T_0 has been calculated on the basis of the corrected x_{0i}'s, the desired composition is given by the relationship,

$$X_{Di} = y_{0i} = K_{0i}(x_{0i})_{co}$$

The total molal flow rates in the stripping section are calculated in the usual manner by use of material and enthalpy balances presented in Chapters 3 and 5, respectively. The condenser duty is determined by use of enthalpy and material balances which enclose the condenser. Then the reboiler duty is found by use of over-all enthalpy and material balances.

Total Reboil in the Stripping Section

When a finite value is specified for L_0 and when D is taken equal to F, the condition of total reboil in the stripping section is realized. The following material-balance equations for the stripping section are developed in a manner similar to that described for the case of total reflux in the rectifying section.

$$\frac{x_{Ni}}{y_{N+1,i}} = 1$$

$$\frac{x_{N-1,i}}{y_{N+1,i}} = .K_{Ni}$$

$$\frac{x_{N-2,i}}{y_{N+1,i}} = K_{N-1,i}K_{Ni}$$

$$\vdots$$

$$\frac{x_{ji}}{y_{N+1,i}} = K_{j+1,i}K_{j+2,i}\ldots K_{N-1,i}K_{Ni}, \quad j > f \qquad (9\text{--}9\text{a})$$

and

$$\frac{\bar{x}_{f-1,i}}{y_{N+1,i}} = K_{fi}K_{f+1,i}\ldots K_{N-1,i}K_{Ni} \qquad (9\text{--}9\text{b})$$

For total reboil in the stripping section, positive compositions are assured by use of the relationship for the liquid flow rates at the feed plate, $(\bar{l}_{f-1,i}/v_{N+1,i})_{ca}$. Therefore, for a feed of any given thermal condition

$$\left(\frac{v_{N+1,i}}{d_i}\right)_{ca} = \frac{(l_{f-1,i}/d_i)_{ca} + l_{Fi}/FX_i}{(\bar{l}_{f-1,i}/v_{N+1,i})_{ca}} \qquad (9\text{--}10)$$

The following equations are developed in a manner analogous to that given for Equations (9–3) through (9–8).

$$(d_i)_{co} = FX_i \qquad (9\text{--}11)$$

$$(v_{N+1,i})_{co} = \theta_0(v_{N+1,i}/d_i)_{ca}(d_i)_{co} \qquad (9\text{--}12)$$

$$V_{N+1} = \sum_{i=1}^{c} \theta_0(v_{N+1,i}/d_i)_{ca}(d_i)_{co} \qquad (9\text{--}13)$$

$$(y_{N+1,i})_{co} = \frac{(v_{N+1,i}/d_i)_{ca}(d_i)_{co}}{\sum\limits_{i=1}^{c} (v_{N+1,i}/d_i)_{ca}(d_i)_{co}} \tag{9-14}$$

$$x_{ji} = \frac{(l_{ji}/d_i)_{ca}(d_i)_{co}}{\sum\limits_{i=1}^{c} (l_{ji}/d_i)_{ca}(d_i)_{co}},$$

$$0 \leq j \leq f - 1 \tag{9-15}$$

$$x_{ji} = \frac{(x_{ji}/y_{N+1,i})_{ca}(y_{N+1,i})_{co}}{\sum\limits_{i=1}^{c} (x_{ji}/y_{N+1,i})_{ca}(y_{N+1,i})_{co}},$$

$$f \leq j \leq N + 1 \tag{9-16}$$

The total liquid and vapor rates in the rectifying section are calculated by use of the appropriate material and enthalpy balances stated in Chapters 3 and 5, respectively. Again, neither $(v_{N+1,i})_{co}$ or θ_0 need be evaluated. However, the flow rate V_{N+1} is needed in the calculation of $(\bar{l}_{f-1,i}/v_{N+1,i})_{ca}$ as described previously. V_{N+1} may be obtained as follows: (1) an enthalpy and material balance enclosing the condenser gives the condenser duty, Q_c, (2) an enthalpy and material balance enclosing the entire column yields Q_R, and (3) an enthalpy balance enclosing the reboiler gives V_{N+1}.

Note that the temperature of the reboiler may be calculated by either of two ways. It may be found by use of a dew point calculation based on the y_{N+1}'s as given by Equation (9-14) or by use of a bubble point calculation based on the x_{N+1}'s as computed by use of Equation (9-16). When the desired solution to the problem is obtained, the temperatures found by these methods are, of course, equal.

Total Recycle

Total recycle may be defined in two ways (3). From an operational point of view, a column that contains enough vapor and liquid to be operational at steady state but has neither entering nor leaving streams ($D = 0$, $B = 0$, $F = 0$) is said to be at total recycle. Thus, a column operating at steady state at both total reflux ($D = 0$) and total reboil ($B = 0$) and at a feed rate equal to zero is said to be at total recycle. The diameters of such columns, as well as the flow rates of the vapor and liquid throughout the column, are finite.

From the standpoint of column design an alternate but equivalent definition is useful. This definition is equivalent to the previous one in that they both lead to the same sets of compositions and temperatures throughout the column. According to this definition the condition of total recycle is said to exist throughout a distillation column when

$$\lim_{L_{j-1} \to \infty} \left(\frac{V_j}{L_{j-1}} \right) = 1 \tag{9-17}$$

In the following development some finite number greater than zero (and less than F) is assumed to be specified for D (or B), and throughout the column the limiting condition of total recycle, $V_j/L_{j-1} = 1$, is assumed to prevail. Since F, D and B are finite, it follows that

$$F = D + B \tag{9-18}$$

and

$$FX_i = d_i + b_i \tag{9-19}$$

However, since the vapor and liquid flow rates throughout the column are extremely large, it is readily shown that

$$\bar{v}_{fi} = v_{fi} + v_{Fi} = v_{fi} \tag{9-20}$$

and

$$\bar{l}_{f-1,i} = l_{f-1,i} + l_{Fi} = l_{f-1,i} \tag{9-21}$$

In a manner similar to that outlined previously, the following expressions are obtained for the rectifying and stripping sections.

$$\frac{x_{1i}}{X_{Di}} = \frac{1}{K_{1i}K_{0i}}, \quad \text{(for a total condenser } K_{0i} = 1)$$

$$\frac{x_{2i}}{X_{Di}} = \frac{1}{K_{2i}K_{1i}K_{0i}}$$

$$\vdots$$

$$\frac{x_{ji}}{X_{Di}} = \frac{1}{K_{ji}K_{j-1,i}\cdots K_{1i}K_{0i}}, \quad 0 \le j \le N+1 \tag{9-22a}$$

and

$$\frac{x_{N+1,i}}{X_{Di}} = \frac{x_{Bi}}{X_{Di}} = \frac{1}{K_{N+1,i}K_{N,i}\cdots K_{1i}K_{0i}} \tag{9-22b}$$

After $(x_{Bi}/X_{Di})_{ca}$ has been evaluated by use of Equation (9–22b) on the basis of an assumed temperature profile, the value of $(b_i/d_i)_{ca}$ is computed as follows:

$$\left(\frac{b_i}{d_i}\right)_{ca} = \left(\frac{B}{D}\right)\left(\frac{x_{Bi}}{X_{Di}}\right)_{ca} \qquad (9\text{--}23)$$

As shown in Chapter 4, the corrected value of d_i is given by

$$(d_i)_{co} = \frac{FX_i}{1 + \theta_0(b_i/d_i)_{ca}} \qquad (9\text{--}24)$$

where θ_0 is the positive root of $g_0(\theta_0)$, where

$$g_0(\theta_0) = \sum_{i=1}^{c} \frac{FX_i}{1 + \theta_0(b_i/d_i)_{ca}} - D \qquad (9\text{--}25)$$

The corrected compositions are computed by use of the following formula.

$$x_{ji} = \frac{(x_{ji}/X_{Di})_{ca}(X_{Di})_{co}}{\displaystyle\sum_{i=1}^{c} (x_{ji}/X_{Di})_{ca}(X_{Di})_{co}}, \quad 0 \leq j \leq N + 1 \qquad (9\text{--}26)$$

where

$$(X_{Di})_{co} = \frac{(d_i)_{co}}{D} \qquad (9\text{--}27)$$

COMPLEX COLUMNS

In general the calculational procedures and convergence methods for complex columns at total reflux and total reboil follow closely those described for conventional columns at the same operating conditions. For complex columns having one feed plate and one or more side-streams withdrawn in addition to the distillate and bottoms, the following calculational procedures and convergence methods are recommended.

1. *Side-Stream W_1 Withdrawn from the Rectifying Section. Specifications*: L_0 *is finite,* $D = 0$, $W_1 = 0$ *and* $B = F$

The treatment for this set of specifications is the same as that given previously for "Total Reflux in the Rectifying Section." When W_1 is withdrawn as a liquid from any plate p of the rectifying section, the composition of W_1 is the same as that of the liquid leaving plate p. Thus the composition of W_1 is given by Equation (9–1a) by taking $j = p$. If W_1 is withdrawn from plate p as a vapor, the compositions are given by $y_{pi} = K_{pi}x_{pi}$.

2. *Side-Stream W_1 Withdrawn from the Rectifying Section. Specifications:*
L_0 *is Finite,* $D = 0,\ 0 < W_1 < F$

This case is illustrated by supposing the side-stream W_1 to be withdrawn from plate p of the rectifying section. From the top of the column down to plate p, calculations are carried out as indicated by Equation (9–1a). After x_{pi}/x_{0i} has been computed, the following molal ratio may be evaluated.

$$\frac{w_{1i}}{l_{0i}} = \left(\frac{W_1}{L_0}\right)\left(\frac{x_{pi}}{x_{0i}}\right) \tag{9–28}$$

Also, since $y_{p+1,i} = x_{pi}$ it follows that

$$\frac{v_{p+1,i}}{l_{0i}} = \left(\frac{V_{p+1}}{L_0}\right)\left(\frac{x_{pi}}{x_{0i}}\right) \tag{9–29}$$

where V_{p+1} is the vapor rate assumed for plate $p + 1$. After these ratios have been evaluated, calculations may be continued to the feed plate as indicated by the following equations.

$$\frac{v_{p+2,i}}{l_{0i}} = A_{p+1,i}\left(\frac{v_{p+1,i}}{l_{0i}}\right) + \frac{w_{1i}}{l_{0i}} \tag{9–30a}$$

$$\vdots$$

$$\frac{\bar{v}_{fi}}{l_{0i}} = A_{f-1,i}\left(\frac{v_{f-1,i}}{l_{0i}}\right) + \frac{w_{1i}}{l_{0i}} \tag{9–30b}$$

For the stripping section the calculations are carried out as described in Chapter 3 for conventional columns. The calculated results for the two sections may be combined to give a value for b_i/w_{1i} as shown by Equation (9–35). The corrected set of rates is that set which satisfies the over-all material balance

$$FX_i = (w_{1i})_{co} + (b_i)_{co} \tag{9–31}$$

and which is related to the calculated values as follows:

$$\left(\frac{b_i}{w_{1i}}\right)_{co} = \theta_1\left(\frac{b_i}{w_{1i}}\right)_{ca} \tag{9–32}$$

These two equations may be solved to give

$$(w_{1i})_{co} = \frac{FX_i}{1 + \theta_1(b_i/w_{1i})_{ca}} \tag{9–33}$$

where the quantity θ_1 is the positive root of $g_1(\theta_1)$,

$$g_1(\theta_1) = \sum_{i=1}^{c} \frac{FX_i}{1 + \theta_1(b_i/w_{1i})_{ca}} - W_1 \tag{9-34}$$

The calculated value of b_i/w_{1i} is obtained by use of the following matching equation which applies for a feed of any given thermal condition

$$\frac{b_i}{w_{1i}} = \frac{(l_{f-1,i}/w_{1i}) + (l_{Fi}/FX_i)}{(v_{fi}/b_i) + (v_{Fi}/FX_i)} \tag{9-35}$$

After $l_{f-1,i}/l_{0i}$ has been computed by use of the equations for the rectifying section, the quantity $l_{f-1,i}/w_{1i}$ follows by division of $l_{f-1,i}/l_{0i}$ by w_{1i}/l_{0i}. Once θ_1 has been determined by use of Equation (9–34), the quantity of θ_0 is given directly by Equation (9–5). The remainder of the calculations are performed in a manner similar to that described previously.

3. *Side-Stream W_1 Withdrawn from the Stripping Section. Specifications:*
   L_0 is finite, $D = 0$, $0 < W_1 < F$

For the rectifying section, calculations are carried out as described under "Total Reflux in the Rectifying Section." For the stripping section the material balances are the same as those given for complex columns in Chapter 7. The equations for the convergence method are the same as those given previously for the case of a side-stream ($W_1 > 0$) in the rectifying section.

4. *Total Recycle with Side-Streams W_1 and W_2 Withdrawn for the Rectifying*
   and Stripping Sections, Respectively

For this set of specifications, the material balances are represented by Equations (9–22a) and (9–22b). The calculated value of b_i/d_i is obtained by use of Equation (9–23). Also,

$$(w_{1i}/d_i)_{ca} = (W_1/D)(x_{pi}/X_{Di})_{ca} \tag{9-36}$$

$$(w_{2i}/d_i)_{ca} = (W_2/D)(x_{qi}/X_{Di})_{ca} \tag{9-37}$$

where the side-streams W_1 and W_2 are withdrawn as liquids from plates p and q of the rectifying and stripping sections, respectively. Three θ's are contained in the equations representing the convergence method. These equations are identical with those given in Chapter 7. Also, the θ's may be determined by one of the procedures discussed in Chapter 7. The remaining calculations are carried out in the usual manner.

If in the case of total recycle any number of feeds are introduced between the two side-streams, the corresponding calculational procedure is the same as the one described above in Item 4. The procedures described for the other cases may be extended to include the introduction of multiple feeds between the side-stream withdrawals. For the plates above and below the uppermost and lowermost feed plates, respectively, the calculational procedure is the same as described in Items 1, 2, and 3. However, in order to minimize round-off error in the treatment of the plates between the top and bottom feed plates, the flow rates for these plates must be determined by making calculations both down from the top and up from the bottom of

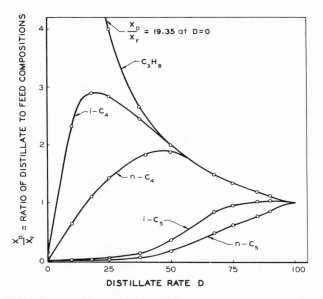

Figure 9–1. Variation of the distillate rate D at a fixed reflux rate $L_0 = 125$. (Reproduced by permission of *Hydrocarbon Processing & Petroleum Refiner*)

the column. Again, before the step by step calculations between the feed plates may be performed, the terminal rates must be determined by use of expressions similar in form to Equation (9–35).

Illustrative Examples

The following examples were taken from the work of Lyster *et al.* (2). Several examples having the same feed composition and certain common specifications as shown in Table 9–1 were solved in order to illustrate some of the operational characteristics of a column. The results obtained for total reflux in the rectifying section are given in Tables 9–2 through 9–4. Table 9–4 illustrates the fact that although $V_j = L_{j-1}$ in the rectifying

TABLE 9-1 Feed composition and specifications for the examples

Component	FX	Specifications
C_3H_8	5.0	Boiling point liquid feed, partial condenser, column pressure = 300 psia, three rectifying plates and eight stripping plates plus a reboiler. Use the equilibrium and enthalpy data given in Tables A–4 and A–8 of the Appendix.
$i\text{-}C_4$	15.0	
$n\text{-}C_4$	25.0	
$i\text{-}C_5$	20.0	
$n\text{-}C_5$	35.0	
	100.0	

Reproduced by permission of *Hydrocarbon Processing & Petroleum Refiner*

section (for $D = 0$), V_j is not necessarily equal to V_{j+1}. Although the constant-composition method could have been employed, the conventional method for making enthalpy balances was used as necessary in the solution of the examples shown in this chapter.

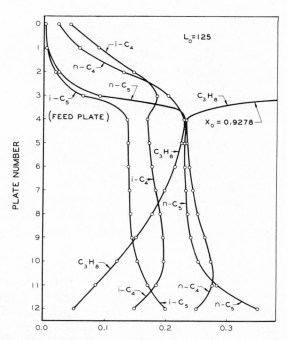

Figure 9–2. Composition profiles at total reflux in the rectifying section. (Reproduced by permission of *Hydrocarbon Processing & Petroleum Refiner*)

Figure 9–1 shows the operational characteristics of a column at a fixed reflux rate, L_0, and at various distillate rates. The range of operation extends from total reflux $(D = 0)$ in the rectifying section to total reboil $(B = 0)$ in the stripping section. Note that at $D = 0$, the lightest component of the feed has its maximum mole fraction. As D is increased, the mole fraction of each of the other components except the heaviest one in the feed passes through a maximum. When D is increased to the condition of total reboil $(D = F, B = 0)$ in the stripping section, the composition of the distillate is equal to that of the feed. Results analogous to those shown in Figure 9–1 are obtained when a plot of x_{Bi}/X_i versus B is made. At the

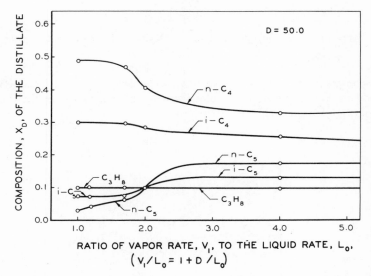

Figure 9–3. Variation of the reflux rate L_0 at a fixed distillate rate D. (Reproduced by permission of *Hydrocarbon Processing & Petroleum Refiner*)

condition of total reflux $(D = 0)$, the final liquid compositions on each plate (at $D = 0$) are shown in Figure 9–2.

When the distillate rate is fixed and the reflux rate is varied, the compositions obtained for the same example are shown in Figure 9–3. As V_1/L_0 approaches 1, total recycle throughout the column is approached. The solution of this example by the proposed method of convergence is presented in Tables 9–5 and 9–6. The range of operation displayed in Figure 9–3 extends from total recycle, $V_1/L_0 = 1$, to the limiting condition of no liquid reflux $(L_0 = 0)$ for the rectifying section. In the limit as L_0 approaches zero, X_{Di} approaches $\bar{y}_{fi}$, the mole fraction of component i in the vapor that enters the plate above the feed plate.

TABLE 9-2 Temperature profiles and reflux rates at $D = 0$, $B = F$, and $L_0 = 125$

Plate No.	Initial profile	Temperature (°F), Trial Number								
		1	2*	3	4	5	6	7	8	9
0 (Distillate)	140.00	138.29	138.32	138.89	139.82	140.22	140.33	140.34	140.34	140.34
1	150.76	141.80	141.93	143.27	145.34	146.21	146.45	146.47	146.46	146.45
2	161.52	150.00	150.52	153.54	157.83	159.56	160.00	160.01	159.97	159.95
3	172.29	169.38	170.59	176.29	183.50	186.14	186.64	186.56	186.44	186.40
4 (Feed)	183.05	209.53	209.53	216.15	223.92	226.31	226.47	226.16	225.95	225.88
5	193.81	209.12	210.32	216.84	224.36	227.00	227.44	227.28	227.10	227.02
6	204.57	211.13	212.71	218.67	225.59	228.23	228.86	228.83	228.71	228.63
7	215.33	215.40	216.81	221.85	227.83	230.25	230.94	231.01	230.94	230.88
8	226.09	221.67	222.64	226.54	231.32	233.31	233.95	234.07	234.04	234.00
9	236.86	229.69	230.16	232.86	236.30	237.74	238.23	238.36	238.36	238.34
10	247.62	239.47	239.58	241.17	243.21	244.10	244.41	244.51	244.54	224.54
11	258.38	251.87	251.87	252.54	253.13	253.51	253.73	253.85	253.91	253.94
12 (Reboiler)	269.14	269.14	269.14	269.14	269.14	269.14	269.14	269.14	269.14	269.14
L_0 (Calculated)	—	114.72	118.41	87.47	81.28	107.12	121.46	125.78	125.96	125.39

* All profiles other than the one for trial no. 1 are averaged. Vapor rates assumed constant at 125 for the first two trials.

Reproduced by permission of *Hydrocarbon Processing & Petroleum Refiner*

TABLE 9–3 Final composition for $D = 0$, $B = F$ and $L_0 = 125$

Component	FX	$X_D{}^*$
C_3H_8	5.0	0.96757089
$i\text{-}C_4$	15.0	$0.23468365 \times 10^{-1}$
$n\text{-}C_4$	25.0	$0.87593467 \times 10^{-2}$
$i\text{-}C_5$	20.0	$0.13173418 \times 10^{-3}$
$n\text{-}C_5$	35.0	$0.83762787 \times 10^{-4}$

* Used to denote mole fraction of the vapor in equilibrium with the liquid stream L_0.

TABLE 9–4 Final vapor rates for $D = 0$, $B = F$ and $L_0 = 125$

Plate No.	Vapor rate
1	125.00
2	119.10
3	109.07
4 (Feed)	97.47
5	86.98
6	87.42
7	88.03
8	88.87
9	90.00
10	91.41
11	92.88
12 (Reboiler)	94.06

TABLE 9-5 Temperature profiles, total distillate rates and values of θ at total recycle,
$D = B = 50$

Plate No.	Initial profile	Temperature (°F), Trial Number			
		1	2*	3	4
O (Distillate)	140	224.60	224.84	224.83	224.83
1	150	265.33	255.55	255.69	255.76
2	160	286.98	271.43	271.87	272.08
3	170	304.26	286.82	287.52	287.85
4 (Feed)	180	315.21	300.11	300.87	301.23
5	190	321.38	310.36	311.00	311.30
6	200	324.84	317.61	318.07	318.28
7	210	326.94	322.48	322.78	322.92
8	220	328.37	325.70	325.89	325.97
9	230	329.46	327.86	327.98	328.03
10	240	330.38	329.38	329.45	329.48
11	250	331.18	330.51	330.55	330.56
12 (Reboiler)	260	331.90	331.39	331.42	331.43
D (Calculated)		7.16	52.37	50.68	50.00
θ		3.92×10^{-6}	1.57	1.16	1.001

* All profiles other than the one for trial No. 1 are averaged.

TABLE 9-6 Final distillate rates at total recycle

Component	FX	d
C_3H_8	5.0	4.9999
i-C_4	15.0	14.9921
n-C_4	25.0	24.8659
i-C_5	30.0	3.7926
n-C_5	35.0	1.3494
	100.0	49.9999

NOTATION

(See Chapters 2 through 8)

h = Heavy key component; a component for which the ratio of b/d is specified

PROBLEMS

9-1   Beginning with material balances and equilibrium relationships, develop the expressions given by Equation 9-1 for total reflux in the rectifying section.

9-2   For the case of total reboil in the stripping section, show that the expressions given by Equation (9-9) follow from material balance and equilibrium relationships.

9-3   Show that the two expressions given for x_{ji} by Equation (9-6) are equivalent.

9-4   Beginning with an expression for x_{ji} of the form given by Equation (9-15), show that the expression given by Equation (9-16) is equivalent.

9-5   By the same procedure as outlined for Problems 9-1 and 9-2, develop Equation (9-22b).

9-6   (a) Develop Equations (9-30a) and (9-30b).

       (b) Develop Equations (9-34) and (9-35).

9-7 Show that for a column with a partial condenser, a reboiler, and for a system whose relative volatilities remain constant throughout the column, that the well-known relationship,

$$b_i/d_i = (b_h/d_h)(\alpha_h/\alpha_i)^{N+2}$$

developed by Fenske (1), may be obtained from Equation (9-22b). The symbol "h" is used to denote the component selected as the heavy key. Show that for a column with a total condenser, $(N + 2)$ should be replaced by $(N + 1)$.

9-8 Show that for any given set of values for the α_i's, N, and b_h/d_h that the corresponding distillate rate at total recycle is given by

$$D = \sum_{i=1}^{c} \frac{FX_i}{1 + (b_h/d_h)(\alpha_h/\alpha_i)^{N+2}}$$

where D and B are considered finite while the diameter of the column is taken to be infinite.

9-9 (a) Determine the total number of equilibrium stages required to obtain the specified separations for components 1 and 3 (the heavy and light keys, respectively) given in the following table.

Component No.	FX_i	α_i	Specifications
1	33.3	1	The column is to have a total condenser.
2	33.3	2	$b_1/d_1 = 6.0$
3	33.4	3	$b_3/d_3 = 0.2$

(b) If $(N + 1)$ is held fixed at the value found in part (a), find the value of b_1/d_1 required to give a D equal to 50. Also, for $D = 50$, compute b_i/d_i for the other components.

9-10 (a) On the basis of the values of b_i/d_i obtained in part (a) of Problem 9-9 and the FX_i's given in this problem, find the value of θ required to give $g(\theta) = 0$, where

$$g(\theta) = \sum_{i=1}^{c} \frac{FX_i}{1 + \theta(b_i/d_i)} - 50$$

(b) Compare the values of $\theta(b_i/d_i)$ with the corresponding values of b_i/d_i obtained in part (b) of Problem 9-9.

9–11 (a) If at total recycle the distillate rate D_1 is obtained for a given set of values for $(N + 1)$ and $(b_3/d_3)_1$ and for the same value of $(N + 1)$ and another value for b_3/d_3 [denoted by $(b_3/d_3)_2$], the distillate rate D_2 is found, show that

$$\theta = \frac{(b_3/d_3)_1}{(b_3/d_3)_2}$$

(b) For these values of D_1 and D_2 plot $\ln (b_i/d_i)_1$ and $\ln (b_i/d_i)_2$ versus $\ln(\alpha_i/\alpha_h)$, where $(N + 1)$ is considered fixed. Locate $\ln \theta$ on this graph.

(c) Using the results given in Table 4–2 for the first trial in the solution of Example 3–1 by the θ-method, plot $\ln (b_i/d_i)_{ca}$ and $\ln (b_i/d_i)_{co}$ versus $\ln (\alpha_i/\alpha_h)$. Locate $\ln \theta$ on this graph.

9–12 Winn (4) has shown that many components have K-values which obey the following relationship

$$K_i = \beta_i K_h{}^{\gamma i}$$

over wide ranges of temperature at constant pressure. The quantities β_i and γ_i are independent of temperature and depend only upon the identities of components i and h (the heavy key). Show that at total recycle Winn's formula

$$b_i/d_i = (b_h/d_h)^{\gamma i}(D/B)^{\gamma_i - 1}\beta_i^{-(N+2)}$$

is obtained for a column in which the distillate is removed as a vapor.

LITERATURE CITED

1. Fenske, M. R., "Fractionation of Straight-Run Pennsylvania Gasoline," *Ind. Eng. Chem.*, **24,** 482 (1932).

2. Lyster, W. N., S. L. Sullivan, Jr., J. A. McDonough, and C. D. Holland, "Figure Distillation This New Way: Part 4—Explore Operating Characteristics of a Column," *Petroleum Refiner*, **39,** No. 8, 121 (1960).

3. Robinson, C. S. and E. R. Gilliland, *Elements of Fractional Distillation*, 4 ed. (New York: McGraw-Hill Book Company, Inc., 1950), p. 128.

4. Winn, F. W., "New Relative Volatility Method for Distillation Calculations," *Petroleum Refiner*, **37,** No. 5, 216 (1958).

Conventional and Complex Columns at Minimum Reflux* 10

The θ-method of convergence may be extended to include the treatment of conventional and complex columns at minimum reflux. Unlike the earlier analytical approaches of Underwood (13), Murdoch and Holland (9), and Acrivos and Amundson (1) that were based on constant-molal overflows and constant-relative volatities between the rectifying and stripping section pinches, the θ-method permits variations in both the flow rates and the relative volatilities. Brown and Holcomb (3) demonstrated the use of the calculational procedure of Lewis and Matheson for the treatment of minimum reflux. The method presented in this chapter uses the general calculational procedure of Thiele and Geddes. Among the first to suggest the use of this procedure were Shiras, Hanson, and Gibson (11). Also, Bachelor (2) made use of the equations of Thiele and Geddes in the treatment of minimum reflux.

In the treatment of minimum reflux a conventional column is considered first, and then these results are extended to include complex columns. The recommended calculational procedures and convergence methods follow closely those recently proposed by McDonough (7) and McDonough and Holland (8).

CONVENTIONAL COLUMNS

When the θ-method of convergence is used to treat conventional columns at minimum reflux, any one of several different types of specifications may be chosen. In this chapter the specifications are considered to be L_0

* A summary of this material was presented in a paper by J. A. McDonough, W. J. Tomme, and C. D. Holland at the Technical Meeting of the South Texas Section of the A.I.Ch.E. at Galveston, Texas, October 20, 1961.

(or V_1),D, and an infinity of plates in both the rectifying and stripping sections. In addition, the thermal condition and composition of the feed, the type of condenser, and the column pressure are specified. For these specifications the problem is to find the product distribution.

The extension of the θ-method of convergence to this particular set of specifications is presented first because the resulting minimum reflux problem is very closely related to the application of a combination of the Thiele and Geddes calculational procedure and the θ-method of convergence to conventional columns (5). In principle, the problem differs from the one considered previously for conventional columns in that infinitely many rather than a finite number of plates are specified in each section of the column. In the next chapter the combination of the Thiele and Geddes calculational procedure and the θ-method of convergence is extended to include other types of specifications such as b_i/d_i for two components instead of L_0 and D.

The minimum reflux ratio is usually defined from the standpoint of design. According to this definition the minimum reflux ratio is the smallest value of L_0/D that may be employed to obtain specified separations of two key components. These separations require infinitely many plates in both the rectifying and stripping sections of the column. The components for which the specifications are made are commonly called the "light" and "heavy keys" and denoted by the subscripts "h" and "l." The light and heavy keys are defined as the most and least volatile components that appear in both the top and bottom products. Components having volatilities between those of the keys are commonly called "split-key" components. The collection of the key and split-key components is referred to as the "distributed" components. Again components which appear in the gas phase alone are referred to as single phase lights (sometimes called inerts) and are identified by the subscript "L." Those components which appear only in the liquid phase are called single phase heavies and they are identified by the subscript "H."

At minimum reflux there is in each section of the column a region (called a rectifying or a stripping pinch) extending over an infinity of plates within which there is no change in composition from plate to plate. The pinch in the rectifying section occurs after those components heavier than the heavy key have been separated, and the pinch in the stripping section occurs after those components lighter than the light key have been separated. Thus when the keys consist of the lightest and heaviest components of the feed, both pinches occur at and adjacent to the feed plate. A system of this type has been treated previously (6, 11).

Except for minor changes, the calculational procedure of Thiele and Geddes is applied as described in Chapter 4. On the basis of assumed L/V and temperature profiles, the molal flow rates of all components between the two pinches are calculated by material balances and equilibrium relations. The convergence method is applied to these results, and the composition of the vapor and liquid leaving each plate, as well as the corresponding corrected temperature profile, is obtained. Then the total molal flow rates of vapor and liquid between the rectifying and stripping pinches are determined by use of enthalpy balances. The entire procedure is repeated until the temperature profiles obtained by successive trials are in satisfactory agreement. In the application of the calculational procedure of Thiele and

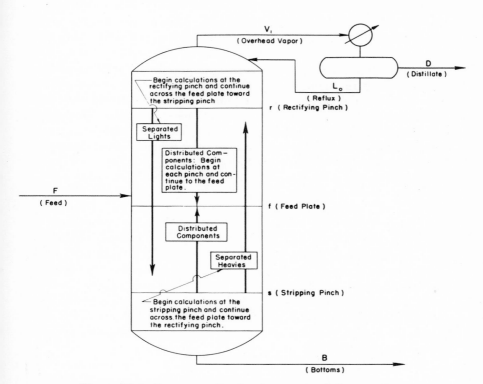

Figure 10–1. For conventional columns at minimum reflux calculations are carried out in the directions indicated.

Geddes to minimum reflux, calculations for the heavy key and all lighter components are made from the rectifying pinch to the feed plate. For all components lighter than the light key, calculations are continued to the stripping pinch. Similarly, for the light key and all components heavier, calculations are begun at the stripping pinch and continued to the feed plate. For all components heavier than the heavy key, calculations are continued from the feed plate to the rectifying pinch. A schematic representation of this procedure is presented in Figure 10–1.

When L_0, D and the other quantities stated previously are specified, the problem to be solved consists of the selection of the key and split-key components and the determination of the corresponding product distribution. Also, for calculational purposes it is necessary to select a suitable number of plates between the pinches. The specification of infinitely many plates in each section of the column is imposed in the statement of the pinch equations which follow.

Pinch Equations

The plates are numbered down from the top of the column. The top plate is assigned the number "1," the rectifying pinch is denoted by the subscript "r," the feed plate by the subscr pt "f," and the pinch in the stripping section by the subscript "s." In the material balances that follow, the single phase lights and heavies are not included.

A material balance enclosing the top of the column and plate $(j-1)$ gives

$$\frac{v_{ji}}{d_i} = \frac{l_{j-1,i}}{d_i} + 1 \tag{10–1}$$

for the heavy key and all components lighter than the heavy key compo⁻ nent. Since $l_{j-1,i} = A_{j-1,i}v_{j-1,i}$. Equation (10–1) may be stated as follows:

$$v_{ji}/d_i = A_{j-1,i}(v_{j-1}/d_i) + 1 \tag{10–2}$$

The conditions at the "rectifying pinch" are implied by the following limit:

$$\lim_{j\to\infty} \frac{v_{ji}}{d_i} = \frac{v_{j-1,i}}{d_i} = \frac{v_{ri}}{d_i} \tag{10–3}$$

The existence of this limit is established in a subsequent section, where it is also shown that at the rectifying pinch, Equation (10–2) takes the form

$$\frac{v_{ri}}{d_i} = \frac{1}{1 - A_{ri}} \tag{10–4}$$

Similarly, the light key and all components heavier are represented by the following equation at the stripping section pinch.

$$\frac{l_{si}}{b_i} = \frac{1}{1 - S_{si}} \tag{10–5}$$

Selection of the Key and Split-Key Components

On the basis of an assumed set of L/V's and temperatures, the heavy key is the heaviest component of the mixture that gives a positive number less than ρ for v_{ri}/d_i, Equation (10–4), where ρ is a number of the order of magnitude of the upper limit of the computer. Similarly, the light key is the lightest component of the mixture that gives a positive number less than ρ for l_{si}/b_i, Equation (10–5). Distributed components are those that satisfy the following inequalities, simultaneously:

$$0 < v_{ri}/d_i < \rho \tag{10–6}$$

$$0 < l_{si}/b_i < \rho \tag{10–7}$$

A separated heavy component is one for which

$$A_{ri} \geqq 1$$

Similarly, for a separated light component

$$S_{si} \geqq 1$$

Use of these criteria, which are based on Equations (10–4) and (10–5), eliminates the necessity for making calculations for all components from the top of the column down and from the bottom of the column up toward the feed plate in order to detect the separated lights and heavies, as was described in Chapter 6 for conventional and complex columns with a finite number of plates. (Note that in practice the value used for ρ is 10^{-8} because in eight-digit arithmetic absolute values of $(A_{ri} - 1)$ less than 10^{-8} are treated as zero.) The proof that a component may be separated and the conditions required for such a separation are presented in a subsequent section.

Material Balances

The material balances are written around the top of the column and plates r through $(f - 1)$ as follows. Since the conditions at the rectifying pinch may be determined independently of the conditions existing between plates 1 and r, the flow rates and temperatures of these intermediate plates are not needed in the determination of the product distribution. In practice, the pinches are considered to be located a finite number of plates from the feed plate. The adjustment of the locations assumed initially is discussed in a subsequent section. Equations (10–8) and (10–9), which follow, do not apply for the single phase lights and heavies. The treatment of these is given in a following section.

1. *Material Balances for the Heavy Key and all Lighter Components*

$$\frac{v_{ri}}{d_i} = \frac{1}{1 - A_{ri}} \tag{10-8a}$$

$$\frac{v_{j+1,i}}{d_i} = A_{ji}\left(\frac{v_{ji}}{d_i}\right) + 1, \quad r \leq j \leq f - 2 \tag{10-8b}$$

$$\frac{\bar{v}_{fi}}{d_i} = A_{f-1,i}\left(\frac{v_{f-1,i}}{d_i}\right) + 1 \tag{10-8c}$$

For any component lighter than the light key, calculations are continued to the stripping pinch as follows. For these components $d_i = FX_i$. Thus

$$l_{f-1,i} = A_{f-1,i}\left(\frac{v_{f-1,i}}{d_i}\right) FX_i \tag{10-8d}$$

A material balance enclosing the bottom of the column and the feed plate gives

$$v_{fi} = l_{f-1,i} + l_{Fi} \tag{10-8e}$$

The remaining material balances are represented by

$$v_{j+1,i} = A_{ji}v_{ji}, \quad f \leq j \leq s - 1 \tag{10-8f}$$

2. *Material Balances for the Light Key and all Heavier Components*

These balances enclose the bottom of the column and either plate s or any plate above s, as indicated. Again, the following material balances do not apply for the single phase light and heavy components.

$$\frac{l_{si}}{b_i} = \frac{1}{1 - S_{si}} \tag{10-9a}$$

$$\frac{l_{j-1,i}}{b_i} = S_{ji}\left(\frac{l_{ji}}{b_i}\right) + 1, \quad f + 1 \leq j \leq s \tag{10-9b}$$

$$\frac{\bar{l}_{f-1,i}}{b_i} = S_{fi}\left(\frac{l_{fi}}{b_i}\right) + 1 \tag{10-9c}$$

For any component heavier than the heavy key, $b_i = FX_i$. Thus

$$v_{fi} = S_{fi}\left(\frac{l_{fi}}{b_i}\right) FX_i \tag{10-9d}$$

Next a material balance enclosing the top of the column and plate $(f - 1)$ gives

$$l_{f-1,i} = v_{fi} + v_{Fi} \tag{10-9e}$$

The remainder of the material balances for all components heavier than the heavy key are represented by

$$l_{j-1,i} = S_{ji} l_{ji}, \quad r + 1 \leqq j \leqq f - 1 \tag{10-9f}$$

Calculation of b_i/d_i

After the material balance calculations have been completed, the calculated value of b/d for each distributed component is found by use of Equation (3-22). If the value of b_i/d_i obtained satisfies the following inequality

$$\frac{1}{\rho} < \frac{b_i}{d_i} < \rho \tag{10-10}$$

this fact implies that a proper classification of components was made for the given trial calculation. If a value of $b_i/d_i > \rho$ is obtained, the component should be reclassified as a separated heavy, and the calculations indicated by Equation (10-9) should be performed. Similarly, if $b_i/d_i < 1/\rho$, the component should be reclassified as a separated light, and the calculations indicated by Equation (10-8) should be performed.

Proof of the Existence of the Rectifying and Stripping Section Pinches

Since the existence of each of these is established in the same manner, the proof is given for only one, the rectifying pinch. The proof makes use of a basic idea stated by Robinson and Gilliland (10). If calculations are made by the procedure of Lewis and Matheson (which consists of alternate material balance and bubble point calculations) from the top of the column down toward the feed plate on the basis of any given set of d_i's whose sum is D and a set of L's and V's related by $V = L + D$ for all plates, a set of constant compositions will be obtained in the limit as the number of step-by-step calculations are increased without bound.

Let the components in D be numbered in the order of decreasing volatility to give

$$K_{j1} > K_{j2} > K_{j3} > \ldots > K_{jc} \tag{10-11}$$

for any plate j. By the calculational procedure of Lewis and Matheson, a temperature is found for each plate j such that the dew point equation

$$\sum_{i=1}^{c} \frac{y_{ji}}{K_{ji}} = 1 \qquad (10\text{--}12)$$

is satisfied. Since the sum of the y_{ji}'s is by definition equal to unity, it follows from Equation (10–11) that for some of the components, $K_{ji} < 1$, and for the remainder, $K_{ji} \geq 1$. Thus for the most volatile component $K_{j1} > 1$ for all j; furthermore, this is the only component for which this statement can be made with certainty. The calculational procedure of Lewis and Matheson leads to a temperature profile and a set of flow rates for each component. The temperatures may be used to compute a set of A_{j1}'s, which may be used to represent the flow rates by use of the following equations:

$$\frac{v_{1,1}}{d_i} = A_{01} + 1 \qquad (10\text{--}13)$$

$$\frac{v_{j+1,1}}{d_i} = A_{j1}\left(\frac{v_{j1}}{d_1}\right) + 1 \qquad (10\text{--}14)$$

Repeated substitution of the expression for v_{j1}/d_1 into the one for $v_{j+1,1}/d_1$ gives

$$\frac{v_{j+1,1}}{d_1} = 1 + A_{j1} + A_{j1}A_{j-1,1} + A_{j1}A_{j-1,1}A_{j-2,1} + \cdots$$

$$\cdots + A_{j1}A_{j-1,1}\ldots A_{j-k,1} + \cdots + A_{j1}A_{j-1,1}\ldots A_{01} \qquad (10\text{--}15)$$

Now consider the series obtained by taking $K_{j1} = 1$ for all j,

$$\frac{v_{j+1,1}}{d_i} < t_{j1} = 1 + \frac{L}{V} + \left(\frac{L}{V}\right)^2 + \cdots + \left(\frac{L}{V}\right)^j + \left(\frac{L}{V}\right)^j\left(\frac{L}{D}\right) \qquad (10\text{--}16)$$

The first j terms of this series are recognized as a geometric series whose sum is well known. Thus

$$t_{j1} = \frac{1 - (L/V)^{j+1}}{1 - (L/V)} + \left(\frac{L}{V}\right)^j\left(\frac{L}{D}\right) \qquad (10\text{--}17)$$

Now let j take on all values to give an infinite series. Since $V > L$ and V/D is finite, the infinite series converges to the sum given by

$$\lim_{j\to\infty} t_{j1} = \frac{1}{1 - (L/V)} \qquad (10\text{--}18)$$

By the comparison test [see Reference (12)] the series for $v_{j+1,1}/d_1$, Equation (10–15), converges as j increases because each term of this series is smaller than the corresponding term of Equation (10–16). Also its sum, denoted by v_{r1}/d_1, is less than the one given by Equation (10–18).

  The series for each of the remaining components has a limit as j is increased without bound. The same approach used for component 1 can not be followed in the remainder of the proof of the proposition because for some of the components for which $K_{ji} < 1$, it may be that $A_{ji} > 1$, particularly component c, for which $K_{jc} < 1$ for all j. The proof is as follows. By definition of the mole fraction

$$y_{j+1,1} = 1 - \sum_{i=2}^{c} y_{j+1,i} \qquad (10\text{–}19)$$

The limit of $y_{j+1,1}$ exists as j approaches infinity, since

$$y_{j+1,1} = \left(\frac{v_{j+1,1}}{d_1}\right)\left(\frac{d_1}{V}\right)$$

Hence the limit of the right hand side exists and has the value

$$\lim_{j\to\infty} \sum_{i=2}^{c} \left(\frac{v_{j+1,i}}{d_i}\right)\left(\frac{d_i}{V}\right) = 1 - \left(\frac{v_{r1}}{d_1}\right)\left(\frac{d_1}{V}\right)$$

Also, since all of the d_i's are finite as well as V,

$$\lim_{j\to\infty} \sum_{i=2}^{c} \frac{v_{j+1,1}}{d_i}$$

exists, or the infinite series,

$$(c-1) + \sum_{i=2}^{c} A_{ji} + \sum_{i=2}^{c} A_{ji}A_{j-1,i} + \sum_{i=2}^{c} A_{ji}A_{j-1,i}A_{j-2,i} + \cdots$$

$$+ \sum_{i=2}^{c} A_{ji}A_{j-1,i}\ldots A_{j-k,i} + \cdots + \sum_{i=2}^{c} A_{ji}A_{j-1,i}\ldots A_{0i} + \cdots \qquad (10\text{–}20)$$

converges. Upon comparison of the series for component c with the one given by Equation (10–20), the series for component c is seen to converge, since each term of the series for this component is less than the corresponding term of Equation (10–20). Similarly, the series for each of the remaining components is shown to converge. Thus

$$\lim_{j\to\infty} \left(\frac{v_{j+1,i}}{d_i}\right) = \frac{v_{ri}}{d_i} \quad \text{for all } i$$

Since each $y_{j+1,i}$ has a limit, y_{ri}, the temperature also has a limit which follows from Equation (10–12). Thus A_{ji} has the limit A_{ri}. With this fact established, Equation (10–4) is readily developed. In the limit as j approaches infinity, Equation (10–14) becomes

$$\frac{v_{ri}}{d_i} = A_{ri}\left(\frac{v_{ri}}{d_i}\right) + 1 \tag{10–21}$$

which may be solved for v_{ri}/d_i to give Equation (10–4). Since each term in the series for $v_{j+1,i}/d_i$ is positive for all values of j, v_{ri}/d_i is positive and hence $A_{ri} < 1$ for all components in the distillate. Similarly, the existence of a pinch in the stripping section is established.

The above proof is readily extended to include the variable-L/V problem. First, observe that the proof shown is valid for any set of L/V's (provided, of course, $L/V < 1$). If the condenser duty is specified and the distillate composition and rate are known, one could perform step-by-step calculations of the Lewis and Matheson type for each of several sets of L/V's to obtain the corresponding conditions at the pinch. (Note: Fixing Q_c amounts to fixing V_1 (or L_0) since both the rate and composition of the distillate are considered fixed for all sets of L/V.) The results so obtained could be used to determine the condenser duty by an enthalpy balance. Obviously, this procedure could be repeated until a set of L/V's in agreement with the specified condenser duty is found. The final results of such a sequence of calculations give rise to a particular set of A_{ji}'s, denoted by $A_{ri} = (L_r/K_{ri}V_r)$. Now consider the following model in which the A_{ji}'s are allowed to take on any finite, positive set of values (such as those determined by equilibrium relations and enthalpy balances) on each of the first n plates. It is to be understood that n remains fixed and finite throughout the argument. For all $j > n$, the model consists of taking $A_{ji} = A_{ri}$ as the set which satisfies equilibrium relations and enthalpy balances at the pinch. The value of v_{ni}/d_i for the first n plates may be computed by use of Equation (10–15). Let this sum be denoted by M_i. Then

$$\frac{v_{n+1,i}}{d_i} = A_{ri}\left(\frac{v_{ni}}{d_i}\right) + 1 = 1 + A_{ri}M_i$$

$$\frac{v_{n+2,i}}{d_i} = A_{ri}\left(\frac{v_{n+1,i}}{d_i}\right) + 1 = 1 + A_{ri} + A_{ri}^2 M_i$$

$$\vdots$$

$$\frac{v_{n+m,i}}{d_i} = 1 + A_{ri} + A_{ri}^2 + \ldots + A_{ri}^{m-2} + A_{ri}^{m-1} + A_{ri}^m M_i$$

$$= \frac{1 - A_r^m}{1 - A_{ri}} + A_{ri}^m M_i \tag{10–22}$$

Since $A_{ri} < 1$ as shown previously,

$$\lim_{m \to \infty} \frac{v_{n+m,i}}{d_i} = \frac{1}{1 - A_{ri}}$$

which gives the same limit obtained previously. Hence the pinch equations apply for variable L/V problems.

Proof of the Separation of Certain Components

For any given set of d_i's and an infinite number of plates in the rectifying section, the existence of a pinch in this part of the column has been established. The proof of its existence did not depend upon the conditions in the stripping section. Similarly, the proof of the existence of a stripping pinch is independent of the conditions in the rectifying section. In order for a set of d_i's and corresponding b_i's to be the correct set for a column, it is necessary that these terminal rates not only satisfy the pinch equations but also the equations for plates between the two pinches. Frequently, it is found that in order to satisfy all equations simultaneously, some of the components which appear in D do not appear in B, and conversely. The separation of a relative heavy component corresponds to and is detected in a very similar manner to that described previously for a conventional column in which a heavy component was taken to be separated ($d_i = 0$) when a j was found such that v_{ji}/d_i exceeded some large preassigned number. With an infinite number of plates, the detection is made at the pinch. If for a given L_r/V_r and T_r, $A_{ri} = 1$, the component is said to be separated since v_{ri}/d_i either becomes an infinitely large positive number or a negative number. The latter implies that the series, Equation (10–15), diverges as j approaches infinity.

First, if $A_{ji} \geq 1$ for all plates in the rectifying section and $S_{ji} < 1$ for all plates in the stripping section, then $d_i = 0$. In the rectifying section let $A_{ji} = 1$ for all j. In the stripping section let $S_{ji} = V_s/L_s$ (where $L_s = V_s + B$) for all j except $j = N + 1$; and for the reboiler let $S_{N+1,i} = V_s/B$, which amounts to taking $K_{ji} = 1$ for all j. At the stripping pinch the value of l_{si}/b_i is given by an expression similar to Equation (10–15) and denoted by M_i; that is

$$\frac{l_{si}}{b_i} = M_i$$

Continuation of the calculations for an infinity of plates between the stripping section pinch and the feed plate yields

$$\frac{v_{fi}}{b_i} = \frac{(V_s/L_s)}{1 - (V_s/L_s)} \qquad (10\text{–}23)$$

(Note: the quantity M_i does not appear in this expression because the term which included it vanished in the limit.) The result obtained by making calculations to the top of a column with a finite number of plates may be represented by Equation (3–22), where,

$$\frac{l_{f-1,i}}{d_i} = A_{f-1,i} + A_{f-1,i}A_{f-2,i} + A_{f-1,i}A_{f-2,i}A_{f-3,i} + \cdots$$

$$+ A_{f-1,i}A_{f-2,i}\ldots A_{1i}A_{0i}$$

For $A_{ji} = 1$ in the rectifying section, it is seen that $l_{f-1,i}/d_i = f$. Substitution of this result together with the one given by Equation (10–23) into Equation (3–22) and taking the limit gives

$$\lim_{f\to\infty}\left(\frac{d_i}{b_i}\right) = \lim_{f\to\infty}\left[\frac{\dfrac{V_s/L_s}{1-(V_s/L_s)}+\dfrac{v_{Fi}}{FX_i}}{f+\dfrac{l_{Fi}}{FX_i}}\right] = 0 \qquad (10\text{–}24)$$

Since B is finite, it follows that each b_i is finite and hence $d_i = 0$. Extension of this proof to include variable-L/V problems is analogous to that shown in the proof of the existence of the pinches.

Convergence Method

After the calculated values of b_i/d_i for the distributed components have been obtained, the θ-method is applied in the usual way. Compositions are calculated by use of Equations (6–3) through (6–7). Separated components are treated in the same way as that shown in Chapter 6. After the compositions have been computed, the temperatures are calculated by use of the bubble point procedure.

Enthalpy Balances

The condenser duty must be determined prior to the calculation of the molal rates of flow between the two pinches. On the basis of the corrected d_i's, the temperature of the distillate is obtained by making a bubble point calculation. (When a partial condenser is specified, a dew point calculation is made.) Then the l_{0i}'s are readily obtained since L_0 and D are known. The flow rate of each component in the overhead vapor is given by $v_{1i} = l_{0i} + d_i$. The temperature of the top plate is found by making a dew point calculation on the basis of the v_{1i}'s.

The flow rates throughout the column may be determined by use of a combination of the constant-composition and Q-methods for making enthalpy balances as follows:

$$Q_c = L_0[H(x_0)_1 - h_0] + D[H(X_D)_1 - H_D] \qquad (10\text{--}25a)$$

For the plates between the two pinches

$$L_r = \frac{D(H_D - H(X_D)_r] + Q_c}{[H(x_r)_r - h_r]} \qquad (10\text{--}25b)$$

$$L_j = \frac{D[H_D - H(X_D)_{i+1}] + Q_c + \sum_{k=r}^{j-1} Q_k}{[H(x_j)_{i+1} - h_j]}, \quad r + 1 \leqq j \leqq f - 2 \qquad (10\text{--}25c)$$

$$L_{f-1} = \frac{D[H_D - H(X_D)_f] + Q_c + V_F[H(y_F)_f - H_F] + \sum_{k=r}^{f-2} Q_k}{[H(x_{f-1})_f - h_{f-1}]} \qquad (10\text{--}25d)$$

$$L_j = \frac{D[H_D - H(X_D)_{i+1}] + Q_c - F[H - H(X)_{i+1}] + \sum_{k=r}^{j-1} Q_k}{[H(x_j)_{i+1} - h_j]},$$
$$f \leqq j \leqq s - 1. \qquad (10\text{--}25e)$$

The corresponding total vapor rates are given by the following material balances:

$$V_i = L_{j-1} + D, \quad r \leqq j \leqq f - 1 \qquad (10\text{--}26a)$$

(Note: $L_{r-1} = L_r$)

$$\bar{V}_f = L_{f-1} + D \qquad (10\text{--}26b)$$

$$V_f = \bar{L}_{f-1} - B \qquad (10\text{--}26c)$$

$$V_i = L_{j-1} - B, \quad f + 1 \leqq j \leqq s \qquad (10\text{--}26d)$$

(Note: $L_{s-1} = L_s$)

For the given set of specifications, calculations are initiated at the top of the column as implied by Equation (10–25). After the intercooler (or heater) duties have been determined for the stripping pinch and all plates above it, the over-all enthalpy balance

$$Q_R = DH_D + Bh_B + Q_c + \sum_{k=r}^{s} Q_k - FH \qquad (10\text{-}27)$$

is used to compute the combined duty for the reboiler and all plates between it and the stripping pinch.

Selection of a Suitable Finite Set of Plates Between the Two Pinches

This selection was made by use of a concept described by Bachelor (2). When the keys are two distinct components other than the lightest and heaviest of the feed, the pinches are separated by infinitely many plates. The pinches occur in the limit as the "separated" components are separated in the rectifying and stripping sections. That is, for any preassigned positive number less than unity, there exists a plate (going from the feed plate toward the top of the column) beyond which the mole fraction for component $(h - 1)$ is less than the preassigned number. Thus, too few plates may be selected, but not too many. In view of this, some arbitrary number of plates may be selected for the first trial, say five in the rectifying and five in the stripping section. At the end of each trial the original estimate may be adjusted by the addition of one plate to each section of the column. (Of course it is necessary from a practical point of view to set an upper limit on the total number of plates.) In the rectifying section a plate is added just above the pinch for the previous trial and becomes the pinch-plate r for the next trial. In the stripping section it is added just below the previous pinch and becomes the pinch-plate s for the next trial. The total molal rates of flow for the added pinch plates are taken equal to those calculated for the respective pinches by the previous trial. The temperatures of the pinches (the two plates added) are taken equal to the corrected values obtained for the plates denoted by r and s in the previous trial. For all problems that were considered, solutions were obtained with less than sixty plates above and below the feed plate.

Direct Solutions for Special Cases

When all of the components are distributed, the pinches in the rectifying and stripping sections occur at and adjacent to the feed plate. A method which consists of a direct solution to this problem has been presented previously (6). Example 10–2 (see Table 10–1) was solved by the general procedure presented in this chapter and the same results were obtained as those found previously (6). These results are presented in Table 10–3.

When all of the components are separated (a perfect split) or when there is only one distributed component, a direct solution to the problem is obtained by solving each of two pairs of equations simultaneously. Since the conditions at the rectifying pinch are independent of the plates between the top plate and the rectifying pinch, the calculational procedure of Lewis and Matheson reduces to a single equation (where it is of course understood that the L/V's are fixed). Similarly, it reduces to a single equation for all plates between the reboiler and the stripping pinch. Also, since the product distribution is known where either all components or all except one are separated, the calculations need not be carried out between the two pinches. In the application of the general calculational procedure systems of these types were found. Several trials were carried out by use of the general procedure in order to make fairly certain that a system classified as a special case had been found. Then the general calculational procedure was abandoned, and the equations that follow were solved directly. These equations are based on adiabatic operation for all plates between the respective pinches and the top and the bottom of the column. The equations for the rectifying pinch are developed as follows. In the interest of simplicity all of the components are taken to be volatile; that is, no single phase lights and heavies are present. Since the vapor and liquid are in equilibrium at the pinch in the rectifying section, it follows from Equation (10–4) that

$$\frac{l_{ri}}{d_i} = \frac{A_{ri}}{1 - A_{ri}} \tag{10–28}$$

which may be written as follows:

$$x_{ri} = \frac{X_{Di}}{1 - \psi_r(1 - K_{ri})} \tag{10–29}$$

where

$$\psi_r = V_r/D$$

Summing both sides of Equation (10–29) over all components present in the rectifying pinch leads to the following material-balance function,

$$P_1(\psi_r, T_r) = \sum_{i=1}^{c} \frac{X_{Di}}{1 - \psi_r(1 - K_{ri})} - 1 \tag{10–30}$$

It is to be understood that $X_{Di} = 0$ for all of the separated heavy components in this and other equations to follow for the rectifying pinch.

After Q_c has been found by use of Equation (10–25a), the conditions at the top of the column have been completely determined since the composition of the distillate is known and since D and V_1 are specified. An enthalpy balance enclosing the top of the column and the rectifying pinch takes the form

$$L_r[H(x_r)_r - h_r] + D[H(X_D)_r - H_D] - Q_c = 0 \qquad (10\text{--}31)$$

Recall that

$$H(x_r)_r - h_r = \sum_{i=1}^{c} (H_{ri} - h_{ri})x_{ri} = \sum_{i=1}^{c} \lambda_{ri} x_{ri}$$

The x_{ri}'s in this expression may be eliminated by use of Equation (10–29). Making use of the result so obtained, Equation (10–31) may be rearranged to give the following expression for the enthalpy-balance function:

$$P_2(\psi_r,\ T_r)\ =\ (1 - \psi_r)\ \sum_{i=1}^{c} \frac{\lambda_{ri} X_{Di}}{1 - \psi_r(1 - K_{ri})} + \left[H(X_D)_r - H_D - \frac{Q_c}{D} \right]$$

$$(10\text{--}32)$$

Equations (10–30) and (10–32) represent two independent equations in two unknowns ψ_r and T_r. The desired solution is that pair of positive values of ψ_r and T_r that not only give $P_1 = P_2 = 0$ but that also satisfy the conditions:

$$1 < \psi_r < \frac{1}{1 - K_{rh}}$$

$$T_{\text{D.P.}} < T_r < T_h$$

where $T_{\text{D.P.}}$ is that temperature obtained by making a dew point calculation on the basis of the X_{Di}'s and T_h is that temperature at which $K_{rh} = 1$. The function P_1 has two trivial solutions: one at $\psi_r = 0$ (for any T_r) and the other one at $\psi_r = 1$ (for $T_r = T_{\text{D.P.}}$). The desired value of ψ_r is the positive root of the function P_1 which lies between $\psi_r = 1$ and

$$\psi_r = 1/(1 - K_{rh}).$$

In order for the function P_1 to have a positive root bounded in this manner, it is necessary that the assumed value of T_r lie between $T_{\text{D.P.}}$ and T_h. The behavior of the function P_1 in the neighborhood of the desired positive root is shown in Figure 10–2. These functions are of the same general form as the material and enthalpy balance functions for the adiabatic flash which were presented in Chapter 2. Equations (10–30) and (10–32) may be solved for the desired values of ψ_r and T_r by the same procedures (Newton-Raphson and interpolation (*regula falsi*)) as described in Chapter 2, provided that all of the assumed values of the variables satisfy the inequalities stated previously.

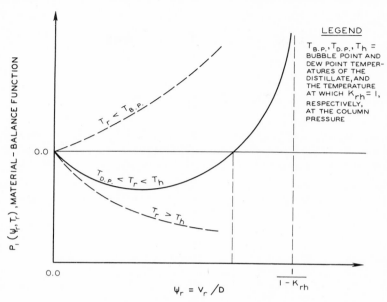

Figure 10–2. The rectifying pinch is represented by that pair of values of T_r and ψ_r, which not only give $P_1 = P_2 = 0$ but also satisfy the following conditions:

$$1 < \psi_r < \frac{1}{1 - K_{rh}} \quad \text{and} \quad T_{D.P.} < T_r < T_h.$$

In a similar manner the following equations for the stripping pinch are developed. The material-balance function is

$$p_1(\psi_s,\ T_s) = \sum_{i=1}^{c} \frac{x_{Bi}}{1 - \psi_s(K_{si} - 1)} - 1 \qquad (10\text{–}33)$$

where

$$\psi_s = V_s/B$$

Also, it is to be understood that $x_{Bi} = 0$ for all of the separated light components in this and other equations for the stripping pinch. The enthalpy-balance function for the stripping pinch is as follows:

$$p_2(\psi_s,\ T_s) = (\psi_s + 1) \sum_{i=1}^{c} \frac{\lambda_{si} x_{Bi}}{1 - \psi_s(K_{si} - 1)}$$

$$- \left[h_B - H(x_B)_s - \frac{Q_R}{B} \right] \qquad (10\text{–}34)$$

After Q_R has been computed by use of an over-all enthalpy balance, Equations (10–33) and (10–34) are solved by use of either the Newton-Raphson method or interpolation (*regula falsi*) for the positive values of ψ_s and T_s that not only give $p_1 = p_2 = 0$, but that also satisfy the conditions

$$0 < \psi_s < \frac{1}{K_{sl} - 1}$$

$$T_l < T_s < T_{\text{B.P.}}$$

where T_l is the temperature at which $K_{sl} = 1$ and $T_{\text{B.P.}}$ is the boiling point of the bottoms at the column pressure. On the basis of the solution (ψ_r, T_r, ψ_s, and T_s), the components are reclassified. If no more than one component is found to be distributed, the solution is valid; otherwise, a return to the general calculational procedure is required.

Frequently when a distillate rate,

$$D = \sum_{i=1}^{k} FX_i, \qquad k < c \tag{10–35}$$

equal to the sum of the FX_i's for the first k components (numbered in the order of decreasing volatility) is specified, a perfect separation is obtained when infinitely many plates are used in each section of the column. A separation is said to be perfect when components $i = 1$ through $i = k$ are separated lights,

$$d_i = FX_i, \qquad i = 1, 2, \ldots, k \tag{10–36}$$

and components $i = k + 1$ through $i = c$ are separated heavies,

$$b_i = FX_i, \qquad i = k + 1, k + 2, \ldots, c \tag{10–37}$$

Since pinches also occur at the top and at the bottom of a column in addition to those at the feed plate for the case of the perfect separation of a binary mixture at minimum reflux, pinches at the top and bottom of a column might be expected to exist for a multicomponent system. However, as shown in the next section, these additional pinches do not exist for multicomponent systems. For multicomponent systems in which the separations are perfect, the conditions at the rectifying and stripping section pinches are found by use of Equations (10–30), (10–32), (10–33) and (10–34).

Proof of the Absence of Certain Pinches for Multicomponent Systems

First, it will be shown that if a multicomponent mixture is perfectly separated, a pinch does not occur at the top of the column. The truth of this statement will be established by means of an indirect proof. By this method the contrary of the given statement will be assumed, and a contradiction will be obtained. In the following proof a column with a partial condenser is selected for consideration. If it is now assumed that a pinch exists at the top of the column, the following relationships may be stated:

$$X_{Di} = y_{0i} = y_{1i} = y_{2i} = \ldots$$

$$x_{0i} = x_{1i} = x_{2i} = \ldots$$

$$V_1 = V_2 = V_3 = \ldots \tag{10-38}$$

$$L_0 = L_1 = L_2 = \ldots$$

A material balance around the condenser yields

$$V_1 y_{0i} = L_0 x_{0i} + D X_{Di} \tag{10-39}$$

Since $X_{Di} = y_{0i} = K_{0i} x_{0i}$, Equation (10–39) reduces to

$$(V_1 - D)(K_{0i}) = L_0$$

and since $V_1 - D = L_0$, the result

$$K_{0i} = 1 \tag{10-40}$$

is obtained. This is recognized as a contradiction because it was given that the distillate leaves the column as a dew point vapor. Since the K_i's differ for each component, it follows from Equation (10–12) that some of the K_i's are less than unity and the remainder are greater than unity (except for not more than one component which may have a K-value equal to unity). Therefore, the original statement is true. For a column with a total condenser the proof is constructed in an analogous manner. In like manner, the possibility of a pinch at the bottom of the column is ruled out.

Illustrative Examples

A wide variety of problems have been solved successfully by the procedures proposed by McDonough (7). In order to illustrate these methods, a fairly simple problem was selected (see Table 10–1) by McDonough and Holland (8).

The operating conditions were varied as required in order to produce different arrays of separated components. In Example 10–1 three components were separated, in Example 10–2 all components were distributed, and in Example 10–3 all components were separated. The solutions are presented in Tables 10–2 through 10–4.

In these examples, the temperatures of the distillate and the bottoms were correct to within 4 or 5 digits of the final values at the end of five or ten trials. This accuracy in the terminal temperatures suggests a corresponding accuracy in the product distribution, the determination of which is the primary objective of the general calculational procedure.

However, in order to obtain the same accuracy for the pinch temperatures, several additional trials were required. This was caused in part by an insufficient number of plates between the pinches. When this situation exists, a sizable mole fraction of a separated heavy component, for example, is computed at the rectifying pinch by use of Equation (10–9f). Thus additional trials are required for such examples in order to provide a sufficient number of plates between the pinches. This need was most pronounced for cases where either all components or all except one were separated. However, for such examples the pinch temperatures may be found by means of a direct solution, which is of course recommended. Also, for such examples the terminal temperatures and rates at the end of the first five or ten trials were either equal to or very nearly equal to the correct values as shown in Tables 10–2 and 10–3. When all of the components are separated, θ is set equal to unity in all of the formulas in which it appears. The results presented in Tables 10–2 through 10–4 indicate that the rate of convergence of problems solved by the general calculational procedure tends to increase as the number of components of the mixture involved in the determination of θ increases.

In order to determine the effect of the number of plates selected initially on the rate of convergence, the three examples were solved by the general calculational procedure for two cases. In the first, 10 plates and in the second case, 102 plates between the pinches were selected. The results are given in Table 10–5. Although there is perhaps a better number of plates with which to begin than 10, little is gained by commencing with a large number of plates. Moreover, the only examples that required an appreciable number of trials by the general calculational procedure could and should be solved directly.

COMPLEX COLUMNS

The calculational procedures described for conventional columns operating at minimum reflux may be extended to include complex columns. The resulting procedures are presented and demonstrated for the case of a column with one feed plate and one side-stream withdrawn (in addition to the distillate and bottoms). Equations are developed for the case where the side-stream is withdrawn as a liquid from a plate located above the feed plate. Each of two locations for the side-stream W_1 are considered. In the first, the side-stream is withdrawn a finite number of plates from the top of the column; and in the second, it is withdrawn a finite number of

TABLE 10–1 Statement and specifications for Examples 10–1, 10–2, and 10–3

Component	Component No.	Examples 10–1, 10–2, 10–3 FX	Specifications			
			Example	V_1	D	Others
C_3H_8	1	20	10–1	150	40	For all examples: column pressure = 400 psia, partial condenser, thermal condition of the feed is boiling point liquid. Initial temperature profile: linear between pinches (252–282°F). Initial vapor rates: $V_j = V_1$ for all j. For all examples: $V_{min} = 5$, and $V_{max} = 250$. Use the equilibrium and enthalpy data given in Tables A–5 and A–8 of the Appendix.
i-C_4	2	20	10–2	55	40	
n-C_4	3	20	10–3	200	60	
i-C_5	4	20				
n-C_5	5	20				

Reproduced by permission of *Hydrocarbon Processing & Petroleum Refiner*

TABLE 10–2 Temperature and vapor rate profiles obtained in the solution of Example 10–1 (the solution shows components 1, 4, and 5 are separated.)

Plate No.	Temperature* profiles (°F) Trial No.				Final vapor rates (Trial No. 20)	Final product distribution (Trial No. 20)		
	5	10	15	20		Component	d	b
0 (Distillate)	217.57	217.63	217.64	217.64		C_3H_8	20	0.0
r	245.23	244.92	244.89	244.88	151.388	i-C_4	14.575759	5.4242396
r + 1	245.50	244.95	244.89	244.88	151.388	n-C_4	5.4242396	14.575759
r + 2	246.12	245.03	244.90	244.88	151.387	i-C_5	0.0	20
r + 3	247.18	246.16	244.91	244.88	151.385	n-C_5	0.0	20
f (Feed)	272.29	272.03	272.05	272.05	136.562			
s − 2	288.62	289.72	289.90	289.93	151.374			
s − 1	289.26	289.83	289.92	289.93	151.377			
s	289.57	289.88	289.93	289.94	151.380			
N + 1 (Bottoms)	323.25	323.22	323.21	323.21				
D (Calculated)	40.034	40.00000	39.9992	39.99997				
θ	1.0042	0.999999	0.999896	0.999996				
Separated components	1, 4, 5	1, 4, 5	1, 4, 5	1, 4, 5				

Reproduced by permission of *Hydrocarbon Processing & Petroleum Refiner*

TABLE 10–3 Solution of Example 10–2 (the solution shows all components are distributed)

Plate No.	Temperature profile (°F) Trial No.		Final vapor rates	Final product distribution (Trial No. 10)		
	5	10	(Trial No. 10)	Component	d	b
0 (Distillate)	253.43	253.33		C_3H_8	17.168039	2.831960
r	267.39	267.34	54.706	i-C_4	9.501945	10.498054
$r+1$	267.39	267.34	54.706	n-C_4	7.361634	12.638365
$r+2$	267.39	267.34	54.706	i-C_5	3.440505	16.559494
$r+3$	267.39	267.34	54.706	n-C_5	2.527875	17.472125
f (Feed)	267.36	267.34	54.706			
$s-2$	267.33	267.34	54.706			
$s-1$	267.33	267.34	54.706			
s	267.33	267.34	54.706			
$N+1$ (Bottoms)	304.21	304.29				
D (Calculated)	39.983	39.99995				
θ	0.9990	0.999997				
Distributed components	All	All				

Reproduced by permission of *Hydrocarbon Processing & Petroleum Refiner*

TABLE 10-4 Solution of Example 10-3 (the solution shows all components are separated)

Plate No.	Temperature profiles (°F) Trial No.				Final vapor rates	
	5	10	25	(*)	25	(*)
0 (Distillate)	237.57	237.00	237.00	237.00		
r	306.14	284.25	254.87	254.36	203.416	206.403
r + 1	306.14	284.36	254.88		203.416	
r + 2	306.14	284.57	254.89		203.398	
r + 3	306.14	284.86	254.90		203.382	
f (Feed)	307.92	288.37	284.24		182.391	
s − 2	319.82	313.97	341.53		207.754	
s − 1	320.23	314.26	341.63		205.181	
s	320.43	314.41	341.67	352.88	205.181	201.452
N + 1 (Bottoms)	355.41	354.96	354.96	354.96		
D (Calculated)	65.95	60.00000	60.00000			
θ	77.96	1.000000	1.00000			
Separated components	1, 2, 3	All	All			

* Values obtained by direct solution.

Reproduced by permission of *Hydrocarbon Processing & Petroleum Refiner*

TABLE 10–5 Effect of the number of plates selected initially on the number of trials required to give variations less than 0.006°F of respective temperatures between successive trials

Example	Results obtained by starting with 10 plates and adding as described to give a total of 120	Results obtained by starting with 102 plates and adding as described to give a total of 120
10–1 (components 1, 4, 5 are separated)	20	15
10–2 (All components are distributed)	9	24
10–3 (all components are separated)	60 T_r came into the correct value but T_s came into 356.09°F compared with the correct value of 352.88°F, obtained by the direct solution.	50 The correct value for T_r was obtained, and T_s came into 352.87°F compared with the correct value of 352.88°F.

Reproduced by permission of *Hydrocarbon Processing & Petroleum Refiner*

plates above the feed plate. Also, for columns which contain more than one feed plate, a calculational procedure which minimizes round-off error is presented.

In the following development the specifications are taken to be L_0, D, W_1, and an infinity of plates in both the rectifying and stripping sections. In addition to these specifications the type of condenser, the column pressure, the flow rate of the feed as well as its composition and thermal condition are specified, and the location of the side-stream withdrawal are specified. For this set of specifications, the problem is to find the product distribution. The extension of the θ-method of convergence to this particular set of specifications is given first because the resulting minimum reflux problem is very closely related to the application of a combination of the Thiele and Geddes calculational procedure and the θ-method of convergence to complex columns (4, 5). In principle, the problem considered in this chapter differs from the one considered previously for complex columns in that infinitely many plates rather than a finite number are specified in each

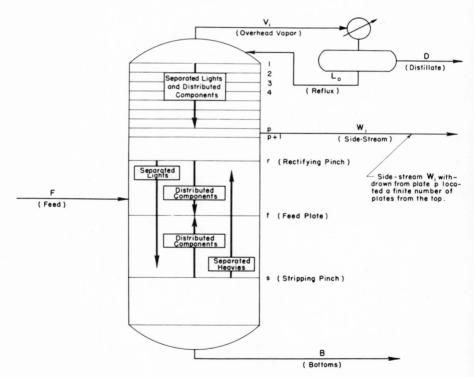

Figure 10–3: When W_1 is withdrawn a finite number of plates below the top of the column, calculations are carried out in the directions indicated.

section of the column. In the next chapter, the combination of the Thiele and Geddes calculational procedure and the θ-method of convergence is extended to include other types of specifications for complex columns such as b_i/d_i for two components instead of L_0 and D. The calculational procedures for each of two possible withdrawal locations for the side-stream W_1 follow.

SIDE-STREAM, W_1, WITHDRAWN A FINITE NUMBER OF PLATES BELOW THE TOP OF THE COLUMN

For this system, the material balances for the rectifying and stripping sections are as follows. Calculations are carried out in the directions shown in Figure 10–3. In the interest of simplicity single phase lights and heavies are not considered in the statement of the equations.

$$\frac{l_{0i}}{d_i} = A_{0i} \tag{10-41a}$$

$$\frac{v_{1i}}{d_i} = A_{0i} + 1 \qquad \text{(balance around condenser)} \tag{10-41b}$$

$$\frac{v_{ji}}{d_i} = A_{j-1,i}\left(\frac{v_{j-1,i}}{d_i}\right) + 1, \quad 2 \leq j \leq p \tag{10-41c}$$

$$\frac{l_{pi}}{d_i} = A_{pi}\left(\frac{v_{pi}}{d_i}\right); \qquad \frac{w_{1i}}{d_i} = \left(\frac{W_1}{L_p}\right)\left(\frac{l_{pi}}{d_i}\right) \tag{10-41d}$$

$$\frac{v_{ri}}{d_i + w_{1i}} = \frac{1}{1 - A_{ri}}, \quad \text{or} \quad \frac{v_{ri}}{d_i} = \frac{C_{1i}}{1 - A_{ri}} \tag{10-41e}$$

$$\frac{v_{j+1,i}}{d_i} = A_{ji}\left(\frac{v_{ji}}{d_i}\right) + C_{1i}, \quad r \leq j \leq f - 2 \tag{10-41f}$$

$$\frac{\bar{v}_{fi}}{d_i} = A_{f-1,i}\left(\frac{v_{f-1,i}}{d_i}\right) + C_{1i} \tag{10-41g}$$

where

$$C_{1i} = 1 + \frac{w_{1i}}{d_i}$$

Stripping Section

$$\frac{l_{Ni}}{b_i} = S_{N+1,i} + 1 \qquad \text{(balance around reboiler)} \qquad (10\text{--}42a)$$

$$\frac{l_{si}}{b_i} = \frac{1}{1 - S_{si}} \qquad\qquad (10\text{--}42b)$$

$$\frac{l_{j-1,i}}{b_i} = S_{ji}\left(\frac{l_{ji}}{b_i}\right) + 1, \quad f + 1 \leqq j \leqq s \qquad (10\text{--}42c)$$

$$\frac{\bar{l}_{f-1,i}}{b_i} = S_{fi}\left(\frac{l_{fi}}{b_i}\right) + 1 \qquad\qquad (10\text{--}42d)$$

The equations for the rectifying section apply for the heavy key and all components lighter. For the separated heavy components,

$$d_i + w_{1i} = 0 \qquad\qquad (10\text{--}43)$$

In the stripping section the flow rates for the separated heavy components are calculated by Equation (10–42), and in the rectifying section the equations stated previously in this chapter for conventional columns are applicable. For a separated light component ($b_i = 0$), the flow rates in the rectifying section are calculated by use of Equation (10–41); and in the stripping section equations analogous to those given previously for conventional column at minimum reflux are readily developed. The difference between the two sets of equations is that for the particular complex column, $d_i = FX_i/C_{1i}$, whereas for conventional columns $d_i = FX_i$.

The following formula for the calculation of b_i/d_i for any distributed component is derived as discussed in Chapters 3 and 7.

$$\frac{b_i}{d_i} = \frac{(l_{f-1,i}/d_i) + C_{1i}(l_{Fi}/FX_i)}{(v_{fi}/b_i) + (v_{Fi}/FX_i)} \qquad (10\text{--}44)$$

In the classification of the components the same scheme is followed as the one described for conventional columns.

Other Relationships

After the calculated values of b_i/d_i and w_{1i}/d_i have been obtained, the θ-method is applied in the same way as described for complex columns in Chapter 7. Compositions are computed by the formulas given in Chapter 6. On the basis of these compositions, the temperatures are determined by the bubble point procedure.

Enthalpy Balances

Before the presentation of the enthalpy balances, one variation in the material balances from the conventional procedure of Thiele and Geddes should be mentioned. Calculations from the top of the column down through plate p are made as indicated by Equation (10–41). After l_{pi} has been evaluated, the vapor rate, $v_{p+1,i}$, is computed by the material balance:

$$v_{p+1,i} = l_{pi} + d_i$$

The temperature of plate $p + 1$ is determined by making a dew point calculation on the basis of the $y_{p+1,i}$'s (obtained from the $v_{p+1,i}$'s). The equations that follow represent enthalpy balances which enclose the top of the column and any plate j, where the constant-composition and Q-methods are employed.

$$Q_c = L_0[H(x_0)_1 - h_0] + D[H(X_D)_1 - H_D] \tag{10-45a}$$

$$L_1 = \frac{D[H_D - H(X_D)_2] + Q_c}{[H(x_1)_2 - h_1]} \tag{10-45b}$$

$$L_j = \frac{D[H_D - H(X_D)_{j+1}] + Q_c + \sum_{k=1}^{j-1} Q_k}{[H(x_j)_{j+1} - h_j]}, \quad 2 \leq j \leq p \tag{10-45c}$$

$$L_r = \frac{D[H_D - H(X_D)_r] + W_1[h_p - H(x_p)_r] + Q_c + \sum_{k=1}^{p} Q_k}{[H(x_r)_r - h_r]} \tag{10-45d}$$

$$L_j = \frac{D[H_D - H(X_D)_{j+1}] + W_1[h_p - H(x_j)_{j+1}] + Q_c + \sum_{k=1}^{p} Q_k + \sum_{k=r}^{j-1} Q_k}{[H(x_j)_{j+1} - h_j]},$$
$$r \leq j \leq f - 2 \tag{10-45e}$$

$$L_{f-1} = \frac{D[H_D - H(X_D)_f] + W_1[h_p - H(x_{f-1})_f] + V_F[H(y_F)_f - H_F]}{[H(x_{f-1})_f - h_{f-1}]}$$
$$+ \frac{Q_c + \sum_{k=1}^{p} Q_k + \sum_{k=r}^{f-2} Q_k}{[H(x_{f-1})_f - h_{f-1}]} \tag{10-45f}$$

$$L_j = \frac{D[H_D - H(X_D)_{j+1}] + W_1[h_p - H(x_j)_{j+1}] - F[H - H(X)_{j+1}]}{[H(x_j)_{j+1} - h_j]}$$

$$+ \frac{Q_c + \sum\limits_{k=1}^{p} Q_k + \sum\limits_{k=r}^{f-2} Q_k}{[H(x_j)_{j+1} - h_j]}, \quad f \leqq j \leqq s - 1 \tag{10–45g}$$

The liquid flow rates are held within the specified limits by use of the Q-method. The corresponding vapor rates are found by use of appropriate material balances.

Solutions for Special Cases

When either all components are separated (they appear either in D and W_1 or B) or all components except one are separated, the following procedure is recommended. It corresponds very nearly to a direct solution. In either the general calculational procedure or the one presented below for the special cases, only θ_1 must be determined by trial when either all components or all except one are separated. The material balance

$$(w_{1i})_{co} + (d_i)_{co} = FX_i - (b_i)_{co} \tag{10–46}$$

may be solved for $(d_i)_{co}$ to give

$$(d_i)_{co} = \frac{FX_i - (b_i)_{co}}{1 + \theta_1(w_{1i}/d_i)_{ca}} \tag{10–47}$$

Observe that $(b_i)_{co}$ is equal to zero for all components except the single distributed component, and for it the value of $(b_i)_{co}$ is known. Thus

$$g_0(\theta_1) = \sum_{i=1}^{c} (d_i)_{co} - D \tag{10–48}$$

which is solved for θ_1 in the usual way. For a system with one distributed component, θ_0 is calculated (after θ_1 has been determined) by use of the definition, Equation (7–1). When all components are separated, θ_0 is taken equal to unity. For each separated heavy, $(d_i)_{co}$ is taken equal to zero in Equation (10–48) as well as in those which follow for the rectifying pinch.

Several trials were carried out by use of the general calculational procedure in order to make fairly certain that a system classified as a special case had been found. Then the general calculational procedure was abandoned, and the one that follows was used.

Since the calculated and corrected values of w_{1i} and d_i for the separated lights (or the separated lights and one distributed component) are independent of the conditions at the rectifying and stripping pinches, the correct distribution of all components appearing in D and W_1 may be determined by consideration of the top part of the column (plates 0 through p) alone. Successive trials are performed by use of the equations representing the material and enthalpy balances for plates zero through p. The corresponding values of θ_1 are found by use of Equation (10–48). When a value of $\theta_1 = 1$ is obtained, a solution to the top part of the column has been found. Then the conditions at the pinches are determined in a manner analogous to that described for conventional columns. At the rectifying pinch the desired set of values for ψ_r and T_r is that positive set which gives $P_1 = P_2 = 0$. The functions P_1 and P_2 are defined as follows:

$$P_1(\psi_r,\ T_r) \ = \ \sum_{i=1}^{c} \frac{(d_i + w_{1i})/(D + W_1)}{1 - \psi_r(1 - K_{ri})} - 1 \tag{10–49}$$

$$P_2(\psi_r,\ T_r) \ = \ (\psi_r - 1) \sum_{i=1}^{c} \frac{[(d_i + w_{1i})/(D + W_1)]\lambda_{ri}}{1 - \psi_r(1 - K_{ri})}$$

$$+ \left(\frac{D}{D + W_1}\right)[H(X_D)_r - H_D] + \left(\frac{W_1}{D + W_1}\right)[H(x_p)_r - h_p] - \frac{Q_c}{D + W_1}$$

$$\tag{10–50}$$

where

$$\psi_r = \frac{V_r}{D + W_1}.$$

In the application of these equations observe that for the separated heavy components $(d_i + w_{1i}) = 0$. The development as well as the method of solution of Equations (10–49) and (10–50) is analogous to that shown and described for Equations (10–30) and (10–32).

Similarly, the conditions $(V_s,\ T_s)$ at the stripping pinch are found by the simultaneous solution of $p_1(\psi_s,\ T_s)$ and $p_2(\psi_s,\ T_s)$, Equations (10–33) and (10–34).

SIDE-STREAM, W_1, WITHDRAWN A FINITE NUMBER OF PLATES ABOVE THE FEED PLATE

When the side-stream is withdrawn below the rectifying pinch, the corresponding calculational procedure is very nearly the same as that shown for the previous case. Calculations are carried out as indicated in Figure 10–4. The material balances for the stripping section are given by

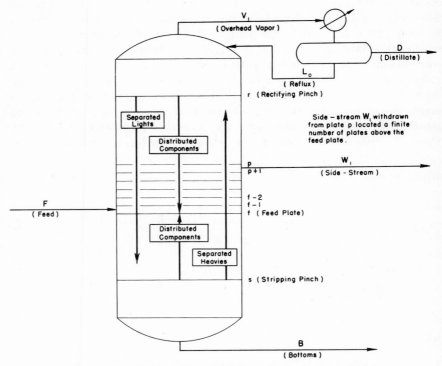

Figure 10–4. When W_1 is withdrawn a finite number of plates above the feed plate, calculations are carried out in the directions indicated.

Equation (10–42). For the rectifying section the material balances are as follows:

$$\frac{l_{0i}}{d_i} = A_{0i} \tag{10–51a}$$

$$\frac{v_{1i}}{d_i} = A_{0i} + 1 \tag{10–51b}$$

$$\frac{v_{ri}}{d_i} = \frac{1}{1 - A_{ri}} \tag{10–51c}$$

$$\frac{v_{j+1,i}}{d_i} = A_{ji}\left(\frac{v_{ji}}{d_i}\right) + 1, \quad r \le j \le p \tag{10–51d}$$

$$\frac{l_{pi}}{d_i} = A_{pi}\left(\frac{v_{pi}}{d_i}\right), \qquad \frac{w_{1i}}{d_i} = \left(\frac{W_1}{L_p}\right)\left(\frac{l_{pi}}{d_i}\right) \tag{10–51e}$$

$$\frac{v_{j+1,i}}{d_i} = A_{ji}\left(\frac{v_{ji}}{d_i}\right) + C_{1i}, \quad p+1 \leqq j \leqq f-2 \tag{10–51f}$$

$$\frac{\bar{v}_{fi}}{d_i} = A_{f-1,i}\left(\frac{v_{f-1,i}}{d_i}\right) + C_{1i} \tag{10–51g}$$

Equations (10–42) and (10–51) apply for all of the distributed components. For a separated light component calculations are made down from the top of the column to the feed plate as indicated by Equation (10–51). Then in a manner analogous to that shown for conventional columns, calculations are continued from the feed plate toward the pinch in the stripping section.

For a separated heavy component, calculations are made from the bottom of the column to the feed plate as indicated by Equation (10–42). From the feed plate calculations are continued to plate p in the rectifying section by use of the following equations, which represent material balances that enclose the top of the column and any plate j above the feed plate.

$$\frac{l_{f-1,i}}{b_i} = \left(\frac{v_{fi}}{b_i} + \frac{v_{Fi}}{b_i}\right) - \frac{w_{1i}}{b_i} \tag{10–52a}$$

$$\frac{l_{ji}}{b_i} = S_{j+1,i}\left(\frac{l_{j+1,i}}{b_i}\right) - \frac{w_{1i}}{b_i}, \quad p+1 \leqq j \leqq f-2 \tag{10–52b}$$

$$\frac{l_{pi}}{b_i} = S_{p+1,i}\left(\frac{l_{p+1,i}}{b_i}\right) \tag{10–52c}$$

$$\frac{w_{1i}}{b_i} = \left(\frac{W_1}{L_p}\right)\left(\frac{l_{pi}}{b_i}\right) \tag{10–52d}$$

$$\frac{l_{ji}}{b_i} = S_{j+1,i}\left(\frac{l_{j+1,i}}{b_i}\right), \quad f \leqq j \leqq p-1 \tag{10–52e}$$

Prior to the application of Equation (10–52), w_{1i}/b_i must be evaluated. By repeated substitution of the expression for $l_{j+1,i}/b_i$ into the one for l_{ji}/b_i, the following expression for w_{1i}/b_i is obtained:

$$\frac{w_{1i}}{b_i} = \frac{\phi_i[(v_{fi}/b_i) + (v_{Fi}/FX_i)]}{(L_p/W_1) + \phi_i(l_{Fi}/FX_i) + \Phi_i} \tag{10–53}$$

where

$$\phi_i = S_{p+1,i}S_{p+2,i}\ldots S_{f-2,i}S_{f-1,i}$$

$$\Phi_i = S_{p+1,i} + S_{p+1,i}S_{p+2,i} + \ldots + S_{p+1,i}S_{p+2,i}\ldots S_{f-3,i}S_{f-2,i}$$

After w_{1i}/b_i has been determined by Equation (10–53) and the bottoms rate determined by the over-all material balance

$$b_i = \frac{FX_i}{1 + (w_{1i}/b_i)} \tag{10–54}$$

the flow rates for a separated heavy component in the rectifying section may be calculated by use of Equation (10–52).

In the selection of the number of plates between the two pinches, the same procedure as described for conventional columns is employed except that the initial value of r is selected such that the rectifying pinch is located above plate p. The remaining calculational procedures are either the same as or analogous to those described for the first type of specification.

Illustrative Examples

In order to demonstrate the type of results that may be obtained by use of the proposed calculational procedure, three examples are presented. The statements and specifications for these examples are given in Table 10–6, and the solutions appear in Tables 10–7 through 10–9. These examples were taken from References (7, 8).

CALCULATIONAL PROCEDURE FOR COLUMNS WITH MULTIPLE FEED PLATES

The general calculational procedure for such columns is about the same as that described in detail in Chapter 7. For illustrative purposes consider a column with two feed plates located a finite number of plates below the withdrawal of the side-stream W_1.

First consider the calculational procedure for the distributed components. Calculations are commenced at each end of the column and continued from the top to the upper feed and from the bottom to the lower feed plate. Before the flow rates between the upper and lower feed plates can be calculated, the terminal rates must be determined. In the same manner as shown for the development of Equation (10–53), a formula for the evaluation of b_i/d_i is obtained. This expression may be obtained either as a function of the A_{ji}'s by carrying out the substitutional process from the top feed plate to the lower one or as a function of the S_{ji}'s by carrying out the substitutional process from the lower to the upper feed plate. Since these formulas are nearly independent of round-off error, they give about the same value for b_i/d_i. Thus only one of the formulas is needed. After the b_i/d_i's and the corresponding terminal rates have been determined, the flow rates between the two feed plates are calculated either by making

TABLE 10-6 Statement and specifications for Examples 10-4, 10-5, and 10-6

Component	Component No.	Examples FX	Example	V_1	D	W_1	Others
C₃H₈	1	20	10-4	150	30	20	For all examples: column pressure = 400 psia, partial condenser, thermal condition of the feed is boiling point liquid, Initial temperature profile: linear between the pinches (252–282°F) for all examples. For Examples 10-4 and 10-5 the initial temperature profile was taken to be linear between 227 and 242°F for plates 1 through 5 and the temperature of the distillate was taken to be 217°F. Initial vapor rates: $V_j = V_1$ for all j. For all examples: $V_{min} = 5$ and $V_{max} = 250$. In Examples 10-4 and 10-5, the liquid side-stream W_1 is withdrawn from plate 5 (numbering down from the top plate), and in Example 10-6 it is withdrawn five plates above the feed plate. Use the equilibrium and enthalpy data given in Tables A-5 and A-8 of the Appendix.
i-C₄	2	20	10-5	200	20	40	
n-C₄	3	20	10-6	100	30	15	
i-C₅	4	20					
n-C₅	5	20					

The "Specifications" heading spans the columns Example, V_1, D, W_1, and Others.

Reproduced by permission of *Hydrocarbon Processing & Petroleum Refiner*

TABLE 10-7 Temperature and Vapor Rate Profiles Obtained in the Solution of Example 10-4 (W_1 is Withdrawn from Plate 5)

Plate No.	Temperature* profiles Trial No.			Final vapor rates	Comp.	Final product distribution (Trial No. 26)		
	5	15	26	(Trial No. 26)		d	b	W_1
0 (Distillate)	210.89	211.21	211.21		C_3H_8	16.9733	0.0	3.0267
5 (plate p)	240.76	241.49	241.50	151.74	$i\text{-}C_4$	9.9098	0.7052	9.3850
r	260.90	246.46	246.14	151.79	$n\text{-}C_4$	3.1169	9.2948	7.5883
$r+1$	261.11	246.52	246.14	151.79	$i\text{-}C_5$	0.0	20.0000	0.0
$r+2$	261.55	246.65	246.14	151.79	$n\text{-}C_5$	0.0	20.0000	0.0
f (Feed)	285.40	277.51	277.43	135.59				
$s-2$	299.92	293.98	293.96	149.83				
$s-1$	300.22	293.99	293.96	149.83				
s	300.36	293.99	293.96	149.83				
$N+1$ (Bottoms)	337.80	337.22	337.22					
D (Calculated)	30.885	29.995	30.000					
θ_0	1.89720	0.99711	0.99999					
W_1 (Calculated)	22.213	19.988	20.000					
θ_1	0.99971	1.00003	0.99999					
Distributed components	3	2, 3	2, 3					

* Averaged values are given.

Reproduced by permission of *Hydrocarbon Processing & Petroleum Refiner*

TABLE 10–8 Temperature and vapor rate profiles obtained in the solution of Example 10–4 (W_1 is withdrawn from plate 5)

Plate No.	Temperature profiles (°F) Trial No.				Final vapor rates		Product distribution			
	5	10	25	*	25	*	Component	d	b	w_1
0 (Distillate)	196.84	196.93	196.93	196.93			C_3H_8	14.430	0.0	5.5700
5 (plate p)	245.11	245.07	245.07	245.07	200.56		i-C_4	4.0671	0.0	15.9329
r	265.32	259.33	254.10	254.08	202.47	202.50	n-C_4	1.50291	0.0	18.4971
r + 1	265.48	258.77	254.11		202.48		i-C_5	0.0	20.0	0.0
r + 2	266.94	259.24	254.12		202.46		n-C_5	0.0	20.0	0.0
f (Feed)	294.72	287.88	285.82		181.14					
s − 2	310.81	317.36	344.77		196.56					
s − 1	310.52	316.95	345.09		196.58					
s	310.80	317.21	345.24	352.88	196.52	200.90				
N + 1 (Bottoms)	354.96	354.96	354.96	354.96						
D (Calculated)	19.934	20.000	20.000							
θ_0	—	—	—							
W_1 (Calculated)	40.066	40.000	40.000							
θ_1	0.99243	0.999999	0.999999							
Separated components	all	all	all							

* At the end of the 25th trial, the general calculational procedure was abandoned by the program and the solution found directly as described in the text.

Reproduced by permission of *Hydrocarbon Processing & Petroleum Refiner*

TABLE 10-9 Temperature and vapor rate profiles obtained in the solution of Example 10-6 (W_1 is withdrawn 5 plates above the feed plate)

Plate No.	Temperature* profiles Trial No.			Final vapor rates	Final product distribution (Trial No. 20)			
	5	10	20	(Trial No. 20)	Component	d	b	w_1
0 (Distillate)	210.78	211.10	211.13	100.36	C_3H_8	17.344	0.0	2.6564
r	239.36	239.62	239.62	100.36	$i\text{-}C_4$	8.9474	6.8042	4.2484
$r+1$	239.47	239.63	239.62	100.36	$n\text{-}C_4$	3.7091	11.3418	4.9490
$r+2$	239.70	239.67	239.62	100.36	$i\text{-}C_5$	0.0	17.9732	2.0267
p (side-stream)	252.98	255.34	255.45	94.17	$n\text{-}C_5$	0.0	18.881	1.1193
f (Feed)	272.55	271.96	271.96	89.23				
$s-2$	295.06	295.22	295.44	102.15				
$s-1$	295.35	295.30	295.44	102.16				
s	295.50	295.34	295.44	102.16				
$N+1$ (Bottoms)	369.36	365.87	366.02					
D (Calculated)	30.004	29.984	30.000					
θ_0	1.0321	1.0011	1.0000					
W_1 (Calculated)	15.579	15.045	15.000					
θ_1	0.9717	0.9957	0.99999					
Separated components	1, 4, 5	1, 4, 5	1, 4, 5					

Reproduced by permission of *Hydrocarbon Processing & Petroleum Refiner*

calculations down from the upper feed plate to the lower one or by making calculations from the lower feed plate to the upper one. Except for round-off error, which may be appreciable, the rates are the same. That set of rates possessing the minimum round-off error is retained and the other one discarded. This selection is made by use of the simple ratio test.

For the separated lights, the calculations are made from the rectifying pinch past both feed plates to (or toward) the stripping pinch.

For the case of a separated heavy component, calculations are made up from the stripping pinch to the lower feed plate. Before further calcula-tions may be performed, terminal rates must be evaluated. This evaluation is accomplished with the aid of a formula for w_{1i}/b_i developed in a manner analogous to that shown for Equation (10–53). The substitutional process is commenced at the lower feed plate and continued past the upper feed plate to the location of the withdrawal of side-stream W_1. After the terminal rates have been computed, the flow rates between the lower feed plate and the rectifying pinch are calculated in the usual way. Note that when W_1 is withdrawn a finite number of plates from the top of the column, the flow rates for the separated heavies are evaluated by making calculations from the bottom of the column to the rectifying pinch.

NOTATION

$k, m, n =$ Integers used for counting

$M_i =$ Sum of a series of terms; used in some of the intermediate steps of the derivations

$p_1, p_2 =$ The material balance and enthalpy balance functions, respectively, for the stripping section pinch

$P_1, P_2 =$ The material balance and enthalpy balance functions, respectively, for the rectifying pinch

$t_j =$ Sum of a particular series considered in the derivations

$T_{\text{B.P.}} =$ Bubble point temperature computed on the basis of the x_{Bi}'s (or X_{Di}'s) and the column pressure

$T_{\text{D.P.}} =$ Dew point temperature computed on the basis of the X_{Di}'s and the column pressure

$T_h =$ Temperature at which $K_{rh} = 1$ at the column pressure

$T_l =$ Temperature at which $K_{sl} = 1$ at the column pressure

$T_r, T_s =$ Temperatures of the rectifying and stripping section pinches, respectively

$\lambda_{ri}, \lambda_{si}$ = Latent heats of vaporization for component i at the rectifying and stripping section pinches, respectively

ψ_r, ψ_s = Vapor flow rates at the pinches relative to the respective terminal rates; $\psi_r = V_r/D$, $\psi_s = V_s/B$. Also, for a complex column symbol ψ_r is also used to denote $(V_r)/(D + W_1)$

Subscripts

h = Heavy key component

H = Single phase heavy component

f = Feed plate

l = Light key component

L = Single phase light component

r = Rectifying pinch

s = Stripping pinch

PROBLEMS

10–1 Beginning with first principles, develop Equations (10–8a) through (10–9f), and (10–25a) through (10–27).

10–2 Develop the formulas for the P-functions given by Equations (10–30), (10–32), (10–33), and (10–34).

10–3 By use of material balances and equilibrium relationships, develop Equations (10–41a) through (10–44).

10–4 Verify the expressions for the enthalpy balances given by Equations (10–45a) through (10–45g).

10–5 Develop the expressions given by Equations (10–49) and (10–50) for the functions P_1 and P_2, respectively.

10–6 Develop Equations (10–51a) through (10–53).

10–7 (a) For the case where the keys are the lightest and heaviest components of a mixture in a conventional column at minimum reflux and the action at the feed plate is the same as that stated in Chapter 3, revise Figures 3–1 through 3–5 as required to describe this type of operation.

(b) Let the thermal condition of the feed be defined in terms of "q" as follows:

$$L_s = L_r + qF, \quad \text{or} \quad V_r - V_s = (1 - q)F$$

By use of the diagram of part (a) and the necessary equilibrium and material balance relationships show that the q-line,

$$X_i = (1 - q)y_{ri} + qx_{ri}$$

holds for bubble point liquid, dew point vapor, subcooled, and superheated feeds.

(c) Show that the q-line may be rearranged to the following form

$$p(T) = \sum_{i=1}^{c} \frac{X_i}{q + (1 - q)K_{ri}} - 1$$

10–8   Construct proofs for the relationships stated in the following table:

Thermal condition of the feed	Relationships (where the keys are the lightest and heaviest components of the mixture)
Boiling point liquid	$y_{ri} = y_{si},\ x_{ri} = x_{si},\ X_i = x_{ri},$ and $T_F = T_r = T_s.$
Subcooled liquid	$y_{ri} = y_{si},\ x_{ri} = x_{si},\ T_r = T_s,$ and T_r is that $T > 0$ which makes $p(T) = 0$ (see Part (c) of Problem 10–7).
Partially vaporized	$y_{ri} = y_{si} = y_{Fi},\ x_{ri} = x_{si} = x_{Fi},$ and $T_r = T_s = T_F.$
Dew point vapor	$x_{ri} = x_{si},\ y_{ri} = y_{si},\ T_r = T_s,\ X_i = y_{ri},$ and $T_F = T_r = T_s.$
Superheated vapor	$x_{ri} = x_{si},\ y_{ri} = y_{si},\ T_r = T_s,$ and T_r is that $T > 0$ which makes $p(T) = 0$ (see Part (c) of Problem 10–7).

Except for a partially vaporized feed, a direct method of proof may be used which makes use of the Figures of Part (a) of Problem 10–7 and certain material balance and equilibrium relationships. A proof for the relationships given for a partially vaporized feed may be obtained by use of the indirect method. An outline of this proof follows. In order to prove that $T_F = T_r = T_s$, make the supposition that $T_F < T_r$, and then obtain a contradiciton. Next suppose T_F to be greater than T_r, and obtain a contradiction. This leads to the conclusion: $T_F = T_r$. Similarly, show $T_F = T_s$. After these two proofs have been obtained, the equality of the compositions readily follows. [Hint: When you are ready to give up, see Reference (6)].

10–9   For feeds of different thermal conditions, outline calculational procedures (of a direct nature) for the determination of the product distribution for specified values of V_1 and D where the keys are the lightest and heaviest components of the feed.

10–10 (a) Develop the component-material balance expressions that apply for distributed components for the case of a conventional column in which an infinity of plates are specified for the rectifying reaction and a finite number of plates are specified for the stripping section.

 (b) For the system described in Part (a), describe the procedures that should be used for the detection of the separated light and separated heavy components.

 (c) Develop the component-material balance expressions for the separated components.

LITERATURE CITED

1. Acrivos, Andreas, and N. R. Amundson, "On the Steady State Fractionation of Multicomponent and Complex Mixtures in an Ideal Cascade: Part 2—The Calculation of the Minimum Reflux Ratio," *Chem. Eng. Sci.*, **4**, No. 2, 68 (1955).

2. Bachelor, J. B., "How to Figure Minimum Reflux," *Petroleum Refiner*, **36**, No. 6, 161 (1957).

3. Brown, G. G., and D. E. Holcomb, "Vapor-Liquid Phase Equilibria in Hydrocarbon Systems," *Petroleum Engineer*, **11**, 23 (August 1940).

4. Canik, L. J., B. W. Hardy, and C. D. Holland, "Figure Distillation This New Way: Part 7—Absorbers With Reboilers," *Petroleum Refiner*, **40**, No. 12, 161 (1961).

5. Lyster, W. N., S. L. Sullivan, Jr., D. S. Billingsley, and C. D Holland, "Figure Distillation This New Way: Part 1—New Convergence Method Will Handle Many Cases," *Petroleum Refiner*, **38**, No. 6, 221 (1959); "Part 2—Product Purity Can Set Conditions for Column," **38**, No. 7, 151 (1959); and "Part 3—Consider Multi-Feed Columns with Side-Streams," **38**, No. 10, 139 (1959).

6. McDonough, J. A., C. D. Holland, and H. L. Bauni, "Determination of the Conditions at Minimum Reflux When the Keys are the Most and Least Volatile Components," *Chem. Eng. Sci.*, **16**, Nos. 3 and 4, 143 (1961).

7. McDonough, J. A., "Calculational Procedures for Minimum Reflux in Complex and Conventional Columns," Ph.D. dissertation, A. and M. College of Texas, College Station, Texas, January 1962.

8. McDonough, J. A. and C. D. Holland, "Figure Separations This New Way: Part 9—How to Figure Minimum Reflux," *Petroleum Refiner*, **41**, No. 3, 153 (1962); and "Part 10—Minimum Reflux for Complex Columns," **41**, No. 4, 135 (1962).

9. Murdoch, P. G. and C. D. Holland, "Multicomponent Distillation: IV—Determination of Minimum Reflux," *Chem. Eng. Prog.*, **48,** No. 6, 287 (1952).

10. Robinson, C. S. and E. R. Gilliland, *Elements of Fractional Distillation* (New York: McGraw-Hill Book Company, Inc., 1950), p. 241.

11. Shiras, R. N., D. N. Hanson, and G. H. Gibson, "Calculation of Minimum Reflux in Distillation Columns," *Ind. Eng. Chem.*, **42,** 871 (1950).

12. Sokolnikoff, I. S. and E. S. Sokolnikoff, *Higher Mathematics for Engineers and Physicists* (New York: McGraw-Hill Book Company, Inc., 1941), p. 21.

13. Underwood, A. J. V., "Fractional Distillation of Multicomponent Mixtures," *Chem. Eng. Prog.*, **44,** 603 (1948).

Determination of the Minimum Reflux for Conventional and Complex Columns

11

In Chapter 10 the specifications were stated from an operational point of view, whereas in the present chapter the specifications are stated from the standpoint of design. Instead of specifying V_1 (or L_0) and D for a conventional column as was done in Chapter 10, separation specifications (b_i/d_i) for each of two components are fixed and the problem is to find the V_1 (or L_0) and the corresponding D required to effect these separations when an infinite number of plates are used in both sections of the column. Similarly, instead of the set of specifications consisting of V_1 (or L_0), D, and W_1 for a complex column, two values of b_i/d_i and the withdrawal rate W_1 are specified. The smallest value of V_1 (or L_0) needed to satisfy the specifications must be found. The final solution also gives the total distillate rate and the complete product distribution. Calculational procedures and convergence methods follow first for a conventional and then for a complex column. These are based on the work of Anthony (2) and Abdel-Aal (1).

CONVENTIONAL COLUMNS

When both sections of a column contain infinitely many plates, the equations for the material balances and the formulas for the calculation of the compositions are the same as those given in Chapter 10. The component having the smallest specified value of b_i/d_i is referred to as the light key, and the other component for which b_i/d_i is specified is called the heavy key. Components lighter and heavier than the keys are classified again as the separated lights and heavies, respectively. Also, the collection of components consisting of the two keys and the components having volatilities intermediate to those of the keys are referred to as the distributed components.

290

Convergence Method

This application differs from the general θ-method described previously in that a θ is to be selected for each of the distributed components; that is,

$$\left(\frac{b_i}{d_i}\right)_{co} = \theta_{0i} \left(\frac{b_i}{d_i}\right)_{ca} \tag{11-1}$$

Since the corrected values of b_i/d_i are known for the keys, $i = h$ (heavy key)

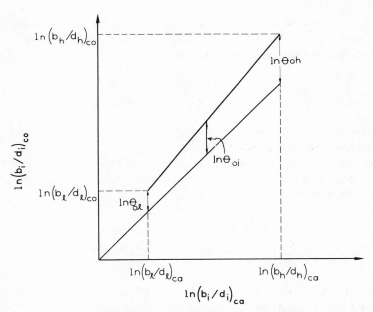

Figure 11-1. When convergence is obtained, the line

$$[\ln (b_i/d_i)_{co} \text{ versus } \ln (b_i/d_i)_{ca}]$$

coincides with the 45° diagonal.

and $i = l$ (light key), θ_{0l} and θ_{0h} are computed directly by use of Equation (11-1). However, the multipliers of components having volatilities between the two keys cannot be determined directly. It appeared reasonable to suppose that the θ_0's for these components should lie between those for the keys. The following relationship, based on a linear variation between the logarithms of the corrected and calculated values of b_i/d_i (see Figure 11–1), was found to give satisfactory results.

$$\theta_{0i} = \theta_{0l} \left(\frac{\theta_{0h}}{\theta_{0l}}\right)^{\eta_i} \tag{11-2}$$

where

$$\eta_i = \frac{\ln\left(\dfrac{b_i/d_i}{b_l/d_l}\right)_{ca}}{\ln\left(\dfrac{b_h/d_h}{b_l/d_l}\right)_{ca}}$$

After θ_{0i} has been determined for a given component by use of Equation (11–2) and $(b_i/d_i)_{co}$ by Equation (11–1), the corrected distillate rate for each distributed component is given by

$$(d_i)_{co} = \frac{FX_i}{1 + (b_i/d_i)_{co}} = \frac{FX_i}{1 + \theta_{0i}(b_i/d_i)_{ca}} \tag{11-3}$$

The total distillate rate is taken as the sum of the corrected rates for the components in the top product.

The compositions are calculated by use of Equations (6–3) through (6–7). For a system that does not contain single-phase components, these formulas reduce to

$$x_{ji} = \frac{(l_{ji}/b_i)_{ca}(b_i)_{co}}{\displaystyle\sum_{i=1}^{c}(l_{ji}/b_i)_{ca}(b_i)_{co}}, \quad y_{ji} = \frac{(v_{ji}/d_i)_{ca}(d_i)_{co}}{\displaystyle\sum_{i=1}^{c}(v_{ji}/d_i)_{ca}(d_i)_{co}} \tag{11-4}$$

In the calculation of the compositions, the calculated flow rates of the separated lights should be altered to reflect the fact that the value of V_1 assumed to make the given trial calculation was not the correct one. This alteration was accomplished through a procedure that made use of the following postulates. For the separated heavies

$$(b_i/d_i)_{co} = \theta_{0h}(b_i/d_i)_{ca} \tag{11-5}$$

and for the separated lights it is postulated that

$$(b_i/d_i)_{co} = \theta_{0l}(b_i/d_i)_{ca} \tag{11-6}$$

For a separated light component $[(b_i)_{ca} = 0 \text{ and } (b_i)_{co} = 0]$, the product

$[(l_{ji}/b_i)_{ca}](b_i)_{co}$ which appears in Equation (11–4) is replaced by its equivalent,

$$\left(\frac{l_{ji}}{b_i}\right)_{ca}(b_i)_{co} = \left[\left(\frac{l_{ji}}{d_i}\right)_{ca}\left(\frac{d_i}{b_i}\right)_{ca}\right]\left[\theta_{0l}\left(\frac{b_i}{d_i}\right)_{ca}(d_i)_{co}\right]$$

$$= \theta_{0l}\left(\frac{l_{ji}}{d_i}\right)_{ca}(d_i)_{co} = \theta_{0l}(l_{ji})_{ca} \qquad (11\text{–}7)$$

Similarly, for a separated heavy component $[(d_i)_{ca} = 0$ and $(d_i)_{co} = 0]$, the indeterminate form which appears in Equation (11–4) is replaced by its equivalent,

$$\left(\frac{v_{ji}}{d_i}\right)_{ca}(d_i)_{co} = \frac{(v_{ji})_{ca}}{\theta_{0h}} \qquad (11\text{–}8)$$

On the basis of the compositions given by Equation (11–4), the calculated temperatures are found by making bubble point calculations. In all problems and for all trials after the first one, the assumed profile for the next trial was obtained by averaging the calculated temperatures plate by plate with those used to make the given trial.

Selection of Trial Values for V_1 (or L_0)

After the temperature profile for the next trial has been determined, the value of V_r required to effect the separation may be found. Then the liquid rate, L_r, is found by material balance, since the corrected distillate rate will have been determined as described in the previous section. For constant-L/V problems, the remaining flow rates in the rectifying section were taken equal to the corresponding rates at the rectifying pinch. For such problems the flow rates in the stripping section were found by use of appropriate material balances that took into account the thermal condition of the feed.

For the general case where the total rates of flow are determined by enthalpy balances, V_1 (or L_0) is calculated by use of an appropriate enthalpy balance after V_r has been determined as shown in a subsequent section. The value of V_r to be used for the next trial is found by use of the material balance function corresponding to the pinch in the rectifying section. This function is developed as follows. At the rectifying pinch

$$\frac{v_{ri}}{d_i} = \frac{1}{1 - A_{ri}} \qquad (11\text{–}9)$$

Since $l_{ri}/d_i = A_{ri}(v_{ri}/d_i)$, it follows that

$$l_{ri} = \frac{(d_i)_{co}}{S_{ri} - 1} = \frac{(d_i)_{co}L_r}{K_{ri}V_r - L_r} \tag{11-10}$$

Since $V_r = L_r + D$,

$$x_{ri} = \frac{(d_i)_{co}}{K_{ri}V_r - L_r} = \frac{X_{Di}}{1 - \psi_r(1 - K_{ri})} \tag{11-11}$$

where

$$X_{Di} = (d_i)_{co}/D = (d_i)_{co}/\sum_{i=h}^{c} (d_i)_{co}$$

$$\psi_r = V_r/D.$$

Summation of both sides of Equation (11–11) over all components followed by rearrangement yields

$$P(\psi_r) = \sum_{i=1}^{c} \frac{X_{Di}}{1 - \psi_r(1 - K_{ri})} - 1 \tag{11-12}$$

where it is understood that $X_{Di} = 0$ for each of the separated heavy components. Values of the K_{ri}'s and X_{Di}'s obtained for the last trial for the previously assumed value of V_r (or V_1) are employed in the determination of the next best value of V_r. Thus the problem of the selection of the next value of V_r reduces to finding that positive value of ψ_r such that $P(\psi_r) = 0$. As described in Chapter 10, this may be done by use of either Newton's method or interpolation (*regula falsi*). Rather than determining the next best value of V_1 by use of the material balance function $P(\psi_r)$, the corresponding material balance function for the stripping section pinch may be employed. By solving a wide variety of problems, Anthony (2) showed that the use of the value of V_r as given by Equation (11–12) generally leads to overcorrections. These were reduced by restricting the variation in V_r for successive trials in the following manner. For the first five trials the value of V_r to be used for the next trial through the column was allowed to differ by no more than 1.2 and 1/1.2 times the value used to make the last trial calculation. After the first five trials the restrictions were altered at the end of each third successive trial as follows: 1.1 and 1/1.1, 1.05 and 1/1.05, and 1.025 and 1/1.025. For all subsequent trials restrictions of 1.0125 and 1/1.0125 were used. If the value of V_r found by use of Equation (11–12) lay within the prescribed limits, it was averaged with the V_r used to make the last trial calculation.

A check which was included in the proposed calculational procedure merits a brief description. The possibility of the selection of values for

V_r, V_s, T_r, and T_s that give negative values for either v_{ri}/d_i or l_{ri}/d_i or both for one or more of the distributed components exists. Such a selection is seldom made except in the initiation of the general calculational procedure. In the event of the selection of a value of V_r such that a negative number is obtained for v_{ri}/d_i for one or more of the distributed components, values of V_r lying between the values of V_r used to make the last trial calculation and the one computed by use of the P-function should be selected and tested until one is found which gives a positive value for v_{ri}/d_i for each of the distributed components. In the event that the V_r selected leads to a value of V_s that gives a negative value for l_{si}/b_i for any one of the distributed components, this value of V_s is discarded and replaced by the one which makes $p_1(\psi_s) = 0$ (see Equation (10–33)). For constant-L/V problems, V_s is found by material balance, and for the general case V_s is determined by use of enthalpy balances as described in the next section.

Enthalpy Balances

When the total rates of flow are determined by use of enthalpy balances, the same general calculational procedure described previously is employed with certain modifications. After V_r for the next trial calculation has been selected as described previously, the remaining rates are determined by use of enthalpy balances.

In making these balances, the enthalpies are calculated by the constant-composition method, and the flow rates throughout the column are maintained within the specified limits by use of the Q-method. These balances are commenced by the determination of the external reflux L_0 by means of an enthalpy balance enclosing the rectifying pinch and the top plate of the column,

$$V_r H_r + L_0 h_0 = V_1 H_1 + L_r h_r \qquad (11\text{–}13a)$$

which reduces to

$$L_0 = \frac{D[H(X_D)_r - H(X_D)_1] + L_r[H(x_r)_r - h_r]}{[H(x_0)_1 - h_0]} \qquad (11\text{–}13b)$$

since

$$V_r H_r = \sum_{i=h}^{c} H_{ri}(l_{ri} + d_i) = L_r H(x_r)_r + DH(X_D)_r$$

$$V_1 H_1 = L_0 H(x_0)_1 + DH(X_D)_1$$

The condenser duty is given by

$$Q_c = D[H(X_D)_r - H_D] + L_r[H(x_r)_r - h_r] - Q_1 \qquad (11\text{–}13c)$$

For the plates between the two pinches

$$L_j = \frac{D[H_D - H(X_D)_{j+1}] + Q_c + Q_1 + \displaystyle\sum_{k=r+1}^{j-1} Q_k}{[H(x_j)_{j+1} - h_j]},$$

$$r + 1 \leqq j \leqq f - 2 \qquad (11\text{--}13\text{d})$$

$$L_{f-1} = \frac{D[H_D - H(X_D)_f] + Q_c + Q_1 + V_F[H(y_F)_f - H_F]}{[H(x_{f-1})_f - h_{f-1}]}$$

$$+ \frac{\displaystyle\sum_{k=r+1}^{j-1} Q_k}{[H(x_{f-1})_f - h_{f-1}]} \qquad (11\text{--}13\text{e})$$

$$L_j = \frac{D[H_D - H(X_D)_{j+1}] + Q_c + Q_1 - F[H - H(X)_{j+1}]}{[H(x_j)_{j+1} - h_j]}$$

$$+ \frac{\displaystyle\sum_{k=r+1}^{j-1} Q_k}{[H(x_j)_{j+1} - h_j]}, \quad f \leqq j \leqq s \qquad (11\text{--}13\text{f})$$

The reboiler duty is given by

$$Q_R = DH_D + Bh_B + Q_c + Q_1 + \sum_{k=r+1}^{s} Q_k - FH \qquad (11\text{--}13\text{g})$$

In making these calculations, the compositions and temperatures for the plates immediately above and below the pinches are taken to be the same as those of the respective pinches; that is, $x_{r-1,i} = x_{ri}$, $T_{r-1} = T_r$, $x_{si} = x_{s+1,i}$, and $T_s = T_{s+1}$. After the liquid rates have been determined by Equation (11–13), the rates are calculated as follows:

$$V_1 = L_0 + D \qquad (11\text{--}14\text{a})$$

$$V_j = L_{j-1} + D, \quad r \leqq j \leqq f - 1 \qquad (11\text{--}14\text{b})$$

(Note: $L_{r-1} = L_r$)

$$\bar{V}_f = L_{f-1} + D \qquad (11\text{--}14\text{c})$$

$$V_f = \bar{L}_{f-1} - B \qquad (11\text{--}14\text{d})$$

$$V_j = L_{j-1} - B, \quad f + 1 \leqq j \leqq s + 1 \qquad (11\text{--}14\text{e})$$

(Note: $L_{s-1} = L_s$)

The intercooler (or heater) duties are calculated in the same manner as described in Chapter 10. Best results were obtained when the variations in the flow rates between successive trials were limited as follows. The first three trials were made with the same set of L/V's. For all subsequent trials the rates were determined by enthalpy balances. For corresponding trials the same restrictions were placed on the V_j's calculated by enthalpy balance as those used for V_r. Other procedures described in Chapter 10 were employed, such as the selection of a suitable finite set of plates between the pinches.

In order to illustrate the convergence method, the solution of Example 11–1 is presented (see Tables 11–1 and 11–2). This problem was formulated by taking certain results obtained in the solution of Example 10–1 as the specifications for Example 11–1. The agreement between the results of the two examples is seen to be good. Example 11–2 (see Tables 11–3 and 11–4) demonstrates the adequacy of the basic postulate given by Equation (11–1) for the estimation of the θ_{0i}'s for components having K-values's between those of the keys.

Anthony (2) developed the set of restrictions for the vapor rates stated in a preceding section by solving a wide variety of examples. The tendency toward obtaining values for the θ_0's that were alternately too large and too small increased as the specified values of b/d for the light and heavy keys were decreased and increased, respectively. For all problems considered, the proposed restrictions on the vapor rates gave satisfactory results provided the specified values of b/d for the keys satisfied the two inequalities

$$b_l/d_l > 0.15 \tag{11–15}$$

and

$$b_h/d_h < 10 \tag{11–16}$$

For specified values of b/d smaller and larger than these more severe restrictions are required.

COMPLEX COLUMNS

In order to demonstrate the application of the general convergence method to complex columns, a particular unit was selected; detailed treatment of this unit is given. The column selected has one side stream, W_1, withdrawn (as a liquid) in addition to the distillate and the bottoms. The withdrawal of W_1 is located on plate p, which is taken to be a finite number of plates from the top of the column. The specifications are taken to be the b_i/d_i's for two components and the withdrawal rate W_1. The smallest value of V_1 needed to effect this separation is to be found. The equations repre-

TABLE 11-1 Station and specifications for Example 11-1

Component	Component No.	FX	Specifications
C_3H_8	1	20	The light key is i-C_4 and the heavy key is n-C_4; $b_l/d_l = 0.37214114$ and $b_h/d_h = 2.6871523$. The column pressure = 400 psia. A partial condenser is to be employed. The thermal condition of the feed is boiling point liquid: $V_{min} = 5$ and $V_{max} = 250$. Equilibrium and enthalpy data given in Tables A-5 and A-8 of the Appendix are to be employed. Initial temperature profile to be linear between the pinches (252–282°F). The initial vapor rates are: $V_j = V_1 = 250$, for all j. (Note: Since the keys are adjacent, the product distribution and the corrected distillate rate is completely determined.)
i-C_4	2	20	
n-C_4	3	20	
i-C_5	4	20	
n-C_5	5	20	

TABLE 11-2 Temperature and vapor rate profiles obtained in the solution of Example 11-1

| Plate No. | Temperature profiles,* (°F) Trial No. | | | | Final vapor rates |
	5	10	25	38	(Trial No. 38)
0 (Distillate)	217.64	217.64	217.64	217.64	
r	236.39	245.95	245.84	244.88	151.378
$r + 1$	236.79	246.99	245.84	244.88	151.378
$r + 2$	237.59	246.07	245.84	244.88	151.378
$r + 3$	238.76	246.23	245.84	244.88	151.378
f (Feed)	255.39	273.55	273.20	272.03	136.555
$s - 2$	269.55	286.18	291.09	289.93	151.375
$s - 1$	269.59	286.26	291.09	289.93	151.375
s	269.63	286.29	291.09	289.93	151.375
$N + 1$ (Bottoms)	323.21	323.21	323.21	323.21	
D_{co}	40	40	40	40	
θ_{ol}	0.27112	0.5496	1.0443	1.00008	
θ_{oh}	0.98292	1.1166	0.94263	1.0004	
V_1	106.796	146.79	158.60	149.991	

* These temperatures were obtained by the averaging procedure. At the end of 38 trials the successive temperatures for each plate differed by no more than 3×10^{-3}.

TABLE 11-3 Statement and specifications for Example 11-2

Component	Component No.	FX	Specifications
C_3H_8	1	15	The light key is i-C_4 and the heavy key is n-C_5; $b_l/d_l = 0.2$ and $b_h/d_h = 8.0$. The column pressure is 400 psia, the thermal condition of the feed is boiling point liquid, and a partial condenser is to be employed. $V_{min} = 5$ and $V_{max} = 250$. Equilibrium and enthalpy data given in Tables A–5 and A–8 of the Appendix are to be employed. Initial temperature profile is to be linear between the pinches (303–337°F). The initial vapor rates are: $V_j = V_1 = 55$ for all j. The initial value assumed for D was 40. The initial L_j's were obtained by use of appropriate material balances.
i-C_4	2	15	
n-C_4	3	20	
i-C_5	4	20	
n-C_5	5	15	
n-C_8	6	15	

TABLE 11-4 Solution of Example 11-2

Plate No.	Temperature profiles,* (°F) Trial No.				Final vapor rates (Trial No. 35)	Final product distribution (Trial No. 35)		
	5	10	25	35		Component	d	b
0 (Distillate)	255.55	253.32	256.05	256.62		C_3H_8	15.0000	0.0
r	285.74	271.46	286.81	284.43	86.94	$i\text{-}C_4$	12.5000	2.5000
$r+1$	285.74	271.46	286.81	284.43	86.94	$n\text{-}C_4$	11.7616	8.2384
$r+2$	285.74	271.46	286.81	284.43	86.94	$i\text{-}C_5$	4.0879	15.9121
$r+3$	285.75	271.32	286.74	284.43	86.94	$n\text{-}C_5$	1.6667	13.3333
f (Feed)	306.08	285.75	301.80	299.39	80.28	$n\text{-}C_8$	0.0	15.0000
$s-2$	318.05	305.76	318.10	316.51	92.89			
$s-1$	318.41	305.87	318.10	316.51	92.89			
s	318.54	305.93	318.10	316.51	92.89			
$N+1$ (Bottoms)	372.99	372.40	376.61	376.98				
D_{co}	43.19	42.39	44.72	45.02				
θ_{01}	4.8327	1.1663	0.9468	0.9997				
θ_{03}	1.9578	1.2300	1.0393	0.9994				
θ_{04}	0.8995	1.2957	1.1806	0.9989				
θ_{0h}	0.6078	1.3156	1.2392	0.9987				
V_1	84.09	68.20	88.00	88.70				

* These temperatures were obtained by use of the averaging procedure. At the end of 35 trials the successive temperatures for each plate differed by no more than 3×10^{-3}.

senting the component-material balances for this unit have been stated in Chapter 10. Again the relationship of the θ_{0i}'s as given by Equation (11–1) is assumed to apply. Also, for all components heavier than the heavy key, θ_{0i} is taken equal to θ_{0h}; and for all components lighter than the light key, θ_{0i} is set equal to θ_{0l}. The corrected rates for all components are further restricted by the requirement that they satisfy the component-material balance

$$FX_i = (d_i)_{co} \left[1 + \left(\frac{b_i}{d_i} \right)_{co} + \left(\frac{w_{1i}}{d_i} \right)_{co} \right] \tag{11–17}$$

and the specification W_1. These requirements are met by the selection of a $\theta_1 > 0$ such that $g_1(\theta_1) = 0$ where

$$g_1(\theta_1) = \sum_{i=1}^{c} (w_{1i})_{co} - W_1 \tag{11–18}$$

The formulas for the corrected rates, $(w_{1i})_{co}$ and $(d_i)_{co}$, are

$$(w_{1i})_{co} = \theta_1 \left(\frac{w_{1i}}{d_i} \right)_{ca} (d_i)_{co} \tag{11–19}$$

$$(d_i)_{co} = \frac{FX_i}{1 + \theta_{0i}(b_i/d_i)_{ca} + \theta_1(w_{1i}/d_i)_{ca}} \tag{11–20}$$

After these have been determined, $(b_i)_{co}$ is computed by use of Equation (11–1). Since the pinch occurs an infinity of plates below the top of the column and those components heavier than the heavy key are separated at the rectifying pinch, it follows that for each separated heavy component $(w_{1i})_{ca} = 0$, $(w_{1i})_{co} = 0$, and $(b_i)_{co} = FX_i$. Compositions are calculated by use of Equation (11–4). For the separated lights

$$\left(\frac{l_{ji}}{b_i} \right)_{ca} (b_i)_{co} = \left[\left(\frac{l_{ji}}{d_i} \right)_{ca} \left(\frac{d_i}{b_i} \right)_{ca} \right] \left[\theta_{0l} \left(\frac{b_i}{d_i} \right)_{ca} (d_i)_{co} \right]$$

which reduces to

$$\left(\frac{l_{ji}}{b_i} \right)_{ca} (b_i)_{co} = \theta_{0l} \left(\frac{l_{ji}}{d_i} \right)_{ca} (d_i)_{co} \tag{11–21}$$

Also, for a separated light, the formula for $(d_i)_{co}$, Equation (11–20), reduces to

$$(d_i)_{co} = \frac{FX_i}{1 + \theta_1(w_{1i}/d_i)_{ca}} \tag{11–22}$$

On the basis of these compositions temperatures are calculated by use of the bubble point procedure. After the first trial, the profile to be used for the next trial was obtained by "quartering," which consists of the following calculation:

T (new assumed value) $= T$ (last assumed value)

$$+ \left[\frac{T \text{ (calculated value)} - T \text{ (last assumed value)}}{4} \right]$$

In the same manner as was described for conventional columns, each trial calculation through the column is made on the basis of an assumed value for V_r. After the corrected d_i's and w_{1i}'s have been found, the corrected temperature profile is obtained as described in the preceding paragraph. On the basis of these results, the V_r to be used for the next trial calculation is found by use of the material balance function for the rectifying pinch,

$$P(\psi_r) = \sum_{i=1}^{c} \frac{(d_i + w_{1i})/(D + W_1)}{1 - \psi_r(1 - K_{ri})} - 1 \qquad (11\text{--}23)$$

where

$$\psi_r = V_r/(D + W_1)$$

This expression is developed in a manner analogous to that shown for Equation (11–12). In the application of Equation (11–23), observe that for the separated heavy components $(d_i + w_{1i}) = 0$. The value of $\psi_r > 0$ required to give $P(\psi_r) = 0$ is found in the usual way. The corresponding value of V_r follows immediately from this result. On the basis of the V_r so obtained and the value of V_r employed to make the last trial, the value of V_r to be employed for the next trial was selected by essentially the same procedure as that used for conventional columns. For complex columns the maximum deviation of the vapor rates between successive trials was reduced to one-half of each of those stated for conventional columns. Also, when the value of V_r given by the P-function was within the permitted limits of variation, the value of V_r to be employed for the next trial was obtained by quartering (same as the procedure described previously for the selection of temperatures) instead of averaging as was done in the case of conventional columns. For constant-L/V problems the flow rates throughout the column were determined by use of material balances in the same manner described for conventional columns.

Enthalpy Balances

After V_r and L_r have been determined by use of the P-function and the associated forcing procedure for V_r, L_p may be found by means of an enthalpy balance enclosing plate $p + 1$ and plate r of the rectifying pinch.

$$V_rH_r + L_ph_p = V_{p+1}H_{p+1} + L_rh_r + W_1h_p \tag{11-24a}$$

But

$$V_rH_r = \sum_{i=1}^{c} H_{ri}(l_{ri} + d_i + w_{1i})$$

$$V_rH_r = L_rH(x_r)_r + DH(X_D)_r + W_1H(x_p)_r$$

$$V_{p+1}H_{p+1} = \sum_{i=1}^{c} H_{p+1,i}(l_{pi} + d_i) = L_pH(x_p)_{p+1} + DH(X_D)_{p+1}$$

Then in view of these expressions Equation (11–24a) reduces to

$$L_p = \frac{[L_rH(x_r)_r - h_r] + W_1[H(x_p)_r - h_p] + D[H(X_D)_r - H(X_D)_{p+1}]}{[H(x_p)_{p+1} - h_p]} \tag{11-24b}$$

If this value of L_p is not within the limits, the quantity Q_{p+1} is computed in the usual way. The temperature of plate $p + 1$ is determined by the same procedure as described in Chapter 10. Next L_{p-1} is computed by use of the enthalpy balance which is represented by

$$L_{p-1} = \frac{L_r[H(x_r)_r - h_r] + W_1[H(x_p)_r - h_p] + D[H(X_D)_r - H(X_D)_p] + Q_{p+1}}{[H(x_{p-1})_p - h_{p-1}]} \tag{11-24c}$$

If this value of L_{p-1} is not within the prescribed limits, Q_p is computed. This process is continued until L_0 has been computed by use of

$$L_0 = \frac{L_r[H(x_r)_r - h_r] + W_1[H(x_p)_r - h_p] + D[H(X_D)_r - H(X_D)_1] + \sum_{k=2}^{p+1} Q_k}{[H(x_0)_1 - h_0]} \tag{11-24d}$$

If this value of L_0 is not within the prescribed limits, Q_1 is determined. The condenser duty is given by

$$V_rH_r = L_rh_r + DH_D + W_1h_p + Q_c + \sum_{k=1}^{p+1} Q_k \tag{11-24e}$$

and since

$$V_rH_r = L_rH(x_r)_r + DH(X_D)_r + W_1H(x_p)_r$$

the desired expression for Q_c is as follows:

$$Q_c = D[H(X_D)_r - H_D] + L_r[H(x_r)_r - h_r] + W_1[H(x_p)_r - h_p] - \sum_{k=1}^{p+1} Q_k$$

$$(11\text{--}24\text{f})$$

After Q_c has been determined, enthalpy balances are written around the top of the column and the plates between the two pinches. Thus

$$L_j = \frac{D[H_D - H(X_D)_{j+1}] + W_1[h_p - H(x_p)_{j+1}] + Q_c + \sum_{k=1}^{p+1} Q_k + \sum_{k=r+1}^{j-1} Q_k}{[H(x_j)_{j+1} - h_j]},$$

$$r + 1 \leq j \leq f - 2 \qquad (11\text{--}24\text{g})$$

$$L_{f-1} = \frac{D[H_D - H(X_D)_f] + W_1[h_p - H(x_p)_f] + V_F[H(y_F)_f - H_F] + Q_c}{[H(x_{f-1})_f - h_{f-1}]}$$

$$+ \frac{\sum_{k=1}^{p+1} Q_k + \sum_{k=r+1}^{j-1} Q_k}{[H(x_{f-1})_f - h_{f-1}]} \qquad (11\text{--}24\text{h})$$

and in the stripping section

$$L_j = \frac{D[H_D - H(X_D)_{j+1}] + W_1[h_p - H(x_p)_{j+1}] + F[H(X)_{j+1} - H] + Q_c + \sum_{k=1}^{p+1} Q_k}{[H(x_j)_{j+1} - h_j]}$$

$$+ \frac{\sum_{k=r+1}^{j-1} Q_k}{[H(x_j)_{j+1} - h_j]}, \quad f \leq j \leq s \qquad (11\text{--}24\text{i})$$

and the reboiler duty is given by

$$Q_R = DH_D + Bh_B + W_1h_p + Q_c + \sum_{k=1}^{p+1} Q_k + \sum_{k=r+1}^{s} Q_k - FH \qquad (11\text{--}24\text{j})$$

The proposed calculational procedure and convergence method for the particular complex column is demonstrated by the solution of Example 11–3 (see Tables 11–5 and 11–6). Other cases such as the one in which the side stream W_1 is withdrawn a finite number of plates above the feed plate may be treated in a manner analogous to the one shown. Also, the calculational procedure is readily modified to include the case where one or more side-streams are withdrawn from the stripping section.

TABLE 11–5 Statement and specifications for Example 11–3

Component	Component No.	FX	Specifications
C_3H_8	1	20	Column pressure = 400 psia, partial condenser, thermal condition of the feed is boiling point liquid, Components 2 and 3 are the keys for which the following separations are specified: $b_l/d_l = 0.15$ and $b_h/d_h = 2.9820$. The withdrawal rate W_1 is 20. The initial profile was taken to be linear between 247 and 248.5°F for plates 1 through 5, and the initial temperature of the distillate was taken to be 247°F. Between the pinches the initial temperature profile was taken to be linear between 260 and 274°F. Initial vapor rates: $V_j = V_1 = 200$ for all j. Initial distillate rate of 40 was used. The equilibrium and enthalpy data are to be taken from Tables A–5 and A–8 of the Appendix.
i-C_4	2	20	
n-C_4	3	20	
i-C_5	4	20	
n-C_5	5	20	

TABLE 11-6 Solution of Example 11-3

Plate No.	Temperature profiles,* (°F) Trial No.				Final vapor rates (Trial No. 25)
	5	10	20	25	
0 (Distillate)	210.41	210.22	210.72	210.68	
5 (Plate p)	241.71	242.28	240.77	240.88	142.04
r	243.52	246.90	245.01	245.23	142.32
$r+1$	243.68	246.93	245.02	245.24	142.32
$r+2$	244.08	247.12	245.04	245.26	142.30
f (Feed)	274.14	278.73	277.89	277.84	126.76
$s-2$	300.61	293.72	295.47	295.23	141.24
$s-1$	300.69	293.72	295.47	295.23	141.24
s	300.73	293.76	295.47	295.23	141.24
$N+1$ (Bottoms)	355.91	355.99	355.78	355.79	
D_{co}	29.438	29.499	29.337	29.350	
θ_{01}	0.33155	2.3846	0.94406	1.0005	
θ_{0h}	0.51620	0.97156	0.96520	1.0004	
θ_1	1.0137	0.9948	0.9996	0.9987	
W_1 (Calc.)	16.37	20.35	19.84	20.02	
V_1	138.89	155.33	139.37	140.61	

Final product distribution (Trial No. 25)

Component	d	b	w
C_3H_8	16.8319	0.0	3.1681
$i\text{-}C_4$	9.4211	1.4132	9.16575
$n\text{-}C_4$	3.0973	9.2365	7.6661
$i\text{-}C_5$	0.0	20.0000	0.0
$n\text{-}C_5$	0.0	20.0000	0.0

* These temperatures were obtained by use of the quartering procedure. At the end of 25 trials the successive temperature profiles agreed to within 5 digits.

The applications of the convergence method presented in this chapter are more limited (see Equations (11–15) and (11–16)) than is the one given in Chapter 10. The method proposed here was subject to overcorrections which were more difficult to dampen than those produced by the method given in Chapter 10.

NOTATION

(See also Chapter 10)

Subscripts

h = heavy key component; a component for which the ratio of b/d is specified

l = light key component; a component for which the ratio of b/d is specified

PROBLEMS

11–1 Commencing with Equation (11–1) and the postulate beneath it, show that Equation (11–2) follows.

11–2 Develop the expression for $P(\psi_r)$ as given by Equation (11–23).

11–3 For the case where plate p is located a finite number of plates from the top of the column (see Figure 10–3), construct a proof of the existence of the rectifying pinch.

11–4 For the case described in the previous problem, show that

$$d_i + w_{1i} = 0$$

for a separated heavy component.
(Hints: (1) Develop a formula for $(d_i + w_{1i})/b_i$ by matching at the feed plate. (2) See Equation (10–24).)

11–5 For the case where the side-stream W_1 is withdrawn a finite number of plates above the feed plate (see Figure 10–4), construct a proof of the existence of the rectifying pinch.

11–6 For the same case described in the previous problem, show that for a separated heavy component, $d_i = 0$ and $w_{1i} = 0$.

11–7 For the case of a column similar to those shown in Figures 10–3 and 10–4 except that the side stream W_1 is withdrawn as a liquid from the rectifying pinch (if it exists), construct a proof of the existence of the rectifying pinch.

11-8 For the column described in the previous problem, show that for a separated heavy component, $d_i = 0$ and $w_{1i} = 0$.

LITERATURE CITED

1. Abdel-Aal, H. K., "Separation Specifications for Complex Columns at Minimum Reflux," M.S. thesis, A. and M. College of Texas, College Station, Texas, January 1962.

2. Anthony, R. G., "Determination of Minimum Reflux for Conventional Columns," M.S. thesis, A. and M. College of Texas, College Station, Texas, January 1962.

Systems: Treatment of Distillation Columns with Side Strippers 12

A complex column with an attached side stripper represents one type of a distillation system. A more general treatment of systems is presented in the next chapter. The special case where the stripping medium, steam, is considered to be a single phase component is treated in this chapter. The method presented follows closely the one proposed in References (2, 3). In it, the side stripper is considered in the same convergence loop as the primary distillation column. This relationship permits the simultaneous convergence of these units. In effect, the strippers are considered as parts of the distillation column. This procedure differs from the one recently shown by Amundson *et al.* (1) in which solutions were obtained alternately for the distillation column and the side stripper. In order to focus attention on the inclusion of a side stripper in the same convergence loop as the distillation column, the equations are stated for a distillation column with one feed plate and one side-stream withdrawn. This side stream is treated by a steam stripper. Steam denoted by the subscript "L" is taken to be the only component which appears in the vapor phase alone. A component denoted by the subscript "H" is considered to be the only one which appears in the liquid phase alone. All components except steam are assumed to enter in the feed F.

MATERIAL BALANCES

In order to distinguish the flow rates and other quantities for the stripper from those of the distillation column, symbols with "primes" are employed for the stripper as required for clarity. As shown in Figure 12–1, the side-stream from the distillation column is stripped by use of a steam stripper and the vapor from the stripper is returned to plate p, the same plate from

310

which the side-stream is withdrawn. When the vapor is returned to some plate other than the one from which the liquid was withdrawn, the plates of the column between the withdrawal and the return of the side-stream together with the stripper are referred to as an "internal loop" (see Figure 12–2). Since the treatment of an internal loop is a logical extension of that which is developed for the system shown in Figure 12–1, it is left as an exercise (see Problems 12–1 and 12–2).

Material Balances for the Distillation Column

For the system shown in Figure 12–1, the following material balances for the rectifying section of the distillation column apply for all of the distributed components.

$$\frac{v_{1i}}{d_i} = A_{0i} + 1, \quad \text{(balance around the condenser)} \qquad (12\text{–}1\text{a})$$

$$\frac{v_{ji}}{d_i} = A_{j-1,i}\left(\frac{v_{j-1,i}}{d_i}\right) + 1, \quad 2 \leq j \leq p - 1 \qquad (12\text{–}1\text{b})$$

$$\frac{\bar{v}_{pi}}{d_i} = A_{p-1,i}\left(\frac{v_{p-1,i}}{d_i}\right) + 1 \qquad (12\text{–}1\text{c})$$

$$\frac{v_{p+1,i}}{d_i} = A_{pi}\left(\frac{v_{pi}}{d_i}\right) + \left(1 - \frac{v'_{1i}}{d_i}\right) \qquad (12\text{–}1\text{d})$$

$$\frac{v_{ji}}{d_i} = A_{f-1,i}\left(\frac{v_{j-1,i}}{d_i}\right) + C_{1i}, \quad p + 2 \leq j \leq f - 1 \qquad (12\text{–}1\text{e})$$

$$\frac{\bar{v}_{fi}}{d_i} = A_{f-1,i}\left(\frac{v_{f-1,i}}{d_i}\right) + C_{1i} \qquad (12\text{–}1\text{f})$$

where

$$C_{1i} = 1 + w_{1i}/d_i$$

$$\bar{v}_{pi} = v_{pi} + v'_{1i}$$

For the stripping section Equations (3–9) through (3–11) are applicable.

The flow rates of the single phase components at all points throughout the system are either known or readily computed. On the basis of assumed L/V and temperature profiles, fixed values for V_1, D, and W_1, calculations are initiated at the top of the column and carried out as indicated by Equations (12–1a) through (12–1c). The computations lead to a numerical

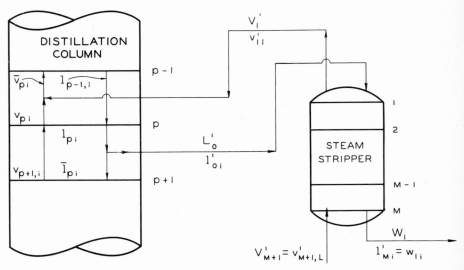

Figure 12–1. Steam stripper for the side-stream withdrawn from the distillation column. (Reproduced by permission of *Hydrocarbon Processing & Petroleum Refiner*)

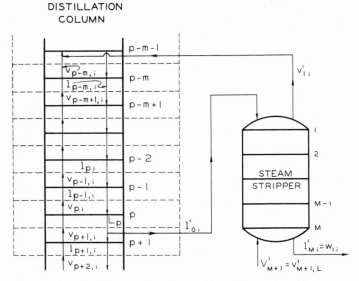

Figure 12–2. Diagram of an internal loop. (Reproduced by permission of *Hydrocarbon Processing & Petroleum Refiner*)

value for $\bar{v}_{pi}/d_i$. However, before further calculations for the distillation column may be made, v'_{1i}/d_i must be evaluated. After the value of the latter has been found, the quantities v_{pi}/d_i and w_{1i}/d_i, appearing in Equations (12–1d) and (12–1e), are readily calculated. The development of the expression for the computation of v'_{1i}/d_i follows.

Material Balances for the Side Stripper

For the side stripper the material balances for all of the distributed components are represented by

$$\frac{l'_{j-1,i}}{d_i} = S_{ji}\left(\frac{l'_{ji}}{d_i}\right) + \frac{l'_{Mi}}{d_i}, \quad 1 \leq j \leq M \tag{12–2}$$

From the analysis given in Chapter 8, it follows that round-off error is minimized in the side stripper by use of Equation (12–2). Continued substitution of the expression for l'_{ji}/d_i into the one for $l'_{j-1,i}/d_i$ leads to the following relationship.

$$\frac{l'_{Mi}}{d_i} = \frac{(l'_{0i}/d_i)}{\Phi_i} \tag{12–3}$$

where

$$\Phi_i = 1 + S_{1i} + S_{1i}S_{2i} + \ldots + S_{1i}S_{2i}\ldots S_{M-1,i}S_{Mi}$$

An over-all balance is given by

$$\frac{v'_{1i}}{d_i} = \frac{l'_{0i}}{d_i} - \frac{l'_{Mi}}{d_i} \tag{12–4}$$

When Equations (12–3) and (12–4) are solved for v'_{1i}/d_i, one obtains

$$\frac{v'_{1i}}{d_i} = \left(\frac{\Phi_i - 1}{\Phi_i}\right)\left(\frac{l'_{0i}}{d_i}\right) \tag{12–5}$$

The quantities l'_{0i}/d_i and v_{pi}/d_i are related as follows:

$$\frac{l'_{0i}}{d_i} = \left(\frac{L'_0}{L_p}\right)\left(\frac{l_{pi}}{d_i}\right) = \left(\frac{L'_0}{L_p}\right)(A_{pi})\left(\frac{v_{pi}}{d_i}\right) \tag{12–6}$$

Elimination of l'_{0i}/d_i from Equations (12–5) and (12–6) gives

$$\frac{v'_{1i}}{d_i} = \left(\frac{\Phi_i - 1}{\Phi_i}\right)\left(\frac{L'_0 A_{pi}}{L_p}\right)\left(\frac{v_{pi}}{d_i}\right) \tag{12–7}$$

The value of L_0' to be employed in this expression is calculated as described in a subsequent section. Since $\bar{v}_{pi}/d_i = v_{pi}/d_i + v_{1i}'/d_i$, the following expression is readily obtained from Equation (12–7).

$$\frac{v_{1i}'}{d_i} = \frac{(\bar{v}_{pi}/d_i)}{1 + [\Phi_i/(\Phi_i - 1)](L_p/L_0'A_{pi})} \qquad (12\text{–}8)$$

After v_{1i}'/d_i has been calculated by use of Equation (12–8), v_{pi}/d_i is computed by use of Equation (12–7) and l_{Mi}'/d_i (which is equal to w_{1i}/d_i) is calculated by Equation (12–3). After w_{1i}/d_i has been evaluated, the calculations indicated by Equation (12–2) may be performed for all components except steam.

After these computations for the stripper have been made, calculations are continued to the feed plate of the distillation column in the usual manner as indicated by Equations (12–1d) through (12–1f). Likewise, the calculations for the stripping section of the distillation column are performed as indicated by Equations (3–9) through (3–11). After these calculations have been made, b_i/d_i for each distributed component is computed by use of Equation (10–44).

The return of the vapor stream V_1' to the column at a plate different from the one from which the side stream is withdrawn is called an internal loop. When V_1' is returned to plate "q" located above p, the treatment of the side stripper is similar to that shown except that the material balances for the plates between q and p of the distillation column are also described by a series.

CONVERGENCE METHOD

In the following considerations assume that F, D, W_1, V_1', V_{M+1}', f, N, M, the type of overhead condenser for the distillation column, the system pressure, and the thermal conditions of the feeds F and V_{M+1}' have been specified.

Each trial calculation through the system leads to a set of calculated values for b_i/d_i and w_{1i}/d_i. The corrected rates are given by Equations (7–1) and (7–2) in terms of the multipliers θ_0 and θ_1. These give rise to two functions, $g_0(\theta_0, \theta_1)$ and $g_1(\theta_0, \theta_1)$ (see Equations (7–6) and (7–7)), which may be solved for the desired values of θ_0 and θ_1 as described in Chapter 7. Compositions in the distillation column are calculated by use of Equations (6–3) through (6–7). For a side stripper the following formulas are applicable.

$$y'_{ji} = \left(\frac{V'_j - v'_{jL}}{V'_j}\right) \frac{(v'_{ji}/d_i)_{ca}(d_i)_{co}}{\sum\limits_{i\neq H,L} (v'_{ji}/d_i)_{ca}(d_i)_{co}}, \quad i \neq H, L \qquad (12\text{–}9a)$$

$$y'_{jL} = v'_{jL}/V'_j \qquad (12\text{–}9b)$$

$$x'_{ji} = \left(\frac{L'_j - l'_{jH}}{L'_j}\right) \frac{(l'_{ji}/b_i)_{ca}(b_i)_{co}}{\sum\limits_{i\neq H,L} (l'_{ji}/b_i)_{ca}(b_i)_{co}}, \quad i \neq H, L \qquad (12\text{–}9c)$$

$$x'_{jH} = \frac{l'_{jH}}{L'_j} \qquad (12\text{–}9d)$$

The same approach used to obtain these expressions readily shows that, for a system containing any number of side strippers, the corresponding equations for the calculation of the compositions are of the same form as Equation (12–9).

The total vapor and liquid flow rates appearing in these formulas are the correct values. If all of the flow rates are fixed by the specifications, then these values are used in Equation (12–9). Usually V'_{M+1} and W_1 (also denoted by L'_M) are the only flow rates specified. For the remainder of the rates the following approximations were found to give satisfactory results.

$$V'_j = \sum_{i\neq H,L} \left(\frac{v'_{ji}}{b_i}\right)_{ca} (b_i)_{co} + v'_{jL}, \quad j \neq 1 \qquad (12\text{–}10)$$

$$L'_j = \sum_{i\neq H,L} \left(\frac{l'_{ji}}{b_i}\right)_{ca} (b_i)_{co} + l'_{jH}, \quad j \neq 0, M \qquad (12\text{–}11)$$

$$V'_1 = \sum_{i\neq H,L} \theta_1 \left(\frac{v'_{1i}}{d_i}\right)_{ca} (d_i)_{co} + v'_{1L} \qquad (12\text{–}12)$$

$$L'_0 = \sum_{i\neq H,L} \theta_1 \left(\frac{l'_{0i}}{d_i}\right)_{ca} (d_i)_{co} + w_{1H} \qquad (12\text{–}13)$$

For the particular system under consideration, note that $v'_{jL} = V'_{M+1}$ and $l'_{jH} = w_{1H} = 0$ in Equations (12–9) through (12–13).

The development of Equations (12–9), (12–10), and (12–11) is presented in the next section. Equations (12–12) and (12–13) are developed in the following manner. The material balances lead to a set of terminal rates for all of the distributed components. For the stripper, the following values are obtained.

$$\left(\frac{l'_{0i}}{d_i}\right)_{ca} = \left(\frac{v'_{1i}}{d_i}\right)_{ca} + \left(\frac{w_{1i}}{d_i}\right)_{ca} \tag{12-14}$$

Multiplication of both sides of this equation by $\theta_1(d_i)_{co}$ gives upon rearrangement

$$\theta_1 \left(\frac{l'_{0i}}{d_i}\right)_{ca} (d_i)_{co} - \theta_1 \left(\frac{v'_{1i}}{d_i}\right)_{ca} (d_i)_{co} = \theta_1 \left(\frac{w_{1i}}{d_i}\right)_{ca} (d_i)_{co} \tag{12-15}$$

Recall that the θ's are calculated such that for each component, the term on the right hand side of Equation (12–15) is $(w_{1i})_{co}$. Furthermore, this corrected rate is in over-all material balance, which is expressed as follows:

$$FX_i = (d_i)_{co} + (b_i)_{co} + (w_{1i})_{co} \tag{12-16}$$

Since the corrected value of w_{1i} has been fixed by the convergence method for the combined unit, the number of corrected sets of values for v'_{1i} and l'_{0i} that satisfy an over-all balance around the stripper has been reduced. That is for each distributed component,

$$(l'_{0i})_{co} - (v'_{1i})_{co} = (w_{1i})_{co} \tag{12-17}$$

One such set of values for l'_{0i} and v'_{1i} is obtained by taking the left hand members of Equation (12–15) to be individually equal to $(l'_{0i})_{co}$ and $(v'_{1i})_{co}$ as follows

$$(l'_{0i})_{co} = \theta_1 \left(\frac{l'_{0i}}{d_i}\right)_{ca} (d_i)_{co} \tag{12-18}$$

$$(v'_{1i})_{co} = \theta_1 \left(\frac{v'_{1i}}{d_i}\right)_{ca} (d_i)_{co} \tag{12-19}$$

Summation over all distributed components yields the desired results, Equations (12–12) and (12–13). These values of L'_0 and V'_1 are in over-all material balance with the specified withdrawal rate W_1 from the stripper. As a consequence of the procedure used for the calculation of these values of V'_1 and L'_0, each component is also in material balance. The values of v'_{1i} and V'_1 given by Equations (12–19) and (12–12) are used to calculate the composition of the vapor leaving the stripper.

Development of Equations (12-9), (12-10), and (12-11)

Consider a side stripper for which V'_j and L'_j are fixed for each plate by use of the required intercoolers (or heaters). Suppose a trial calculation has been carried out for the distillation column and the stripper and that the set of corrected values for w_{1i}, l'_{0i} and v'_{1i} has been obtained as described previously. Expressions suitable for the calculation of the compositions on each plate may be developed on the basis of the following postulates. Let σ_j be defined by

$$(v'_{ji})_{co} = \sigma_j \left(\frac{v'_{ji}}{v'_{1i}}\right)_{ca} (v'_{1i})_{co}, \qquad i \neq H, L \qquad (12\text{-}20)$$

$$1 \leq j \leq M$$

and τ_j by

$$(l'_{ji})_{co} = \tau_j \left(\frac{l'_{ji}}{w_{1i}}\right)_{ca} (w_{1i})_{co}, \qquad i \neq H, L \qquad (12\text{-}21)$$

$$1 \leq j \leq M$$

For $j = 0$ and $j = M + 1$, more general definitions are permitted for τ and σ; namely,

$$(v'_{M+1,i})_{co} = \sigma_{M+1,i} \left(\frac{v'_{M+1,i}}{v'_{1i}}\right)_{ca} (v'_{1i})_{co}, \quad i \neq H, L \qquad (12\text{-}22)$$

$$(l'_{0i})_{co} = \tau_{0i} \left(\frac{l'_{0i}}{w_{1i}}\right)_{ca} (w_{1i})_{co}, \quad i \neq H, L \qquad (12\text{-}23)$$

As shown below, the ratio of $\sigma_{M+1,i}$ to τ_{0i} is not independent of i for the particular selection of the corrected values of w_{1i}, l'_{0i} and v'_{1i} stated in the previous section.

Equations (12–9) through (12–11) are shown to follow on the basis of the given postulates. Expressions for V'_j and L'_j are obtained by summing both sides of Equations (12–20) and (12–21) over all distributed components followed by the addition of v'_{jL} and l'_{jH} to each side of the respective equations to give

$$V'_j = \sum_{i \neq H,L} \sigma_j \left(\frac{v'_{ji}}{v'_{1i}}\right) (v'_{1i})_{co} + v'_{jL}, \quad 1 \leq j \leq M \qquad (12\text{-}24)$$

$$L'_j = \sum_{i \neq H,L} \tau_j \left(\frac{l'_{ji}}{w_{1i}}\right)_{ca} (w_{1i})_{co} + l'_{jH}, \quad 1 \leq j \leq M \qquad (12\text{-}25)$$

By use of the conventional definition of the mole fraction and Equations (12–20) and (12–24) it follows that

$$y'_{ji} = \frac{\sigma_j (v'_{ji}/v_{1i})_{ca} (v'_{1i})_{co}}{\displaystyle\sum_{i \neq H,L} \sigma_j (v'_{ji}/v'_{1i})_{ca} (v'_{1i})_{co} + v'_{jL}} \qquad (12\text{-}26)$$

When Equation (12–24) is solved for σ_j one obtains

$$\sigma_j = \frac{V'_j - v'_{jL}}{\sum_{i \neq H,L} (v'_{ji}/v'_{1i})_{ca} (v'_{1i})_{co}} \tag{12–27}$$

Substitution of this expression for σ_j into Equation (12–26) gives

$$y'_{ji} = \left(\frac{V'_j - v'_{jL}}{V'_j}\right) \frac{(v'_{ji}/v_{1i})_{ca} (v'_{1i})_{co}}{\sum_{i \neq H,L} (v'_{ji}/v'_{1i})_{ca} (v'_{1i})_{co}} \tag{12–28}$$

When $(v'_{1i})_{co}$ is given by Equation (12–19), each term in the summation of Equation (12–28) may be written in the form

$$\left(\frac{v'_{ji}}{v'_{1i}}\right)_{ca} (v'_{1i})_{co} = \theta_1 \left(\frac{v'_{ji}}{d_i}\right)_{ca} (d_i)_{co} \tag{12–29}$$

Substitution of this expression into Equation (12–28) gives the desired result, Equation (12–9a). When V'_j and L'_j are unknown, the approximations given by Equations (12–10) and (12–11) may be employed. In the development of these expressions, it is convenient to begin with a further examination of the multipliers, σ and τ.

When the solution is obtained, $\sigma_j = \tau_j = 1$ for all j. Use of the postulates represented by Equations (12–18), (12–19), (12–20), and (12–21) gives several values of σ and τ that are also equal to unity for each trial. The values of j for which σ_j and τ_j are equal to unity as well as the values of $\sigma_{M+1,i}$ and τ_{0i} follow. For $j = 1$, note that Equation (12–24) requires that $\sigma_1 = 1.0$; and for $j = M$, Equation (12–25) requires that $\tau_M = 1.0$. When the distributed components do not appear in V'_{M+1}, the expression for $\sigma_{M+1,i}$ follows immediately from Equation (12–22). Since the stripping medium is specified to consist of steam alone, both $(v'_{M+1,i})_{ca}$ and $(v'_{M+1,i})_{co}$ are equal to zero for $i = 2$ through c, where steam is given the component number 1. Thus Equation (12–22) reduces to

$$1 = \sigma_{M+1,i} \frac{(v'_{1i})_{co}}{(v'_{1i})_{ca}} \tag{12–30}$$

Elimination of $(v'_{1i})_{co}$ from this expression by use of Equation (12–19) yields

$$\frac{1}{\sigma_{M+1,i}} = \theta_1 \frac{(d_i)_{co}}{(d_i)_{ca}}$$

The quantity τ_{0i} is evaluated as follows. Elimination of $(l'_{0i})_{co}$ from Equations (12–18) and (12–23) gives

$$\theta_1 \frac{(d_i)_{co}}{(d_i)_{ca}} = \tau_{0i} \frac{(w_{1i})_{co}}{(w_{1i})_{ca}} \tag{12–31}$$

When $(w_{1i})_{co}$ is replaced by its equivalent as given by Equation (7–2), it is found that

$$\frac{\tau_{0i}(w_{1i})_{co}}{(w_{1i})_{ca}} = \frac{\tau_{0i}(w_{1i}/d_i)_{ca}(d_i)_{co}}{(w_{1i})_{ca}} = \tau_{0i}\theta_1 \frac{(d_i)_{co}}{(d_i)_{ca}} \tag{12–32}$$

Comparison of this expression with Equation (12–31) shows that $\tau_{0i} = 1.0$.
   Equations (12–24) and (12–29) may be combined to give

$$V'_j = \sum_{i \neq H,L} (\sigma_j \theta_1) \left(\frac{v'_{ji}}{d_i}\right)_{ca} (d_i)_{co} + v'_{jL}, \quad 1 \leq j \leq M \tag{12–33}$$

Equation (12–10) is seen to be an approximation of this expression in that the combined multiplier, $(\sigma_j \theta_1)$, is taken equal to unity when the value of σ_j is unknown. Similarly, Equation (12–25) may be restated in the following form.

$$L'_j = \sum_{i \neq H,L} \left(\tau_j \frac{\theta_1}{\theta_0}\right) \left(\frac{l'_{ji}}{b_i}\right)_{ca} (b_i)_{co} + l'_{jH}, \quad 1 \leq j \leq M \tag{12–34}$$

Equation (12–11) represents an approximation of Equation (12–34). Again, when the value of τ_j is unknown, the combined multiplier, $[\tau_j(\theta_1/\theta_0)]$, is taken equal to unity. These approximations are based on the results obtained by Dickey (2), who solved a wide variety of examples and found these to be the best of the approximations considered.

OTHER RELATIONSHIPS

   After a given trial has been carried out to give corrected compositions and the corresponding temperatures, values of V'_1, L'_0, V'_j and L'_j are determined by use of a combination of the constant-composition and Q-methods for making enthalpy balances. These flow rates are used in the stripping factors for the stripper for the next trial. For the distillation column, the enthalpy balances were written around the top of the column and any given plate below it. Where V'_{M+1}, W_1, and the enthalpy of the steam is specified for the side stripper, the enthalpy balances for this unit are commenced at the bottom and carried out step-by-step to the top of the stripper.

Illustrative Example

The statement and specifications for Example 12–1 are given in Table 12–1. In the solution of this example, the temperatures were determined by use of the bubble point procedure; and for every trial after the first the temperature profile to be used for the next trial calculation was obtained by averaging. The total flow rates in both the distillation column and the stripper were determined by use of a combination of the constant-composition and Q-methods. The variation of the rates between successive trials was restricted in about the same manner as described in Chapter 5. Prior to the initiation of the procedure for making enthalpy balances, the first three trials for both the distillation column and the side stripper were made at a fixed set of vapor and liquid rates. For the next four trials, the vapor rates were permitted to vary by not more than 20 percent, and for all subsequent trials the change permitted was 5 percent. It should be mentioned that the same solution may be obtained by use of other restrictions of the same order of magnitude as those employed. The solution of Example 12–1 is given in Tables 12–2, 12–3, and 12–4. Note that for the specified steam enthalpy a heating duty was required for the bottom plate of the side stripper. This may be effected either by use of a reboiler on the bottom plate of the side stripper or by use of steam having an enthalpy such that the heater duty required for plate M is zero.

TABLE 12-1 Statement and specifications for Example 12-1

Component	FX	Specifications
C_3H_8	5	$N = 16, f = 11, M = 9, W_1$ to be withdrawn from plate 9 of the distillation column. $D = 25$ (vapor), partial
$i\text{-}C_4$	8	condenser, $W_1 = 45$ (liquid), $V_{M+1} = 5$, and the system pressure $= 300$ psia. The feed enters the distillation
$n\text{-}C_4$	12	column as a liquid at its bubble point. Flow rates to be determined by enthalpy balances. The initial tem-perature profile for the column is to linear with plate number between 140 and 480°F and in the side stripper,
$i\text{-}C_5$	30	linear between 200 and 360°F. The initial vapor rates for the distillation column are as follows: $V_j = $ 225, $1 \leqq j \leqq 8$ and $V_j = 220, 9 \leqq j \leqq 12$. For the side stripper, $V_j = V'_{M+1} = 5, 1 \leqq j \leqq 9$. L_0' to be
$i\text{-}C_5$	25	calculated by enthalpy balance. For the column: $V_{min} = 100, V_{max} = 55$. Enthalpy of the entering steam
$n\text{-}C_6$	12	is 15,000 Btu per lb-mole. Enthalpy of and equilibrium data to be taken from Tables A–4 and A–8 of the Appendix. For steam: $H^\natural = -40.48668 + 0.48685T - 3.112164 \times 10^{-4}T^2$, $(T°R)$. Data for the curve
$n\text{-}C_7$	8	fit were taken from *Chemical Engineers' Handbook*, 3 ed., J. H. Perry, editor (New York: McGraw-Hill Book Company, Inc., 1960), p. 279.

Reproduced by permission of *Hydrocarbon Processing & Petroleum Refiner*

TABLE 12-2* Temperatures and vapor rates obtained for the distillation column in the solution of Example 12-1

Plate No.	Temperatures and vapor rates				Plate No.	Temperatures and vapor rates			
	Temp., °F Trial No.		Vapor rates Trial No.			Temp., °F Trial No.		Vapor rates Trial No.	
	8	24	8	24		8	24	8	24
0	190.6	189.6	25.0	25.0	9	307.6	306.2	185.2	187.4
1	225.6	223.9	225.0	225.0	10	314.9	314.6	188.1	190.2
2	235.8	233.0	253.8	254.7	11	323.4	323.1	185.3	186.1
3	246.2	242.1	249.8	251.5	12	332.2	331.9	195.0	194.9
4	257.9	252.6	243.5	245.3	13	338.8	338.4	199.9	200.2
5	270.2	264.5	237.4	238.3	14	345.3	344.8	201.6	202.2
6	281.8	276.5	233.4	232.8	15	354.2	353.4	200.1	200.9
7	291.4	287.3	231.6	229.8	16	368.5	367.4	194.9	195.6
8	299.0	296.2	231.3	228.7	17	391.9	390.8	186.4	186.7

*The temperatures shown are those calculated at the end of the trial indicated. At the end of 24 trials, the assumed and calculated temperatures agreed to within 5 digits, and at the end of 30 trials to within 8 digits.

Reproduced by permission of *Hydrocarbon Processing & Petroleum Refiner*

TABLE 12-3* Temperatures and vapor rates obtained in the side stripper in the solution of Example 12.1

Plate No.	Temperature, (°F) Trial No.			Vapor rates Trial No.			Intercooler duties (Btu per hr) Trial No.		
	8	12	24	8	12	24	8	12	24
1	274.9	287.7	291.9	40.7	37.6	40.5	-17.8×10^3	0.0	0.0
2	236.8	257.7	270.7	15.1	18.4	19.3	58.2×10^3	24.6×10^3	0.0
3	227.8	243.5	257.8	11.9	14.5	14.8	0.0	28.6×10^2	0.0
4	223.0	234.4	248.8	10.5	12.8	12.9	78.6×10^2	60.4×10^2	0.0
5	222.5	230.6	242.5	10.1	11.7	11.8	0.0	0.0	0.0
6	222.0	228.9	237.8	10.2	10.9	11.2	0.0	0.0	0.0
7	220.2	228.0	234.3	10.5	10.7	10.7	25.9×10^2	0.0	0.0
8	219.0	227.8	231.6	10.6	10.4	10.4	24.1×10^2	0.0	0.0
9	220.1	228.2	229.1	10.0	10.0	10.0	74.9×10^3	-72.9×10^3	-66.3×10^3

*The temperatures shown are those calculated at the end of the trial indicated. At the end of 24 trials, the assumed and calculated temperatures agreed to within 5 digits, and at the end of 30 trials to within 8 digits.

Reproduced by permission of *Hydrocarbon Processing & Petroleum Refiner*

TABLE 12-4 Solution of Example 12-3

Trial No.	Variation of D and W_1 with trial No.				Product distribution (Trial No. 24)			
	D	W_1	θ_0	θ_1	Component	d	b	w_1
1	17.64	67.75	1.041	0.170	C_3H_8	4.862	5.161×10^{-4}	1.370×10^{-1}
4	23.67	49.59	0.974	0.738	$i\text{-}C_4$	6.864	1.918×10^{-3}	1.134
8	24.62	47.12	1.042	0.909	$n\text{-}C_4$	8.048	1.046×10^{-1}	3.847
12	25.04	45.03	1.015	1.010	$i\text{-}C_5$	2.010×10^{-1}	5.550	1.925×10
16	25.06	45.02	1.021	1.015	$n\text{-}C_5$	4.200×10^{-2}	1.116×10	1.884×10
20	25.005	44.978	1.0001	1.001	$n\text{-}C_6$	1.860×10^{-7}	1.045×10	1.555
24	24.999	44.999	1.0009	0.9999	$n\text{-}C_7$	3.280×10^{-10}	7.714	2.000×10^{-1}

Reproduced by permission of *Hydrocarbon Processing & Petroleum Refiner*

NOTATION

(See also Chapters 2 through 11)

M = total number of plates in the side stripper

Q'_j = intercooler (or heater) duty for plate j of the side stripper

PROBLEMS

12–1 Develop the component-material balances for the rectifying section of the distillation column for the system containing the internal loop as shown in Figure 12–2.

12–2 (a) Show that the equations developed in Problem 12–1 may be solved to give

$$\frac{v_{pi}}{d_i} = \omega_i \left(\frac{v_{p-m,i}}{d_i}\right) + (\Omega_i - \omega_i)\left(1 - \frac{v'_{1i}}{d_i}\right)$$

where

$$\Omega_i = 1 + A_{p-1,i} + A_{p-1,i}A_{p-2,i} + \ldots + A_{p-1,i}A_{p-2,i}\ldots A_{p-m+1,i}A_{p-m,i}$$

$$\omega_i = A_{p-1,i}A_{p-2,i}\ldots A_{p-m+1,i}A_{p-m,i}$$

(b) Show that the expression given by Equation (12–7) is applicable for the system under consideration.

(c) Then show that

$$\frac{v'_{1i}}{d_i} = \frac{\Omega_i + \omega_i\left[(\bar{v}_{p-m,i}/d_i) - 1\right]}{\Omega_i + (\Phi_i/(\Phi_i - 1))(L_p/L'_0 A_{pi})}$$

where

$$\frac{\bar{v}_{p-m,i}}{d_i} = \frac{v_{p-m,i}}{d_i} + \frac{v'_{1i}}{d_i}$$

LITERATURE CITED

1. Amundson, N. R., A. J. Pontinen, and J. W. Tierney, "Multicomponent Distillation on a Digital Computer—Generalization with Side-Stream Stripping," *A.I.Ch.E. Journal,* **5,** 295 (1959).

2. Dickey, B. R., "Calculational Procedure for Multicomponent Distillation Columns with Side-Stream Strippers," M.S. thesis, A. and M. College of Texas, College Station, Texas, January 1962.

3. Dickey, B. R., C. D. Holland, and Ralph Cecchetti, "Figure Separations This New Way: Part 8—Distillation with Side-Strippers," *Petroleum Refiner,* **41,** No. 2, 143 (1962).

The Θ-Method of Convergence for Systems of Distillation Columns* 13

Since the procedure for including one unit as a part of another (as was done in Chapter 12 in the treatment of side strippers) becomes cumbersome when several units are involved, efforts were directed by Tomme (2) and Tomme *et al.* (3) toward the extension of the θ-method for the treatment of systems. As a result of this work, a generalized "Θ-Method for Systems" was developed. It is distinguished from the "θ-method" for a single column by use of a capital "Θ." However, when the system consists of a single unit, the Θ-method for systems reduces to the θ-method for a single column.

When the output from one unit is the input to the next, the θ-method for a single column is employed by obtaining the solution for each unit in succession. However, the Θ-method for systems is employed when units are connected in series and a recycle or feedback stream between units is involved. In the treatment of systems of this type, the calculational procedure of Thiele and Geddes is employed for each unit. Round-off error is minimized by the procedures described previously. The total flow rates throughout each unit are determined by use of a combination of the constant-composition and Q-methods for making enthalpy balances. Temperatures are calculated by use of the bubble point procedure. After a set of terminal rates has been calculated for each unit, the Θ-method is used to find a corrected set which is in component-material balance for each unit and for the entire system and which is in agreement with the specified terminal flow rates.

DEVELOPMENT OF THE Θ-METHOD FOR SYSTEMS

The Θ-method is perhaps best understood by consideration of a specific system such as the one shown in Figure 13–1, which consists of a reboiler-

* A summary of this work was presented in a paper by J. A. McDonough, W. J. Tomme, and C. D. Holland at the Technical Meeting of the South Texas Section of the A.I.Ch.E. at Galveston, Texas, October 20, 1961.

absorber (Unit I) and a conventional distillation column (Unit II). In this
application the terminal flow rate D is specified; this rate determines V_1
since the feed rate F is fixed. Also, the recycle rate L_N (or B) is specified;
this rate in turn determines B (or L_N). In addition, for each unit the type
of condenser, the pressure, the number of plates, and the locations of feed
plates are specified. Also, the composition and thermal condition of the
feed F to Unit I, as well as the liquid reflux rate (L_0) for the second unit,
is fixed.

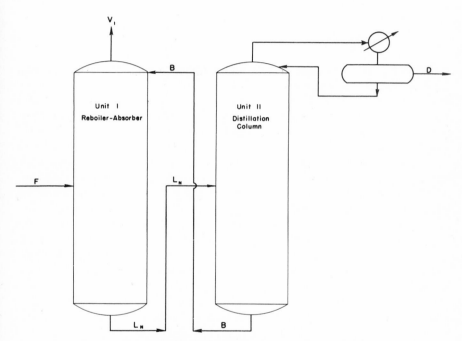

Figure 13–1. A system with recycle or feedback. (Reproduced by
permission of *Hydrocarbon Processing & Petroleum Refiner*)

In order to initiate the calculational procedure for the system, L/V
and temperature profiles, as well as a set of b_i's and a set of l_{Ni}'s, must be
assumed. On this basis, trial calculations are carried out for each unit as
discussed in greater detail in a subsequent section. At this point in the
argument, suffice it to say that, on the basis of the assumed values stated
above, the following calculated values are obtained. For Unit I, the rates
$(v_{1i})_{ca}$ and $(l_{Ni})_{ca}$ and the ratios $(v_{ji}/v_{1i})_{ca}$ and $(l_{ji}/l_{Ni})_{ca}$ are obtained.
Similarly for the second unit, the terminal rates $(d_i)_{ca}$ and $(b_i)_{ca}$ and the
ratios $(v_{ji}/d_i)_{ca}$ and $(l_{ji}/b_i)_{ca}$ are determined. Again the compositions on

each plate are altered in a manner reflecting the deviation of the terminal rates from the specified values of D and L_N. For Unit I

$$y_{ji} = \frac{(v_{ji}/v_{1i})_{ca}(v_{1i})_{co}}{\displaystyle\sum_{i=1}^{c}(v_{ji}/v_{1i})_{ca}(v_{1i})_{co}} \quad \text{and} \quad x_{ji} = \frac{(l_{ji}/l_{Ni})_{ca}(l_{Ni})_{co}}{\displaystyle\sum_{i=1}^{c}(l_{ji}/l_{Ni})_{ca}(l_{Ni})_{co}} \tag{13-1}$$

For Unit II

$$y_{ji} = \frac{(v_{ji}/d_i)_{ca}(d_i)_{co}}{\displaystyle\sum_{i=1}^{c}(v_{ji}/d)_{ca}(d_i)_{co}} \quad \text{and} \quad x_{ji} = \frac{(l_{ji}/b_i)_{ca}(b_i)_{co}}{\displaystyle\sum_{i=1}^{c}(l_{ji}/b_i)_{ca}(b_i)_{co}} \tag{13-2}$$

When the system contains single phase lights and heavies, the formulas for the y_{ji}'s and x_{ji}'s are preceded by

$$\frac{V_j - \displaystyle\sum_{L} v_{jL}}{V_j} \quad \text{and} \quad \frac{L_j - \displaystyle\sum_{H} l_{jH}}{L_j}$$

respectively. The development of these formulas from basic postulates is analogous to that described previously in Chapter 4. This approach readily shows that the corrected terminal rates and the calculated rates may be related by use of two multipliers as follows:

$$\left(\frac{l_{Ni}}{v_{1i}}\right)_{co} = \Theta_0 \left(\frac{l_{Ni}}{v_{1i}}\right)_{ca} \tag{13-3}$$

$$\left(\frac{b_i}{d_i}\right)_{co} = \Theta_1 \left(\frac{b_i}{d_i}\right)_{ca} \tag{13-4}$$

The "capital Θ" is employed in order to emphasize the fact that the corrected rates obtained by use of these multipliers must satisfy the over-all material balance for each unit of the system instead of only one unit, which is the case when the "lower case θ" is employed. Specifically, for each unit a corrected set of terminal rates must be found that satisfy the independent component-material balances enclosing each unit and the specifications D and L_N. For two units two independent over-all material balances exist, which may be taken as a balance around the entire system,

$$FX_i = (v_{1i})_{co} + (d_i)_{co} \tag{13-5}$$

and a balance enclosing the first unit,

$$FX_i = (v_{1i})_{co} + (l_{Ni})_{co} - (b_i)_{co} \tag{13-6}$$

Note that the equation representing a material balance for Unit II was taken to be dependent. This dependency is readily shown by combining Equations (13–5) and (13–6) to produce the relationship. The development of the formulas for $(v_{1i})_{co}$ and $(d_i)_{co}$ in terms of the calculated rates and the Θ's follows. After these expressions have been developed, formulas for $(l_{Ni})_{co}$ and $(b_i)_{co}$ are produced by making use of Equations (13–3) and (13–4). When Equation (13–5) is solved for $(d_i)_{co}$, one obtains

$$(d_i)_{co} = \frac{FX_i}{1 + (v_{1i}/d_i)_{co}} \tag{13–7}$$

Similarly, Equation (13–6) may be solved for $(v_{1i})_{co}$ to give

$$(v_{1i}) = \frac{FX_i}{1 + \Theta_0(l_{Ni}/v_{1i})_{ca} - \Theta_1(b_i/d_i)_{ca}(d_i/v_{1i})_{co}} \tag{13–8}$$

Dividing the members of Equation (13–7) by the corresponding ones of Equation (13–8) and solving for $(d_i/v_{1i})_{co}$ yields

$$\left(\frac{d_i}{v_{1i}}\right)_{co} = \frac{\Theta_0(l_{Ni}/v_{1i})_{ca}}{1 + \Theta_1(b_i/d_i)_{ca}} \tag{13–9}$$

Substitution of this expression into Equations (13–7) and (13–8) gives the desired formulas,

$$(d_i)_{co} = \frac{\Theta_0(l_{Ni}/v_{1i})_{ca}FX_i}{1 + \Theta_0(l_{Ni}/v_{1i})_{ca} + \Theta_1(b_i/d_i)_{ca}} \tag{13–10}$$

$$(v_{1i})_{co} = \frac{[1 + \Theta_1(b_i/d_i)_{ca}]FX_i}{1 + \Theta_0(l_{Ni}/v_{1i})_{ca} + \Theta_1(b_i/d_i)_{ca}} \tag{13–11}$$

The formulas for $(l_{Ni})_{co}$ and $(b_i)_{co}$ are readily produced from Equations (13–3), (13–4), (13–10), and (13–11).

In order to determine Θ_0 and Θ_1, two independent equations are required. These equations are developed on the basis of the two independent specifications, which are taken to be D and L_N. Since these specifications must be satisfied by the corrected rates, the desired set of values for Θ_0 and Θ_1 is that positive set which makes $G_0 = G_1 = 0$, simultaneously, where

$$G_0(\Theta_0, \Theta_1) = \sum_{i=1}^{c} (d_i)_{co} - D \tag{13–12}$$

$$G_1(\Theta_0, \Theta_1) = \sum_{i=1}^{c} (l_{Ni})_{co} - L_N \tag{13–13}$$

Of course the expression given by Equation (13–10) is understood to be used for $(d_i)_{co}$ in the function G_0, and the following expression for $(l_{Ni})_{co}$ is understood to be used in the function G_1,

$$(l_{Ni})_{co} \ = \ \Theta_0(l_{Ni}/v_{1i})_{ca}(v_{1i})_{co}$$

or

$$(l_{Ni})_{co} \ = \ \frac{\Theta_0(l_{Ni}/v_{1i})_{ca}[1 \ + \ \Theta_1(b_i/d_i)_{ca}]FX_i}{1 \ + \ \Theta_0(l_{Ni}/v_{1i})_{ca} \ + \ \Theta_1(b_i/d_i)_{ca}} \qquad (13\text{–}14)$$

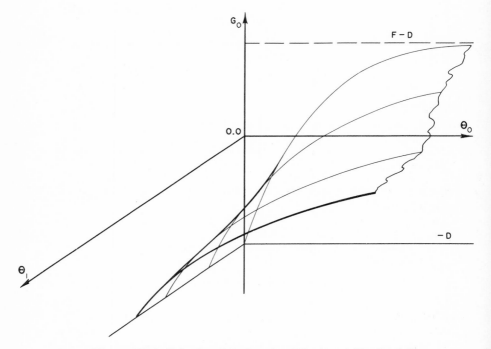

Figure 13–2. Behavior of the function G_0 in the neighborhood of the positive roots.

The behavior of each of these functions in the neighborhood of the set of positive roots is shown in Figures 13–2, 13–3, and 13–4. The θ's may be determined by use of the Newton-Raphson method as described in Chapters 1 and 7. If the feed F contains single phase lights and heavies the function G_1 is modified as follows:

$$L_N \text{ is replaced by } (L_N \ - \ \sum_H l_H)$$

Such components are treated in a manner analogous to that described in Chapters 6 and 7.

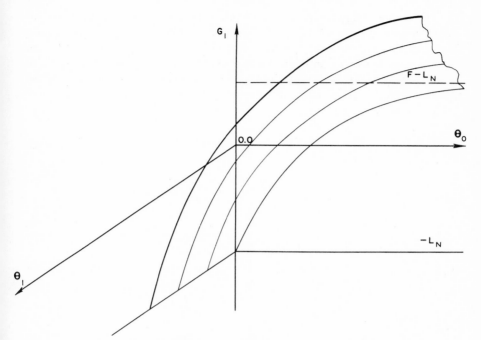

Figure 13–3. Behavior of the function G_1 in the neighborhood of the positive roots.

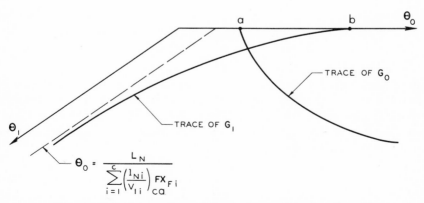

Figure 13–4. Intersections of the surfaces of the functions G_0 and G_1 with the $\overline{\Theta_0 \Theta_1}$ plane.

Treatment of Separated Components

The development of the formulas to be employed for separated components for the system shown in Figure 13–1 is similar to the one presented in Chapter 6 for single columns. Again as components are separated, certain ratios become indeterminate. For a heavy component separated in the reboiler-absorber, both $(v_{1i})_{ca}$ and $(v_{1i})_{co}$ are equal to zero and the product $[(v_{ji}/v_{1i})_{ca}(v_{1i})_{co}]$, which appears in Equation (13–1), is replaced by its equivalent; namely,

$$\left(\frac{v_{ji}}{v_{1i}}\right)_{ca}(v_{1i})_{co} = \left(\frac{v_{ji}}{l_{Ni}}\right)_{ca}\left(\frac{l_{Ni}}{v_{1i}}\right)_{ca}(v_{1i})_{co}$$

$$= \left(\frac{v_{ji}}{l_{Ni}}\right)_{ca}\left(\frac{l_{Ni}}{v_{1i}}\right)_{ca}\left(\frac{1}{\Theta_0}\right)\left(\frac{v_{1i}}{l_{Ni}}\right)_{ca}(l_{Ni})_{co}$$

$$= \left(\frac{1}{\Theta_0}\right)\left(\frac{v_{ji}}{l_{Ni}}\right)_{ca}(l_{Ni})_{co} \qquad (13\text{–}15)$$

Similarly, for a light component separated in the reboiler-absorber, $(l_{Ni})_{ca} = 0$ and $(l_{Ni})_{co} = 0$, and it is readily shown that

$$\left(\frac{l_{ji}}{l_{Ni}}\right)_{ca}(l_{Ni})_{co} = \Theta_0\left(\frac{l_{ji}}{v_{1i}}\right)_{ca}(v_{1i})_{co} \qquad (13\text{–}16)$$

Formulas for the corrected terminal rates of the separated components are developed in the following manner. For a heavy component separated in the reboiler-absorber, it follows from Equation (13–5) that

$$(d_i)_{co} = FX_i \qquad (13\text{–}17)$$

The formula for $(l_{Ni})_{co}$ is found by first restating Equation (13–6) in the form

$$FX_i = (l_{Ni})_{co}\left[1 - \left(\frac{b_i}{d_i}\right)_{co}\left(\frac{d_i}{l_{Ni}}\right)_{co}\right]$$

Elimination of $(b_i/d_i)_{co}$ and $(d_i)_{co}$ from this expression by use of Equations (13–4) and (13–17), respectively, followed by rearrangement gives

$$(l_{Ni})_{co} = FX_i\left[1 + \Theta_1\left(\frac{b_i}{d_i}\right)_{ca}\right] \qquad (13\text{–}18)$$

The formula for $(b_i)_{co}$ for the separated heavy component follows upon combination of Equations (13–4) and (13–18). For a light component that is separated in the reboiler-absorber, $(l_{Ni})_{co} = 0$, $(b_i)_{co} = 0$, $(d_i)_{co} = 0$, and $(v_{1i})_{co} = FX_i$.

Components separated in the distillation column are described by the following formulas, which are developed in a manner analogous to that shown for the reboiler-absorber. For a heavy component separated in the distillation column, $(d_i)_{ca} = 0$ and $(d_i)_{co} = 0$, and

$$\left(\frac{v_{ji}}{d_i}\right)_{ca}(d_i)_{co} = \left(\frac{1}{\Theta_1}\right)\left(\frac{v_{ji}}{b_i}\right)_{ca}(b_i)_{co} \tag{13–19}$$

$$(l_{Ni})_{co} = (b_i)_{co} = \Theta_0\left(\frac{l_{Ni}}{v_{1i}}\right)_{ca} FX_i \tag{13–20}$$

$$(v_{1i})_{co} = FX_i \tag{13–21}$$

For a light component separated in the distillation column, $(b_i)_{ca} = 0$, $(b_i)_{co} = 0$, and

$$(l_{ji}/b_i)_{ca}(b_i)_{co} = \Theta_1(l_{ji}/d_i)_{ca}(d_i)_{co} \tag{13–22}$$

Also,
$$(v_{1i})_{co} = \frac{FX_i}{1 + \Theta_0(l_{Ni}/v_{1i})_{ca}} \tag{13–23}$$

$$(d_i)_{co} = (l_{Ni})_{co} = \Theta_0(l_{Ni}/v_{1i})_{ca}(v_{1i})_{co} \tag{13–24}$$

TREATMENT OF A SYSTEM OF COMPLEX COLUMNS

The Θ-method is readily applied to a system of complex columns such as the one shown in Figure 13–5. The withdrawal of two side streams creates two additional degrees of freedom which permit two additional specifications to be made. In the following treatment, these are taken to be the flow rates W_1 and W_2. Again compositions for each unit are computed by use of Equations (13–1) and (13–2). For each of the streams (W_1 and W_2) withdrawn from the system a corresponding multiplier is obtained,

$$(w_{1i}/v_{1i})_{co} = \Theta_2(w_{1i}/v_{1i})_{ca} \tag{13–25}$$

$$(w_{2i}/d_i)_{co} = \Theta_3(w_{2i}/d_i)_{ca} \tag{13–26}$$

Thus for the system shown in Figure 13–2, the corrected and calculated rates are related by Equations (13–3), (13–4), (13–25), and (13–26). The Θ's are to be determined such that the over-all material balances,

$$FX_i = (v_{1i})_{co} + (d_i)_{co} + (w_{1i})_{co} + (w_{2i})_{co} \tag{13–27}$$

$$FX_i = (v_{1i})_{co} + (l_{Ni})_{co} + (w_{1i})_{co} - (b_i)_{co} \tag{13–28}$$

and the specifications D, L_N, W_1, and W_2 are satisfied. The set of positive

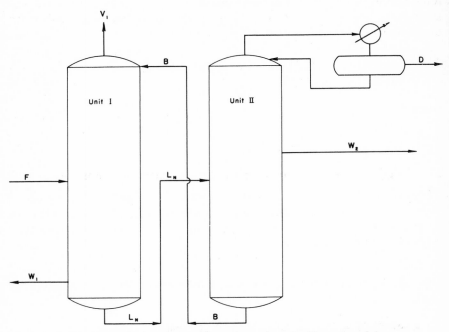

Figure 13–5. A system of complex columns. (Reproduced by permission of *Hydrocarbon Processing & Petroleum Refiner*)

Θ's that makes $G_0 = G_1 = G_2 = G_3 = 0$, simultaneously, satisfy these conditions. In a manner similar to that shown in Chapter 7, the following functions are developed.

$$G_0(\Theta_0, \Theta_1, \Theta_2, \Theta_3) = \sum_{i=1}^{c} (d_i)_{co} - D \qquad (13\text{–}29)$$

$$G_1(\Theta_0, \Theta_1, \Theta_2, \Theta_3) = \sum_{i=1}^{c} (l_{Ni})_{co} - L_N \qquad (13\text{–}30)$$

$$G_2(\Theta_0, \Theta_1, \Theta_2, \Theta_3) = \sum_{i=1}^{c} (w_{1i})_{co} - W_1 \qquad (13\text{–}31)$$

$$G_3(\Theta_0, \Theta_1, \Theta_2, \Theta_3) = \sum_{i=1}^{c} (w_{2i})_{co} - W_2 \qquad (13\text{–}32)$$

The following formulas for the corrected terminal rates for the individual components that appear in these functions are developed by use of the same approach shown for the first system.

$$(d_i)_{co} = \frac{\Theta_0(l_{Ni}/v_{1i})_{ca}FX_i}{R_1 + R_2R_3} \tag{13-33}$$

$$(v_{1i})_{co} = \frac{R_3FX_i}{R_1 + R_2R_3} \tag{13-34}$$

where

$$R_1 = [\Theta_0(l_{Ni}/v_{1i})_{ca}][1 + \Theta_3(w_{2i}/d_i)_{ca}]$$

$$R_2 = 1 + \Theta_2(w_{1i}/v_{1i})_{ca}$$

$$R_3 = 1 + \Theta_1(b_i/d_i)_{ca} + \Theta_3(w_{2i}/d_i)_{ca}$$

The formulas for $(l_{Ni})_{co}$, $(b_i)_{co}$, $(w_{1i})_{co}$, and $(w_{2i})_{co}$ readily follow by use of these results and Equations (13-3), (13-4), (13-25), and (13-26). Again, the Θ's may be determined by using the Newton-Raphson method as described in Chapters 1 and 7.

USE OF THE Θ-METHOD FOR THE SOLUTION OF SYSTEMS OF INTERRELATED UNITS

The term "interrelated units" means that the particular units are related by one or more recycle streams. Although the convergence characteristics of the Θ-method have not been investigated for any systems other than the combination of two distillation columns, the potential use of this method for solving problems involving interrelated units should be recognized. These units need not be distillation columns! In general, after a trial calculation has been performed for any system of units, the Θ-method may be employed to choose for each unit a corrected set of terminal rates that are in component-material balance and in agreement with the specified total flow rates for each unit. Also, it should be observed that the Θ-method of convergence may be extended to include specifications other than those considered herein. As a general rule, any information which is known with certainty about a unit or a system of units may be incorporated in the Θ multipliers.

SIGNIFICANCE OF THE MULTIPLIER Θ

In the meshing of units, it is necessary to obtain a relationship between the distribution of products and the composition of the feed to the column. In the previous development the multipliers (Θ) represent such a relationship. Further significance of these multipliers is afforded by consideration of a conventional column at total recycle. Components 1 through c are understood to appear in all of the feeds (to be considered) to the column, and regardless of composition the total feed rate F is understood to be held fixed. Further, suppose that the same distillate rate D is specified for each of feed compositions and that the α's are constant. Such a system is represented by Fenske's (1) equation,

$$b_i/d_i = (b_k/d_k)(\alpha_i/\alpha_k)^{-(N+2)} \tag{13–35}$$

where $(N + 2)$ is the total number of equilibrium stages (the number of plates plus the reboiler plus the partial condenser) and the base component is denoted by the subscript "k." An over-all material balance leads to

$$d_i = \frac{FX_i}{1 + (b_i/d_i)} \tag{13–36}$$

Summing both sides of this equation over all components gives

$$D = \sum_{i=1}^{c} \frac{FX_i}{1 + (b_i/d_i)} = \sum_{i=1}^{c} \frac{FX_i}{1 + (b_k/d_k)(\alpha_i/\alpha_k)^{-(N+2)}} \tag{13–37}$$

In view of Equation (13–37), it is convenient to define the function G as follows:

$$G(b_k/d_k) = \sum_{i=1}^{c} \frac{FX_i}{1 + (b_k/d_k)(\alpha_i/\alpha_k)^{-(N+2)}} - D \tag{13–38}$$

Equation (13–38) shows that for a given column at total recycle and a specified value of D, a b_k/d_k exists for each set of feed compositions; namely, the value that gives $G(b_k/d_k) = 0$. Since each feed contains the same set of components, the same values of $(\alpha_i/\alpha_k)^{-(N+2)}$ appear in Equation (13–38) for each set of feed compositions. Graphically the problem is represented in Figure 13–6 for two different feeds. This treatment parallels the one in which the total distillate rate is varied instead of the composition of the feed (see Problems 9–8 through 9–11).

    An expression for the multiplier θ for a conventional column at total recycle is developed in the following manner. When the distillate is withdrawn at the rate D and a feed having a composition denoted by the subscript "1" is fed to the column, the process may be represented by Equation (13–35) rearranged to the following form.

$$\log (b_i/d_i)_1 = \log (b_k/d_k)_1 - (N + 2) \log (\alpha_i/\alpha_k) \tag{13–39}$$

Similarly, when a feed consisting of the same components but of different composition is fed to the same column and when the distillate is withdrawn at the same rate D as for the previous case, the operation is represented by

$$\log (b_i/d_i)_2 = \log (b_k/d_k)_2 - (N + 2) \log (\alpha_i/\alpha_k) \qquad (13\text{--}40)$$

Observe that $(b_k/d_k)_1$ and $(b_k/d_k)_2$ are the values required to give $G(b_k/d_k) = 0$ for the specified value of D and for the respective sets of feed compositions. When Equation (13–40) is subtracted from Equation

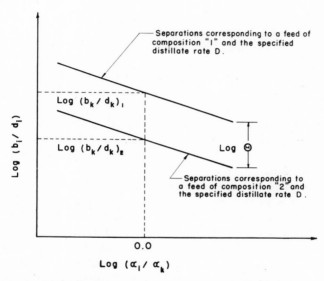

Figure 13–6. Significance of Θ at total recycle. (Reproduced by permission of *Hydrocarbon Processing & Petroleum Refiner*)

(13–41), the result is as follows:

$$\log \frac{(b_i/d_i)_1}{(b_i/d_i)_2} = \log \frac{(b_k/d_k)_1}{(b_k/d_k)_2} \qquad (13\text{--}41)$$

Thus

$$(b_i/d_i)_1 = \left[\frac{(b_k/d_k)_1}{(b_k/d_k)_2}\right] (b_i/d_i)_2 \qquad (13\text{--}42)$$

Since the multiplier enclosed by brackets is the same for all components, Equation (13–42) may be written in the form,

$$(b_i/d_i)_1 = \Theta (b_i/d_i)_2 \qquad (13\text{--}43)$$

Therefore, at total recycle, Θ corresponds to a direct solution.

CALCULATIONAL PROCEDURES

Only the best of the calculational procedures investigated is described here. These procedures dealt primarily with the manner in which the convergence methods are applied. In all of them the compositions of L_N and B were assumed first along with L/V and temperature profiles for each unit. Then a trial calculation for the distillation column and the reboiler-absorber was carried out as described in Chapters 6 and 7, respectively. After the terminal rates had been determined, the Θ-method was applied. Temperatures were determined by use of the bubble point procedure. Because of the similarities of this approach to those described in Chapters 6 and 7, computer programs for different units may be tied together. In fact the θ-method for each unit may be left in the respective programs, and identically the same set of terminal rates will be determined. That is, if the Θ's are defined in terms of the corrected rates for each unit (as determined by the θ-method), the resulting terminal rates for the system are the same as those found where the Θ's are defined in terms of the calculated rates, Equations (13–3) and (13–4). A proof of this statement is presented in the next section.

The second and all subsequent trials through the complete system differ from the first one in that the system is placed in material balance by use of the Θ-method after the step-by-step calculations for each unit have been performed. For example, suppose the first trial has been carried out and a corrected set of terminal rates for the system has been determined. On the basis of these corrected rates the next trial calculation for the first unit is carried out in the usual way to give a set of calculated rates for the first unit. This set of calculated rates, together with the last set of corrected rates for the second unit, is used with the Θ-method to determine another set of corrected rates for the system. (Instead of using the corrected rates for the second unit, the last set of calculated rates for this unit may be employed to give the same set of corrected rates for the system. This is proved in a manner analogous to the second proof shown in the next section.) Then the temperature profiles for each unit are determined. For the illustrative example presented in Tables 13–1 through 13–3, the assumed profile for the next trial for each unit was taken equal to the last calculated profile. (Averaging of the profiles would be necessary for systems that contain a substantial amount of methane in the feed F.) After the temperature profile for the second unit has been determined, the step-by-step calculations are carried out on the basis of the feed composition obtained by the last application of the Θ-method. Upon completion of these calculations, the Θ-method is again applied to the set of calculated rates obtained for the second unit and the last set of corrected rates for the first unit to give another set of corrected rates for the system.

TABLE 13–1 Statement and specifications for Example 13–1

Component	FX	Flow rates	Specifications Other specifications
C_2H_4	5	$F = 100$	*For the Reboiler-Absorber:* $N = 11$, the feed F enters on plate 7 as a liquid at its bubble point at the column pressure.
C_2H_6	5	$V_1 = 70$	
C_3H_6	10	$B = 70$	*For the Distillation Column:* $N = 10, f = 5$, a total condenser is employed. Operating pressure for each unit is 300 psia. The overhead vapor rate is 150. The equilibrium and enthalpy data were taken from Tables A–4 and A–8 of the Appendix.
C_3H_8	5	$L_N = 100$	
$i\text{-}C_4H_8$	10	$D = 30$	
$i\text{-}C_4H_{10}$	10		
$n\text{-}C_4H_{10}$	15		
$i\text{-}C_5$	10		
$n\text{-}C_5$	10		
$n\text{-}C_6$	10		
$n\text{-}C_7$	5		
$n\text{-}C_8$	5		

Reproduced by permission of *Hydrocarbon Processing & Petroleum Refiner*

TABLE 13-2 Solution of Example 13-1

Trial No.	θ_0	θ_1	T (°F) of V_1	T (°F) of L_N	T (°F) of B	T (°F) of D
3	0.762	3.915	374.39	374.16	494.86	266.81
	1.001	0.970				
10	0.995	0.924	372.98	305.29	402.02	196.36
	1.000	0.999				
20	0.997	1.114	375.32	411.45	405.42	202.43
	0.999	1.001				
30	0.999	1.019	374.95	411.53	406.58	202.48
	0.999	1.000				

Reproduced by permission of *Hydrocarbon Processing & Petroleum Refiner*

TABLE 13-3 Product distribution for Example 13-1

Component	v_{1i}	l_{Ni}	b_i	d_i
C_2H_4	4.9664	0.0336	0.0000	0.0336
C_2H_6	4.8933	0.1067	0.0000	0.1067
C_3H_6	6.5505	3.4557	0.0061	3.4495
C_3H_8	2.8185	2.1887	0.0072	2.1815
$i\text{-}C_4H_8$	2.9717	8.4508	1.4225	7.0283
$i\text{-}C_4H_{10}$	2.7097	8.0851	0.7949	7.2903
$n\text{-}C_4H_{10}$	5.7953	13.2471	4.0424	9.2047
$i\text{-}C_5$	9.5109	10.3882	9.8990	0.4891
$n\text{-}C_5$	9.7888	10.8411	10.6299	0.2112
$n\text{-}C_6$	9.9951	14.6399	14.6350	0.0049
$n\text{-}C_7$	4.9999	10.9281	10.9280	0.0001
$n\text{-}C_8$	5.0000	17.6350	17.6350	0.0000

Reproduced by permission of *Hydrocarbon Processing & Petroleum Refiner*

Stability and convergence were enhanced by carrying out the first three trials for each unit at a fixed set of L/V's. The flow rates for all subsequent trials were determined by use of the constant-composition and Q-methods. The variation of the rates for each unit between successive trials was restricted. The vapor rates for the reboiler-absorber were limited to changes no greater than 20 percent, and for the distillation column the limit was 3 percent. For the example shown an adiabatic solution was obtained.

Although only the single system consisting of two units is considered here, the Θ-method of convergence is readily extended to include a system of any number of columns (see Problem 13–3).

PROOF OF THE EXISTENCE OF THE Θ'S

For a system such as the one shown in Figure 13–1, proof of the existence of the two Θ's is presented. This proof follows the one given by Tomme (2). Although a general proof of the existence of the Θ's for those systems with convergence formulas having three or more Θ's has not been constructed, a numerical example has not been found where the Θ's failed to exist.

In the following arguments all of the calculated terminal rates are understood to be known positive numbers, and D, L_N, and F are assumed to be specified positive numbers such that $F - D > 0$, $F - L_N > 0$, and $B > 0$. After the proof for the case where $F - L_N > 0$ has been presented, it is extended to include the case where $F - L_N < 0$. Under these conditions a set of Θ's always exist such that $G_0 = G_1 = 0$, simultaneously, where G_0 and G_1 are defined by Equations (13–12) and (13–13).

For convenience, this proof is divided into three parts. In the first and second parts, the existence of the traces shown in Figure 13–4 for all sets of positive, finite values of Θ_1 and for all positive values of Θ_0 greater than the asymptotic value of Θ_0 is proved. In the third part point "a" is shown to be always to the left of point "b" (see Figure 13–4). In the fourth part, the proof is extended to include the case where $F - L_N < 0$.

1. Existence of the Trace of the Function G_0 in the $\overline{\Theta_0 \Theta_1}$ Plane

In order to prove the existence of the trace of G_0 for all positive and finite values of Θ_0 and Θ_1, the fact that the function G_0 will always intersect the Θ_0-axis must be shown. That is, for $\Theta_1 = 0$ a Θ_0 exists such that $G_0(\Theta_0, 0) = 0$. Therefore, note that Equation (13–12) demonstrates that $G_0(0, 0) = -D$ and that

$$\lim_{\Theta_0 \to \infty} G_0(\Theta_0, 0) = F - D = V_1 > 0$$

Since the partial derivative of G_0 with respect to Θ_0 (at $\Theta_1 = 0$) decreases uniformly from its value at $\Theta_0 = \Theta_1 = 0$ to zero as Θ_0 becomes infinite, the surface of the function G_0 intersects the positive Θ_0-axis at one and only one point (denoted by $\Theta_0 = $ "a" in Figure 13–4).

This conclusion holds not only for $\Theta_1 = 0$ but also for any finite value of $\Theta_1 > 0$. Since the value of the function G_0 changes from minus to plus as Θ_0 goes from zero to infinity,

$$G_0(0, \Theta_1) = -D$$

$$\lim_{\Theta_0 \to \infty} G_0(\Theta_0, \Theta_1) - F - D = V_1 > 0$$

there exists at least one value of Θ_0 such that

$$G_0(\Theta_0, \Theta_1) = 0$$

An examination of $\partial G_0/\partial \theta_0$ shows that only one such Θ_0 is possible.

Also observe from Equation (13–12) that as Θ_1 is increased, the corresponding value of Θ_0 required to give $G_0(\Theta_0, \Theta_1) = 0$ increases. Thus for $\Theta_1 > 0$, the intersections of the surface of G_0 with the $\overline{\Theta_0 \Theta_1}$ plane occur at values of $\Theta_0 > a$ and result in a trace such as the one shown in Figure 13–4.

2. Existence of the Trace of the Function G_1 in the $\overline{\Theta_0 \Theta_1}$ Plane

First, where the specifications are made such that $F - L_N > 0$, the function G_1 intersects the Θ_0-axis. That is, for $\Theta_1 = 0$, a Θ_0 must be shown to exist such that $G_1(\Theta_0, 0) = 0$. In Figure 13–4 this value of Θ_0 is denoted by "b." Observe from Equation (13–13) that

$$G_1(0, 0) = -L_N$$

and that

$$\lim_{\Theta_0 \to \infty} G_1(\Theta_0, 0) = F - L_N > 0$$

Also, the partial derivative of G_1 with respect to Θ_0 decreases steadily from its value at the point $(0, 0)$ to zero as Θ_0 increases without bound. These two results lead to the conclusion that G_1 intersects the positive Θ_0-axis at one and only one point.

Before presenting the generalization of this result for values of $\Theta_1 > 0$, the existence of the asymptote shown in Figure 13–4 will be demonstrated. The value of the asymptote is obtained as follows:

$$\lim_{\Theta_1 \to \infty} G_1(\Theta_0, \Theta_1) = \sum_{i=1}^{c} \Theta_0 \left(\frac{l_{Ni}}{v_{1i}}\right)_{ca} FX_i - L_N$$

Thus, the value of Θ_0 required to make $G_1(\Theta_0, \infty) = 0$ is

$$\Theta_0 = \frac{L_N}{\sum\limits_{i=1}^{c} (l_{Ni}/v_{1i})_{ca} FX_i}$$

Although this information is not required in the proof, the asymptote may, depending upon the particular set of specifications, be shown to lie either to the right or to the left of the point $(a, 0)$.

For any finite, positive value of Θ_1, the surface of G_1 intersects the $\overline{\Theta_0\ \Theta_1}$ plane because

$$G_1(0, \Theta_1) = -L_N$$

and

$$\lim_{\Theta_0 \to \infty} G_1(\Theta_0, \Theta_1) = \sum_{i=1}^{c} \left[1 + \Theta_1 \left(\frac{b_i}{d_i}\right)_{ca} \right] FX_i - L_N > F - L_N > 0$$

and the partial derivative of G_1 with respect to Θ_0 has its maximum value at $\Theta_0 = 0$ and decreases steadily to zero as Θ_0 is increased without bound. Also, these conditions permit only one intersection. Comparison of $G_1(\Theta_0, 0)$ with $G_1(\Theta_0, \infty)$ shows that the point $(0, b)$ is always to the right of the asymptote. Thus as Θ_1 is increased, the trace of the function G_1 in the $\overline{\Theta_0\ \Theta_1}$ plane moves from the point $(0, b)$ toward the asymptote.

3. Proof That $b > a$ (See Figure 13-4)

Since for all $\Theta_1 > 0$, the Θ_0 that gives $G_0(\Theta_0, \Theta_1) = 0$ is greater than "a" and the Θ_0 that makes $G_1(\Theta_0, \Theta_1) = 0$ is less than "b," the traces of G_0 and G_1 in the $\overline{\Theta_0\ \Theta_1}$ plane intersect, provided $b > a$. Proof of this inequality is established in the following manner. In view of the fact that

$$\frac{\partial G_0(\Theta_0, 0)}{\partial \Theta_0} = \frac{\partial G_1(\Theta_0, 0)}{\partial \Theta_0}$$

and that

$$| G_0(0, 0) | < | G_1(0, 0) |$$

it follows that $b > a$.

4. Extension of the Proof to Include Those Specifications Where $F - L_N < 0$ and $B > 0$

For this case the trace of the function G_0 in the $\overline{\Theta_0\ \Theta_1}$ plane has the same properties established previously. However, when $F - L_N < 0$, the surface of G_1 does not cut the positive Θ_0-axis. In fact it gets no closer than the asymptote,

$$\Theta_1 = \frac{L_N - F}{\sum\limits_{i=1}^{c} (b_i/d_i)_{ca} F X_i}$$

which is obtained by taking the limit of $G_1(\Theta_0, \Theta_1)$ as Θ_0 becomes infinite and then solving for the value of Θ_1 required to give $G_1(\infty, \Theta_1) = 0$. Thus as Θ_0 is reduced from an infinitely large value to the asymptotic value, the trace of the function G_1 in the $\overline{\Theta_0 \Theta_1}$ plane moves from the asymptotic value of Θ_1 toward the asymptotic value of Θ_0. Since the trace of G_1 is bounded in this manner and since the value of Θ_0 required to make $G_0(\Theta_0, \Theta_1) = 0$ increases as Θ_1 increases, the traces of G_0 and G_1 intersect in the $\overline{\Theta_0 \Theta_1}$ plane.

PROOF OF THE EQUALITY OF CERTAIN TERMINAL RATES

The corrected set of terminal rates defined by Equations (13–44) and (13–45) will be shown to be equivalent to those defined by Equations (13–3) and (13–4). More specifically, suppose a set of corrected terminal rates must be found that satisfy the material balances (Equations (13–5) and (13–6)) and the specifications L_N and D simultaneously, where the multipliers are defined by

$$(l_{Ni}/v_{1i})_{co} = \overline{\Theta}_0 (l_{Ni}/v_{1i})_c \tag{13–44}$$

$$(b_i/d_i)_{co} = \overline{\Theta}_1 (b_i/d_i)_c \tag{13–45}$$

The subscript "c" is used to denote the corrected rates obtained by the θ-method for each unit. In the application of the θ-method to each unit, the feed compositions (x_{Bi} and x_{Ni}) that were assumed in order to carry out the first trial for the system are taken to be correct. The θ's for each unit are defined as follows:

$$(l_{Ni}/v_{1i})_c = \theta_0 (l_{Ni}/v_{1i})_{ca} \tag{13–46}$$

$$(b_i/d_i)_c = \theta_1 (b_i/d_i)_{ca} \tag{13–47}$$

Each of the θ's is determined independently of the other. The first, θ_0, is determined such that the specified value of L_N (or V_1) and the material balance

$$FX_i + Bx_{Bi} = (l_{Ni})_c + (v_{1i})_c \tag{13–48}$$

are satisfied simultaneously. The second multiplier, θ_1, is determined such that the specification D and the material balance

$$L_N x_{Ni} = (b_i)_c + (d_i)_c \tag{13–49}$$

are satisfied simultaneously. Each procedure just described for the determination of the θ for each unit is the θ-method for a single column, and it would ordinarily be in the program for the given unit.

The definitions of the Θ's as given by Equations (13–44) and (13–45) will be shown to lead to identically the same set of terminal rates as those resulting from Θ's as defined by Equations (13–3) and (13–4). Again, Equations (13–5), (13–6), (13–44), and (13–45) may be combined to give expressions for $(d_i)_{co}$ and $(l_{Ni})_{co}$ of the same form as Equations (13–10) and (13–14). For any given trial, these expressions contain the two variables $\overline{\Theta}_0$ and $\overline{\Theta}_1$, and the remaining terms are constants. Since any constant may be represented by a combination of two other constants, the corrected rates, $(l_{Ni}/v_{1i})_c$ and $(b_i/d_i)_c$, may be replaced by their equivalents as given by Equations (13–46) and (13–47). The resulting expressions are as follows:

$$(d_i)_{co} = \frac{\overline{\Theta}_0 \theta_0 (l_{Ni}/v_{1i})_{ca} FX_i}{1 + \overline{\Theta}_0 \theta_0 (l_{Ni}/v_{1i})_{ca} + \overline{\Theta}_1 \theta_1 (b_i/d_i)_{ca}} \tag{13–50}$$

and

$$(l_{Ni})_{co} = \frac{\overline{\Theta}_0 \theta_0 (l_{Ni}/v_{1i})_{ca}[1 + \overline{\Theta}_1 \theta_1 (b_i/d_i)_{ca}] FX_i}{1 + \overline{\Theta}_0 \theta_0 (l_{Ni}/v_{1i})_{ca} + \overline{\Theta}_1 \theta_1 (b_i/d_i)_{ca}} \tag{13–51}$$

Examination of Equations (13–50) and (13–51) shows that with each $\overline{\Theta}_0$ a θ_0 appears and with each $\overline{\Theta}_1$ a θ_1 appears. Thus if the following changes of variable

$$\overline{\overline{\Theta}}_0 = \overline{\Theta}_0 \theta_0 \qquad \overline{\overline{\Theta}}_1 = \overline{\Theta}_1 \theta_1$$

are made, the resulting expressions are identically the same as Equations (13–10) and (13–14) except for the symbols by which the variables are denoted. Hence

$$\Theta_0 = \overline{\overline{\Theta}}_0 = \overline{\Theta}_0 \theta_0$$

and

$$\Theta_1 = \overline{\overline{\Theta}}_1 = \overline{\Theta}_1 \theta_1$$

and thus the two sets of definitions of the multipliers (Equations (13–3) and (13–4) and Equations (13–44) and (13–45)) lead to the same set of terminal rates.

NOTATIONS

(See Chapters 2 through 7)

$G_0,\ G_1,\ G_2,\ G_3$ = functions of the Θ's

$R_1,\ R_2,\ R_3$ = products defined after Equation (13–34)

θ = multiplier used in the treatment of a single distillation column

Θ = multiplier employed in the treatment of a system of columns

PROBLEMS

13–1 Beginning with Equations (13–3), (13–4), (13–5), and (13–6), develop the expressions for $(d_i)_{co}$ and $(v_{1i})_{co}$ as given by Equations (13–10) and (13–11).

13–2 Similarly, develop the expressions for $(d_i)_{co}$ and $(v_{1i})_{co}$ as given by Equations (13–33) and (13–34).

13–3 For each of the following combinations of three units, develop the formulas for the corrected rates and the expressions for the G-functions (or g-function where a unit is not interrelated by a recycle stream). Also, the product of $\Theta(b_i/d_i)_{ca}$ should be replaced by r_i. For example, for a system in which three Θ's are involved, let

$$(b_i^1/d_i^1)_{co} = \Theta_1(b_i^1/d_i^1)_{ca} = r_{1i}$$

$$(b_i^2/d_i^2)_{co} = \Theta_2(b_i^2/d_i^2)_{ca} = r_{2i}$$

$$(b_i^3/d_i^3)_{co} = \Theta_3(b_i^3/d_i^3)_{ac} = r_{3i}$$

(a) Two units interrelated by a recycle stream as shown in Figure P13–3a.

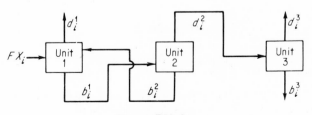

Figure P13–3a

Hint: Two G-functions and one g-function should be obtained.

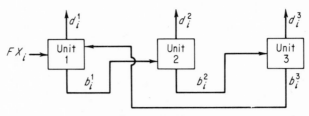

Figure P13–3b

(b) Three units interrelated as shown in Figure P13–3b.

Hint: First show that

$$(d_i^1)_{co} = \frac{FX_i(1 + r_{2i})(1 + r_{3i})}{(1 + r_{1i})(1 + r_{2i} + r_{3i}) + r_{2i}r_{3i}}$$

$$(d_i^2)_{co} = \frac{FX_i r_{1i}(1 + r_{3i})}{(1 + r_{1i})(1 + r_{2i} + r_{3i}) + r_{2i}r_{3i}}$$

$$(d_i^3)_{co} = \frac{FX_i r_{1i}r_{2i}}{(1 + r_{1i})(1 + r_{2i} + r_{3i}) + r_{2i}r_{3i}}$$

(c) Three units interrelated as shown in Figure P13.3c.

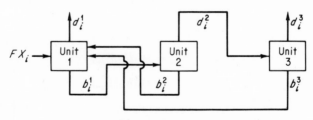

Figure P13–3c

LITERATURE CITED

1. Fenske, M. R., "Fractionation of Straight-Run Pennsylvania Gasoline," *Ind. Eng. Chem.*, **24,** 482 (1932).

2. Tomme, W. J., "A Convergence Method for Distillation Systems," Ph.D. dissertation, A. and M. College of Texas, College Station, Texas, 1963.

3. Tomme, W. J. and C. D. Holland, "Figure Distillation This New Way: Part 11—When Columns are Operated as a Unit," *Petroleum Refiner*, **41,** No. 6, 139 (1962).

Use of Efficiencies for Mass and Heat Transfer in Conventional and Complex Columns

14

In order to approach more closely the actual operating conditions within a column, efficiencies for mass and heat transfer have been included in the treatment of conventional columns by Taylor (7) and in complex columns by Lynch (4). The approach presented in this chapter is a combination of the calculational procedure of Thiele and Geddes and the θ-method of convergence. It follows closely the approach taken by Taylor (7). Flow rates throughout the column are calculated by use of a combination of the constant-composition and Q-methods.

The efficiency of mass transfer is customarily called plate efficiency. Two expressions for plate efficiencies are considered. The first of these represents a slight modification of the well-known Murphree plate efficiency. The second consists of a modification of the "vaporization efficiency" defined by McAdams (2) in the batch-steam distillation of a system consisting of one volatile (two-phase) component. This treatment was extended by Holland and Welch (3) to include any number of volatile components. From a calculational point of view the modified vaporization efficiency is superior to the modified Murphree plate efficiency. For each of these modified plate efficiencies, the corresponding calculational procedures for conventional columns are presented. For complex columns the procedure for the use of the modified vaporization efficiencies is given. Also, a general procedure is presented in which a combination of the two types of modified efficiencies is employed.

Corresponding to the plate efficiencies for mass transfer, two efficiencies for heat transfer are presented. They were found to be about equally satisfactory in the solution of numerical examples (7).

No doubt other definitions for the plate efficiency, such as the one proposed by Ravicz (6), could be employed successfully with the θ-method of convergence.

THE MODIFIED MURPHREE PLATE EFFICIENCY

The modified Murphree efficiency is defined by

$$E_{ji}^M = \frac{y_{ji} - y_{j+1,i}}{Y_{ji} - y_{j+1,i}} \tag{14-1}$$

The mole fraction of component i in the vapor V_{j+1} that enters plate j is denoted by $y_{j+1,i}$. In the vapor, V_j, leaving plate j, the symbol y_{ji} is used. These mole fractions are sometimes referred to as average values because $V_{j+1}y_{j+1,i}$ and $V_j y_{ji}$ represent the actual molal rates at which component i respectively enters and leaves plate j. The quantity Y_{ji} is defined by

$$Y_{ji} = K_{ji}x_{ji} \tag{14-2}$$

where K_{ji} is evaluated at the actual temperature and pressure at which the liquid leaves plate j. The actual composition of the liquid leaving plate j is represented by the x_{ji}'s. When it is specified (or assumed) that the liquid leaving plate j is at its bubble point at the column pressure (this amounts to requiring that the sum of the Y_{ji}'s be equal to unity), Equation (14-1) reduces to the definition proposed by Murphree (5). As will be shown, if it is specified that the liquid leaving plate j is at its bubble point, at most only $(c - 1)$ values of the efficiencies may be specified.

The fact is readily shown that the liquid leaving a given plate need not be at its bubble point in order to develop Equation (14-1) from first principles. As proposed by Brown (1), the rate of mass transfer of a component from a bubble of vapor having a surface area A to the liquid is given by

$$r = K_G A (\bar{f}^v - \bar{f}^L) \tag{14-3}$$

where

A = Interfacial area per bubble
$\bar{f}^L$ = Fugacity of the particular component in the liquid; it is evaluated at the composition, total pressure, and temperature of the liquid
$\bar{f}^v$ = Fugacity of the particular component in the vapor; it is evaluated at the composition, the total pressure, and the temperature of the vapor
K_G = Over-all coefficient of mass transfer
r = Moles of a given component transferred from the vapor to the liquid per unit time

A further insight into this expression may be gained if the vapor is assumed to be a perfect gas and the liquid phase is assumed to obey Raoult's law. Then

$$\bar{f}^v = Py \quad \text{and} \quad \bar{f}^L = P^*x$$

where P is the total pressure in the gas phase and P^* is the vapor pressure of the pure component evaluated at the actual temperature of the liquid. Thus on the basis of the suppositions, Equation (14-3) reduces to

$$r = K_G A P \left(y - \frac{P^* x}{P} \right)$$

Since nothing in the preceding argument requires that the liquid be at its bubble point,

$$\sum_{i=1}^{c} (P_i^* x_i / P)$$

need not be equal to unity. When the liquid is required to be at its bubble point, $(P^* x)/P$ is commonly replaced by y^* (the mole fraction a component would have in the vapor if the vapor were in equilibrium with the liquid). If the liquid is not required to be at its bubble point, the ratio $(P^* x)/P$ is replaced by Y to give

$$r = K_G A P(y - Y) \tag{14-4}$$

However, be sure to note that Y is not to be referred to as a mole fraction. Calling Y a mole fraction is tantamount to specifying that the liquid be at its bubble point because the definition of a mole fraction requires that the sum of the Y's be equal to unity, which condition is precisely the same as that for the liquid at its bubble point.

For the rate of mass transfer an expression of the same form as Equation (14-4) may be obtained on the basis of a set of postulates more general than those employed in the previous case. If the fugacity of the given component in the vapor phase is assumed to be given by the ideal solution law,

$$\bar{f}^v = f^v y$$

and in the liquid phase by the general relationship

$$\bar{f}^L = \gamma^L f^L x$$

then

$$r = K_G A f^v [y - (\gamma^L f^L / f^v) x] = K_G A f^v [y - Y] \tag{14-5}$$

where

f^v = Fugacity of the pure component in the vapor state at the total pressure and at the temperature of the vapor.

f^L = Fugacity of the pure component in the liquid state at the total pressure and at the temperature of the liquid.

γ^L = Activity coefficient of the given component in the liquid phase.

Although the vapor and liquid phases are under approximately the same total pressure, the use of a K-value for $(\gamma^L f^L)/f^v$ may constitute a minor approximation. In the conventional definition of K the fugacities f^L and f^v are evaluated at the same temperature and total pressure. Although f^v is primarily a function of the total pressure, it does vary to some extent with temperature. The approximation arises when the temperature of the vapor is taken to be different from that of the liquid. In this connection recall that the equality of the temperatures of the two phases is a necessary, but not a sufficient, condition for equilibrium. Also, when K is taken equal to $(\gamma^L f^L)/f^v$, the effect of composition is understood to be included in the definition of K.

When the rate of mass transfer for a component is defined by Equation (14–5) and the other postulates made by Murphree (5) are invoked, a relationship between the plate efficiency and the dynamics of the plate is readily obtained. This relationship is of the same form as the one found by Murphree except for the fact that the expression for the plate efficiency (Equation (14–1)) contains Y instead of y^*.

From a calculational point of view, the modified Murphree efficiency was found to be far superior to the Murphree plate efficiency. In the application of Equation (14–1), c values of the E_{ji}^M's are specified. All of the compositions are assumed to be known (which is the case when the Thiele and Geddes calculational procedure is employed), and the temperature of plate j must be found subject to the conditions,

$$\sum_{i=1}^{c} y_{ji} = 1 \quad \text{and} \quad \sum_{i=1}^{c} y_{j+1,i} = 1 \tag{14–6}$$

and that the efficiency is given by Equation (14–1). When the latter is solved for Y_{ji}, the result

$$Y_{ji} = y_{j+1,i} + \frac{y_{ji} - y_{j+1,i}}{E_{ji}^M} \tag{14–7}$$

is obtained. Elimination of Y_{ji} from Equations (14–2) and (14–7) yields

$$E_{ji}^M K_{ji} x_{ji} = E_{ji}^M y_{j+1,i} + y_{ji} - y_{j+1,i}$$

When each side of this equation is summed over all components, the result is

$$\sum_{i=1}^{c} E_{ji}^M K_{ji} x_{ji} = \sum_{i=1}^{c} E_{ji}^M y_{j+1,i} \tag{14–8}$$

since

$$\sum_{i=1}^{c} y_{ji} - \sum_{i=1}^{c} y_{j+1,i} = 0$$

by Equation (14–6). Thus the temperature of the liquid leaving plate j is that value of T_j which gives $f(T_j) = 0$ when

$$f(T_j) = \sum_{i=1}^{c} E_{ji}^{M} K_{ji} x_{ji} - \sum_{i=1}^{c} E_{ji}^{M} y_{j+1,i} \qquad (14–9)$$

When this value of T_j is substituted into the right hand side of Equation (14–2), the sum of the $K_{ji} x_{ji}$'s will not in general be equal to unity.

THE MODIFIED VAPORIZATION EFFICIENCY

For any component i this efficiency is defined by

$$E_{ji}^{0} = y_{ji} / Y_{ji} \qquad (14–10)$$

where Y_{ji} is again defined by Equation (14–2). This efficiency was found to be far more convenient to use than the modified Murphree efficiency, particularly in the treatment of complex columns. Elimination of Y_{ji} from Equations (14–2) and (14–10) yields

$$E_{ji}^{0} K_{ji} x_{ji} = y_{ji} \qquad (14–11)$$

Thus the temperature of the liquid leaving plate j is that positive value of T_j which gives $f(T_j) = 0$, where

$$f(T_j) = \sum_{i=1}^{c} E_{ji}^{0} K_{ji} x_{ji} - 1 \qquad (14–12)$$

For a liquid of known composition and c specified values for the E_{ji}^{0}'s, Equation (14–12) is readily solved for T_j by use of either Newton's method or interpolation (*regula falsi*) as described in Chapter 2. Again the sum of the corresponding Y_{ji}'s is not generally found equal to unity.

If the liquid leaving plate j be required to be at its bubble point (i.e. $\sum_{i=1}^{c} Y_{ji} = 1$), then the conventional bubble point function is obtained by use of Equation (14–2), namely;

$$f(T_j) = \sum_{i=1}^{c} K_{ji} x_{ji} - 1$$

After T_j has been found, the corresponding values of Y_{ji} (or y_{ji}^{*}) are calculated by use of Equation (14–2). Then from the definition of E_{ji}^{0}, Equation (14–10), the y_{ji}'s are computed for $(c - 1)$ of the components; that is, for all components except component "k," the one for which an E_{ji}^0 is not specified. The mole fraction, y_{jk}, is computed as follows:

$$y_{jk} = 1 - \sum_{i \neq k} y_{ji}$$

After y_{jk} has been determined, the vaporization efficiency is calculated by use of Equation (14–10). Similar relationships may be developed for Murphree efficiencies. From a calculational point of view, the requirement that the liquid leaving plate j be at its bubble point leads to several awkward situations. First, the value of y_{jk} (obtained as described previously) may be negative. If this condition occurs, the other efficiencies must be adjusted in some manner, which at best would be of rather an arbitrary nature. Secondly, how should the k'th component be selected? The results (solution) might well depend on the selection of this component.

In conclusion, the requirement that the liquid be at its bubble point appeared to lead to too many computational problems which could be avoided by use of the modified efficiencies.

EFFICIENCY OF HEAT TRANSFER

In a manner analogous to the development of the expression for the Murphree plate efficiency (5), the following expression for the efficiency of heat transfer,

$$e_j = \frac{T_{j+1}^v - T_j^v}{T_{j+1}^v - T_j^L} \tag{14–13}$$

is readily shown to be related exponentially to the over-all coefficient of heat transfer, the heat capacity of the vapor, and the contact time between the vapor and liquid on plate j, where

T_j^L = Temperature of the liquid leaving plate j, calculated by use of either Equation (14–9) or (14–12) (whichever is appropriate)

T_j^v = Temperature of the vapor leaving plate j

T_{j+1}^v = Temperature of the vapor entering plate j

Actually, the complete expression for e_j consists of a rearrangement of the well-known heat transfer relationship, $q = UA\Delta T_m$. Ravicz (6) also employed this relationship in his treatment of heat transfer in columns. Corresponding to the definition of the vaporization efficiency, the alternate definition for the efficiency of heat transfer may be employed,

$$e_j^0 = T_j^v / T_j^L \tag{14–14}$$

Each of the efficiencies was investigated and found to give satisfactory results.

USE OF THE MODIFIED MURPHREE PLATE EFFICIENCY IN THE TREATMENT OF CONVENTIONAL COLUMNS

A hypothetical flow rate defined as follows is used in the application of the modified efficiencies to distillation:

$$v_{ji}^* = V_j Y_{ji} \tag{14-15}$$

When the definition of Y_{ji} as given by Equation (14-2) is substituted into this expression, the following result is obtained.

$$v_{ji}^* = V_j Y_{ji} = V_j K_{ji} x_{ji} = (V_j K_{ji}/L_j) L_j x_{ji}$$

Thus

$$v_{ji}^* = S_{ji} l_{ji}, \quad \text{or} \quad l_{ji} = A_{ji} v_{ji}^* \tag{14-16}$$

When the modified Murphree plate efficiencies are employed in the description of a conventional distillation column, the following material balances are obtained for the rectifying and stripping sections.

Rectifying Section

For a partial condenser:

$$\frac{d_i^*}{d_i} = \frac{(V_1/D) - (1 - E_{0i}^M)}{(V_1/D) E_{0i}^M + (1 - E_{0i}^M) A_{0i}} \tag{14-17a}$$

$$l_{0i}/d_i = A_{0i}(d_i^*/d_i) \tag{14-17b}$$

$$v_{1i}/d_i = (l_{0i}/d_i) + 1 \tag{14-17c}$$

For a total condenser:

$$v_{1i}/d_i = (L_0/D) + 1 \tag{14-17d}$$

In general:

$$\frac{v_{j+1,i}}{d_i} = \frac{(V_{j+1}/V_j)[E_{ji}^M + A_{ji}(v_{ji}/d_i)]}{(V_{j+1}/V_j) E_{ji}^M + (1 - E_{ji}^M) A_{ji}}, \quad 1 \leq j \leq f - 2 \tag{14-17e}$$

$$\frac{\bar{v}_{fi}}{d_i} = \frac{(V_f/V_{f-1})[E_{f-1,i}^M + A_{f-1,i}(v_{f-1,i}/d_i)]}{(V_f/V_{f-1}) E_{f-1,i}^M + (1 - E_{f-1,i}^M) A_{f-1,i}} \tag{14-17f}$$

$$l_{ji}/d_i = (v_{j+1,i}/d_i) - 1, \quad 1 \leq j \leq f - 2 \tag{14-17g}$$

$$l_{f-1,i}/d_i = (\bar{v}_{fi}/d_i) - 1 \tag{14-17h}$$

Stripping Section

$$\frac{v_{N+1,i}}{b_i} = E^M_{N+1,i}\, S_{N+1,i} \tag{14–18a}$$

$$\frac{v_{ji}}{b_i} = E^M_{ji} S_{ji} \left(\frac{v_{j+1,i}}{b_i} + 1\right) + \left(\frac{V_j}{V_{j+1}}\right)\left(\frac{v_{j+1,i}}{b_i}\right)(1 - E^M_{ji}),$$

$$f \leqq j \leqq N \tag{14–18b}$$

$$l_{ji}/b_i = (v_{j+1,i}/b_i) + 1, \quad f \leqq j \leqq N \tag{14–18c}$$

Equations (14–17a) through (14–17h) for the rectifying section are developed in the following manner. For a partial condenser

$$E^M_{0i} = \frac{X_{Di} - y_{1i}}{Y_{0i} - y_{1i}} = \frac{(V_1/D)d_i - v_{1i}}{(V_1/D)d^*_i - v_{1i}} \tag{14–19}$$

where $d^*_i = D Y_{0i}$. Equation (14–19) may be arranged to give

$$E^M_{0i}\left(\frac{d^*_i}{d_i}\right) - 1 = \left(\frac{v_{1i}}{d_i}\right)\left(\frac{D}{V_1}\right)[E^M_{0i} - 1] \tag{14–20}$$

The ratio, v_{1i}/d_i, is eliminated from Equation (14–20) by use of Equations (14–17b) and (14–17e) to give the desired expression for d^*_i/d_i, Equation (17a). After the formula for d^*_i/d_i has been developed, the formulas for l_{0i}/d_i and v_{1i}/d_i, Equations (14–17b) and (14–17c), follow immediately.

The expression for v_{2i}/d_i is obtained by beginning with a material balance around the top plate,

$$\frac{v_{2i}}{d_i} = \frac{l_{1i}}{d_i} + 1$$

and the efficiency for this plate

$$E^M_{1i} = \frac{(V_2/V_1)v_{1i} - v_{2i}}{(V_2/V_1)v^*_{1i} - v_{2i}}$$

as well as Equation (14–2) from which it is shown that

$$l_{1i}/d_i = A_{1i}(v^*_{1i}/d_i)$$

Elimination of v^*_{1i}/d_i and l_{1i}/d_i from these three equations produces the desired result, which can be generalized to give Equation (14–17e). The remainder of the equations for the rectifying section are developed in a similar manner.

The equations for the stripping section are developed by commencing at the bottom of the column. For the reboiler, the expression for the modified Murphree plate efficiency reduces to

$$E^M_{N+1,i} = y_{N+1,i}/Y_{N+1,i} = v_{N+1,i}/v^*_{N+1,i}$$

Also

$$v^*_{N+1,i}/b_i = S_{N+1,i}$$

These two equations are readily solved to give the desired result, Equation (14–18a). Equation (14–18b) is obtained in the following manner. A material balance around plate N yields

$$\frac{l_{Ni}}{b_i} = \frac{v_{N+1,i}}{b_i} + 1$$

This result follows from Equation (14–18c) for $j = N$. Also, for plate N

$$E^M_{Ni} = \frac{(V_{N+1}/V_N)v_{Ni} - v_{N+1,i}}{(V_{N+1}/V_N)v^*_{Ni} - v_{N+1,i}}$$

and

$$v^*_{Ni} = S_{Ni}l_{Ni}$$

These three relationships may be solved for v_{Ni}/b_i to give Equation (14–18b), for $j = N$. Continuation of this procedure leads to the remainder of the equations stated for the stripping section.

Selection of a Suitable Set of Modified Murphree Plate Efficiencies

The form of the expression for the modified Murphree plate efficiency leads to a rather serious disadvantage inasmuch as many apparently reasonable values for the plate efficiencies yield negative rates of flow. A procedure for the detection and modification of the troublesome values for the efficiencies was developed. Basically, the procedure is as follows. Each of the equations is examined and it is determined whether or not the specified value of E^M_{ji} would give a negative flow rate. If such a value of E^M_{ji} is found, another value for E^M_{ji} (one near the specified value) is selected as required to maintain positive rates of flow. An examination of the equations for each section of the column follows.

1. Examination of the E^M_{ji}'s for the Rectifying Section

Consider first the numerator of Equation (14–17a). Since V_1/D is always greater than unity, the numerator of this equation is positive. If the denominator of this equation is negative, it is set equal to zero and solved to give the maximum value of the efficiency,

$$(E_{0i}^M)_{max} = \frac{A_{0i}}{A_{0i} - (V_1/D)} \tag{14-21}$$

Then the following value for the efficiency is used in Equation (14-17a).

$$E_{0i}^M = \frac{(E_{0i}^M)_{max}}{1 + p} \tag{14-22}$$

The symbol "p" is used to denote a small positive number of the order of 10^{-8}. Satisfactory results were obtained by taking $p = 5 \times 10^{-8}$.

It is necessary that the value of $v_{j+1,i}/d_i$ given by Equation (14-17e) be greater than unity in order to satisfy the material balances represented by Equation (14-17g). If the value of $v_{j+1,i}/d_i$ obtained is greater than unity, no further testing is required. If not, further examinations are made by use of the following expression,

$$\frac{l_{ji}}{d_i} = \frac{A_{ji}[(V_{j+1}/V_j)(v_{ji}/d_i) - (1 - E_{ji}^M)]}{(V_{j+1}/V_j)E_{ji}^M + (1 - E_{ji}^M)A_{ji}} \tag{14-23}$$

which is obtained by elimination of $v_{j+1,i}/d_i$ from Equations (14-17e) and (14-17g). If the numerator of Equation (14-23) is negative, it is set equal to zero and solved for the minimum value of the efficiency,

$$(E_{ji}^M)_{min} = 1 - (V_{j+1}/V_j)(v_{ji}/d_i) \tag{14-24}$$

Then the following value for the efficiency is computed and used in Equation (14-17e).

$$E_{ji}^M = (1 + p)(E_{ji}^M)_{min} \tag{14-25}$$

The procedure for testing the denominator of Equation (14-23) is analogous to that described for Equation (14-17a). The maximum value of E_{ji}^M is defined by

$$(E_{ji}^M)_{max} = \frac{A_{ji}}{A_{ji} - (V_{j+1}/V_j)} \tag{14-26}$$

If the denominator of Equation (14-23) is negative, the following value for the efficiency

$$E_{ji}^M = \frac{(E_{ji}^M)_{max}}{1 + p} \tag{14-27}$$

is employed in Equation (14-17e).

2. Examination of the E_{ji}^M's for the Stripping Section

Material balance relationships permit v_{ji}/d_i to take on any positive value. Thus if the v_{ji}/d_i as determined by use of Equation (14–18b) is negative, the expression is set equal to zero and solved for the maximum value of the efficiency

$$(E_{ji}^M)_{\max} = \frac{(V_j/V_{j+1})\,(v_{j+1,i}/b_i)}{(V_j/V_{j+1})\,(v_{j+1,i}/b_i) \,-\, S_{ji}[(v_{j+1,i}/b_i) \,+\, 1]} \qquad (14\text{–}28)$$

Then the following value for the efficiency,

$$E_{ji}^M = \frac{(E_{ji}^M)_{\max}}{1 + p} \qquad (14\text{–}29)$$

is used in Equation (14–18b).

USE OF THE MODIFIED VAPORIZATION EFFICIENCY IN THE TREATMENT OF CONVENTIONAL COLUMNS

The modified vaporization efficiency, defined by Equation (14–10) leads to a much simpler calculational procedure than does the modified Murphree plate efficiency. When modified vaporization efficiencies are employed, the material balances are found to be essentially the same as those shown in Chapter 3 for conventional columns. In fact, the equations become formally the same by use of modified absorption and stripping factors defined as follows:

$$A_{ji}^0 = \frac{A_{ji}}{E_{ji}^0} = \frac{L_j}{E_{ji}^0 K_{ji} V_j} \qquad (14\text{–}30)$$

$$S_{ji}^0 = E_{ji}^0 S_{ji} = E_{ji}^0 K_{ji} V_j / L_j \qquad (14\text{–}31)$$

USE OF A COMBINATION OF THE MURPHREE AND THE VAPORIZATION EFFICIENCIES

This procedure consists of the use of successive sets of E_{ji}^0's as the first approximations of the specified set of E_{ji}^M's. On the basis of a selected set of E_{ji}^0's, each trial calculation through the column is made in the usual way. This procedure has the advantage over the direct use of E_{ji}^M's in that the necessity for the examination of each plate efficiency as calculations are carried out through the column is eliminated. In the case of absorbers and complex columns, such an examination is impossible because the terminal flow rates must be determined prior to either the initiation or completion of the step-by-step calculations. Expressions corresponding to Equation (8–4) for the calculation of the terminal rates for an absorber would involve all of the plate efficiencies. Thus, if modified Murphree plate efficiencies were employed directly, negative values for the terminal rates could be obtained. It would then be necessary to determine which of the E_{ij}^M's gave the negative rates. The following procedure eliminates this difficulty. In order to describe this calculational method, suppose a set of E_{ij}^M's are known for each plate of a conventional distillation column. The first two or three trials (two trials were used) through the column may be made on the basis of $E_{ji}^0 = 1$ for all plates and components. At the end of every subsequent trial, a better set of E_{ji}^0's are computed on the basis of the specified E_{ij}^M's and the compositions obtained by the last trial. The two efficiencies are related as follows:

$$E_{ji}^0 = E_{ji}^M + (1 - E_{ji}^M)(y_{i+1,i}/Y_{ji}) \tag{14–32}$$

If a negative value for E_{ji}^0 is given by Equation (14–32), the expression is set equal to zero and solved for the maximum value of the efficiency,

$$(E_{ji}^M)_{\max} = \frac{y_{i+1,i}}{y_{i+1,i} - Y_{ji}} \tag{14–33}$$

On the basis of the maximum value, an E_{ji}^M is calculated by use of Equation (14–27). Then this E_{ji}^M is used to compute E_{ji}^0 by Equation (14–32).

If formulas based on experimental results are available for the calculation of a better set of E_{ji}^M's on the basis of improved sets of temperatures and compositions, they should be employed prior to the calculation of the E_{ji}^0's by Equation (14–32).

Other Relationships

The formulas for the calculation of the b_i/d_i's for conventional columns as well as those for the computation the compositions (y_{ji}'s and x_{ji}'s) are the same as those shown in Chapter 3. The total flow rates throughout the column are calculated by use of a combination of the constant-composition and Q-methods for making enthalpy balances as described in Chapter 5. When efficiencies for heat-transfer are employed, the vapor enthalpies are evaluated at the temperatures required by the specified heat-transfer efficiencies.

USE OF MODIFIED VAPORIZATION EFFICIENCIES IN THE TREATMENT OF COMPLEX COLUMNS

The calculational procedure resulting from the use of modified vaporization efficiencies in the treatment of complex columns is far superior to the procedure corresponding to the direct use of the modified Murphree efficiencies. In the treatment of complex columns the use of a combination of modified Murphree and vaporization efficiencies was investigated and found to give satisfactory results.

Absorbers were used to investigate the use of efficiencies in the treatment of complex columns. The material balances for an absorber may be represented by equations that include either the top of the column and any given plate j,

$$\frac{v_{ji}}{v_{1i}} = A^{0}_{j-1,i}\left(\frac{v_{j-1,i}}{v_{1i}}\right) + \left(1 - \frac{l_{0i}}{v_{1i}}\right), \quad 2 \leqq j \leqq N+1 \quad (14\text{--}34)$$

or the bottom of the column and any plate j,

$$\frac{l_{j-1,i}}{l_{Ni}} = S^{0}_{ji}\left(\frac{l_{ji}}{l_{Ni}}\right) + \left(1 - \frac{v_{N+1,i}}{l_{Ni}}\right), \quad 1 \leqq j \leqq N \quad (14\text{--}35)$$

The corresponding liquid and vapor flow rates may be computed from the vapor and liquid rates given by Equations (14–34) and (14–35) by respective use of the relationships: $l_{ji} = A^{0}_{ji}v_{ji}$ and $v_{ji} = S^{0}_{ji}l_{ji}$. Before calculations may be initiated by use of either Equation (14–34) or (14–35), the terminal flow rates must be evaluated by use of

$$\frac{l_{Ni}}{v_{1i}} = \frac{\omega^{0}_{i}l_{0i} + (\Omega^{0}_{i} + \omega^{0}_{i} - 1)v_{N+1,i}}{\Omega^{0}_{i}l_{0i} + v_{N+1,i}} \quad (14\text{--}36)$$

where

$$\omega^{0}_{i} = A^{0}_{Ni}A^{0}_{N-1,i}\ldots A^{0}_{2i}A^{0}_{1i}$$

$$\Omega^{0}_{i} = 1 + A^{0}_{Ni} + A^{0}_{Ni}A^{0}_{N-1,i} + \ldots + A^{0}_{Ni}A^{0}_{N-1,i}\ldots A^{0}_{3i}A^{0}_{2i}$$

and the over-all material balance,

$$v_{1i} = \frac{v_{N+1,i} + l_{0i}}{1 + (l_{Ni}/v_{1i})} \quad (14\text{--}37)$$

Round-off error is minimized by application of these equations in the same manner as described in Chapter 8. Also, it should be remarked that Equations (14–36) through (14–37) differ from those in Chapter 8 only by the superscript zero on the absorption and stripping factors. Similarly, the equations for columns from which side-streams are withdrawn differ from those stated in Chapter 7 only in the superscript zero.

If a set of modified Murphree efficiencies is specified instead of a set of modified vaporization efficiencies, the procedure described making use of a combination of the two types of efficiencies is recommended. It is applied to complex columns in the same manner described (see Equations (14–32), (14–33), and (14–34)) for conventional columns.

Illustrative Examples

The use of the two types of modified efficiencies in the treatment of conventional columns was investigated by the solution of a wide variety of numerical examples, three of which are shown here. Example 14–1 was selected in order to demonstrate the direct use of modified Murphree efficiencies. The same problem (called Example 14–2) was solved by use of a combination of the modified Murphree and modified vaporization efficiencies. For Examples 14–1 and 14–2, the efficiencies were ordered in different ways as shown in Table 14–1. In order to further test the procedure for the use of a combination of the modified Murphree and vaporization efficiencies, a bounded set of random efficiencies was selected using a program that generated random numbers. The efficiencies so obtained (listed in Table 14–2) were taken as specifications for Example 14–3. After solutions had been obtained, the bubble point temperatures corresponding to the final liquid compositions were computed and tabulated in Tables 14–3 and 14–6. In view of the wide range of efficiencies employed in the solution of the examples, the bubble point temperatures are surprisingly close to the actual temperatures.

Note that if E_{ji}^M has the same value for each component, the actual and the bubble point temperatures are equal. This conclusion follows immediately from Equation (14–9). Because of the manner in which the efficiencies were ordered for Examples 14–1 and 14–2, the efficiency for each component is equal to 0.9 on plate 2. On this plate the actual and bubble point temperatures are seen to be equal in Table (14–3).

In the solution of Examples 14–1, 14–2, and 14–3 (shown in Tables 14–3 through 14–6), the temperature of the vapor leaving each plate was assumed to be equal to the temperature of the liquid leaving the given plate. This amounts to taking the efficiency for heat transfer equal to unity for each plate, $e_j = e_j^0 = 1$. The use of heat transfer efficiencies is illustrated by the solution of Example 14–4. Except for the specification of the heat transfer efficiencies, this problem is the same as Example 14–3. The random set of e_j's selected for Example 14–4 are given in Table 14–7 with the final solution.

The use of a combination of modified Murphree and vaporization efficiencies in the treatment of complex columns is illustrated by Example 14–5 (see Tables 14–8 through 14–10). The solution to this example was obtained by Lynch (4).

TABLE 14-1 Statements and specifications for Examples 14-1, 14-2, 14-3, and 14-4

Component No.	Component	FX	Specifications
1	CH_4	2.0	For all examples: $N = 11$, $f = 4$, $V_1 = 94.8$, $D = 31.6$ (vapor), partial condenser, and the feed enters as a liquid at its bubble point at the column pressure. The column pressure is 300 psia. Initial temperature profile is linear with plate number between 50 and 450°F. Initial vapor rates: $V_j = 94.8$ for all j. Maximum and minimum vapor rates: $47.4 = V_{min} \leq V_j \leq V_{max} = 161.16$. For Examples 14-1 and 14-2 the modified Murphee efficiencies to be employed are as follows. For components 1 through 6: $E_{ji}^M = 0.7 + j(0.1)$. For components 7 through 11; $E_{ji}^M = 1.0 - j(0.05)$. Efficiencies for Example 14-3 are given in Table 14-2. For Examples 14-1, 14-2, and 14-3, $e_j = e_j^0 = 1.0$. The specifications for Example 14-4 are the same as those for Example 14-3 except for the heat transfer efficiencies. For Example 14-4, a random set of e_j's was selected as shown in Table 14-7. Equilibrium and enthalpy data from Tables A-4 and A-8 of the Appendix are to be employed.
2	C_2H_6	10.0	
3	C_3H_6	6.0	
4	C_3H_8	12.5	
5	$i\text{-}C_4$	3.5	
6	$n\text{-}C_4$	15.0	
7	$n\text{-}C_5$	15.2	
8	$n\text{-}C_6$	11.3	
9	$n\text{-}C_7$	9.0	
10	$n\text{-}C_8$	8.5	
11	400	7.0	

TABLE 14-2 Modified Murphree efficiencies specified for Example 14-3

(Random values for the efficiencies lying between 0.01 and 2.0 were selected for all plates except the reboiler, and for the latter the random values were between 0.5 and 1.5.)

Efficiencies

Component No.

Plate No.	1	2	3	4	5	6	7	8	9	10	11
0	0.284	1.659	1.632	1.105	0.162	1.483	0.340	1.032	0.051	1.003	0.941
1	0.823	0.142	0.890	1.840	0.635	1.644	1.208	0.469	1.022	0.519	0.155
2	0.327	1.823	0.745	0.026	0.545	1.014	1.287	0.830	0.690	0.750	1.003
3	1.322	1.383	1.334	1.469	1.110	0.392	1.342	1.014	0.484	1.014	1.004
4	0.866	0.394	1.623	1.997	0.236	1.482	0.085	1.858	1.174	1.054	0.826
5	0.710	0.308	1.924	0.196	1.273	1.929	0.839	1.876	1.177	1.267	1.523
6	1.933	0.155	0.653	1.303	0.654	0.759	1.866	1.228	0.350	0.229	1.432
7	1.253	0.704	1.354	0.552	0.097	0.345	0.517	1.435	0.444	1.790	1.587
8	0.683	1.713	1.174	0.726	1.497	0.681	1.433	0.784	1.280	1.205	1.053
9	1.321	1.506	1.272	1.774	0.887	0.670	1.292	1.086	0.865	0.626	1.653
10	1.869	0.533	1.778	0.339	1.722	0.807	0.111	0.119	1.134	0.715	1.123
11	1.809	0.576	1.018	0.934	1.374	0.814	0.536	0.154	1.343	1.257	0.238
12	1.132	0.908	1.147	1.290	1.013	1.032	0.844	1.226	0.731	1.034	1.040

TABLE 14-3 Solution of Example 14-1 obtained by making direct use of modified Murphree efficiencies

Plate No.	Temperature profiles (°F)* Trial No.				Bubble point temp. of liquid Trial No. 17	Vapor rates Trial No. 17	Component No.	Product distribution (Trial No. 17)	
	2	7	12	17				d	b
0	87.01	96.91	97.12	97.13	97.08		1	2.000	4.849×10^{-11}
1	115.11	123.32	123.49	123.50	123.40	94.8	2	10.000	1.143×10^{-5}
2	136.89	140.06	140.09	140.08	140.08	94.0	3	5.992	7.743×10^{-3}
3	160.67	158.23	158.11	158.11	158.88	89.7	4	12.446	5.425×10^{-2}
4	206.63	201.33	200.88	200.92	201.64	78.6	5	0.648	2.852
5	226.27	222.39	222.39	223.33	223.33	105.9	6	0.511	14.489
6	242.11	238.74	238.85	238.83	239.88	119.8	7	2.409×10^{-3}	15.198
7	255.21	250.94	251.29	251.40	252.40	130.9	8	3.696×10^{-5}	11.300
8	266.77	259.10	259.77	259.74	261.08	140.4	9	1.527×10^{-5}	9.000
9	278.39	264.32	265.23	265.21	267.01	147.3	10	1.175×10^{-7}	8.500
10	291.93	268.52	269.24	269.25	271.71	151.0	11	7.430×10^{-9}	7.000
11	310.73	277.02	276.82	276.83	278.57	149.7			
12	358.30	328.63	327.68	327.65	267.04	125.0			
D (Calculated)	31.68	31.56	31.601	31.601					
θ	0.609	0.967	1.00077	0.99999					

* Averaged temperatures. Each calculated temperature profile was averaged plate by plate with the profile used to make the given trial calculation.

TABLE 14-4 Solution of Example 14-2 by use of a combination of modified Murphree and vaporization efficiencies

Plate No.	Temperature profiles (°F) Trial No.				E_{ji}^0	Intermediate efficiencies Trial No.			
	2	7	12	17		2	7	12	17
0	97.82	97.12	97.13	97.13	$E_{0,1}^0$	0.823	0.795	0.795	0.795
1	128.28	123.73	123.51	123.51	$E_{1,11}^0$	25.748	25.255	25.380	25.386
2	153.82	140.50	140.09	140.09	$E_{2,10}^0$	8.948	10.608	10.719	10.720
3	179.69	158.52	158.10	158.11	$E_{3,9}^0$	3.589	4.175	4.215	4.212
4	222.42	202.51	200.87	200.92	$E_{4,8}^0$	1.030	1.070	1.074	1.074
5	238.35	223.18	222.36	222.39	$E_{5,7}^0$	1.039	1.066	1.068	1.068
6	251.68	239.19	238.81	238.83	$E_{6,5}^0$	0.989	0.948	0.951	0.951
7	264.55	251.33	251.25	251.27	$E_{7,6}^0$	0.980	0.941	0.943	0.943
8	278.12	259.51	259.73	259.74	$E_{8,3}^0$	1.255	1.217	1.221	1.221
9	293.59	264.60	265.20	265.21	$E_{9,4}^0$	1.303	1.243	1.247	1.247
10	312.61	268.31	269.23	269.25	$E_{10,2}^0$	1.525	1.501	1.502	1.502
11	338.73	276.18	276.82	276.83	$E_{11,1}^0$	1.722	1.720	1.720	1.720
12	387.59	329.52	327.70	327.65	$E_{12,7}^0$	0.400	0.400	0.400	0.400
D (Calculated)	31.263	31.574	31.598	31.600					
θ	0.74102	0.97664	0.99821	1.0000					

TABLE 14-5 Final set of modified vaporization efficiencies obtained for Example 14-2

Plate No.	Modified vaporization efficiencies Component No.										
	1	2	3	4	5	6	7	8	9	10	11
0	0.795	0.875	1.057	1.101	1.549	1.850	1.000	1.000	1.000	1.000	1.000
1	0.975	0.945	0.988	1.004	1.169	1.282	1.278	1.910	3.677	8.923	25.386
2	1.004	0.990	0.987	0.991	1.044	1.084	1.386	2.246	4.481	10.720	34.477
3	1.000	1.000	1.000	1.000	1.000	1.000	1.363	2.195	4.212	9.535	33.383
4	1.089	1.059	1.012	1.001	0.945	0.957	1.073	1.074	1.084	1.098	1.082
5	1.179	1.128	1.053	1.036	0.936	0.937	1.068	1.069	1.076	1.097	1.075
6	1.269	1.201	1.105	1.084	0.951	0.934	1.060	1.066	1.073	1.082	1.073
7	1.360	1.277	1.163	1.138	0.978	0.943	1.052	1.071	1.081	1.092	1.086
8	1.451	1.352	1.221	1.193	1.009	0.955	1.048	1.093	1.118	1.140	1.139
9	1.542	1.428	1.278	1.247	1.039	0.964	1.048	1.137	1.197	1.249	1.267
10	1.633	1.502	1.336	1.302	1.069	0.971	1.046	1.196	1.317	1.428	1.491
11	1.720	1.575	1.396	1.360	1.099	0.972	0.987	1.166	1.324	1.477	1.585
12	1.900	1.900	1.900	1.900	1.900	1.900	0.400	0.400	0.400	0.400	0.400

TABLE 14-6 Solution of Example 14-3 for which a random set of modified Murphree efficiencies was specified

Plate No.	Temperature profiles (°F) Trial No.				Bubble point temp. of liquid	Vapor rates	Component No.	Product distribution (Trial No. 20)	
	2	7	12	20	Trial No. 20			d	b
0	89.69	100.05	100.47	100.47	96.53		1	2.000	3.022×10^{-10}
1	116.73	130.24	130.79	130.76	121.84	94.8	2	9.998	1.634×10^{-3}
2	134.49	147.86	147.94	147.83	139.15	95.1	3	5.980	1.980×10^{-2}
3	139.97	148.06	148.38	148.32	155.81	97.4	4	12.132	3.678×10^{-1}
4	182.90	202.25	200.83	200.92	190.55	77.9	5	1.489	2.011
5	223.20	233.26	233.16	233.12	201.74	105.2	6	5.369×10^{-4}	15.000
6	220.60	226.68	227.40	227.34	222.85	151.1	7	1.046×10^{-19}	15.200
7	230.55	228.42	229.39	229.36	242.56	131.2	8	1.271×10^{-9}	11.300
8	263.76	255.81	256.93	256.90	255.80	113.8	9	7.897×10^{-9}	9.000
9	285.15	276.74	277.77	277.74	278.72	134.6	10	1.262×10^{-15}	8.500
10	295.19	268.76	268.80	268.80	288.45	160.2	11	1.031×10^{-16}	7.000
11	323.67	294.32	293.91	292.90	307.19	125.1			
12	387.06	368.30	367.85	367.82	366.39	107.1			
D (Calc.)	30.833	31.534	31.613	31.600					
θ	0.616	0.949	1.006	1.0001					

TABLE 14-7 Solution of Example 14-4 in which heat transfer efficiencies are also employed

Plate No.	Specified heat transfer efficiency e_j (Eq. 14-13)	Temperature and vapor rate profiles (Trial No. 20)			Product distribution (Trial No. 20)		
		T^L (°F)	T^v (°F)	V_j	Comp. No.	d	b
0	0.877	100.65	104.54		1	2.000	3.326×10^{-10}
1	0.949	131.40	132.40	94.8	2	9.998	1.754×10^{-3}
2	0.980	150.43	150.92	94.7	3	12.123	2.083×10^{-2}
3	0.607	148.72	174.44	90.7	4	5.979	3.772×10^{-1}
4	0.569	200.44	214.12	75.4	5	1.499	2.001
5	0.717	233.19	232.17	105.6	6	1.066×10^{-3}	14.999
6	0.975	228.11	229.56	150.1	7	1.014×10^{-19}	15.200
7	0.724	229.77	239.73	127.2	8	1.346×10^{-9}	11.300
8	0.610	257.10	265.81	110.7	9	7.891×10^{-9}	9.000
9	0.835	278.66	279.43	134.1	10	1.247×10^{-15}	8.500
10	0.743	270.82	283.30	150.9	11	1.003×10^{-16}	7.000
11	0.613	293.21	319.32	114.7			
12	0.981	367.75	360.71	110.0			

TABLE 14-8 Statement and specifications for Example 14-5

Component No.	Component	Feed		Specifications
		V_{N+1}	L_0	
1	CH_4	70		For this example, $N = 8$, $V_1 = 85$, column pressure = 300 psia. The lean oil enters at 90°F. The adiabatic solution is desired. The constant-composition and Q-methods are to be used in making the enthalpy balances. The initial temperature profile is given by beginning with 260°F for plate 1 and subtracting 10°F per plate. Modified Murphree efficiencies for components 1 through 3 are, $E_{ji}^M = 0.7 + j$ (0.1); for components 4 through 6, $E_{ji}^M = 1.0 - j$ (0.05). Equilibrium and enthalpy data given in Tables A–4 and A–8 of the Appendix are to be used. Minimum and maximum vapor rates of 85 and 100 are to be employed. In view of the large amount of methane take $\theta = 1$ (direct-iteration) for each trial as discussed in Chapter 8.
2	C_2H_6	15		
3	C_3H_8	10		
4	$n\text{-}C_4$	4		
5	$n\text{-}C_4$	1		
6	$n\text{-}C_8$		20	

TABLE 14-9 Solution of Example 14-5 by use of a combination of modified Murphree and vaporization efficiencies

Plate No.	Temperature profiles (°F) Trial No.				$E_{j,i}^0$	Intermediate efficiencies Trial No.			
	6	16	21	30		6	16	21	30
1	97.55	106.13	106.22	106.19	$E_{1,5}^0$	7.122	2.380	2.378	2.383
2	99.19	109.53	109.58	109.53	$E_{2,6}^0$	0.919	0.915	0.914	0.914
3	96.40	110.06	109.97	109.90	$E_{3,2}^0$	1.000	1.000	1.000	1.000
4	89.58	109.26	109.02	108.94	$E_{4,1}^0$	0.995	1.000	1.000	1.000
5	85.05	108.26	107.84	107.79	$E_{5,4}^0$	0.750	0.750	0.750	0.750
6	86.64	104.42	104.04	104.01	$E_{6,3}^0$	1.300	1.300	1.300	1.300
7	98.26	97.91	97.37	97.41	$E_{7,5}^0$	0.650	0.650	0.650	0.650
8	70.33	77.57	77.50	77.50	$E_{8,1}^0$	1.032	1.038	1.038	0.600
$(V_1)_{ca}$	84.090	85.015	85.002						

TABLE 14–10 Final set of modified vaporization efficiencies obtained for Example 14–5

Plate No.	Modified vaporization efficiencies Component No.					
	1	2	3	4	5	6
1	0.994	1.012	1.088	1.085	2.383	0.972
2	0.999	1.000	1.014	1.157	7.498	0.914
3	1.000	1.000	1.000	1.372	84.753	0.850
4	1.000	1.000	1.005	2.167	0.800	0.800
5	1.001	1.000	1.016	0.750	0.750	0.750
6	1.000	1.010	1.300	0.700	0.700	0.700
7	1.004	1.400	1.400	0.650	0.650	0.650
8	1.038	0.996	0.773	1.318	2.177	0.600

NOTATION

(See also Chapters 2 through 8)

A = interfacial area per bubble of vapor

e_j = efficiency of heat transfer; defined by Equation (14–13)

e_j^0 = modified efficiency of heat transfer; defined by Equation (14–14)

E_{ji}^M = modified Murphree plate efficiency (for mass transfer); defined by Equation (1)

E_{ji}^0 = modified vaporization efficiency; defined by Equation (14–10)

$f^L, \bar{f}^L$ = fugacity of a pure component in the liquid state and the fugacity of a component in a liquid mixture, respectively; definitions follow Equations (14–3) and (14–5)

$f^v, \bar{f}^v$ = fugacity of a pure component in the vapor state and the fugacity of a component in a vapor mixture, respectively; definitions follow Equations (14–3) and (14–5)

K_G = over-all coefficient for the transfer of mass from the vapor to the liquid phase

P = total pressure in the vapor phase

P^* = vapor pressure of a pure component evaluated at the temperature of the liquid leaving a given plate

r = rate of mass transfer; see Equation (14–3)

$T_j^v,\ T_j^L$ = actual temperatures of the vapor and liquid leaving plate j, respectively

v_{ji}^* = a hypothetical flow rate; defined by Equation (14–15)

y_{ji}^* = mole fraction a component would have in the vapor if the vapor were in equilibrium with the liquid leaving plate j

Y_{ji} = product of K_{ji} and x_{ji}, where these quantities are evaluated at the actual conditions of the liquid leaving plate j

PROBLEMS

14–1 (a) By use of the mean value theorems presented in Chapter 4 and a material balance, develop the following differential equation that describes the rate of transfer of a component from the vapor to the liquid phase as the vapor passes through the liquid on plate j.

$$-d(Vy_i)/dz = K_{Gi}a\bar{S}(y_i - Y_i)$$

where

a = Interfacial area per unit volume of the liquid-vapor mixture on plate j

K_{Gi} = Coefficient of mass transfer for component i on the j'th plate. (Note: this K_G differs from the one appearing in Equation (14–5))

$\bar{S}$ = Mean cross-sectional area of the plate (i.e. the volume of the mixture on plate j is equal to $z_t\bar{S}$)

z = Depth of the liquid-vapor mixture on plate j; measured from the surface of the plate ($z = 0$) to the top of the liquid-vapor mixture ($z = z_t$)

(b) Show that

$$E_{ji}^M = 1 - \exp(-K_{Gi}a\bar{S}z_t/V_j)$$

and state the assumptions involved in the integration.

1. Repeat Part (a) of Problem 14–1 for heat-transfer and show that for any plate j

$$-d(VH)/dz = Ua\bar{S}(T^v - T^L)$$

where

V = mass rate of flow of the vapor

H = enthalpy per unit mass of vapor

2. Show that
$$d(VH)/dz = Vc_p(dT^v/dz)$$
and state the assumptions implied by this relationship.

3. Show that the following expression is obtained for the efficiency of heat transfer.
$$e_j = 1 - \exp(-Ua\bar{S}z_t/Vc_p)$$
and state the assumptions required in order to obtain this expression by integration of the differential equations given in Part (a).

14-2 Develop Equations (14–17a) through (14–18c).

14-3 Show that, when modified vaporization efficiencies are employed, the expressions for the material balance for a conventional column are as given by Equations (3–6) through (3–11) except that A_{ji}^0 and S_{ji}^0 appear instead of A_{ji} and S_{ji}.

LITERATURE CITED

1. Brown, G. G. and Associates, *Unit Operations* (New York: John Wiley & Sons, Inc., 1953), p. 525.

2. *Chemical Engineers' Handbook*, 3 ed., J. H. Perry, editor (New York: McGraw-Hill Book Company, Inc., 1950).

3. Holland, C. D. and N. E. Welch, "Steam Batch Distillation Calculation," *Petroleum Refiner*, **36**, No. 5, 251 (1957).

4. Lynch, R. P., personal communication.

5. Murphree, E. V., "Rectifying Column Calculations," *Ind. Eng. Chem.*, **17**, 747 (1925).

6. Ravicz, A. E., "Non-Ideal State Multicomponent Absorber Calculations by Automatic Digital Computer," Ph.D. dissertation, University of Michigan, Ann Arbor, Michigan, 1958.

7. Taylor, D. L., "Use of Plate Efficiencies in the Treatment of Conventional Columns," M.S. thesis, A. and M. College of Texas, College Station, Texas, January 1962.

Determination of Plate Efficiencies and Other Topics $\quad$ 15

The first part of this chapter is concerned with the determination of a set of plate efficiencies on the basis of the usual available operational data. Other topics, some of which have not been thoroughly investigated, are discussed. One of the subjects considered is the reduction of the time required to solve problems.

PLATE EFFICIENCIES

Frequently the determination of a set of plate efficiencies from certain available operational data is desirable. Since this information is usually rather limited in scope, this fact must be recognized in the calculational procedure for the determination of the efficiencies. The method developed supposes that in addition to the usual specifications (such as the number of plates; the location of the feed plate; the type of condenser, D, V_1, F; and the composition and the thermal condition of the feed), the composition of the distillate (or bottoms) and the temperature on each plate are known. Although whether or not each plate operates adiabatically will be known, the total vapor and liquid rates throughout the column are not generally known. Also, the compositions of the various streams throughout the column are seldom known. Because of this a method for the determination of the plate efficiencies was developed by Harris (3) requiring neither the knowledge of the internal flow rates nor the compositions. This procedure as modified by Taylor (5) is presented. By use of it, problems such as Examples 15–1 and 15–2 may be solved in less than 10 minutes with an I.B.M. 709 computer.

Calculational Procedure

Modified vaporization efficiencies were selected for use in the calculational procedure and convergence method because of the relatively simple manner in which they may be combined with the procedure of Thiele and Geddes. Although the definitions of these efficiencies, as well as the modified Murphree efficiencies, were presented previously, they are repeated here for convenience. The modified vaporization efficiency is defined by

$$E^0_{ji} = \frac{y_{ji}}{Y_{ji}} \tag{15-1}$$

and the modified Murphree plate efficiency by

$$E^M_{ji} = \frac{y_{ji} - y_{j+1,i}}{Y_{ji} - y_{j+1,i}} \tag{15-2}$$

The quantity Y_{ji} has the definition

$$Y_{ji} = K_{ji}x_{ji} \tag{15-3}$$

where x_{ji} is the mole fraction of component i in the liquid leaving plate j. The equilibrium constant, K_{ji}, is evaluated at the temperature of the liquid leaving plate j.

As discussed in Chapter 14, the equations stated previously for conventional and complex columns with perfect plates are readily converted to include vaporization efficiencies by replacing the absorption and stripping factors, A_{ji} and S_{ji}, by A^0_{ji} and S^0_{ji}, respectively. These factors were defined by Equations (14-30) and (14-31).

Since the temperature of the liquid leaving each plate j is taken to be one of the specifications, a set of E^0_{ji}'s must be found such that the sum of the y_{ji}'s is unity. Thus

$$\sum_{i=1}^{c} E^0_{ji}K_{ji}x_{ji} = 1 \tag{15-4}$$

which is readily developed by use of Equations (15-1) and (15-3). Further, the E^0_{ji}'s must be selected such that the calculated values of b_i/d_i are in agreement with the specified values.

On the basis of assumed sets of E^0_{ji}'s and L/V's, and the set of specified temperatures, the Thiele and Geddes equations are applied as shown in Chapter 14 to give a set calculated values for b_i/d_i. The θ-method may be applied in the usual way to obtain a better set of values for b_i/d_i, namely,

$$(b_i/d_i)_c = \theta(b_i/d_i)_{ca} \tag{15-5}$$

where the subscript "c" is used to identify the improved set of terminal flow rates. The quantity θ is determined in the usual way such that the improved set of rates are in component-material balance, and in agreement with the specification D. The $(b_i/d_i)_c$'s represent a good estimate of those values which would be obtained if the solution corresponding to the assumed set of E^0_{ji}'s were found by the procedure described in Chapter 14. A measure of the accuracy of the assumed set of E^0_{ji}'s is provided by the following ratio.

$$\theta_i = \frac{(b_i/d_i)_{co}}{(b_i/d_i)_c} \tag{15-6}$$

The specified values of b_i/d_i are identified by means of the subscript "co."

Thus the problem reduces to finding a set of E^0_{ji}'s such that simultaneously, Equation (15-4) is satisfied for each j and Equation (15-6) reduces to $\theta_i = 1$ for each i. At the end of each trial, flow rates throughout the column are found by use of the constant-composition and Q-methods. Compositions needed for carrying out these computations are found by use of Equations (4-9) and (4-10) modified as indicated by Equation (15-10). Also the enthalpies of the pure components are evaluated at the specified temperatures.

If the results obtained by a given trial do not satisfy Equation (15-4) for each j and give $\theta_i = 1$ for each i, another set of E^0_{ji}'s must be selected. This selection may be made by use of the convergence method presented in the next section. After the required set of E^0_{ji}'s has been found, the corresponding set of E^M_{ji}'s is given by the following expression

$$E^M_{ji} = \frac{E^0_{ji} - (y_{j+1,i}/Y_{ji})}{1 - (y_{j+1,i}/Y_{ji})} \tag{15-7}$$

which is readily developed from Equations (15-1) and (15-2).

Convergence Method

In the following development a conventional column with a total condenser, N plates, and a reboiler is considered. The total condenser is assumed to behave perfectly in that the distillate leaves the column at its bubble point at the column pressure. Then in view of Equation (15-6), the specification of the b_i/d_i's alone fixes the temperature, T_D, of the distillate. Since all of the b_i/d_i's are specified, D is fixed. Also, the overhead vapor rate V_1 (or L_0) is assumed to be specified. However, this specification is not available for use in the selection of the E_{ji}^0's because it is commonly employed in the determination of the condenser duty, Q_c.

Thus the problem reduces to the selection of a set of E_{ji}^0's such that the $c + N + 1$ independent specifications (c values of b_i/d_i and $N + 1$ values of T_j) are satisfied. Observe that this relatively small set of specifications does not permit the selection of a set of E_{ji}^0's mutually independent for all j and i. In order to pick such a set, it would be necessary to make at least $c(N + 1)$ independent specifications. This case was not considered because seldom if ever are this many variables known with any significant degree of accuracy.

Although many schemes could be proposed for the selection of $c(N + 1)$ values of E_{ji}^0 in agreement with $c + N + 1$ specifications, the following scheme,

$$E_{ji}^0 = \beta_j \bar{E}_i^0 \tag{15-8}$$

gave satisfactory results for all problems considered by Harris (3). In this expression β_j depends on j alone and $\bar{E}_i^0$ depends on i alone giving $N + 1$ values of β_j and c values of $\bar{E}_i^0$. Rearrangement of Equation (15–4) into functional form leads to the following definition of the function f_j; namely,

$$f_j = \cfrac{1}{\sum\limits_{i=1}^{c} E_{ji}^0 K_{ji} x_{ji}} - 1 \tag{15-9}$$

Again each K_{ji} is evaluated at the specified value of T_j. Also, each x_{ji} is regarded as a dependent variable whose value may be determined for any choice of the independent variables, $\bar{E}_i^0$ and β_j. Since the corrected values of b_i (the specified values) do not reflect the choice of the $\bar{E}_i^0$'s and β_j's, the improved values of b_i that reflect the particular choice of the independent variables should be employed in the calculation of the x_{ji}'s as follows:

$$x_{ji} = \cfrac{(l_{ji}/b_i)_{ca}(b_i)_c}{\sum\limits_{i=1}^{c} (l_{ji}/b_i)_{ca}(b_i)_c} \tag{15-10}$$

The V_j's and L_j's that appear in the Thiele and Geddes equations are also taken to be dependent variables whose values may be found for any choice of the independent variables by use of enthalpy balances. With these intermediate calculations understood, the c values of $\bar{E}_i^0$ and the $N + 1$ values of β_j are to be selected such that $\theta_i = 1$ for all i and $f_j = 0$ for all j

where

$$\theta_1 = \theta_1(\bar{E}_1^0,\ \bar{E}_2^0,\ \ldots,\ \bar{E}_c^0,\ \beta_1,\ \beta_2,\ \ldots,\ \beta_{N+1})$$

$$\theta_2 = \theta_2(\bar{E}_1^0,\ \bar{E}_2^0,\ \ldots,\ \bar{E}_c^0,\ \beta_1,\ \beta_2,\ \ldots,\ \beta_{N+1})$$

$$\vdots \qquad \vdots$$

$$\theta_c = \theta_c(\bar{E}_1^0,\ \bar{E}_2^0,\ \ldots,\ \bar{E}_c^0,\ \beta_1,\ \beta_2,\ \ldots,\ \beta_{N+1})$$

$$f_1 = f_1(\bar{E}_1^0,\ \bar{E}_2^0,\ \ldots,\ \bar{E}_c^0,\ \beta_1,\ \beta_2,\ \ldots,\ \beta_{N+1}) \qquad (15\text{--}11)$$

$$f_2 = f_2(\bar{E}_1^0,\ \bar{E}_2^0,\ \ldots,\ \bar{E}_c^0,\ \beta_1,\ \beta_2,\ \ldots,\ \beta_{N+1})$$

$$\vdots \qquad \vdots$$

$$f_{N+1} = f_{N+1}(\bar{E}_1^0,\ \bar{E}_2^0,\ \ldots,\ \bar{E}_c^0,\ \beta_1,\ \beta_2,\ \ldots,\ \beta_{N+1})$$

After the n'th trial has been made on the basis of a set of variables denoted by $\bar{E}_{i,\,n}^0$ and $\beta_{j,n}$, an improved set for use in the next trial (the $n + 1$'st) may be found by use of the Newton-Raphson equations which follow.

$$1 = \theta_1 + \frac{\partial \theta_1}{\partial \bar{E}_1^0}\,\Delta \bar{E}_1^0 + \frac{\partial \theta_1}{\partial \bar{E}_2^0}\,\Delta \bar{E}_2^0 + \ldots + \frac{\partial \theta_1}{\partial \bar{E}_c^0}\,\Delta \bar{E}_c^0$$

$$+ \frac{\partial \theta_1}{\partial \beta_1}\,\Delta \beta_1 + \frac{\partial \theta_1}{\partial \beta_2}\,\Delta \beta_2 + \ldots + \frac{\partial \theta_1}{\partial \beta_{N+1}}\,\Delta \beta_{N+1}$$

$$\vdots$$

$$1 = \theta_c + \frac{\partial \theta_c}{\partial \bar{E}_1^0}\,\Delta \bar{E}_1^0 + \frac{\partial \theta_c}{\partial \bar{E}_2^0}\,\Delta \bar{E}_2^0 + \ldots + \frac{\partial \theta_c}{\partial \bar{E}_c^0}\,\Delta \bar{E}_c^0$$

$$+ \frac{\partial \theta_c}{\partial \beta_1}\,\Delta \beta_1 + \frac{\partial \theta_c}{\partial \beta_2}\,\Delta \beta_2 + \ldots + \frac{\partial \theta_c}{\partial \beta_{N+1}}\,\Delta \beta_{N+1} \qquad (15\text{--}12)$$

$$0 = f_1 + \frac{\partial f_1}{\partial \bar{E}_1^0}\,\Delta \bar{E}_1^0 + \frac{\partial f_1}{\partial \bar{E}_2^0}\,\Delta \bar{E}_2^0 + \ldots + \frac{\partial f_1}{\partial \bar{E}_c^0}\,\Delta \bar{E}_c^0$$

$$+ \frac{\partial f_1}{\partial \beta_1}\,\Delta \beta_1 + \frac{\partial f_1}{\partial \beta_2}\,\Delta \beta_2 + \ldots + \frac{\partial f_1}{\partial \beta_{N+1}}\,\Delta \beta_{N+1}$$

$$\vdots$$

$$0 = f_{N+1} + \frac{\partial f_{N+1}}{\partial \bar{E}_1^0}\,\Delta \bar{E}_1^0 + \frac{\partial f_{N+1}}{\partial \bar{E}_2^0}\,\Delta \bar{E}_2^0 + \ldots + \frac{\partial f_{N+1}}{\partial \bar{E}_c^0}\,\Delta \bar{E}_c^0$$

$$+ \frac{\partial f_{N+1}}{\partial \beta_1}\,\Delta \beta_1 + \frac{\partial f_{N+1}}{\partial \beta_2}\,\Delta \beta_2 + \ldots + \frac{\partial f_{N+1}}{\partial \beta_{N+1}}\,\Delta \beta_{N+1}$$

where

$$\Delta \bar{E}_i^0 = \bar{E}_{i,n+1}^0 - \bar{E}_{i,n}^0$$

$$\Delta \beta_j = \beta_{j,n+1} - \beta_{j,n}$$

The Newton-Raphson equations represent $(c + N + 1)$ equations in $(c + N + 1)$ unknowns, the $\bar{E}_{i,n+1}^0$'s and $\beta_{j,n+1}$'s. The θ_i's and f_j's are evaluated on the basis of the last set of independent variables, the $\bar{E}_{i,n}^0$'s and $\beta_{j,n}$'s. After the derivatives have been evaluated as described in a subsequent paragraph, the Newton-Raphson equations may be solved for the c values of $\bar{E}_i^0$ and the $(N + 1)$ values of β_j from which the next set of independent variables (the $\bar{E}_{i,n+1}^0$'s and the $\beta_{j,n+1}$'s) are readily obtained.

The partial derivatives appearing in the Newton-Raphson equations were evaluated numerically. The numerical procedure is applied in the same manner as described previously in Chapter 7. After the θ_i's and f_j's have been determined for the last set of variables $(\bar{E}_{i,n}^0, \beta_{j,n})$, the partial derivatives of θ_i and f_j with respect to the $\bar{E}_i^0$'s are computed in the same manner as that described for the k'th component. Let all of the variables be held fixed at those values used for the previous trial except for $\bar{E}_{k,n}^0$ which is selected as follows,

$$\bar{E}_{k,p}^0 = \bar{E}_{k,n}^0 + p \tag{15-13}$$

The rate of convergence of the problem to the desired solution was increased by decreasing the values of p as the E_{ji}^0's converged to the correct set. In general a value of p less than 10^{-5} should not be employed, because for values of p less than this, the effect of round-off error becomes comparable to the effect of the change in E_k^0 on θ_k and the f_j's. The sequence of p's stated in Table 15-1 was found to give satisfactory results. On the basis of this $\bar{E}_{k,p}^0$, the remaining $\bar{E}_{i,n}^0$'s, and the $\beta_{j,n}$'s, another trial calculation through the column is carried out to give values for θ_k and $f_1, f_2, \ldots, f_{N+1}$. On the basis of the θ_k so obtained and the one found by the previous trial, the partial derivative of θ_k with respect to $\bar{E}_k^0$ is computed

$$\frac{\partial \theta_k}{\partial \bar{E}_k^0} = \frac{\theta_k(\bar{E}_{k,p}^0, \beta_{1,n}, \ldots, \beta_{N+1,n})}{p} - \frac{\theta_k(\bar{E}_{k,n}^0, \beta_{1,n}, \ldots, \beta_{N+1,n})}{p} \tag{15-14}$$

The corresponding partial derivatives of the f_j's with respect to $\bar{E}_k^0$ are computed in a manner analogous to that which follows for f_1.

$$\frac{\partial f_1}{\partial \bar{E}_k^0} = \frac{f_1(\bar{E}_{1,n}, \ldots, \bar{E}_{k,p}^0, \ldots, \bar{E}_{c,n}^0, \beta_{1,n}, \ldots, \beta_{N+1,n})}{p}$$

$$- \frac{f_1(\bar{E}_{1,n}^0, \ldots, \bar{E}_{k,n}^0, \ldots, \bar{E}_{c,n}^0, \beta_{1,n}, \ldots, \beta_{N+1,n})}{p} \tag{15-15}$$

The partial derivatives of the θ_i's and the f_j's with respect to any one of the β_j's are computed by the same general approach.

Treatment of Systems Containing Relatively Light and Heavy Components

Methods for the analysis of a mixture of compounds are bound by certain well-known limitations, one of which is the size of the smallest amount of a component which may be determined quantitatively. Examples were solved in which the value of b_i/d_i was assumed to be unknown for any component having either an X_{Di} or an $x_{Bi} < 10^{-2}$. The heaviest component having an $X_{Di} > 10^{-2}$ is referred to as the "heavy key" and indicated by the subscript "h." The lightest component having an $x_{Bi} > 10^{-2}$ is called the "light key" and distinguished by the subscript "l." For all components having either an X_{Di} or an x_{Bi} less than 10^{-2}, the correct (or actual) values of their respective b_i/d_i's are unknown. Thus the number of specifications is in effect reduced by the number of such components unless an equal number of arbitrary specifications are made. Although these specifications are arbitrary, they should be realistic in order to obtain a reasonable set of E_{ji}^0's. Several schemes exist for choosing a set of $(b_i/d_i)_{co}$'s for the components lighter and heavier than the keys. Of these only one is presented. This scheme does not propose to choose a precise set of values for the $(b_i/d_i)_{co}$'s (for $i < l$ and $i > h$) that are independent of trial number. Instead it consists of a procedure for the calculation of a corrected set of b_i/d_i's on the basis of the results obtained for the last trial calculation through the column. More specifically, a single value of θ_i (denoted by $\bar{\theta}$) for $i < l$ and $i > h$ is defined as follows:

$$(b_i/d_i)_{co} = \bar{\theta}(b_i/d_i)_c, \qquad i < l \qquad\qquad (15\text{--}16)$$

$$(b_i/d_i)_{co} = \bar{\theta}(b_i/d_i)_c, \qquad i > h \qquad\qquad (15\text{--}17)$$

This value of $\bar{\theta}$ is found by use of the following g function.

$$g(\bar{\theta}) = \sum_{\substack{i<l \\ i>h}} \frac{FX_i}{1 + \bar{\theta}(b_i/d_i)_c} + \sum_{i=l}^{h} \frac{FX_i}{1 + (b_i/d_i)_{co}} - D \qquad (15\text{--}18)$$

The desired value of $\bar{\theta}$ is the one which makes $g(\bar{\theta}) = 0$. For this value of $\bar{\theta}$, the $(b_i/d_i)_{co}$'s for the "separated components" are both in over-all material balance and in agreement with the specification D as well as the specified values of $(b_i/d_i)_{co}$ for the distributed components (l through h). For the remainder of the trial (the evaluation of the partial derivatives), the values of $(b_i/d_i)_{co}$ given by Equations (15–16) and (15–17) are considered to be the specified values. On the basis of these values of $(b_i/d_i)_{co}$, the derivatives are evaluated in the same manner as that described for the case where the $(b_i/d_i)_{co}$'s are specified at the outset of the given trial or problem. In effect this procedure supposes that T_D is unknown. The particular value obtained by the proposed procedure may differ slightly from the operational value. However, this deviation will probably be within the experimental accuracy of the measurement of this particular variable. Note also that, in the limit as convergence is obtained, the proposed procedure leads to a value of unity for each θ_i.

When a partial condenser instead of a total condenser is employed, $c + N + 2$ equations in $c + N + 2$ unknowns are obtained.

Illustrative Examples

In order to test the convergence properties of the procedures described in this chapter, examples were first solved on the basis of a given set of E_{ji}^0's (computed preassigned sets of values of $\bar{E}_i^0$ and β_j) as described in Chapter 14. The resulting $(b_i/d_i)_{co}$'s and T_j's were taken as the specifications for the problems used to test the procedures described in this chapter. Statements of Examples 15–1 and 15–2 are presented in Table 15–1, and the solutions are given in Tables 15–2 and 15–3. The specifications stated for these examples were found by solving the given problem as described in Chapter 14 on the basis of the following set of values for $\bar{E}_i^0$ and β_j.

$$\bar{E}_i^0 = 0.75 + (i - 1)(0.05)$$

$$\beta_j = 1, \quad \text{for} \quad j = 1, 3, \ldots, 9, 11$$

$$\beta_j = 0.9, \quad \text{for} \quad j = 2, 4, \ldots, 8, 10$$

As shown in Table 15–2, these values were determined by the procedures presented in this chapter. The calculational procedure was followed as described in the development.

For the case where some of the b_i/d_i's are unknown, the proposed calculational procedure is illustrated by the solution of Example 15–2, shown in Table 15–3. The efficiencies for the distributed components are in good agreement with those found in Example 15–1. Although the proposed procedure did not give the same efficiencies as those found in Example 15–1 for the component lighter and heavier than keys, the procedure did lead to convergence and to very nearly the correct set of efficiencies for the distributed components. In view of the specifications for this particular example, the results obtained are as good as may be expected.

Table 15–1 Specifications for Examples 15–1 and 15–2

Component	Component No.	FX	b_i/d_i	Plate No.	T_j (°F)
CH_4	1	0.5	1.3424835×10^{-7}	0	121.5508
C_2H_6	2	1.0	2.2831944×10^{-4}	1	176.6284
C_3H_8	3	6.0	3.0072939×10^{-2}	2	205.9177
C_3H_6	4	12.5	9.1519363×10^{-3}	3	212.6389
$n\text{-}C_4$	5	3.5	2.3065976	4	269.7236
$i\text{-}C_4$	6	15.0	4.1289765×10^{-1}	5	268.5260
$n\text{-}C_5$	7	15.2	7.2210822×10	6	287.0048
$n\text{-}C_6$	8	11.3	1.9111616×10^{3}	7	287.1989
$n\text{-}C_7$	9	9.0	3.7487806×10^{4}	8	312.5138
$n\text{-}C_8$	10	18.5	8.3590640×10^{5}	9	322.3374
500	11	7.5	2.6363920×10^{8}	10	371.0180
				11	418.8843

Specifications

Example	
15–1	$V_1 = 94.8$, $D = 31.6$ (fixed by the specified values of b_i/d_i's), $N = 10$, $f = 4$, column pressure $= 300$ psia, thermal condition of the feed is boiling point liquid, and a total condenser is to be employed. Limiting vapor rates: $V_{min} = 37 \leq V_j \leq 140 = V_{max}$, $2 \leq j \leq 11$. Equilibrium and enthalpy data to be taken from Tables A–4 and A–8 of the Appendix. For the first trial: $E_{ji}^0 = 1.0$ for all i, and $\beta_j = 1.0$ for all j. Initial flow rates, $V_j = V_1$ for all j. The value of p is 0.1 for trials 1 and 2; 0.01 for trials 3 and 4; 0.001 for trials 5 and 6; 0.0001 for trials 7 and 8; and 0.00001 for all subsequent trials.
15–2	Same as Example 15–1 except that the b_i/d_i's for components 1, 2, 9, 10, and 11 are considered to be unknown. Also, the temperature (T_D) of the distillate is taken to be unknown.

TABLE 15-2 Values of $\bar{E}_i^0$, θ_i, β_j, and vapor rates obtained in the solution of Example 15-1

Component No.	$\bar{E}_i^0$ Trial No.			θ_i Trial No.			Plate No.	β_j Trial No.			Final vapor rates Trial No. 10
	1	5	10	1	5	10		1	5	10	10
1	0.8520	0.7500	0.7500	4.1669	0.9995	1.0000	1	1.0000	1.0000	1.0000	94.80
2	0.8583	0.7999	0.8000	2.6282	0.9991	1.0000	2	0.8664	0.8999	0.9000	98.37
3	0.8697	0.8499	0.8500	1.7390	0.9993	1.0000	3	1.0118	0.9998	1.0000	103.44
4	0.8818	0.9000	0.9000	1.2400	0.9992	1.0000	4	0.9441	0.8994	0.9000	79.14
5	0.9062	0.9501	0.9500	0.8908	1.0005	1.0000	5	1.0511	0.9992	1.0000	105.54
6	0.9641	1.0000	1.0000	1.0114	0.9998	1.0000	6	0.9746	0.9000	0.9000	90.61
7	0.9904	1.0504	1.0500	0.7783	1.0021	1.0001	7	1.0640	0.9999	1.0000	114.76
8	1.0443	1.1005	1.1000	0.7856	1.0026	1.0001	8	0.9691	0.9002	0.9000	95.20
9	1.1037	1.1506	1.1500	0.8183	1.0027	1.0001	9	1.0528	0.9999	1.0000	119.71
10	1.1573	1.2006	1.2000	0.8336	1.0028	1.0000	10	0.9351	0.8998	0.9000	95.10
11	1.1573	1.2506	1.2500	0.7072	1.0028	1.0001	11	1.0295	0.9997	1.0000	114.97

TABLE 15-3 Values $\bar{E}_i^0$, b_i/d_i, β_j, and vapor rates obtained in the solution of Example 15-2

Component No.	$\bar{E}_i^0$ Trial No. 1	$\bar{E}_i^0$ Trial No. 5	$\bar{E}_i^0$ Trial No. 10	θ_i Trial No. 10	(b_i/d_i) Trial No. 10	Plate No.	β_j Trial No. 1	β_j Trial No. 5	β_j Trial No. 10	Final vapor rates Trial No. 10
1	0.8951	0.9454	0.9447	1.0001	2.0102×10^{-8}	1	1.0000	1.0000	1.0000	94.80
2	0.8960	0.9455	0.9449	1.0001	5.7366×10^{-5}	2	0.8650	0.8997	0.8999	98.33
3	0.8685	0.8470	0.8471	1.0000	3.0074×10^{-2}	3	1.0013	0.9905	0.9911	103.58
4	0.8804	0.8961	0.8963	1.0000	9.1521×10^{-3}	4	0.9445	0.8968	0.8983	79.73
5	0.9065	0.9510	0.9507	1.0000	2.3066	5	1.0503	0.9976	0.9992	106.59
6	0.9638	0.9987	0.9986	1.0000	0.4129	6	0.9741	0.8968	0.8971	91.53
7	0.9920	1.0559	1.0546	1.0000	7.2211×10	7	1.0602	0.9952	0.9955	116.29
8	1.0460	1.1074	1.1057	1.0000	1.9112×10^{3}	8	0.9632	0.8914	0.8913	96.58
9	0.8648	0.8936	0.8931	1.0001	1.0777×10^{5}	9	1.0376	0.9850	0.9853	122.31
10	0.8641	0.8927	0.8922	1.0001	2.8347×10^{6}	10	0.9260	0.8863	0.8868	97.83
11	0.8635	0.8920	0.8916	1.0001	1.0450×10^{9}	11	1.1021	1.0511	1.0520	119.08

$T_D = 121.5491°F$ (Trial No. 10)

OTHER TOPICS

Speed

In the interest of reducing computing costs, any increase in the rate
of solving problems is always desirable. The bubble point procedure,
Equation (2–2), requires an appreciable percentage of the computing time
for the combination of the Thiele and Geddes calculational procedure and
the θ-method of convergence. Determination of temperature by use of the
bubble point procedure consists of finding a T_j such that $f(T_j) = 0$ (the
actual limit employed was $|f(T_j)| \leq 10^{-5}$). When the temperature of each
plate is calculated with this accuracy, the time required for the determination of these temperatures amounts to anywhere from about one fourth to
one half or more of the total running time. As the number of plates is increased, the relative amount of time required to make the bubble point
calculations increases. Thus the determination of temperatures represents
a rather obvious area worthy of further investigation. Recently, some work
was done along this line by Abdel-Aal, Anthony, Taylor, and Wetherold
(1). The results obtained are promising.

The method considered has as its basis the fact that, as convergence is
obtained, the relative volatility of each component for each plate does
not change between successive trials. (Note, this does not imply that the
relative volatility of a component becomes independent of plate number
as convergence is obtained.) Instead of finding the T_j such that $f(T_j) = 0$,
the method consists of finding a first approximation for T_j indicated by
$T_{j,n+1}$. If the relative volatilities were independent of temperature, the
approximate value, $T_{j,n+1}$, would also be the correct value. In order to
make this calculation, a component is selected as the "base" or reference
component, and its K-value is identified by the subscript "b." (This component need not be present in the mixture under consideration.) Let the
temperature used to make the last set of trial calculations through the
column be indicated by $T_{j,n}$. Then as shown in Chapter 2.

$$K_b \big|_{T_{j,n+1}} = \frac{K_b \big|_{T_{j,n}}}{\left[\sum_{i=1}^{c} K_{ji} \big|_{T_{j,n}} x_{ji}\right]} = \frac{1}{\sum_{i=1}^{c} \alpha_{ji} \big|_{T_{j,n}} x_{ji}} \tag{15–19}$$

Thus if the α's are independent of temperature, this expression gives the
correct value of K_b, and the correct temperature may be obtained from a
curve fit such as:

$$T = a + bK_b + cK_b^2 + dK_b^3 + \dots \tag{15–20}$$

Although the α's may vary with temperature, the value of K_b given by
Equation (15–19) approaches the correct value as convergence is obtained.

Also, the temperature corresponding to the K_b computed by use of Equation (15–19) is the same as the one given by use of the y_{ji}'s; namely,

$$K_b \mid_{T_{j,n+1}} = \sum_{i=1}^{c} y_{ji}/\alpha_{ji} \mid_{T_{j,n}} \tag{15–21}$$

[See Problem 4–2 (d).]

Problems were solved in which each of several hypothetical components were used as the base component. Perhaps, the most unusual of these was the one for which the coefficients in Equation (15–20) have the following values; $a = c = d = \ldots = 0$, and $b = 1$; that is,

$$T = K_b \tag{15–22}$$

However, for the conventional-column problem considered (Example 5–7), the overcorrections which resulted from the use of such a component led to a bouncing of the temperatures from the lower to the upper limits of the curve fits. This component is like a light hydrocarbon in that its value of K is large at the temperatures involved in Example 5–7. It differs from the light hydrocarbons in that for all T its slope, $dK_b/dT = 1$, whereas for the light hydrocarbons, dK/dT approaches zero as T increases as discussed in Chapter 6. As the temperature scale for this base component ($T = K_b$) was changed from °R to °F, the tendency toward overcorrection was diminished. Although this particular base component was investigated no further, additional work might produce a useable procedure.

The use of hypothetical components having simple relationships for T as a function of K_b permits the direct determination of $T_{j,n+1}$ once the corresponding value of K_b has been computed by use of Equation (15–19). The use of such components avoids the necessity for the determination of a set of coefficients $(a, b, c, d, \ldots)$ for K_b as a function of T. Other hypothetical base components investigated are those having the following relationships between K_b and T,

$$K_b = a + bT \tag{15–23}$$

$$\ln K_b = (b/T) + a \tag{15–24}$$

Of these, the second has a K_b versus T relationship most nearly like that of a hydrocarbon. In order to define completely a particular base component, two values of K_b at each of two values of T are required. Values of K_b evaluated at the lower and upper temperature limits of the curve fits for each of several components were employed as indicated in Tables 15–4 through 15–9. The component whose K-values at $T_{L.L.}$ and $T_{U.L.}$ are used to determine the constants in Equations (15–23) and (15–24) is called the "hypothetical base component." In Table 15–4, i-C_4 is the "hypothetical base component."

Table 15–4 Solution of Examples 5–7 and 5–1 by use of several different procedures for the determination of the temperatures

Example	Procedure for the determination of the temperatures	Hypothetical base component	No. of trials required† $\|\Delta T\| = 10^{-4}$ (averaging)	No. of trials required $\|\Delta T\| \leqq 10^{-4}$	Calculated value of D^*	θ^*	Total computing time (min.)
5–7 (11 components)	Bubble points, $f(T_j) = 0$	i-C$_4$ Component No. 5	22		31.60000	0.99999959	1.76
5–7	$K_b = 1/\Sigma\alpha x$ $K_b = a + bT$	i-C$_4$ Component No. 5	25		31.60001	1.0000060	1.45
5–7	$K_b = 1/\Sigma\alpha x$ $\ln K_b = \dfrac{b}{T} + a$	i-C$_4$ Component No. 5	20	15	31.60000	0.99999952	1.49
5–1 (5 components)	$K_b = 1/\Sigma\alpha x$ $\ln K_b = \dfrac{b}{T} + a$	i-C$_4$ Component No. 2	18	13	48.899999	1.0000000	

* Values obtained at the end of 20 trials.

† At the end of the number of trials indicated, each of the temperatures used to make a given trial calculation agreed with the corresponding calculated temperatures to within four digits. "Averaging" is used to indicate that for each trial after the first, the temperatures were averaged, as described in Chapter 5.

TABLE 15–5 Effect of the hypothetical base component on the rate of convergence of Example 6–6

Hypothetical base component	Bubble points, $f(T_j) = 0$ $\left|\dfrac{\Delta D}{D}\right| \leqq 10^{-3}$ (averaging)	$K_b = 1/\Sigma\alpha x$ $\ln K_b = \dfrac{b}{T} + a$ $\left|\dfrac{\Delta D}{D}\right| \leqq 10^{-3}$ (averaging)	$K_b = 1/\Sigma\alpha x$ $\ln K_b = \dfrac{b}{T} + a$ $\mid \Delta T \mid \leqq 10^{-4}$ (averaging)	$K_b = 1/\Sigma\alpha x$ $\ln K_b = \dfrac{b}{T} + a$ $\left|\dfrac{\Delta D}{D}\right| \leqq 10^{-3}$	$K_b = 1/\Sigma\alpha x$ $\ln K_b = \dfrac{b}{T} + a$ $\mid \Delta T \mid \leqq 10^{-4}$
			No. of trials required		
CH_4, Component No. 1	9	Bounced back and forth	Bounced	Bounced	Bounced
$n\text{-}C_4$, Component No. 2		7	30	6	17
$i\text{-}C_4$, Component No. 3		6	22	10	35

Table 15-6 Effect of the hypothetical base component on the rate of convergence of conventional columns at minimum reflux

Example	Hypothetical base component	No. of trials required			
		Bubble points, $f(T_j) = 0$ $\|\Delta T\| \leqq 3 \times 10^{-3}$ (averaging)	$K_b = 1/\Sigma \alpha x$ $\ln K_b = \dfrac{b}{T} + a$ $\|\Delta T\| \leqq 3 \times 10^{-3}$ (averaging)	θ_{ol}	θ_{oh}
11–2 (6 components)	C₃H₈, Component No. 1	35	Bounced back and forth	0.9997	0.9987
11–2	i-C₄, Component No. 2		21	1.000008	0.99999
11–2	n-C₄, Component No. 3		21	1.00002	0.99998
11–2	i-C₅, Component No. 4		21	0.99991	1.00013
11–2	n-C₅, Component No. 5		21	1.00011	0.99984
11–2	n-C₆, Component No. 6		26	1.00015	0.99995
11–1 (5 components)		38		1.0008	1.0004
11–1	n-C₄, Component No. 3		20	0.999996	0.99994

Note: In the top data row, θ_{ol} and θ_{oh} columns read: "Values were alternately 0.93 and 1.08" and "Values were alternately 0.93 and 1.04" respectively.

TABLE 15-7 Statement of Example 15-3

Component	v_{N+1}	l_0	Specifications
CH_4	25.0		Column pressure = 300 psia, $V_1 = 85$ and $N = 8$. Lean oil enters at 90°F. Use the equilibrium and enthalpy data given in Tables A–4 and A–8 of the Appendix. Use a combination of the constant-composition and Q-methods, where the vapor rates are bounded as follows: $85 = V_{min} \leq V_j \leq V_{max} = 100, 2 \leq j \leq N$.
C_2H_6	52.5		
C_3H_8	11.25		
n-C_4	7.50		
n-C_5	3.75		
n-C_8		70.0	

TABLE 15–8 Effect of the hypothetical base component on the rate of convergence of absorber problems

Example	Hypothetical base component	No. of trials required			Value of θ	
		Bubble points $f(T_j) = 0$ $\lvert \Delta T \rvert < 10^{-1}$ (averaging)	$K_b = 1/\Sigma\alpha x$ $\ln K_b = \frac{b}{T} + a$ $\lvert \Delta T \rvert < 10^{-1}$ (averaging)	$K_b = 1/\Sigma\alpha x$ $\ln K_b = \frac{b}{T} + a$ $\lvert \Delta T \rvert < 10^{-1}$	$K_b = 1/\Sigma\alpha x$; $\ln K_b = \frac{b}{T} + a$ $\lvert \Delta T \rvert \le 10^{-1}$	
					Temperatures were averaged	Temperatures were not averaged
8–2 (6 components)		25 (used direct-iteration, $\theta = 1$)				
8–2	C_2H_6, Component No. 2		25	Bounced back and forth	1.000000	Values were alternately 1.28 and 0.79
8–2	C_3H_8 Component No. 3		24	23	0.999979	1.000007
8–2	n-C_4, Component No. 4		40	26	1.000133	1.000111
15–3* (6 components)		23			0.999751	
15–3*	C_3H_8, Component No. 3		39	Bounced back and forth	0.999815	Bounced high and low
15–3*	n-C_4, Component No. 4		Not quite in at end of 40 trials	28	At trial 40 $\theta = 1.000414$	0.999878
15–3*	n-C_5, Component No. 5		Not quite in at end of 40 trials	34	At trial 40 $\theta = 1.00382$	0.999767

* Used the criterion $\lvert \Delta T \rvert \le 0.5$ instead of 10^{-1}.

TABLE 15-9 Effect of the hypothetical base component on the rate of convergence of stripper Example 8-3

Hypothetical base component	Bubble points $f(T_j) = 0$ $\|\Delta T\| \leq 0.7$ (averaging)	Number of trials required		Value of θ	
		$K_b = (1 - y_{j,1})/\Sigma\alpha x$ $\ln K_b = \frac{b}{T} + a$ $\|\Delta T\| \leq 0.7$ (averaging)	$K_b = (1 - y_{j,1})/\Sigma\alpha x$ $\ln K_b = \frac{b}{T} + a$ $\|\Delta T\| \leq 0.7$	$K_b = (1 - y_{j,1})/\Sigma\alpha x$; $\ln K_b = \frac{b}{T} + a$; $\|\Delta T\| \leq 0.7$	
				Temperatures were averaged	Temperatures were not averaged
	19			1.00084	
C_3H_8, Component No. 4		Bounced back and forth	Bounced	Values were alternately 3.82 and 0.35	
n-C_4, Component No. 5		38	Bounced	0.999689	Values were alternately 15.3 and 0.02
n-C_5, Component No. 6		49	Bounced	1.00017	Values were alternately 15.3 and 0.05
n-C_6, Component No. 7		56	Bounced	0.999584	Values were alternately 21.7 and .075

The results given in Table 15–4 show that the solution of Example 5–7 is obtained in the smallest amount of time by use of the expression given by Equation (15–24) for K_b, where the hypothetical base component is taken to be i-C_4.

The results given in Tables 15–5 and 15–6 show that the tendency toward making overcorrections increases as lighter and lighter components are used as the hypothetical base component. On the other hand the use of a very heavy component as the base results in overdamping. Both of these tendencies are diminished as the boiling range of the feed is decreased. In general, the best results seem to be obtained for conventional columns by use of either the middle component or the next lighter one as the hypothetical base component. Averaging of the temperatures is also recommended. Although averaging increases the computing time for problems having narrow boiling feeds, it made possible the solution of problems containing a large percentage of methane; see Example 6–6, Table 15–5.

The use of the middle component as the hypothetical base component plus the averaging of temperatures decreased the running time for the minimum-reflux problems by more than one half. The results obtained for several examples are presented in Table 15–6.

In the case of absorbers two problems were considered in order to investigate the effect of the relative amounts of methane in the rich gas and the relative amount of lean oil on the rate of convergence. In Example 8–2 the rich gas contained 70 moles of methane and 20 moles of lean oil (n-C_8), whereas in Example 15–3 (see Table 15–7) the rich gas contained 25 moles of methane and 70 moles of lean oil. The results given in Table 15–8 show that as the amount of methane is decreased and the amount of lean oil is increased, the tendency toward overcorrection is decreased until overdamping is obtained. Again, the choice of the middle component as the hypothetical base component plus the averaging of the temperatures gives good results.

For the particular stripper example considered, the results are presented in Table 15–9. This problem, Example 8–3, contained a relatively large amount of the heavy, 500-component, which tended to promote damping. Again, less computing time was required to obtain the solution by use of K_b's rather than bubble points. However, the amount of time saved by using K_b's rather than bubble points was not appreciable for this particular example.

Design Specifications

Historically the subject of distillation has been approached from the standpoint of design, making necessary the determination of the minimum number of plates required to effect the specified separations for the two key components at a specified value of L_0/D. Of course certain other specifications such as the complete definition of the feed stream, the type of condenser, and the column pressure are made. In practice most of the problems are of an operational nature in that they usually involve the determination of the product distribution that can be expected when a given column is operated at a specified set of conditions. As described in previous chapters, extensive use of the combination of the θ-method of convergence and the Thiele and Geddes calculational procedure has been made in solving problems of the operational type. At the time of this writing no attempt has been made to extend this combination to obtain a direct solution for the design problem. These problems have been solved indirectly by obtaining solutions for each of a series of problems in which the total number of plates, as well as the location of the feed plate, is varied.

It should be pointed out that the product distribution obtained by the θ-method at the end of the first few trials represents a good approximation of the correct distribution. This is particularly true for conventional columns as reflected by the temperatures obtained for the distillate and bottoms (see Example 5–2, Table 5–5). If the product distribution is approximated in this way, the time required to solve several cases would be appreciably reduced. In the neighborhood of the desired solution, it would be desirable to obtain convergence for each case.

Another approach has been taken by Erbar and Maddox (2). They improved an existing graphical correlation in which the number of plates required to effect a specified separation of two components at a given L_0/D is represented as a function of the minimum reflux ratio and the number of equilibrium stages needed to effect the separation at total recycle.

Peiser (4) has described a direct method for solving the design problem that makes use of the calculational procedure of Lewis and Matheson and the θ-method of convergence. With minor modifications, it should be possible to apply this method to the Thiele and Geddes calculational procedure. A suggested combination follows. By this approach a set of values for N (number of rectifying plates) and M (number of stripping plates) that minimize the total number of plates and satisfy the separation specifications at the specified value of L_0/D is found every time a trial calculation through the column is made. The separation specifications may be stated in terms of the θ's as follows:

$$\theta_h = \frac{(b_h/d_h)_{co}}{(b_h/d_h)_{ca}} \leqq 1 \qquad (15\text{--}25)$$

$$\theta_l = \frac{(b_l/d_l)_{co}}{(b_l/d_l)_{ca}} \geqq 1 \qquad (15\text{--}26)$$

where the subscript "*co*" denotes the specified values and "*ca*" the calculated values of b/d. The specifications are stated in terms of inequalities in order to eliminate solutions involving a fractional number of plates. The introduction of these inequalities usually leads to two or more combinations of N and M which both satisfy the specifications and minimize the total number of plates. The further restriction that N is to be minimized as well as the total number of plates reduces the number of solutions to one. A scheme for finding such a set of values for N and M is readily devised. One such is as follows. First let M be held fixed at the upper limit for the number of plates permitted for the stripping section. Then compute the values of b/d for the keys for different values of N until the smallest N that satisfies the separation specifications is found. Next, decrease the value of M by one and repeat the procedure described. Continuation of this process leads to the desired set of values of N and M for the given trial. The calculated d_i's and b_i's corresponding to this set of values for N and M are used as the corrected rates in the formulas for the calculation of the compositions. Also the distillate rate, D, for the next trial is taken equal to the sum of these d_i's. Corresponding to the particular set of values found for N and M, the temperatures and flow rates are found in the usual way. Then the procedure is repeated. In the addition and removal of plates, it is suggested that this be done within each section of the column at the point where

$$| \; T_{j+1} - T_j \; |$$

was a minimum for the previous trial. When the values for N and M and the temperatures do not change between successive trials, the desired solution has been found.

NOTATION

(See Chapters 7 through 14)

LITERATURE CITED

1. Abdel-Aal, H. K., R. G. Anthony, D. L. Taylor, and R. G. Wetherold, personal communication.

2. Erbar, J. H. and R. N. Maddox, "Latest Score: Reflux vs. Trays," *Petroleum Refiner*, **40,** No. 5; 183 (1961).

3. Harris, T. R., "Determination of Plate Efficiencies for Conventional Columns," M.S. thesis, A. and M. College of Texas, College Station, Texas, May 1962.

4. Peiser, A. M., "Better Computer Solution of Multicomponent System," *Chemical Engineering*, **67,** 129 (July 1960).

5. Taylor, D. L. (To be used as part of the research requirement for the Ph.D. degree at the A. and M. College of Texas).

Thermodynamics of Vapor-Liquid Equilibria of Multicomponent Mixtures

16

Many of the thermodynamic relationships for solutions are needed in order to describe various methods proposed for the correlation of vapor-liquid equilibria data. In this chapter certain of these relationships are developed. A knowledge of the thermodynamics of pure components is assumed. In view of this assumption the general development moves rapidly from the first and second laws to the resulting expressions for multicomponent mixtures. Particular attention is devoted to the partial molal quantities and to the fugacities of components in mixtures. All of the thermodynamic relationships needed in Chapter 17 for the correlation of vapor-liquid equilibria data are derived in this chapter.

THE FIRST AND SECOND LAWS OF THERMODYNAMICS

The first law (the energy of the universe is constant) implies that the internal energy function, E, is independent of path. As a consequence of the second law (heat does not of itself flow from a body of lower temperature to one of higher temperature), the entropy function, S, can be shown to be independent of path. For a pure component both the first and second laws are contained in the expression

$$dE = T \, dS - P \, dV \tag{16-1}$$

The expression "independent of path" has physical significance. With respect to vapor-liquid equilibria, it means that the internal energy, E, and the entropy, S, of a system depend only upon the state of the system as described by temperature, pressure, volume, and composition. The functions E and S are also independent of all previous states of the system.

Furthermore, such functions are independent of the history of the system, that is, of all processes which have been employed to change the system from one state to another.

In most applications only the difference in energy between two states of a system is required. Since the energy of a system depends upon the state of the system alone, the difference in energy, ΔE, of two states of a system is given by

$$\Delta E = E_2 - E_1 \qquad (16\text{--}2)$$

where E_1 and E_2 denote the energies of the system in the initial and final states, respectively. In view of this fact functions independent of path are also called "state functions." Functions of this type are also known by names such as, "potential functions," "exact differentials," and "point functions."

The function W (work) and the function Q (heat) are examples of the class of functions called "path functions."

From the standpoint of thermodynamics the most significant mathematical properties of state functions are summarized in the following statement. The necessary and sufficient condition that the line integral

$$I = \int_C M(x, y) \; dx + N(x, y) \; dy \qquad (16\text{--}3)$$

be independent of the path described by curve C is that

$$\partial M/\partial y = \partial N/\partial x \qquad (16\text{--}4)$$

This statement means two things. First, if the line integral I is independent of path, then $\partial M/\partial y = \partial N/\partial x$. Second, if $\partial M/\partial y = \partial N/\partial x$, then the line integral I is independent of path.

Properties of line integrals are described by Sokolnikoff *et al.* (8). Additional exercises are given at the end of this chapter.

Since the internal energy, E, is independent of path,

$$(\partial T/\partial V)_S = -(\partial P/\partial S)_V \qquad (16\text{--}5)$$

which follows from Equation (16–1). This is one of the well-known "Maxwell relations." For convenience these partial derivatives are referred to as the "cross-partials." Another useful property of line integrals is the following one. If the line integral I is independent of path, a function $f(x, y)$ exists such that

$$\partial f(x, y)/\partial x = M(x, y) \quad \text{and} \quad \partial f(x, y)/\partial y = N(x, y) \qquad (16\text{--}6)$$

Thus if I is independent of path, the integrand of Equation (16–3) is seen to be the exact differential of f; namely,

$$df = (\partial f/\partial x) \; dx + (\partial f/\partial y) \; dy$$

Also for such a function, Equation (16–4) states

$$\frac{\partial^2 f}{\partial y \; \partial x} = \frac{\partial^2 f}{\partial x \; \partial y} \qquad (16\text{–}7)$$

Therefore, if the line integral I depends upon path, a function f cannot be found which satisfies simultaneously both of the conditions of Equation (16–6). Equations (16–6) and (16–7) imply that the explicit statement of a function in terms of its independent variables assures its independence of path. Thus for any function I, $M(x, y)$ and $N(x, y)$ are independent of path. For example, suppose $f(x, y) = x^2 + y^2$. Then

$$df = 2x \; dx + 2y \; dy$$

$$\partial M/\partial y = \partial N/\partial x = 0$$

and the function $M = 2x$ is likewise independent of path.

Equation (16–1) implies that E is a function of the independent variables S and V. Thus,

$$dE = (\partial E/\partial S)_V \; dS + (\partial E/\partial V)_S \; dV \qquad (16\text{–}8)$$

Comparison of Equation (16–1) and (16–8) shows $(\partial E/\partial S)_V = T$ and $(\partial E/\partial V)_S = -P$. These relationships also follow from Equations (16–1) and (16–6).

In addition to the functions E and S, other thermodynamic functions in common use are as follows: the enthalpy H, the work function A, and the free energy G. These are also state functions and are defined by the following equations.

$$H = E + PV \qquad (16\text{–}9a)$$

$$A = E - TS \qquad (16\text{–}9b)$$

$$G = H - TS \qquad (16\text{–}9c)$$

Combination of these definitions with Equation (16–1) gives

$$dH = T \; dS + V \; dP \qquad (16\text{–}10a)$$

$$dA = -S \; dT - P \; dV \qquad (16\text{–}10b)$$

$$dG = -S \; dT + V \; dP \qquad (16\text{–}10c)$$

Each of these is an equivalent statement of the first and second laws of thermodynamics for a pure component.

Of these the free energy function G is the most convenient for the consideration of vapor-liquid equilibria because the independent variables P and T are those most easily and commonly measured in the laboratory. This dependence is represented symbolically by $G = G(P, T)$. Thus

$$dG = (\partial G/\partial T)_P \, dT + (\partial G/\partial P)_T \, dP \tag{16-11}$$

and comparison with Equation (16–10c) gives

$$(\partial G/\partial T)_P = -S \quad \text{and} \quad (\partial G/\partial P)_T = V \tag{16-12}$$

For a multicomponent mixture the total free energy is a function not only of P and T but the moles, n_i, of each component present in the mixture, $G = G(P, T, n_1, \ldots, n_c)$. The total differential is given by

$$dG = \left(\frac{\partial G}{\partial T}\right)_{P,n_i} dT + \left(\frac{\partial G}{\partial P}\right)_{T,n_i} dP + \sum_{i=1}^{c} \left(\frac{\partial G}{\partial n_i}\right)_{P,T,n_j} dn_i \tag{16-13}$$

The convention adopted is that the subscript n_i means that all of the n's are held fixed, and

$$(\partial G/\partial n_i)_{P,T,n_j} \quad \text{means} \quad (\partial G/\partial n_1)_{P,T,n_2,n_3,\ldots,n_c}$$

that is, j does not equal i. Since a pure component may be regarded as a mixture in which the composition is held constant, it follows from Equation (16–13) that

$$(\partial G/\partial T)_{P,n_i} = (\partial G/\partial T)_P = -S \quad \text{and} \quad (\partial G/\partial P)_{T,n_i} = (\partial G/\partial P)_T = V \tag{16-14}$$

In view of this result Equation (16–13) reduces to

$$dG = -S \, dT + V \, dP + \sum_{i=1}^{c} \bar{G}_i \, dn_i \tag{16-15}$$

where

$$\bar{G}_i = (\partial G/\partial n_i)_{P,T,n_j}$$

Equation (16–15) may be called the first and second laws of thermodynamics for multicomponent mixtures. The $\bar{G}_i$'s are called the partial molal quantities. The partial molal quantity $\bar{G}_i$ was introduced by Gibbs (2), who called it μ_i, the chemical potential. The physical significance of the partial molal quantities is best described by consideration of the variation of the volume of any solution with respect to the moles of any one of its constituents. After ideal and nonideal solutions have been examined, additional relationships involving the free energy functions are developed.

IDEAL AND NONIDEAL SOLUTIONS

Several equivalent definitions of ideal solutions exist; that is, any one of these may be taken as the definition and the others will follow as consequences. Thus the choice of a particular definition is largely a matter of personal preference. The definition taken here was selected because it describes a physical phenomenon which is easily visualized. Also, it leads to a logical introduction of partial molal volumes for the description of the volumetric behavior of ideal solutions. In addition this approach is helpful in the description of the properties of the partial molal quantities.

An ideal solution is defined simply as one which obeys Amagat's law of additive volumes. That is, the volume of an ideal solution at a given temperature and pressure is equal to the sum of the volumes of its pure constituents at the same temperature and pressure.

$$V = n_1 v_1 + n_2 v_2 + n_3 v_3 + \ldots + n_c v_c \qquad (16\text{--}16)$$

where

n_i = moles of component i; the total moles of solution is denoted by

$$n_T = \sum_{i=1}^{c} n_i$$

v_i = volume of one mole of pure component i at the temperature, T, and pressure, P, of the solution.

V = volume of n_T moles of solution at P and T.

By this definition volume is conserved when components that form an ideal solution are mixed. Many actual mixtures do not obey the simple relationship given by Equation (16–16). Because of the simplicity of this expression, to be able to express the variation of the volume of an actual solution by use of a similar expression would be desirable.

As pointed out by Guggenheim (4), the use of partial molal quantities produces a formula that is not only symmetrical to Equation (16–16) but also gives the correct volume of the mixture. This formula consists of Euler's theorem (8) for homogeneous functions. The extensive thermodynamic functions V, E, S, H, A, and G are all homogeneous of degree 1. This degree is assigned to that class of functions having the common property that

$$V(\lambda n_1, \lambda n_2, \lambda n_3, \ldots, \lambda n_c) = \lambda V(n_1, n_2, \ldots, n_c) \qquad (16\text{--}17)$$

where λ is any real number. For example, if the number of moles of each component in a mixture be doubled (at constant temperature and pressure), the volume of the resulting mixture is twice the initial volume. For such functions Euler's formula is

$$V = n_1\bar{V}_1 + n_2\bar{V}_2 + n_3\bar{V}_3 + \ldots + n_c\bar{V}_c \qquad (16\text{–}18)$$

where

$\bar{V}_i = (\partial V/\partial n_i)_{P,T,n_j}$

    = partial molal volume of component i; evaluated at the pressure, temperature, and composition of the mixture.

Although V is not homogeneous in the intensive variables P and T, it remains a function of these variables.

In the physical interpretation of the partial molal quantities, it is helpful to investigate their deviations with respect to the corresponding molal volumes of pure components at the same temperature and pressure. For an ideal solution, the deviation for each component is zero. This is readily shown by differentiating each side of Equation (16–16) with respect to n_k at a given temperature and pressure as follows:

$$\bar{V}_k = (\partial V/\partial n_k)_{P,T,n_j} = n_k(\partial v_k/\partial n_k)_{P,T,n_j} + v_k(\partial n_k/\partial n_k)_{P,T,n_j}$$

$$+ \sum_{i \neq k} \left(\frac{\partial n_i v_i}{\partial n_k}\right)_{P,T,n_j} \qquad (16\text{–}19)$$

Since v_i and all of the n_i's except n_k are independent of n_k, it follows that

$$\bar{V}_k = v_k(P,\ T) \qquad (16\text{–}20)$$

The representation, $v_k(P,\ T)$, is used to emphasize the fact that the molal volume of the pure component k is at most a function of P and T. Also, note that the equality given by Equation (16–20) holds for each component of the solution defined by Equation (16–16).

Physical significance of the molal and partial molal volumes is afforded by the following examples. First consider a solution whose volume is given by Equation (16–16). Suppose the moles of components 2 through c are held fixed, the moles of component 1 are varied from $n_1 = a$ to $n_1 = b$, and the temperature and pressure are held fixed. This process is represented by the straight line in Figure 16–1. The slope is then given by

$$\left(\frac{\partial V}{\partial n_1}\right)_{P,T,n_j} = \frac{(bv_1 + n_2v_2 \ldots + n_cv_c) - (av_1 + n_2v_2 + \ldots + n_cv_c)}{(b - a)}$$

$$= (b - a)v_1/(b - a) = v_1$$

or

$$\bar{V}_1 = v_1$$

For the case of a nonideal solution whose volume changes as shown in

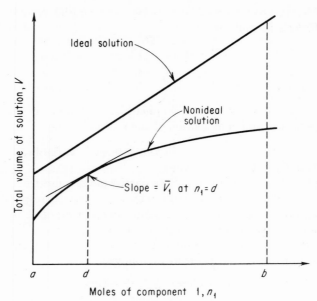

Figure 16–1. Variation of the volume of an ideal and a nonideal solution with respect to the moles of component 1 at constant pressure and temperature.

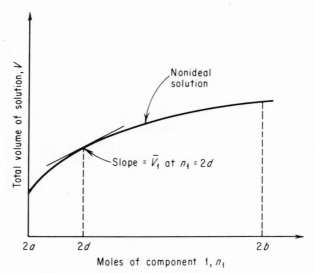

Figure 16–2. Variation of the volume of a nonideal solution containing the same components as the one in Fig. 16–1. Each V in Fig. 16–2 is twice as large as the corresponding V (nonideal solution) in Fig. 16–1 and contains twice as much of each component.

Figure 16–1, the slope of the curve at any given value of n_1 is the partial molal volume. The partial molal volumes depend only on the relative amounts of each component present. This fact is illustrated by comparison of the curves for the nonideal solution in Figures 16–1 and 16–2. In Figure 16–2 the initial solution (at $n_1 = 2a$) contains twice as much of each component as the initial solution (at $n_1 = a$) shown in Figure 16–1. The slope $\bar{V}_1$ at $n_1 = 2a$ in Figure 16–2 is equal to the slope $\bar{V}_1$ at $n_1 = a$ in Figure 16–1. The analytical proof of this property is readily established.*

CERTAIN FUNDAMENTAL RELATIONSHIPS OF THE PARTIAL MOLAL QUANTITIES

Because of the many existing relationships the following discussion is limited primarily to those that are needed in the consideration of vapor-liquid equilibria. In addition to being state functions, E, S, H, A, and G are also homogeneous functions of degree 1 with respect to the n_i's at any given temperature and pressure. At any given temperature and pressure these functions may be stated in terms of their partial molal quantities. For example,

$$H = \sum_{i=1}^{c} n_i \bar{H}_i; \quad S = \sum_{i=1}^{c} n_i \bar{S}_i; \quad G = \sum_{i=1}^{c} n_i \bar{G}_i \qquad (16\text{–}21)$$

* *Proposition*: The partial molal volumes, $\bar{V}_1$, $\bar{V}_2$, $\bar{V}_3$, $\cdots$, $\bar{V}_c$ for a solution containing $n_1, n_2, n_3, \cdots, n_c$ moles of components 1 through c are equal, respectively, to the partial molal volumes of a solution containing $\lambda n_1, \lambda n_2, \lambda n_3, \cdots, \lambda n_c$ moles of each component.

Proof: Since the volume of a solution is homogeneous of degree 1 in the n_i's,

$$V(\lambda n_1, \lambda n_2, \cdots, \lambda n_c) = \lambda V(n_1, n_2, \cdots, n_c)$$

For convenience let Z_i be defined by $Z_i = \lambda n_i$

For definiteness consider component 1. Differentiation of the first expression with respect to Z_1, yields,

$$\frac{\partial V(Z_1, \cdots, Z_c)}{\partial Z_1} = \frac{\lambda \partial V(n_1, \cdots, n_c)}{\partial n_1} \frac{\partial n_1}{\partial Z_1}$$

From the definition of Z_i it follows that

$$\partial n_1 / \partial Z_1 = 1/\lambda$$

Hence

$$\frac{\partial V(Z_1, \cdots, Z_c)}{\partial Z_1} = \frac{\partial V(n_1, \cdots, n_c)}{\partial n_1} = \bar{V}_1$$

Thus in general

$$\frac{\partial V(Z_1, \cdots, Z_c)}{\partial Z_i} = \frac{\partial V(n_1, \cdots, n_c)}{\partial n_i} = \bar{V}_i$$

The line integrals of state functions of several variables are independent of path (8), and Equation (16–4) and others analogous to it apply; that is, the cross-partials of the expression for the total differential are equal. Thus, from Equation (16–15), it follows that

$$(\partial \bar{G}_i / \partial T)_{P,n_i} = -(\partial S / \partial n_i)_{P,T,n_j} = -\bar{S}_i \qquad (16\text{--}22a)$$

$$(\partial \bar{G}_i / \partial P)_{T,n_i} = (\partial V / \partial n_i)_{P,T,n_j} = \bar{V}_i \qquad (16\text{--}22b)$$

and

$$(\partial \bar{G}_h / \partial n_k)_{P,T,n_j} = (\partial \bar{G}_k / \partial n_h)_{P,T,n_j} \qquad (16\text{--}22c)$$

These equations are recognized as the Maxwell relations. Also, in view of the discussion following Equation (16–7), it follows that the partial molal quantities are independent of path.

Another fundamental relationship, called the Gibbs-Duhem equation, is frequently used in the examination of experimental results of vapor-liquid equilibria. It is readily derived by commencing with Equation (16–15) and the expression for G as given by Equation (16–21). The total differential of G as given by Equation (16–21) is

$$dG = \sum_{i=1}^{c} n_i \, d\bar{G}_i + \sum_{i=1}^{c} \bar{G}_i \, dn_i \qquad (16\text{--}23)$$

Subtracting Equation (16–15) from (16–23) yields the well-known Gibbs-Duhem equation

$$0 = S \, dT - V \, dP + \sum_{i=1}^{c} n_i \, d\bar{G}_i \qquad (16\text{--}24)$$

At constant temperature and pressure, this expression reduces to the more familiar form,

$$\sum_{i=1}^{c} n_i \, d\bar{G}_i = 0 \qquad (16\text{--}25)$$

In subsequent developments two other forms of Equations (16–24) and (16–25) are required. In one of these, the partial derivatives of the $\bar{G}_i$ with respect to pressure are employed. Formally this expression is obtained by dividing each differential of Equation (16–24) by ∂P and writing

$$-V + \sum_{i=1}^{c} n_i (\partial \bar{G}_i / \partial P)_{T,n_i} = 0 \qquad (16\text{--}26)$$

The validity of this procedure follows from application of Equation (16–27). For convenience this formula for computing partial derivatives (6) is called the "chain rule." For this development consider the case of a pure component and the functions $G = G(P, T)$, $P = P(u, w)$, and

$T = T(u, w)$, where u and w are any pair of independent variables. The partial derivative of G with respect to u at constant w as given by the chain rule is

$$(\partial G/\partial u)_w = (\partial G/\partial P)_T(\partial P/\partial u)_w + (\partial G/\partial T)_P(\partial T/\partial u)_w \qquad (16\text{-}27)$$

In view of Equation (16-12) this expression reduces to

$$(\partial G/\partial u)_w = -S(\partial T/\partial u)_w + V(\partial P/\partial u)_w \qquad (16\text{-}28)$$

This same result may be obtained from Equation (16-10c) by use of the formal procedure used to obtain Equation (16-26). Hence the operational or algebraic property of ∂u is established.

The Gibbs-Duhem equation stated in the form

$$\sum_{i=1}^{c} n_i \left(\frac{\partial \bar{G}_i}{\partial n_1} \right)_{P,T,n_j} = 0 \qquad (16\text{-}29)$$

is used extensively in Chapter 17 in the treatment of activity coefficients. This expression is developed from Equation (16-25) in a manner analogous to that described for Equation (16-26). Physical significance may be attached to the partial derivatives appearing in Equation (16-29) by construction of the following graphs. From a plot of G versus n_1, the slope of the resulting curve at any given n_1 gives the partial molal free energy, $\bar{G}_1$, in the same manner as illustrated for volume in Figure 16-1. Then a plot of these slopes, $\bar{G}_1$'s, versus n_1 may be made. The slope of the curve so obtained at any given n_1 is

$$(\partial \bar{G}_1/\partial n_1)_{P,T,n_j}$$

Since $\bar{G}_1$ is a function of the composition alone (at any given P and T) plotting $\bar{G}_1$ versus x_1 might appear more desirable. However, confusion is likely to arise, particularly in the interpretation of the partial derivatives because, if x_1 is varied, x_2 through x_c cannot be held constant. The possibility of confusion is avoided by differentiating with respect to n_1 rather than x_1 because it is clear that n_1 may be varied when n_2 through n_c are held fixed. However, in a subsequent section, the partial derivatives of Equation (16-29) are stated in terms of mole fractions and properly interpreted.

A relationship exists between the partial molal free energy, $\bar{G}_i$, and the partial molal enthalpy, $\bar{H}_i$. This relationship is developed as follows. Equations (16-9a) through (16-9c) also serve as the definitions for the functions H, A, and G for mixtures as well as pure components. Partial differentiation of each member of Equation (16-9c) with respect to n_i at constant temperature and pressure yields

$$\bar{G}_i = \bar{H}_i - T\bar{S}_i \qquad (16\text{-}30)$$

Elimination of $\bar{S}_i$ by use of Equation (16–22a) yields

$$\frac{1}{T}\left(\frac{\partial \bar{G}_i}{\partial T}\right)_{P,n_i} - \frac{\bar{G}_i}{T^2} = -\frac{\bar{H}_i}{T^2} \qquad (16\text{–}31)$$

Since it is readily confirmed by differentiation that

$$\left(\frac{\partial \bar{G}_i/T}{\partial T}\right)_{P,n_i} = -\frac{\bar{G}_i}{T^2} + \frac{1}{T}\left(\frac{\partial \bar{G}_i}{\partial T}\right)_{P,n_i}$$

Equation (16–31) reduces to

$$\left(\frac{\partial \bar{G}_i/T}{\partial T}\right)_{P,n_i} = -\frac{\bar{H}_i}{T^2} \qquad (16\text{–}32)$$

THE PERFECT GAS MIXTURE

In this section the relationship between the partial molal free energy and the partial pressure of a component in a perfect gas mixture is de-

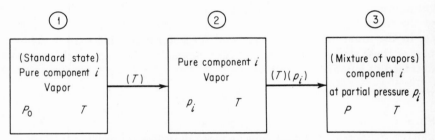

Figure 16–3. Alternate path for the calculation of the change in the partial molal free energy in going from the standard state to the mixture of vapors.

veloped. A perfect gas mixture is defined as one for which the molal volume of each component present in the mixture is given by

$$v_i^v = RT/P \qquad (16\text{–}33)$$

The volume of the mixture is

$$V = \sum_{i=1}^{c} n_i v_i^v = (RT/P)\sum_{i=1}^{c} n_i \qquad (16\text{–}34)$$

Note that the definition of a perfect gas mixture is more restrictive than the definition of an ideal solution. Equation (16–33) requires the molal volumes of each component to be the same function of P and T; whereas, Equation (16–16) permits each v_i to be a different function of P and T.

The difference between the partial molal free energy for a component in its standard state and in a mixture is independent of path and may be evaluated by use of any path such as the one shown in Figure 16–3. Although the standard state of each component is arbitrary (denoted by P_0), it is usually taken to be the pure component in the vapor state at the temperature and total pressure of the mixture ($P_0 = P$).

In Figure 16–3 the variables held fixed in going from one state to another are enclosed in parenthesis. The changes in the partial molal free energy are as follows.

States ① → ②:

$$G_i^v(p_i, T) - G_i^v(P_0, T) = \int_{P_0}^{p_i} v_i^v \, dP = \int_{P_0}^{p_i} \frac{RT}{P} \, dP = RT \ln \frac{p_i}{P_0}$$

States ② → ③:*

$$\bar{G}_i^v(P, T) - G_i^v(p_i, T) = \int_{p_i}^{p_i} v_i^v \, dP = 0$$

Summing the free energy changes yields

$$\bar{G}_i^v(P, T) = G_i^v(P_0, T) + RT \ln (p_i/P_0)$$

When the particular standard state pressure $P_0 = P$ is selected, this expression becomes

$$\bar{G}_i^v(P, T) = G_i^v(P, T) + RT \ln (p_i/P) \qquad (16\text{–}35)$$

which reduces to

$$\bar{G}_i^v(P, T) = G_i^v(P, T) + RT \ln y_i \qquad (16\text{–}36)$$

since the definition of p_i is taken to be

$$p_i = Py_i$$

* Although $\bar{G}_i^v$ may be a function of c values of y_i in addition to P and T, in the interest of brevity this fact is not included in the functional notation $\bar{G}_i^v(P, T)$. Assume that

$$\bar{G}_i^v(P, T) = \bar{G}_i^v(P, T, y_1, y_2, \cdots, y_c)$$

The "bar" suffices to distinguish the partial molal quantities from the G_i's for the pure components. The latter are, of course, functions of P and T alone.

IMPERFECT GAS MIXTURES

The definition of the fugacity which is used to describe imperfect gas mixtures is suggested by consideration of an alternate form of Equation (16–35), obtained by partial differentiation of each member of this equation with respect to P to give

$$\left(\frac{\partial \bar{G}_i^v}{\partial P}\right)_{T,n_i} = \left(\frac{\partial G_i^v}{\partial P}\right)_T + RT\left(\frac{\partial \ln p_i}{\partial P}\right)_{T,n_i} - RT\left(\frac{\partial \ln P}{\partial P}\right)_T$$

$$= \frac{RT}{P} + RT\left(\frac{\partial \ln p_i}{\partial P}\right)_{T,n_i} - \frac{RT}{P}$$

Hence

$$(\partial \bar{G}_i^v/\partial P)_{T,n_i} = RT(\partial \ln p_i/\partial P)_{T,n_i} \tag{16–37}$$

For an imperfect gas mixture the left hand side of Equation (16–37) is equal to $\bar{V}_i^v$, but the right hand side is equal to $v_i^v = RT/P$. A new variable, the fugacity $\bar{f}_i^v$ of a component in a mixture, is defined such that it is always in agreement with both the derivative of $\bar{G}_i^v$ with respect to P and $\bar{V}_i^v$ as follows:

$$(\partial \bar{G}_i^v/\partial P)_{T,n_i} = RT(\partial \ln \bar{f}_i^v/\partial P)_{T,n_i} \tag{16–38}$$

Hence

$$\bar{V}_i^v = RT(\partial \ln \bar{f}_i^v/\partial P)_{T,n_i} \tag{16–39}$$

When the standard state of any component i in the mixture is taken to be the pure component (in the vapor state) at the temperature T and the total pressure P of the mixture, the difference between the partial molal free energy of component i in the mixture and in its standard state may be calculated by use of a path analogous to the one shown in Figure 16–3 to give

$$\bar{G}_i^v(P, T) = G_i^v(P, T) + RT \ln (\bar{f}_i^v/f_i^v) \tag{16–40}$$

where

$G_i^v(P, T)$ = free energy of one mole of the pure component i evaluated at the standard state conditions, P and T

f_i^v = fugacity of pure component i evaluated at the standard state conditions, P and T

$\bar{f}_i^v$ = fugacity of the pure component i in the mixture evaluated at the total pressure P and temperature T of the mixture.

For a pure component in the vapor phase, the fugacity is defined* by

$$(\partial G_i^v/\partial P)_T = RT(\partial \ln f_i^v/\partial P)_T \qquad (16\text{--}41a)$$

and

$$\lim_{P \to 0} (f_i^v/P) = 1 \qquad (16\text{--}41b)$$

By subtracting Equation (16–35) from (16–40) and then taking the limit as P goes to zero, it follows that

$$\lim_{P \to 0} (\bar{f}_i^v/p_i) = 1 \qquad (16\text{--}42)$$

THE LEWIS AND RANDALL RULE FOR THE VAPOR PHASE

Since an ideal solution will be defined in terms of its volumetric behavior, the Lewis and Randall rule (5) should follow as a consequence of

* Alternately, the fugacity of a pure component in the vapor phase may be defined by the equation:

$$G^v = RT \ln f^v + B(T) \qquad (A)$$

where $B(T)$ is the constant of integration obtained by integration of the second expression given by Equation (16–12) for a perfect gas $(Pv = RT)$; namely,

$$G^v = RT \ln P + B(T) \qquad (B)$$

On the basis of this definition and the experimental fact that actual gases approach perfect gases as P tends to zero, that the relationship given by Equation (16–41b) follows as a consequence can be shown.

Proof:

For any known value G^v for an actual substance, a function $\epsilon(P)$ exists such that the correct value of the free energy is given by

$$G^v = RT \ln P + B(T) + \epsilon(P) \qquad (C)$$

From the definition of $\epsilon(P)$, note that for a perfect gas

$$\epsilon(P) = 0$$

for all P. Since all gases become perfect as P approaches zero, it follows that

$$\lim_{P \to 0} \epsilon(P) = 0 \qquad (D)$$

Also from the definition of $\epsilon(P)$, the same value of G^v is given by Equations (A) and (C) for actual substances. Subtraction of Equation (C) from (A) yields

$$RT \ln(P/f^v) = \epsilon(P) \qquad (E)$$

Taking the limit of both sides of Equation (E) as P approaches zero gives the desired result, Equation (16–41b).

this definition. That it does is shown as follows. Partial differentiation of each member of Equation (16–40) with respect to P yields

$$\left(\frac{\partial \bar{G}_i^v}{\partial P}\right)_{T,ni} = \left(\frac{\partial G_i^v}{\partial P}\right)_T + RT\left(\frac{\partial \ln \bar{f}_i^v/f_i^v}{\partial P}\right)_{T,ni}$$

For an ideal solution this expression reduces to

$$v_i^v(P,\ T) = v_i^v(P,\ T) + RT\left(\frac{\partial \ln \bar{f}_i^v/f_i^v}{\partial P}\right)_{T,ni}$$

Thus

$$\left(\frac{\partial \ln \bar{f}_i^v/f_i^v}{\partial P}\right)_{T,ni} = 0 \qquad (16\text{–}43)$$

This equation shows that when the temperature and composition of a mixture are held fixed, the ratio $\bar{f}_i^v/f_i^v$ is independent of pressure. At any given temperature, the general solution of Equation (16–43) is

$$\bar{f}_i^v/f_i^v = \eta_i(y_1,\ \ldots,\ y_c) \qquad (16\text{–}44)$$

A more precise expression for η_i is given by recalling that the limit of $\bar{f}_i^v/f_i^v$ as P goes to zero is y_i; that is,

$$\lim_{P\to 0} \bar{f}_i^v/f_i^v = y_i = \lim_{P\to 0} \eta_i$$

But since $\bar{f}_i^v/f_i^v$ and η_i are independent of P, the following relationship holds at all pressures,

$$\bar{f}_i^v/f_i^v = y_i,\quad \bar{f}_i^v = f_i^v y_i \qquad (16\text{–}45)$$

This is the well-known Lewis and Randall rule for an ideal solution of gases. When this result is substituted into Equation (16–40), the expression

$$\bar{G}_i^v(P,\ T) = G_i^v(P,\ T) + RT \ln y_i \qquad (16\text{–}46)$$

is obtained.

THE LEWIS AND RANDALL RULE FOR THE LIQUID PHASE

In the development that follows, the hypothetical state of a liquid at zero pressure is encountered. Although hypothetical states are perfectly permissible for state functions, it is necessary to define the properties of the mixture in this state because they cannot be determined experimentally. Although the definition of a hypothetical state is arbitrary, once selected it must be retained for all subsequent developments. Thus the properties of a liquid mixture at zero pressure are by definition the same as those of a perfect gas mixture.

In the treatment of vapor-liquid equilibria, the standard state of each component in the liquid mixture is commonly taken as the pure component in the liquid state at the same temperature and pressure as that of the mixture. The difference in the partial molal free energy between the two states is independent of path; it may be calculated by use of a path analogous to the one shown in Figure 16–3. The result

$$\bar{G}_i^L(P, T) = G_i^L(P, T) + RT \ln \bar{f}_i^L / f_i^L \tag{16–47}$$

is readily obtained. This relationship together with the definition of an ideal solution, Equation (16–16), may be used to obtain the Lewis and Randall rule for a pure component in a liquid mixture.

Again, partial differentiation with respect to pressure yields a result analogous to the one given by Equation (16–43). In view of the definition selected for the hypothetical state of a liquid at zero pressure, it follows that

$$\lim_{P \to 0} \bar{f}_i^L / f_i^L = x_i$$

Hence $\bar{f}_i^L / f_i^L = x_i$ at all pressures and gives the desired result

$$\bar{f}_i^L = f_i^L x_i \tag{16–48}$$

Combination of Equations (16–47) and (16–48) give another useful relationship for an ideal solution of liquids,

$$\bar{G}_i^L(P, T) = G_i^L(P, T) + RT \ln x_i \tag{16–49}$$

PHYSICAL EQUILIBRIUM

The necessary conditions for any mixture (nonideal or ideal) of components in each of two phases to be in equilibrium may be taken as follows:

$$T^v = T^L$$

$$P^v = P^L \tag{16–50}$$

$$\bar{G}_i^v = \bar{G}_i^L$$

Beginning with equations of this type, the Gibbs phase rule,

$$\mathcal{P} + \mathcal{V} = c + 2 \tag{16–51}$$

where

$\mathcal{P}$ = number of phases
$\mathcal{V}$ = degrees of freedom
c = number of components

may be deduced as shown by Denbigh (1).

Note that since the fugacity $\bar{f}_i$ of a component in a mixture (vapor or liquid) is defined by a partial differential equation, Equation (16–38),*

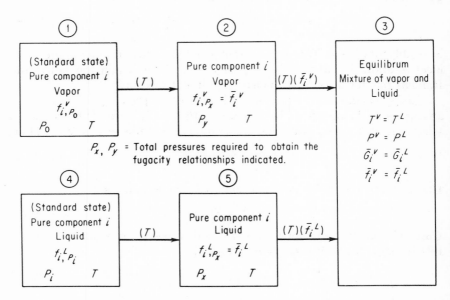

Figure 16–4. Paths used to develop Equations (19–53) and (16–54).

it does not follow immediately that

$$\bar{f}_i^v = \bar{f}_i^L \qquad\qquad (16\text{–}52)$$

For example, if $y = x + 2$, then $dy = dx$, but certainly y is not equal to x. The equality given by Equation (16–52) will be shown to follow as a consequence of the definition of the fugacity, Equation (16–38), and the necessary conditions for equilibrium, Equation (16–50). Furthermore, Equation (16–52) holds regardless of the standard state selected for each component. Gilmont (3) has shown that a sufficient condition for Equa-

---

* The definition of fugacity of a component in a liquid mixture is obtained by replacing the superscript v in this equation by the superscript L.

tion (16–52) to apply is that the same standard state be selected for a component in the liquid phase as that chosen for the pure component in the vapor phase.

For definiteness, suppose the standard state of component i in the vapor phase is taken to be the pure component in the vapor state at a pressure P_o (which differs from the pressure P of the equilibrium mixture) and at the same temperature as the equilibrium mixture. Also, for definiteness let the standard state be taken as the pure component in the liquid state at its vapor pressure P_i at the temperature T of the system. Since $\bar{G}_i$ is independent of path, the difference in free energy between a compo-

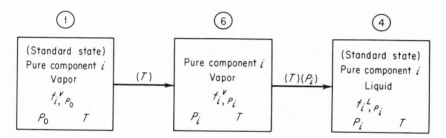

Figure 16–5. Path used to go from the standard state of a component in the vapor phase to the standard state of the same component in the liquid phase.

nent in the equilibrium mixture and in its standard state may be calculated by use of the paths shown in Figure 16–4 and Equation (16–39). The change in the free energy along the path ① → ② → ③ is given by

$$\bar{G}_i^v(P,\, T) = G_i^v(P_0,\, T) + RT \ln\,(\bar{f}_i^v / f_{i,P_0}^v) \qquad (16\text{–}53)$$

If a fugacity is to be evaluated at a pressure other than the equilibrium pressure P, the particular pressure is carried as the second subscript.

For the path ④ → ⑤ → ③, it is readily shown that

$$\bar{G}_i^L(P,\, T) = \bar{G}_i^L(P_i,\, T) + RT \ln\,(\bar{f}_i^L / f_{i,P_i}^L) \qquad (16\text{–}54)$$

In order to complete the proof of the equality given by Equation (16–52), a relationship must be obtained between the free energy of a component in standard state ① and in standard state ④. The desired relationship may be obtained by use of the path between the standard states

① and ④ as shown in Figure 16–5. For this path the following results are obtained.

States ① → ⑥

$$G_i^v(P_i,\ T) - G_i^v(P_0,\ T) = RT \ln (f_{i,P_i}^v / f_{i,P_0}^v) \qquad (16\text{–}55)$$

States ⑥ → ④

$$G_i^L(P_i,\ T) - G_i^v(P_i,\ T) = RT \ln (f_{i,P_i}^L / f_{i,P_i}^v) \qquad (16\text{–}56)$$

For a pure component at a pressure equal to its vapor pressure at the temperature T, the vapor and liquid phases are in equilibrium, and Equation (16–50) reduces to

$$G_i^v(P,\ T) = G_i^L(P_i,\ T) \qquad (16\text{–}57)$$

Therefore, it follows from Equation (16–56) that

$$f_{i,P_i}^v = f_{i,P_i}^L \qquad (16\text{–}58)$$

In view of these relationships Equation (16–55) may be rewritten in the form

$$G_i^L(P_i,\ T) - G_i^v(P_0,\ T) = RT \ln (f_{i,P_i}^L / f_{i,P_0}^v) \qquad (16\text{–}59)$$

For a component in vapor and liquid mixtures which are in equilibrium at P and T,

$$\bar{G}_i^v(P,\ T) = \bar{G}_i^L(P,\ T)$$

by Equation (16–50). Thus the right hand sides of Equations (16–53) and (16–54) are equal. Hence

$$G_i^L(P_i,\ T) - G_i^v(P_0,\ T) = RT \ln (\bar{f}_i^v / \bar{f}_i^L)\,(f_{i,P_i}^L / f_{i,P_0}^v) \qquad (16\text{–}60)$$

Since the left hand sides of Equations (16–59) and (16–60) are equal,

$$(\bar{f}_i^v / \bar{f}_i^L)\,(f_{i,P_i}^L / f_{i,P_0}^v) = f_{i,P_i}^L / f_{i,P_0}^v \qquad (16\text{–}61)$$

from which the desired result, Equation (16–52), is readily obtained.

Note that when the pressure of the equilibrium mixture is taken as the pressure for each of the standard states, Equation (16–59) becomes

$$G_i^L(P,\ T) - G_i^v(P,\ T) = RT \ln f_i^L / f_i^v \qquad (16\text{–}62)$$

which is referred to in subsequent developments.

DEFINITION OF THE EQUILIBRIUM CONSTANT K_i FOR VAPOR-LIQUID EQUILIBRIA

For any component i, K_i is defined as follows:

$$K_i = y_i/x_i \qquad (16\text{--}63)$$

When defined in this way, K_i is independent of the standard states selected for a component in the vapor and liquid phases.

When both the vapor and liquid phases are ideal solutions, K_i is shown to be independent of composition and a function of P and T alone in the following manner. Since at equilibrium, the left hand sides of Equations (16–46) and (16–49) are equal, the right hand sides may be equated to give

$$G_i^L(P,\ T) + RT \ln x_i = G_i^v(P,\ T) + RT \ln y_i$$

When this expression is solved for $y_i/x_i = K_i$, the result

$$K_i = \exp \frac{G_i^L(P,\ T) - G_i^v(P,\ T)}{RT} \qquad (16\text{--}64)$$

is obtained. The molal free energies of a pure component are independent of composition; therefore, the right hand side of Equation (16–64) is a function of P and T alone. Therefore, for an ideal solution (vapor and liquid), K_i is a function only of P and T. In the investigations described in Chapters 2 through 15, K_i was taken to be independent of composition and a function of P and T alone.

When both the vapor and liquid phases of an equilibrium mixture are nonideal solutions, K_i is found to be a function of both the vapor and liquid compositions. For the case of a nonideal vapor solution, partial differentiation of Equation (16–40) with respect to pressure leads to

$$\bar{V}_i^v(P,\ T) - v_i^v(P,\ T) = RT \left(\frac{\partial \ln \bar{f}_i^v/f_i^v}{\partial P} \right)_{T,n_i} \qquad (16\text{--}65)$$

Since the left hand side of this expression is a function of P, T and the composition of the vapor, the right hand side is a function of the same variables. Thus a general solution may be stated in the form

$$\bar{f}_i^v/f_i^v = y_i\gamma_i^v(P,\ T,\ y_1,\ y_2,\ \ldots,\ y_c)$$

or simply

$$\bar{f}_i^v/f_i^v = y_i\gamma_i^v \qquad (16\text{--}66)$$

Note that the left hand side of Equation (16–66) has the limit y_i as P approaches zero. Thus it follows that

$$\lim_{P \to 0} \gamma_i^v = 1$$

For a component in a nonideal liquid, the expression

$$\bar{f}_i^L / f_i^L = x_i \gamma_i^L \tag{16–67}$$

where

$$\gamma_i^L = \gamma_i^L(P, T, x_1, \ldots, x_c)$$

is obtained in a manner analogous to that shown for Equation (16–66). Equation (16–47) is taken as the starting point in the development of Equation (16–67).

Since $\bar{f}_i^L = \bar{f}_i^v$ at equilibrium, Equation (16–66) and (16–67) may be combined to give

$$\gamma_i^v f_i^v y_i = \gamma_i^L f_i^L x_i \tag{16–68}$$

or

$$K_i = \gamma_i^L f_i^L / \gamma_i^v f_i^v \tag{16–69}$$

Equations (16–66) and (16–67) may be rearranged to give the following expressions for the activity coefficients:

$$\gamma_i^v = \bar{f}_i^v / f_i^v y_i \tag{16–70}$$

$$\gamma_i^L = \bar{f}_i^L / f_i^L x_i \tag{16–71}$$

Integral expressions for these activity coefficients are obtained as follows. Integration of Equation (16–65) is indicated by

$$\int_0^P \left(\frac{\partial \ln \bar{f}_i^v / f_i^v}{\partial P} \right)_{T, n_i} dP = \frac{1}{RT} \int_0^P (\bar{V}_i^v - v_i^v) \, dP \tag{16–72}$$

which gives

$$\ln \gamma_i^v = \ln \frac{\bar{f}_i^v}{f_i^v y_i} = \frac{1}{RT} \int_0^P (\bar{V}_i^v - v_i^v) \, dP \tag{16–73}$$

since $\bar{f}_i^v / f_i^v$ has the limit y_i as P approaches zero. Similarly, for a component in the liquid phase,

$$\ln \gamma_i^L = \ln \frac{\bar{f}_i^L}{f_i^L x_i} = \frac{1}{RT} \int_0^P (\bar{V}_i^L - v_i^L) \, dP \tag{16–74}$$

RELATIONSHIP OF THE ENTHALPY OF A COMPONENT TO ITS FUGACITY AND ACTIVITY

In the investigation of the convergence methods, the enthalpy of each phase was calculated by use of the formula for an ideal solution. For any component of an ideal solution of vapor, Equation (16–46) applies. This expression may be rearranged to give,

$$\frac{\bar{G}_i^v(P, T)}{T} = \frac{G_i^v(P, T)}{T} + R \ln y_i \tag{16-75}$$

Partial differentiation with respect to T yields

$$\left(\frac{\partial \bar{G}_i^v / T}{\partial T}\right)_{P, n_i} = \left(\frac{\partial G_i^v / T}{\partial T}\right)_P \tag{16-76}$$

Since the left hand side of this expression is equal to $(-\bar{H}_i^v / T^2)$ and the right hand side is equal to $(-H_i^v / T^2)$, the result

$$\bar{H}_i^v = H_i^v \tag{16-77}$$

follows. Hence

$$H^v = \sum_{i=1}^c n_i \bar{H}_i^v = \sum_{i=1}^c n_i H_i^v \tag{16-78}$$

Similarly, for an ideal liquid solution,

$$\bar{H}_i^L = H_i^L \tag{16-79}$$

and

$$H^L = \sum_{i=1}^c n_i \bar{H}_i^L = \sum_{i=1}^c n_i H_i^L \tag{16-80}$$

where

H_i^v, H_i^L = enthalpy of one mole of vapor and of one mole of liquid, respectively, of component i, evaluated at the temperature and pressure of the respective mixtures.

Actually, the effect of pressure on H_i^v and H_i^L was also neglected in the solution of most of the illustrative examples presented in Chapters 2 through 15.

The partial molal enthalpies of nonideal solutions of vapor and liquid are related to their respective fugacities as follows. Division of each member of the expression for the nonideal vapor, Equation (16–40) by T

followed by partial differentiation with respect to T yields,

$$\left(\frac{\partial \bar{G}_i^v / T}{\partial T}\right)_{P,ni} - \left(\frac{\partial G_i^v / T}{\partial T}\right)_P = R\left(\frac{\partial \ln \bar{f}_i^v / f_i^v}{\partial T}\right)_{P,ni}$$

In view of Equation (16–32), the left hand side reduces to

$$-\left(\frac{\bar{H}_i^v - H_i^v}{RT^2}\right) = \left(\frac{\partial \ln \bar{f}_i^v / f_i^v}{\partial T}\right)_{P,ni} \tag{16–81}$$

The right hand side of Equation (16–81) may be stated in other forms. Since y_i is held constant in the partial differentiation with respect to T, it is evident that

$$-\left(\frac{\bar{H}_i^v - H_i^v}{RT^2}\right) = \left(\frac{\partial \ln \bar{f}_i^v / (f_i^v y_i)}{\partial T}\right)_{P,ni} = \left(\frac{\partial \ln \gamma_i^v}{\partial T}\right)_{P,ni} \tag{16–82}$$

The last equality follows from the definition of γ_i^v, Equation (16–70).

Similarly, for a component in the liquid phase, a development analogous to the one shown for the vapor leads to the results

$$-\left(\frac{\bar{H}_i^L - H_i^L}{RT^2}\right) = \left(\frac{\partial \ln \bar{f}_i^L / f_i^L}{\partial T}\right)_{P,ni} \tag{16–83}$$

and

$$-\left(\frac{\bar{H}_i^L - H_i^L}{RT^2}\right) = \left(\frac{\partial \ln \bar{f}_i^L / f_i^L x_i}{\partial T}\right)_{P,ni} = \left(\frac{\partial \ln \gamma_i^L}{\partial T}\right)_{P,ni} \tag{16–84}$$

Other relationships involving the activity follow.

THERMODYNAMIC RELATIONSHIPS OF THE ACTIVITY COEFFICIENTS

In the development of these relationships the liquid phase is used. Because of the nature of the liquid phase, it generally deviates from an ideal solution far more than does the gas phase. As discussed in the next chapter, several empirical expressions consisting of power series in the compositions have been proposed for the correlation of the experimentally determined activity coefficients at a given temperature and pressure.

These series may be of any arbitrary form provided they satisfy the Gibbs-Duhem equation. In order to test (or select) these series, a statement of the Gibbs-Duhem equation in terms of activity coefficients is needed. This expression is developed by commencing with Equation

(16–29). The partial derivatives appearing in this equation are evaluated by use of the following expression.

$$\bar{G}_i^L(P, T, x_1, \ldots, x_c) = G_i^L(P, T) + RT \ln \gamma_i^L x_i \qquad (16\text{–}85)$$

which was obtained from Equation (16–47) and (16–67). Since $G_i^L(P, T)$ is independent of composition, it follows that

$$\left(\frac{\partial \bar{G}_i^L}{\partial n_1}\right)_{P,T,nj} = RT \left[\left(\frac{\partial \ln \gamma_i^L}{\partial n_1}\right)_{P,T,nj} + \left(\frac{1}{x_i}\right)\left(\frac{\partial x_i}{\partial n_1}\right)_{P,T,nj}\right]$$

Substitution of this expression into Equation (16–29) produces

$$RT \sum_{i=1}^{c} n_i \left(\frac{\partial \ln \gamma_i^L}{\partial n_1}\right)_{P,T,nj} + RT \sum_{i=1}^{c} \left(\frac{n_i}{x_i}\right)\left(\frac{\partial x_i}{\partial n_1}\right)_{P,T,nj} = 0 \qquad (16\text{–}86)$$

Since

$$\frac{n_i}{x_i} = \frac{x_i n_T}{x_i} = n_T, \quad x_1 = \frac{n_1}{n_1 + n_2 + \ldots + n_c}$$

$$x_2 = \frac{n_2}{n_1 + n_2 + \ldots + n_c}, \quad \ldots, \quad x_c = \frac{n_c}{n_1 + n_2 + \ldots + n_c}$$

then

$$\left(\frac{\partial x_1}{\partial n_1}\right)_{T,P,n_j} = -\frac{n_1}{n_T^2} + \frac{1}{n_T} = \frac{n_T - n_1}{n_T^2}$$

$$(\partial x_2/\partial n_1)_{T,P,n_j} = -n_2/n_T^2$$

$$\vdots \qquad \vdots \qquad \vdots$$

$$(\partial x_c/\partial n_1)_{T,P,n_j} = -n_c/n_T^2$$

Thus

$$\sum_{i=1}^{c} \left(\frac{n_i}{x_i}\right)\left(\frac{\partial x_i}{\partial n_1}\right)_{T,P,nj} = n_T \left(\frac{n_T - n_1}{n_T^2}\right) + n_T \left(\frac{-n_2}{n_T^2}\right)$$

$$+ \ldots + n_T \left(\frac{-n_{c-1}}{n_T^2}\right) + n_T \left(\frac{-n_c}{n_T^2}\right) = \frac{n_T - n_1 - n_2 - \ldots - n_c}{n_T} = 0$$

Hence Equation (16–86) reduces to the Gibbs-Duhem equation.

$$\sum_{i=1}^{c} n_i \left(\frac{\partial \ln \gamma_i^L}{\partial n_1}\right)_{P,T,n_j} = 0 \qquad (16\text{–}87)$$

This expression may be stated in terms of mole fractions. First, division of each term by n_T gives

$$\sum_{i=1}^{c} x_i \left(\frac{\partial \ln \gamma_i^L}{\partial n_1} \right)_{P,T,n_j} = 0 \qquad (16\text{–}88)$$

Next, apply the chain rule to obtain

$$(\partial \ln \gamma_i^L / \partial n_1)_{P,T,n_j} = (\partial \ln \gamma_i^L / \partial x_1)_{P,T,n_j} (\partial x_1 / \partial n_1)_{P,T,n_j}$$

$$= (\partial \ln \gamma_i^L / \partial x_1)_{P,T,n_j} [(n_T - n_1/n_T^2)]$$

When this result is substituted into Equation (16–88), the following form of the Gibbs-Duhem equation is obtained.

$$\sum_{i=1}^{c} x_i \left(\frac{\partial \ln \gamma_i^L}{\partial x_1} \right)_{P,T,n_j} = 0 \qquad (16\text{–}89)$$

This formula implies that x_1 is changed by changing n_1 while holding n_2 through n_c fixed. Actually, this type of variation is more restrictive than is necessary. A more general result is obtained as follows.

Suppose the total number of moles, n_T, of the mixture is held fixed, and that for any given variation in n_1, the quantities n_2 through n_c are to be varied in any arbitrary manner whatsoever subject only to the condition that n_T is fixed. Since

$$n_1 + n_2 + n_3 + \ldots + n_c = n_T$$

partial differentiation for this case yields

$$1 + \frac{\partial (n_2 + n_3 + \ldots + n_c)}{\partial n_1} = 0 \qquad (16\text{–}90)$$

Observe that although the individual variations

$$\partial n_2 / \partial n_1, \quad \partial n_3 / \partial n_1, \ldots, \quad \partial n_c / \partial n_1$$

are arbitrary, the value of their sum is fixed by the relationship given by Equation (16–90).

The general development for this case is formally the same as before—down to Equation (16–86). Commencing at this point,

$$\sum_{i=1}^{c} n_i \left(\frac{\partial \ln \gamma_i^L}{\partial n_1} \right)_{P,T,n_T} + \sum_{i=1}^{c} \left(\frac{n_i}{x_i} \right) \left(\frac{\partial x_i}{\partial n_1} \right)_{P,T,n_T} = 0 \qquad (16\text{–}91)$$

But

$$\left(\frac{\partial x_1}{\partial n_1} \right)_{P,T,n_T} = \frac{1}{n_T}; \quad \text{and} \quad \left(\frac{\partial x_i}{\partial n_1} \right)_{P,T,n_T} = \frac{1}{n_T} \left(\frac{\partial n_i}{\partial n_1} \right)_{P,T,n_T} \quad \text{for } i = 2, 3, \ldots, c$$

Thus the second summation of Equation (16–91) has the value

$$\sum_{i=1}^{c} \left(\frac{n_i}{x_i}\right)\left(\frac{\partial x_i}{\partial n_1}\right)_{P,T,nT} = 1 + \left(\frac{\partial(n_2 + \ldots + n_c)}{\partial n_1}\right)_{P,T,nT} = 1 - 1 = 0$$

$$(16\text{–}92)$$

Hence Equation (16–91) reduces to the following form of the Gibbs-Duhem equation:

$$\sum_{i=1}^{c} n_i(\partial \ln \gamma_i^L/\partial n_1)_{P,T,n_T} = 0 \qquad (16\text{–}93)$$

Following a development similar to that used to obtain Equation (16–89) yields

$$\sum_{i=1}^{c} x_i(\partial \ln \gamma_i^L/\partial x_1)_{P,T,n_T} = 0 \qquad (16\text{–}94)$$

If the total moles of the mixture be understood to be held fixed at any value, say 1, the subscript n_T may be dropped.

Further physical significance of the Gibbs-Duhem equation may be demonstrated by use of Equation (16–26), which involves the derivatives of $\bar{G}_i$ with respect to pressure at constant temperature and composition. When these derivatives are replaced by their values as given by Equation (16–22b), the following result, Equation (16–18), is obtained

$$V = \sum_{i=1}^{c} n_i \bar{V}_i$$

This is recognized as Euler's formula for a function which is homogeneous of degree 1. Thus, if a proposed activity function satisfies the Gibbs-Duhem equation, the homogeneous degree of 1 for the volume is preserved.

THE EXCESS FREE ENERGY FUNCTION

In the examination of experimental results, the excess free energy function is found to be useful. The excess free energy per mole of solution, $\mathcal{G}^E$, is defined as follows:

$$\mathcal{G}^E = \mathcal{G} \text{ (actual solution)} - \mathcal{G} \text{ (ideal solution)} \qquad (16\text{–}95)$$

Thus,

$$\mathcal{G}^E = \sum_{i=1}^{c} x_i(\bar{G}_i^L)_{\text{actual}} - \sum_{i=1}^{c} x_i(\bar{G}_i^L)_{\text{ideal}} \qquad (16\text{–}96)$$

For purposes of partial differentiation the expression G^E for the excess free energy for n_T moles of solution is more convenient. Since

$$n_T \mathcal{G}^E = G^E \tag{16-97}$$

it follows that

$$G^E = \sum_{i=1}^{c} n_i (\bar{G}_i^L)_{\text{actual}} - \sum_{i=1}^{c} n_i (\bar{G}_i^L)_{\text{ideal}} \tag{16-98}$$

The excess free energy is readily stated in terms of the activity coefficients. Subtracting Equation (16–49) from (16–47) gives

$$(\bar{G}_i^L)_{\text{actual}} - (\bar{G}_i^L)_{\text{ideal}} = RT \ln \gamma_i^L$$

When this result is substituted into Equation (16–98), the expression,

$$G^E / RT = \sum_{i=1}^{c} n_i \ln \gamma_i^L \tag{16-99}$$

is obtained. Termwise partial differentiation with respect to n_1 yields

$$\frac{1}{RT} \left(\frac{\partial G^E}{\partial n_1} \right)_{T,P,n_j} = \sum_{i=1}^{c} n_i \left(\frac{\partial \ln \gamma_i^L}{\partial n_1} \right)_{T,P,n_j} + \sum_{i=1}^{c} (\ln \gamma_i^L) \left(\frac{\partial n_i}{\partial n_1} \right)_{T,P,n_j} \tag{16-100}$$

The first summation on the right hand side is recognized as the Gibbs-Duhem equation and has the value of zero. In the second summation the derivatives have the following values,

$$\left(\frac{\partial n_1}{\partial n_1} \right)_{T,P,n_j} = 1; \quad \left(\frac{\partial n_2}{\partial n_1} \right)_{T,P,n_j} = \left(\frac{\partial n_3}{\partial n_1} \right)_{T,P,n_j} = \ldots = \left(\frac{\partial n_c}{\partial n_1} \right)_{T,P,n_j} = 0$$

since all of the n's are held fixed except n_1. Thus Equation (16–100) reduces to

$$\frac{1}{RT} \left(\frac{\partial G^E}{\partial n_1} \right)_{T,P,n_j} = \ln \gamma_1^L \tag{16-101}$$

Since component 1 was selected arbitrarily, an analogous result would have been obtained for any other component. Thus Equation (16–101) may be stated in the general form.

$$\frac{1}{RT} \left(\frac{\partial G^E}{\partial n_i} \right)_{T,P,n_j} = \ln \gamma_i^L \tag{16-102}$$

where it is understood that for each choice of i (say $i = 2$), $n_1, n_3, n_4, \ldots, n_c$ are held fixed.

For the case where n_T is held fixed instead of $n_2, n_3, \ldots, n_c$, the following result

$$\frac{1}{RT} \left(\frac{\partial G^E}{\partial n_1} \right)_{P,T,n_T} = \sum_{i=1}^{c} \left(\frac{\partial n_i}{\partial n_1} \right)_{P,T,n_T} (\ln \gamma_i^L) \qquad (16\text{-}103)$$

is obtained instead of Equation (16–101). Until the manner in which each n_i ($i = 2$ through $i = c$) is to be varied with respect to n_1 (with n_T being held fixed) is specified, no further reduction of Equation (16–103) is possible for a general multicomponent mixture. However, for the special case of a binary mixture the precise variation of n_2 with respect to n_1 at constant n_T is determined,

$$\frac{\partial n_1}{\partial n_1} + \frac{\partial n_2}{\partial n_1} = \frac{\partial n_T}{\partial n_1}; \quad 1 + \frac{\partial n_2}{\partial n_1} = 0$$

For a binary mixture in which n_T is held fixed, Equation (16–103) reduces to

$$\frac{1}{RT} \left(\frac{\partial G^E}{\partial n_1} \right)_{P,T,n_T} = \ln \gamma_1^L - \ln \gamma_2^L = \ln \gamma_1^L/\gamma_2^L \qquad (16\text{-}104)$$

This holds for all values of n_1 from $n_1 = 0$ to $n_1 = n_T$ (or $x_1 = 0$ to $x_1 = 1$). This expression is commonly stated in terms of mole fractions. Equation (16–104) is converted to this form as follows. Partial differentiation by the chain rule yields

$$\left(\frac{\partial G^E}{\partial n_1} \right)_{P,T,n_T} = \left(\frac{\partial G^E}{\partial x_1} \right)_{P,T,n_T} \left(\frac{\partial x_1}{\partial n_1} \right)_{P,T,n_T} = \left(\frac{\partial G^E}{\partial x_1} \right)_{P,T,n_T} \left(\frac{1}{n_T} \right)$$

$$= \left(\frac{\partial \mathcal{G}^E}{\partial x_1} \right)_{P,T,n_T}$$

Thus

$$\frac{1}{RT} \left(\frac{\partial \mathcal{G}^E}{\partial x_1} \right)_{P,T,n_T} = \ln \frac{\gamma_1^L}{\gamma_2^L}$$

Integration from $x_1 = 0$ (pure component 2) to $x_1 = 1$ gives

$$\frac{1}{RT} \left[\mathcal{G}^E \big|_{x_1=1} - \mathcal{G}^E \big|_{x_1=0} \right] = \int_0^1 \left(\ln \frac{\gamma_1^L}{\gamma_2^L} \right) dx_1 \qquad (16\text{-}105)$$

Since all solutions consisting of pure components are ideal, $\mathcal{G}^E = 0$ at

$x_1 = 1$ and $x_1 = 0$. Thus Equation (16–105) reduces to the well-known result of Redlich and Kister (7)

$$\int_0^1 \left(\ln \frac{\gamma_1^L}{\gamma_2^L} \right) dx_1 = 0 \qquad (16\text{–}106)$$

for binary mixtures. This expression may be employed to check the thermodynamic consistency of the experimental data by plotting $\ln \gamma_1^L/\gamma_2^L$ versus x_1. For data which are consistent, the total area under this curve from $x_1 = 0$ to $x_1 = 1$ is of course equal to zero.

NOTATION

A = total work function; energy units

c = total number of components

C = name of the curve (or path) prescribed for going from one state (or point) to another

E = internal energy; energy units

ΔE = $E_2 - E_1$; the difference of the energy of the system at states 2 and 1, respectively

$f(x, y)$ = function of the variables x and y, where x and y do not necessarily represent mole fractions

f_i^v, f_i^L = fugacities of pure component i in the vapor and liquid states, respectively; evaluated at the temperature T and total pressure P of the mixture; atm

$\bar{f}_i$ = fugacity of a component i in a mixture; it is evaluated at the temperature and total pressure of the mixture; atm

$\bar{f}_i^v, \bar{f}_i^L$ = fugacities of component i in the vapor and liquid phases (mixtures), respectively; evaluated at the temperature T and total pressure P of the vapor-liquid mixture; atm

$\bar{f}_{i,P_i}^v, \bar{f}_{i,P_i}^L$ = fugacities of component i in the vapor and liquid phases (mixtures), respectively; evaluated at a pressure equal to the vapor pressure which component i exhibits at the temperature T of the vapor-liquid mixture; atm

$\bar{f}_{i,P_o}^v$ = fugacity of component i in the vapor phase (mixture); evaluated at the temperature T of the vapor-liquid mixture and at some arbitrary pressure denoted by P_o; atm

G = total free energy; energy units

G_i = free energy of one mole of pure component i; energy units per mole

G^E = total excess free energy of a solution; defined by Equation (16–98); energy units

$\mathcal{G}^E$ = excess free energy per mole of solution; defined by Equation (16–95); energy units per mole

H = total enthalpy; energy units

H_i = enthalpy of one mole of pure component i; energy units per mole

$\bar{H}_i$ = partial molal enthalpy of component i; energy units per mole

I = value of the line integral along the prescribed curve C from one specified point to another specified point on curve C

K_i = value of y_i/x_i for component i in a vapor-liquid mixture at equilibrium; sometimes called the equilibrium constant, the vaporization-equilibrium constant, the Henry-law constant, and the equilibrium ratio

$M(x, y), N(x, y)$ = functions of the variables x and y, where x and y do not necessarily represent mole fractions

n_i = number of moles of component i; i may take on all values from 1 through c; moles

n_T = total number of moles

p_i = partial pressure of component i in a mixture; defined by $p_i = Py_i$; atm

P = total pressure; the pressure of the vapor-liquid mixture; atm

P_i = vapor pressure of component i at the temperature T of the vapor-liquid mixture; atm

P_0 = arbitrary pressure of a standard state; atm

R = gas constant in consistent units; defined by $R = PV/T$

S = total entropy; energy units per $°R$ (or $°K$)

$\bar{S}_i$ = partial molal entropy of component i; energy units per $°R$ per mole

T = temperature; the temperature of the vapor-liquid mixture; $°R$ or $°K$

V = total volume of solution; evaluated at the temperature and pressure of the solution; volume units (ft³, cm³, liters)

v_i = volume of one mole of pure component i; evaluated at the temperature and pressure of the solution; volume per mole

$\bar{V}_i$ = partial molal volume of component i; evaluated at the temperature and pressure of the solution; volume per mole

y_i, x_i = mole fractions of component i in the vapor and liquid phases, respectively

γ_i^v, γ_i^L = activity coefficients of component i in the vapor and liquid phases, respectively

λ = arbitrary multiplier

$\exp z$ = e^z, where e is the base of natural logarithms

$(\partial G/\partial n_i)_{T,P,n_j}$ = change in G with respect to n_i, where G is regarded as a function of P, T, n_1, n_2, ..., n_c. The subscript n_j means all of the n's are held constant except n_i.

$(\partial G/\partial P)_{T,n_i}$ = change in G with respect to P, where $G = G(P, T, n_1 ..., n_c)$. The subscript n_i means all of the n's are held fixed.

Subscripts

c = total number of components

i = any component of the mixture

Superscripts

E = excess free energy function for the liquid phase

L = liquid phase

v = vapor phase

PROBLEMS

16–1   (a) Evaluate

$$I = \int_C xy \, dx + y \, dy$$

along the path $y = x$ (curve C) from the point $(0, 0)$ to the point $(1, 1)$.   *Ans. $I = 5/6$*

(b) Repeat part (a) for the case where curve C consists of the straight line $y = 2x$ from $(0, 0)$ to $(\frac{1}{4}, \frac{1}{2})$, and then the straight line connecting the points $(\frac{1}{4}, \frac{1}{2})$ and $(1, 1)$.   *Ans. I = 85/96*

(c) Compute the values of

$$\partial M/\partial y \quad \text{and} \quad \partial N/\partial x$$

(d) Attempt to find the function $f(x, y)$ such that $M(x, y) = xy$, and $N(x, y) = y$.

16-2   Evaluate

$$I = \int_{(P_1, T_1)}^{(P_2, T_2)} \left(\frac{-RT}{P^2}\right) dP + \left(\frac{R}{P}\right) dT$$

(a) along the straight line between the two points

$$P_1 = 1.0, \quad T_1 = 492$$

$$P_2 = 2.00, \quad T_2 = 1568$$

where $R = 0.73$.   *Ans. I = 213.16*

(b) along the line $P = 1.0$ to the point $P = 1.0$, $T = 1568$; then along the line $T = 1568$ to the point $P = 2.0$ and $T = 1568$.   *Ans. I = 213.16*

(c) Compute

$$\partial M/\partial T \quad \text{and} \quad \partial N/\partial P$$

(d) Corresponding to the points given in Part (a), compute $V_2 - V_1$ for one mole of a perfect gas.

(e) Find the function such that $M(P, T) = -RT/P^2$ and $N(P, T) = R/P$.

16-3   (a) Evaluate

$$I = \int_C P \, dV$$

along the straight line connecting the points $P_1 = 1$, $V_1 = 359$ and $P_2 = 2$, $V_2 = 718$.   *Ans. I = 1077/2*

(b) Along the straight line $P = 1$ from $V_1 = 359$ to $V_2 = 718$; then along the line $V = 718$ to the point $P_2 = 2$, $V_2 = 718$.   *Ans. I = 359*

(c) If $M(V, P) = P$, what is the implied value of $N(V, P)$ in the integrand of I? Compute

$$\partial M/\partial P \quad \text{and} \quad \partial N/\partial V$$

16-4   Show that

$$(\partial V_1/\partial n_1)_{P,T,n_j} = \lambda(\partial^2 V/\partial Z_1^2)_{P,T,n_j},$$

where $Z_i = \lambda n_i$.

16-5   Show that the expression given by Equation (16-40) is obtained by use of a path analogous to that described in Figure 16-3.

16-6   Derive Equation (16–47) by the procedure indicated in the text.

16-7   Verify the results given by Equations (16–53) and (16–54).

16-8   Beginning with the first principles, show that instead of Equation (16–73), the following expression may be obtained.

$$\ln \frac{\bar{f}_i^v}{Py_i} = \frac{1}{RT} \int_0^P \left(\bar{V}_i^v - \frac{RT}{P} \right) dP$$

16-9   Show that Equation (16–77) holds for the case where the standard state of a component in the vapor phase is the pure component in the vapor phase at the temperature T of the equilibrium mixture and at some arbitrary pressure P_0 independent of the pressure P of the vapor-liquid equilibrium mixture.

16-10   Although in the developments the use of paths for the calculation of the change of the partial molal free energy was employed, do not overlook that $\bar{G}_i$ is independent of path and thus depends only on the initial and final states. Instead of the definition of fugacity given by Equation (16–38), the following more general one which involves total differentials,

$$d\bar{G}_i^v = RT \, d \ln \bar{f}_i^v \tag{A}$$

may be employed where it is understood that $\bar{G}_i^v$ and $\bar{f}_i^v$ are functions of $P, T, y_1, \ldots, y_c$.

Show that:
(a) Equation (16–38) follows as a consequence of Equation (A)
(b) Equations (16–40), (16–53), and (16–62) may be obtained by use of Equation (A) and paths going directly from the initial to the final states.

LITERATURE CITED

1. Denbigh, Kenneth, *The Principles of Chemical Equilibrium* (New York: Cambridge University Press, 1955), p. 182.

2. Gibbs, J. W., *Collected Works*, Vol. I, (New York: Longmans, Green & Co., Inc., 1931), p. 55.

3. Gilmont, Roger, *Thermodynamic Principles* (Englewood Cliffs, N. J.: Prentice-Hall, Inc., 1959), p. 207.

4. Guggenheim, E. A., *Thermodynamics* (New York: Interscience Publishers, Inc., 1949), p. 170.

5. Lewis, G. N. and M. Randall, *Thermodynamics* (New York: McGraw-Hill Book Company, Inc., 1923), p. 222.

6. Mickley, H. S., T. H. Sherwood, and C. E. Reed, *Applied Mathematics in Chemical Engineering* (New York: McGraw-Hill Book Company, Inc., 1957), p. 207.

7. Redlich, O. and A. T. Kister, "Algebraic Representation of Thermodynamic Properties and the Classification of Solutions," *Ind. Eng. Chem.*, **40,** 345 (1948)

8. Sokolnikoff, I. S. and E. S. Sokolnikoff, *Higher Mathematics for Engineers and Physicists*, 2 ed. (New York: McGraw-Hill Book Company, Inc., 1941), pp. 136, 208, and 216.

Correlation of Vapor-Liquid Equilibria Data for Multicomponent Mixtures

17

In the correlation of the K-values for the components of multicomponent mixtures, two general approaches have been taken. In the first, the effect of composition is included as an implicit function of the K-value. In the second, the effect of composition is accounted for by use of separate correlations for the activity coefficients. The first method has proved very successful in the treatment of hydrocarbon mixtures composed of similar compounds, such as paraffins and olefins. Efforts to extend it to include mixtures of paraffins (or olefins) and aromatics have met with only moderate success.

Although the experimental determination of the volumetric (P-V-T) behavior of pure compounds and mixtures and the determination of K-values for both binary and multicomponent mixtures form the basis for the various correlations presented, the description of the experimental techniques is not within the scope of this book.

Many of the K-values now available for hydrocarbon systems were determined experimentally, whereas others were computed on the basis of P-V-T data for either the pure components or K-data for binaries. Although the presentation of all the details pertaining to each method proposed for the correlation of the K-values is impossible, descriptions of the basic principles involved in some of the methods presently available are given.

This chapter is divided into four parts. In Part I, methods that make direct use of thermodynamic relationships for the correlation and calculation of K-values are presented. Part II contains methods based on the use of convergence pressure, and Part III is concerned with the use of activity coefficients. Part IV contains a brief summary of methods for including the effects of temperature, pressure, and composition on enthalpy.

PART I

USE OF FUGACITIES FOR THE CALCULATION OF K-VALUES

Some of the proposed methods of this type are presented in an order which follows their chronological developments fairly closely.

In the earlier applications the K-values were calculated on the basis of *Raoult's* and *Dalton's laws*. *Raoult's law* is given by the relationship

$$p_i = P_i x_i \tag{17-1}$$

The expression

$$p_i = P y_i \tag{17-2}$$

may be taken as the definition of partial pressure, or it may be shown to be a consequence of *Dalton's law*

$$\sum_{i=1}^{c} p_i = P$$

where it is understood that

$$p_i = n_i R T / V \tag{17-3}$$

Elimination of the partial pressure from Equations (17–1) and (17–2) gives

$$P y_i = P_i x_i \tag{17-4}$$

which is commonly called the combination of Raoult's and Dalton's laws. Thus for mixtures that obey both Raoult's and Dalton's laws,

$$K_i = P_i / P \tag{17-5}$$

Observe that this relationship not only neglects the effect of composition on K_i but to some extent the effect of pressure on the behavior of a component in the vapor and liquid phases.

To account for the effect of pressure, Lewis and co-workers (45, 46) used the following expression

$$K_i = f_{i,P_i}^{L} / f_i^{v} \tag{17-6}$$

whereas Souders, Selheimer, and Brown (81) employed

$$K_i = f_i^{L} / f_i^{v} \tag{17-7}$$

For the case where both the vapor and liquid phases are ideal solutions, the relationship of Brown and co-workers is readily obtained by combining Equations (16–62) and (16–64). Since the effect of pressure on the fugacity of a pure component in the liquid state is small for pressures well above its vapor pressure at the system temperature (70), Equations (17–6) and (17–7) are usually very nearly equivalent.

For a pure component that exists as a vapor at its standard state conditions (the total pressure and temperature of the mixture), a formula for the calculation of fugacity at the standard state is obtained by integration of Equation (16–41a). If the given component is a member of a group of compounds having similar physical and chemical properties, it will generally obey the law of corresponding states. Compounds that obey this law have equal compressibility factors at the same reduced temperature and pressure. These variables are defined as follows:

Z = compressibility factor; $Z_i = Pv_i/RT$.
P_R = reduced pressure; $P_R = P/P_c$, where P_c is the critical pressure of component i.
T_R = reduced temperature; $T_R = T/T_c$, where T_c is the critical temperature of component i.

For a pure component, it is readily shown that

$$\ln \frac{f_i^v}{P} = \int_0^{P_R} (Z-1) \frac{dP_R}{P_R} \qquad (17\text{–}8)$$

by use of Equations (16–12), (16–41), and the definition of Z. For components which obey the law of corresponding states, the right-hand side of Equation (17–8) is seen to be independent of the identity of the component at any given reduced temperature. On this basis generalized "fugacity charts" (47) have been prepared from which values of f_i^v/P may be read directly. Generally, f_i^v/P is plotted against P_R at parameters of T_R.

At a pressure equal to the vapor pressure possessed by component i at the temperature of the mixture,

$$f_{i,P_i}^L = f_{i,P_i}^L$$

because this set of values of P and T represent an equilibrium state. Thus the fugacity, f_{i,P_i}^L, of the liquid may be obtained by use of fugacity charts (Equation (17–8)) by taking

$$P = P_i \quad \text{and} \quad P_R = P_i/P_c$$

If the liquid state exists at all pressures between P_i and the total pressure P of the mixture, the fugacity of the liquid is found by integration of Equation (16–41a) (restated for the liquid phase) from P_i to P, which gives

$$f_i^L = f_{i,P_i}^L \exp \frac{v_i^L (P - P_i)}{RT} \qquad (17\text{–}9)$$

In this integration the change in the molal volume of the liquid with pressure was neglected.

Although Equations (17–8) and (17–9) represent direct methods for the calculation of the fugacities appearing in Equations (17–6) and (17–7), many combinations of values of P and T give rise to hypothetical standard states for which other procedures are required for the calculation of the corresponding fugacities. The following combinations of P and T give hypothetical standard states.

(1) If $T < T_c$ and $P > P_i$, the vapor phase does not exist.
(2) If $T < T_c$ and $P < P_i$, the liquid phase does not exist. (However, it does exist for $P \geq P_i$.)
(3) If $T > T_c$, the liquid phase does not exist at any P.

As discussed in Chapter 16, a hypothetical state is thermodynamically permissible; but the properties of the substance in this state must be defined because they are experimentally unattainable. The method of extrapolation from a known physical state to a hypothetical state serves to define the latter. In theory the method of extrapolation is completely arbitrary, thus permitting the selection of a set of extrapolation procedures that give a collection of K-values in reasonable agreement with an experimental set of K-values. Obviously, more than one set of extrapolation procedures may be found. Thus it is understandable that, despite the similarities of the formulas employed by Lewis and Kay and by Brown and co-workers, their methods of extrapolation differed appreciably.

METHOD OF LEWIS AND KAY

For all values of P and T where the vapor phase exists, the fugacity of the vapor is found by use of Equation (17–8) or an equivalent fugacity chart. For values of $T < T_c$ the fugacity of the liquid at its vapor pressure is also found by use of a fugacity chart, as described in the discussion that follows Equation (17–8).

If either the vapor or liquid phase of the pure component does not exist at the respective standard state condition, one of the extrapolation procedures of Lewis and Kay (45) [with minor modifications by others (70, 77)] is used. For the region where the vapor phase of the pure component does not exist ($T < T_c$ and $P > P_i$), the fugacity of the vapor is obtained from a chart for the supersaturated vapor. It was constructed on the basis of fugacities calculated by use of Equation (17–6) rearranged to the following form

$$f_i^v = f_{i,P_i}^L / K_i$$

Experimental values of K_i were used, and f_{i,P_i}^L was computed by use of a fugacity chart (Equation (17–8)); note that $f_{i,P_i}^L = f_{i,P_i}^v$. For $T > T_c$, the liquid state of the pure component is hypothetical. The fugacity f_{i,P_i}^L is obtained by a linear extrapolation of the plot of either

$$\log f_{i,P_i}^L \quad \text{or} \quad \log P_i \quad \text{versus} \quad 1/T_R.$$

METHOD OF SOUDERS, SELHEIMER, AND BROWN

This procedure for the determination of K-values is in many respects similar to the one proposed by Lewis and Kay. The two methods differ primarily by the extrapolation procedures used to define the hypothetical standard states.

For values of P and T such that the standard state for the vapor exists, the fugacity of the vapor is found by use of a fugacity chart [Equation (17–8)]. Similarly, when the standard state of the liquid exists, its fugacity is found by use of a fugacity chart and Equation (17–9).

For sets of values of $P > P_i$ and $T < T_c$, the standard state of the vapor is hypothetical. Also, for all such sets of values of P and T, $K_i < 1$. The division occurs at $P = P_i$ and $T < T_c$, and for all sets of P and T of this type, $K_i = 1$. Values of $K_i < 1$ were determined by extrapolation of a $\log K$ versus $\log P$ plot to values of $P > P_i$ at $T < T_c$.

For $T > T_c$, the liquid state is hypothetical for all values of P. For all such sets of P and T, values of K were found by extrapolation of a plot of $\log K$ versus T_R to values of $T_R > 1$. Experimental values of K_i and heats of solution data formed the basis for the extension of the curve for values of $T > T_R$.

The Lewis-Kay method and the method of Brown and co-workers account for the effect of temperature and pressure on K but largely neglect the effect of composition.

OTHER METHODS WHICH ACCOUNT FOR THE EFFECTS OF TEMPERATURE AND PRESSURE ON K-VALUES

Recently several correlations which include the temperature and pressure effects but neglect composition effects have been published. Among these were the methods of Scheibel and Jenny (76), Hadden (26), Natural Gasoline Supply Men's Association (56), Maxwell (51), and DePriester (15). In general, these correlations are both more accurate and more easily applied than the earlier methods of Lewis *et al.* and Brown *et al.*

In addition to the effects of temperature and pressure, the methods that follow include the effect of composition on K-values.

METHOD OF GAMSON AND WATSON: EFFECT OF COMPOSITION ON K-VALUES

In order to include the effect of composition as well as temperature and pressure on K-values, Gamson and Watson (22) employed standard states which were defined by procedures of extrapolation involving the pseudo-critical temperatures and pressures of the phases. After certain refinements had been made by Smith and Watson (80), Smith and Smith (78) prepared a set of K-charts for hydrocarbons. Values of K are given over wide ranges of temperature and pressure. This method is regarded by Hougen, Watson, and Ragatz (34) as probably the most reliable one for estimating K-values close to the critical point. At conditions removed from the critical, the methods that follow give more accurate K-values than do the charts of Smith and Smith.

USE OF THE BENEDICT-WEBB-RUBIN EQUATION FOR THE CALCULATION OF K-VALUES

Over a period of years investigators have collected a sizeable amount of P-V-T data for pure components and K-values for many binary and a few multicomponent systems. Benedict, Webb, and Rubin (5) used experimental results from about 35 sources in the evaluation of the constants appearing in their equation of state for the 12 hydrocarbons: methane, ethylene, ethane, propylene, propane, i-butylene, i-butane, n-butane, i-pentane, n-pentane, n-hexane, n-heptane. Mentioned most frequently among the sources were the works of B. H. Sage and W. N. Lacey and their co-workers and the works of J. A. Beattie and his co-workers.

In the first of a series of papers Benedict, Webb, and Rubin (3) proposed the following equation of state.

$$P = RT\rho + (B_0 RT - A_0 - C_0/T^2)\rho^2 + (bRT - a)\rho^3 + a\alpha\rho^6$$

$$+ \frac{c\rho^3}{T^2} \left[(1 + \gamma\rho^2) \right] \exp (-\gamma\rho^2) \qquad (17\text{--}10)$$

The parameters A_0, B_0, C_0, a, b, c, α, and γ are constants that depend only on the identity of a component; they are independent of whether the component is in the liquid or in the vapor state. Values of these for the 12 hydrocarbons are given in Reference (5). The molal density (moles per unit volume) is represented by ρ. Again R denotes the gas constant in consistent units. With a single set of constants this equation describes both the vapor and the liquid phases of a substance. Benedict and co-workers elected to take ρ and T as the independent variables and P as the dependent variable because P is single-valued for all choices of ρ and T. The choice of V as the dependent variable with P and T as the independent variables would have required that V be a multivalued function because the vapor and liquid phases have different volumes at the same temperature and pressure.

In the second paper (4) the equation of state is extended to include the description of mixtures. Two methods were considered by Benedict *et al.* (4) for the evaluation of the constants for this case. They recommended the following one because it gives good accuracy and is simple. For the liquid phase the values of the constants, A_0, B_0, C_0, a, b, c, α, and γ for the mixture are calculated on the basis of those for the pure components as follows:

$$A_0 = (\sum_{i=1}^{c} x_i(A_{0i})^{1/2})^2 \tag{17-11a}$$

$$B_0 = \sum_{i=1}^{c} x_i B_{0i} \tag{17-11b}$$

$$C_0 = (\sum_{i=1}^{c} x_i(C_{0i})^{1/2})^2 \tag{17-11c}$$

$$a = (\sum_{i=1}^{c} x_i(a_i)^{1/3})^3 \tag{17-11d}$$

$$b = (\sum_{i=1}^{c} x_i(b_i)^{1/3})^3 \tag{17-11e}$$

$$c = (\sum_{i=1}^{c} x_i(c_i)^{1/3})^3 \tag{17-11f}$$

$$\alpha = (\sum_{i=1}^{c} x_i(\alpha_i)^{1/3})^3 \tag{17-11g}$$

$$\gamma = (\sum_{i=1}^{c} x_i(\gamma_i)^{1/2})^2 \tag{17-11h}$$

By replacing x_i by y_i in Equations (17-11a) through (17-11h), the formulas for the evaluation of the constants for the vapor phase are obtained. The constants (A_{0i}, B_{0i}, C_{0i}, a_i, b_i, c_i, α_i, γ_i) within the summations are those of the pure components, and again they depend only on the component i and are independent of whether the phase under consideration is vapor or liquid.

In the calculation of the fugacities and partial molal quantities, Benedict *et al.* (4, 5) took the standard state of a component in either the vapor or liquid phase to be a perfect gas at a pressure of one atmosphere and at the temperature T of the mixture. Since the partial molal quantities are independent of path, integration of Equation (16–38) from the standard state to the final vapor and liquid states yields

$$\bar{G}_i^v(P,\ T) - G_i^0\ (1,\ T) = RT \ln \bar{f}_i^v \qquad (17\text{–}12a)$$

$$\bar{G}_i^L(P,\ T) - G_i^0(1,\ T) = RT \ln \bar{f}_i^L \qquad (17\text{–}12b)$$

respectively. The superscript zero is used to distinguish the free energy of one mole of a perfect gas from that for one mole of a pure component at the same conditions. To develop Equations (17–12a) and (17–12b) by use of paths from the initial to the final states is both informative and satisfying. One set of paths out of the infinitely many sets that could be proposed is given in Problem 17–2.

Actually, because of the choice of ρ and T (or V and T) rather than P and T as the independent variables, Benedict *et al.* (3, 4, 5) found it more convenient for development purposes to make use of the work function A (see Equation (16–10b)) rather than the free energy function G. For a component in the liquid phase mixture, they obtained the following formula:

$$
\begin{aligned}
RT \ln (\bar{f}_i^L/x_i) = {}& RT \ln \rho RT \\
& + [(B_0 + B_{0i})RT - 2(A_0 A_{0i})^{1/2} - 2(C_0 C_{0i})^{1/2}/T^2]\rho \\
& + \tfrac{3}{2}[RT(b^2 b_i)^{1/3} - (a^2 a_i)^{1/3}]\rho^2 \\
& + \tfrac{3}{5}[a(\alpha^2 \alpha_i)^{1/3} + \alpha(a^2 a_i)^{1/3}]\rho^5 \\
& + \frac{3\rho^2(c^2 c_i)^{1/3}}{T^2}\left[\frac{1 - \exp(-\gamma\rho^2)}{\gamma\rho^2} - \frac{\exp(-\gamma\rho^2)}{2}\right] \\
& - \frac{2\rho^2 c}{T^2}\left(\frac{\gamma_i}{\gamma}\right)^{1/2} \\
& \times \left[\frac{1 - \exp(-\gamma\rho^2)}{\gamma\rho^2} - \exp(-\gamma\rho^2) - \frac{\gamma\rho^2 \exp(-\gamma\rho^2)}{2}\right]
\end{aligned}
$$

$$(17\text{–}13)$$

In the interest of simplicity the superscript "L" was omitted from the density; understand that $\rho = \rho^L$. The formula for the fugacity of a component in a gaseous mixture is obtained from Equation (17–13) by replacing $\bar{f}_i^L$ by $\bar{f}_i^v$, x_i by y_i, and ρ^L by ρ^v. Also, in the evaluation of the constants for the vapor mixture, assume that the y_i's are to be employed in Equations (17–11a) through (17–11h). Except for pressures below atmospheric, Equations (17–10) and (17–13) give accurate results for mixtures of similar compounds. In order to improve the accuracy at low pressures, Benedict *et al.* (5) used values of C_{0i} that depend upon the specified temperature of the mixture.

For a two-phase multicomponent system at equilibrium, the values for c independent variables must be specified in order to fix the system. After c values have been picked, the corresponding values for the dependent variables may be found by use of Equations (17–10) and (17–13).

The necessary conditions for equilibrium to exist between vapor and liquid phases are given by Equation (16–50). Although in theory the choice of the particular variables to be fixed is arbitrary, in practice certain choices are preferred over others because of the characteristics of the equations describing equilibrium.

Benedict *et al.* (4) chose to fix the total pressure, P, the temperature T, and $c - 2$ values of the mole fractions in the liquid phase. (These will be taken as x_i through x_{c-2}). In the counting of the number of variables, only $c - 1$ values of the x_i's and $c - 1$ values of the y_i's are listed. Assume that the values of x_c and y_c are to be computed by use of the defining equations:

$$\sum_{i=1}^{c} x_i = 1 \quad \text{and} \quad \sum_{i=1}^{c} y_i = 1$$

When P is fixed, that $P^v = P$, and $P^L = P$ follows from Equation (16–50). Also, since it has been shown that $\bar{f}_i^L = \bar{f}_i^v$, Equations (17–10) and (17–18) may be applied to give the following $(c + 2)$ equations.

$$P^L(\rho^L, x_{c-1}) = P \tag{17–14a}$$

$$P^v(\rho^v, y_1, y_2, \ldots, y_{c-1}) = P \tag{17–14b}$$

$$RT \ln \bar{f}_1^L(\rho^L, x_{c-1}) = RT \ln \bar{f}_1^v(\rho^v, y_1, y_2, \ldots, y_{c-1}) \tag{17–14c}$$

$$\vdots \qquad\qquad \vdots \qquad\quad \vdots$$

$$RT \ln \bar{f}_c^L(\rho^L, x_{c-1}) = RT \ln \bar{f}_c^v(\rho^v, y_1, y_2, \ldots, y_{c-1}) \tag{17–14d}$$

in $c + 2$ unknowns: x_{c-1}, $(c - 1)$ values of y_i, ρ^L and ρ^v. Obviously, the solution of this set of equations is at best difficult. If a computer is employed to solve them, use of the method of Newton and Raphson (see Chapters 1 and 7) would probably be advantageous. When a solution is obtained, the values of K_i follow immediately for each component, since $K_i = y_i/x_i$.

For the 12 hydrocarbons, the method gives good accuracy. Benedict *et al.* (5) reported that the average deviation of the calculated values of K from the experimental values was less than 5 percent.

THE KELLOG CHARTS

Determination of the equilibrium conditions by solution of Equations (17–14a) through (17–14d) was considered impractical for making distillation calculations. In view of this conclusion, Benedict, Webb, Rubin, and Friend (6) devised a graphical method for the presentation of the K-values determined by use of these equations. A total of 325 charts were required to record the K-values of the 12 hydrocarbons. A collection of charts of this type has been published by the M. W. Kellog Company (54). These charts are commonly called the "Kellog Charts."

A reduction in the number of composition parameters was necessary in order to present the K-values for all possible combinations of vapor and liquid compositions over wide ranges of temperature and pressure on a reasonable number of charts. All of the vapor and liquid compositions can be expressed in terms of two variables, the molal average boiling points of the vapor and the liquid, respectively. These are defined as follows:

$$T_M^v = \sum_{i=1}^{c} y_i T_{Ni} \tag{17–15}$$

$$T_M^L = \sum_{i=1}^{c} x_i T_{Ni} \tag{17–16}$$

where

$T_{Ni} =$ normal boiling point (°R or °K) of component i
$T_M^v,\, T_M^L =$ molal average boiling points (°R or °K) of the vapor and liquid, respectively; these are sometimes referred to in the literature by "*MABP.*"

Each of the 324 charts refers to a particular component at a given pressure. A total of 26 pressures was given. Below 1000 psia, K-values are presented. Between 1000 psia and 3600 psia, the ratio of the fugacity to the mole fraction is given. A schematic representation of a typical chart is presented in Figure 17–1. In the insert the effect of the composition of the vapor on the K-value is given.

The use of these charts for making bubble point and dew point calculations is complicated by the fact that the molal average boiling points for both phases are required in advance. Thus, in the calculation of bubble points (where $x_1, \ldots, x_c$ and P are given), it is necessary to assume trial values for both the bubble point temperature, T, and the molal average boiling point of the vapor, T_M^v. The correct pair of temperatures has been selected when

$$\sum_{i=1}^{c} K_i x_i = \sum_{i=1}^{c} y_i = 1$$

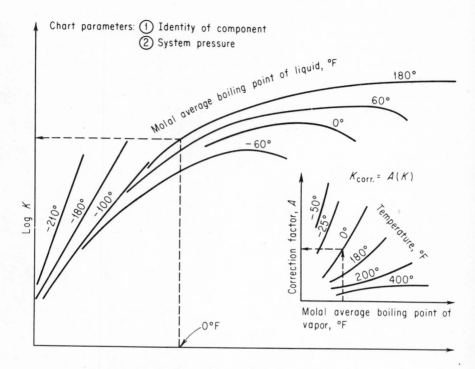

Figure 17–1. Sketch of a typical Kellog Chart.

and

$$T_M^v \text{ (calculated)} - T_M^v \text{ (assumed)} = 0$$

are satisfied simultaneously.

Another disadvantage of the Kellog charts is the necessity for inter-polation between charts with respect to pressure. This limitation was re-moved by DePriester (15).

CORRELATIONS OF DePRIESTER

In addition to the reporting of the experimental K-values for the certain light hydrocarbons present in thirty-three mixtures at temperatures ranging from $-60°F$ to $300°F$, DePriester (15) also presented two graphic correlations. He referred to these as the "general correlation" and the "Pressure-Temperature-Composition" (P.T.C.) charts. The generalized correlation consists of two nomograms that give K as a function of only temperature and pressure. One nomogram is for temperatures from $-100°$

to 70°F and the other one for temperatures from 20°F to 400°F. The nomograms were developed by DePriester for making preliminary calculations prior to the use of the P.T.C. charts.

Twenty-four P.T.C. charts were constructed on the basis of the data presented on 192 Kellog charts. The P.T.C. charts cover the pressure range of 14.7 to 1000 psia, whereas the complete set of Kellog charts cover the range of 14.7 to 3600 psia. Minor corrections of the K-values obtained

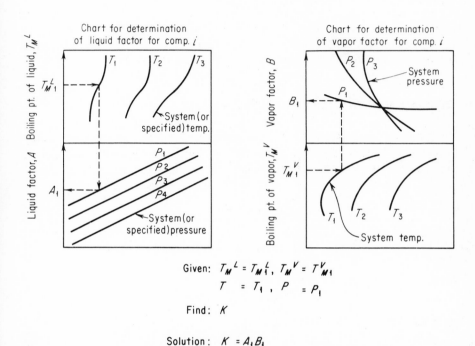

Given: $T_M{}^L = T_M{}^l{}_1, \; T_M{}^V = T_M{}^V{}_1$
$\qquad T \; = \; T_1 \; , \; P \; = P_1$

Find: K

Solution: $K = A_1 B_1$

Figure 17–2. A sketch of a typical set of DePriester Charts (P.T.C.) for a given component i.

from the Kellog charts were made on the basis of available experimental data prior to the construction of the P.T.C. charts.

The P.T.C. charts make use of a liquid factor, A_i, and a vapor factor, B_i, which are defined as follows:

$$A_i = \bar{f}_i^L / P x_i \qquad\qquad (17\text{–}17)$$

$$B_i = P y_i / \bar{f}_i^v \qquad\qquad (17\text{–}18)$$

Then

$$K_i = A_i B_i \qquad\qquad (17\text{–}19)$$

The liquid and vapor factors are seen to differ from the fugacity-mole fraction ratio of Equation (17–13) only by the multiplier P. The effects of the compositions of the vapor and liquid phases on the K-values was again represented by use of the respective molal average boiling points. Two charts were used for each of the 12 hydrocarbons. Schematic representations of the charts for a given component are presented in Figure 17–2.

Bubble point temperatures are computed by use of these charts in the same manner described for the Kellog charts.

For the comparisons made by DePriester (15), the P.T.C. charts gave more accurate results than did the Kellog charts. The average deviations of the calculated values of K from the experimental values were 7.7 and 6.4 percent for the Kellog and P.T.C. charts, respectively.

GENERALIZED K-CHARTS OF EDMISTER AND RUBY

Edmister and Ruby (21) drastically reduced the number of charts required to present the data contained on the Kellog charts. They altered the fugacity-mole fraction ratio employed by Benedict, Webb, and Rubin (4) as follows

For the vapor: $\qquad\qquad \bar{f}_i^v/Py_i$

For the liquid: $\qquad\qquad \bar{f}_i^L/P_ix_i$

Then

$$K_i = \left(\frac{\bar{f}_i^L/P_ix_i}{\bar{f}_i^v/Py_i}\right)\left(\frac{P_i}{P}\right) \qquad (17\text{--}20)$$

The separate ratios for the vapor and liquid may be considered as activity coefficients and were so called by Edmister and Ruby. For the vapor the above ratio is the reciprocal of the B_i employed by DePriester. However, for the liquid the vapor pressure, P_i, of the pure component (evaluated at the equilibrium or system temperature) is employed rather than the total pressure used by DePriester. Introduction of the vapor pressure necessitates a statement of the source of the data employed for temperatures below the critical and the extrapolation procedure employed for temperatures above the critical temperature. At temperatures where the vapor pressures were below atmospheric pressure, the vapor pressure data were taken from A. P. I. Research Project 44; see Reference (1). Between the atmospheric boiling point and the critical temperature, a straight line plot of log P_i versus the reciprocal of the absolute temperature was used. For temperatures above the critical, a straight-line extrapolation of this plot was used to give the vapor pressures.

Edmister and Ruby were able to generalize the results of Benedict *et al.* (6) by introduction of the following parameters.

$$T_R = \frac{T_s}{T_{ci}} = \frac{\text{system temperature (°R)}}{\text{critical temperature (°R) of component } i} \qquad (17\text{–}21)$$

$$P_R = \frac{P_s}{P_{ci}} = \frac{\text{system pressure (psia)}}{\text{critical pressure (psia) of component } i} \qquad (17\text{–}22)$$

$$T_{MR}^v = \frac{T_M^v}{T_{Ni}} = \frac{\text{molal average boiling point (°R) of the vapor } (MABP)}{\text{normal boiling point (°R) of component } i}$$
$$(17\text{–}23)$$

$$T_{MR}^L = \frac{T_M^L}{T_{Ni}} = \frac{\text{molal average boiling point (°R) of the liquid } (MABP)}{\text{normal boiling point (°R) of component } i}$$
$$(17\text{–}24)$$

In addition to these, two intermediate parameters, denoted by θ^v and θ^L, are employed. Except for methane, the parameters θ^v and θ^L are independent of the identity of the component; θ^v is a function of T_{MR}^v and T_R, whereas θ^L is a function of T_{MR}^L and T_R. For methane two additional charts were provided for the determination of θ^v and θ^L. The variables θ^v and θ^L have the property that at the critical temperature ($T_R = 1$) of any component,

$$\theta^v = \theta^L = T_R = 1$$

By use of these parameters, Edmister and Ruby needed only six charts (plus one table containing the vapor pressure data) to present all of the information contained on the Kellog charts. Interpolation between charts with respect to pressure as required by the Kellog charts was also eliminated. A schematic representation of the charts for the vapor phase is presented in Figure 17–3.

The generalized charts of Edmister and Ruby are used to compute bubble points in the same way described for the Kellog charts. A set of the generalized charts* of Edmister and Ruby (21) consist of Figures 1 through 6 of their article. The accuracy of these charts is good. Edmister and Ruby report an average deviation of the calculated K-values from the experimental values of 6.4 percent.

---

* Edmister and Ruby (21) state "Large scale, detailed drawings of Figures 1–6, which can be read to a much higher degree of accuracy are on file with A.D.I. Auxiliary Publications Photo-duplication Service, Library of Congress, Washington, D. C."

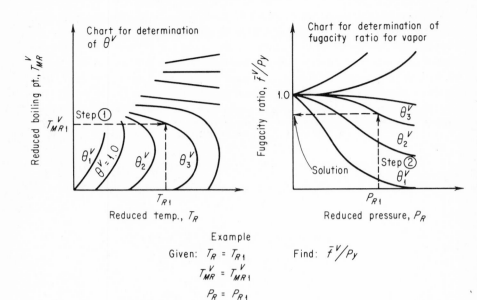

Figure 17–3. Sketches of the generalized charts of Edmister and Ruby.

PART II

USE OF CONVERGENCE PRESSURE IN THE CORRELATION OF K-VALUES

During the same years that the methods resulting from the Benedict-Webb-Rubin equation of state were under development, correlations of K-values based on experimental results were also under development. The correlations resulting from the latter approach have an advantage over the charts (6, 15, 21, 54) that are based on the equation of state of Benedict *et al.* (4) in that less trial and error is required. However, as pointed out by Edmister and Ruby (21), the equation of state of Benedict, Webb, and Rubin has the advantage of giving values of other properties, such as enthalpy, that are thermodynamically consistent with the K-values. For a binary system Brown (8) demonstrated that the convergence pressure is the critical pressure corresponding to the specified temperature of the system. Thus the system temperature becomes the critical temperature of a particular binary mixture. The concept of convergence pressure has either been recognized or employed in the correlation of K-data by a variety of investigators (8, 25, 30, 60, 73, 82, 85). It appears to be an outgrowth of the plots of log K versus log P suggested in 1932 by Souders, Selheimer, and Brown (81). The pressure at which all of the K's of a multicomponent mixture appear to approach unity on a log K versus log P plot at constant temperature has come to be known as the convergence pressure. The possibility of predicting the convergence pressure of a multicomponent mixture by means of an equivalent binary mixture was suggested by Katz and Kurata (38). Eventually such a method was developed by Hadden (26, 27). The development of this method depends upon the phase behavior of binary mixtures, a discussion of which follows.

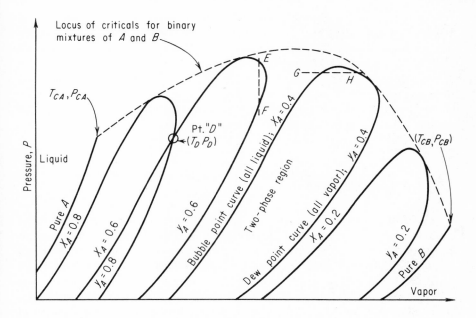

Figure 17–4. Phase behavior and locus of critical temperatures and pressures for binary mixtures of components A and B.

Consider the hypothetical system consisting of components A and B. Figure 17–4 was constructed on the basis of the general characteristics of the experimental results of several investigators (2, 39) and the discussions of others (8, 17, 70, 79); it represents the phase behavior of a typical binary mixture. With respect to concentration the limiting conditions of the mixture are represented by the single curves for pure A and B. These are the vapor pressure curves for pure A and pure B, and they are seen to terminate at the critical temperature and pressure for each component. Each envelope contains all of the two-phase mixtures ranging from bubble point liquid to dew point vapor. The left and right boundaries of each envelope represent the bubble point and dew point curves, respectively.

The intersection of two envelopes gives the composition of the vapor and the liquid at the temperature and pressure that locate the point of intersection. For example point *"D"* of Figure 17–4 defines the equilibrium state:

$$P = P_D, \quad T = T_D$$

$$y_A = 0.8, \quad x_A = 0.6$$

$$K_A = \tfrac{4}{3}, \quad K_B = 0.2/0.4 = \tfrac{1}{2}$$

At the critical temperature and pressure the liquid and vapor phases are indistinguishable. One such point exists for each envelope. The curve connecting the points for all envelopes is called the "locus of criticals."

The phenomenon of "retrograde condensation" is also illustrated by Figure 17–4. As pointed out by Brown (8), if either the bubble point or dew point curve is crossed twice while passing through the two-phase region by either isobaric or isothermal paths, retrograde condensation will occur. Lines *EF* and *GH* represent isothermal and isobaric paths, respectively, which would produce retrograde condensation.

CONVERGENCE PRESSURE

According to the Gibbs phase rule, Equation (16–51), the number of degrees of freedom for a two-phase system is equal to the number of components. Thus for a binary there are two degrees of freedom so long as two phases persist. The fixing of any two variables, such as the system pressure and the system temperature denoted by T_s and P_s, completely determines the properties of the system. That is both of the K_i's, as well as the vapor and liquid compositions, are determined along with convergence pressure, which is the ordinate of the point of intersection of the line $T_s = T_c$ and the locus of criticals as illustrated in Figure 17–5. This type of graph was used by Hadden (27). It consists of a combined graph of the locus of criticals and the associated log P versus log K plot for the binary. This combined plot illustrates that each system temperature selected not only determines the convergence pressure but also the log P versus log K isotherm.

For a ternary system with two phases present, there are three degrees of freedom, and three variables must be fixed in order to completely determine the system. Carter, Sage, and Lacey (12) elected to fix T, P, and the composition parameter C_2, which is defined as follows,

$$C_2 = x_2/(x_2 + x_3) \tag{17–25}$$

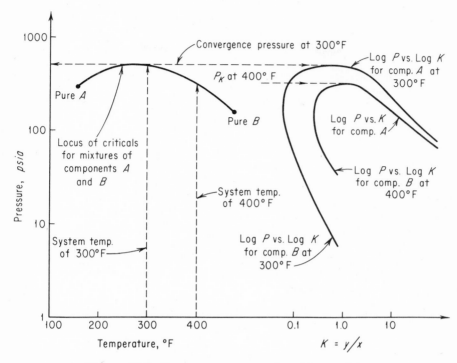

Figure 17–5. Convergence pressures for a binary mixture.

where the components are numbered in the order of decreasing volatility. For each set of values for P, T, and C_2, the convergence pressure is uniquely determined as illustrated in Figure 17–6. The log P versus log K plots were constructed on the basis of one choice of C_2, namely, $C_2 = 0.4$. This figure illustrates the fact that only the specification of C_2 and of the system temperature determines the convergence pressure and the log P versus log K isotherm. Also, this figure demonstrates that a ternary system may be regarded as three binaries; components 1 and 2, components 1 and 3, and components 2 and 3. The broken line in Figure 17–6 represents the locus of criticals for the ternary mixture with $C_2 = 0.4$.

Hadden (27) found that better correlations were obtained by use of a composition parameter based on mass (lb-mass or gm-mass) fractions rather than mole fractions. For a ternary mixture the mass-composition parameter is defined by

$$M_2 = m_2/(m_2 + m_3) \qquad (17\text{–}26)$$

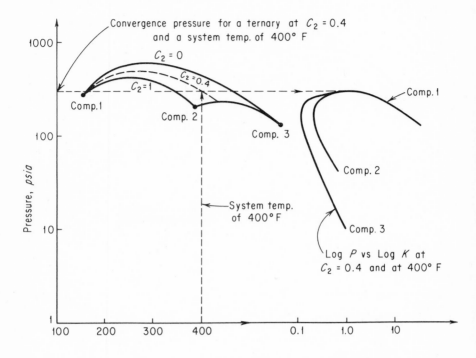

Figure 17–6. Convergence pressure for ternary systems.

The mass fractions are denoted by the m's, which are defined as follows:

$$\sum_{i=1}^{n} m_i = 1$$

Also, note that the letter "n" is used in this definition, rather than "c," to denote the total number of components. For developments in which c is used to identify the critical temperature and pressure, n is used to represent the total number of components.

By using the composition parameter M_2, Hadden found that the critical temperature of a mixture of components 2 and 3 in a ternary mixture at a specified value of M_2 could be computed with sufficient accuracy for use in subsequent correlations by use of the simple proportionality

$$\frac{t_{c3} - t_{c\overline{2}}}{M_2} = \frac{t_{c3} - t_{c2}}{1} \qquad (17\text{–}27)$$

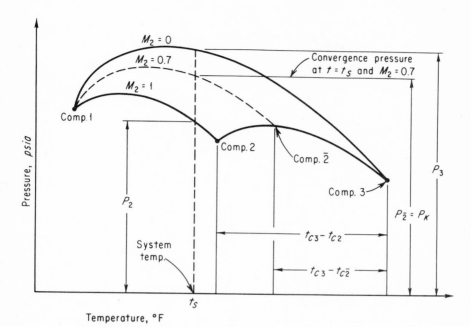

Figure 17–7. Convergence pressure and critical temperature relationships.

where

$t_{c\bar{2}}$ = critical temperature (°F) of a mixture of components 2 and 3 at the specified value of M_2. The lower case "t" is used to emphasize the fact that the temperatures are in °F.

t_{c2}, t_{c3} = critical temperatures of components 2 and 3.

These temperature differences are shown in Figure 17–7. Substitution of the definition of M_2 into Equation (17–27), followed by rearrangement yields

$$t_{c\bar{2}} = \frac{m_2 t_{c2} + m_3 t_{c3}}{m_2 + m_3} \qquad (17\text{–}28)$$

which is recognized as the weight average of the critical temperatures of components 2 and 3.

Calculation of the convergence pressure for a ternary mixture may be accomplished by the following formula, proposed by Winn (86),

$$(P_{\bar{2}} - P_3)/M_2 = (P_2 - P_3)/1 \qquad (17\text{-}29)$$

where

P_2, P_3 = convergence pressures for the binaries composed of components (1, 2) and (1, 3), respectively, at the system temperature t_s. If $t_s > t_{c2}$ then P_2 is taken equal to the critical pressure for component 2; that is $P_2 = P_{c2}$.

$P_K = P_{\bar{2}}$ = convergence pressure for the ternary mixture at the specified values of M_2 and t_s.

These pressure differences are likewise depicted in Figure 17–7, and in view of the definition of M_2, Equation (17–29) reduces to

$$P_K = P_{\bar{2}} = \frac{m_2 P_2 + m_3 P_3}{m_2 + m_3} \qquad (17\text{-}30)$$

Although a composition parameter involving component 1 and excluding either component 2 or 3 may be defined, it was found to be of no practical value (27).

Equations (17–28) and (17–30) and Figure 17–7 strongly suggest the representation of a ternary mixture (at M_2 fixed) as an equivalent binary composed of component 1 and the pseudoheavy component $\bar{2}$. Equation (17–28) serves to define the pseudoheavy as that hypothetical component having a critical temperature $t_{c\bar{2}}$ (the weight average temperature of components 2 and 3 at the specified value of M_2). The binary composed of components 1 and $\bar{2}$ has a convergence pressure $P_K = P_{\bar{2}}$, which is also the convergence pressure of the ternary mixture. Thus for the determination of convergence pressure, the ternary may be replaced by an equivalent binary mixture.

MULTICOMPONENT MIXTURES

By an extension of the procedure described for a ternary, the "equivalent binary" for any multicomponent mixture may be found. The equivalent binary is the one with the same convergence pressure as the multicomponent mixture at the specified system temperature and the specified composition parameters. For each component that is added to a mixture after the second one, a composition parameter is fixed. For example, for a quaternary mixture, the convergence pressure (as well as the log P versus log K plots) is determined by fixing the system temperature t_s and the composition parameters M_2 and M_3. The lightest component of the quaternary mixture is taken as the light component of the equivalent binary. Determination of the "pseudoheavy" component of the equivalent binary mixture is a two-step process. First, $t_{c\overline{3}}$ is determined on the basis of components 3 and 4, and then $t_{c\overline{2}}$ is determined on the basis of components 2 and $\overline{3}$. This brief description of the extension to quaternary mixtures serves to suggest the following set of formulas for the general multicomponent mixture. The composition parameters are defined by

$$\left.\begin{array}{c} M_2 = \dfrac{m_2}{m_2 + m_3 + \ldots + m_n} \\[2em] M_3 = \dfrac{m_3}{m_3 + m_4 + \ldots + m_n} \\[1em] \vdots \qquad \qquad \vdots \\[1em] M_{n-1} = \dfrac{m_{n-1}}{m_{n-1} + m_n} \end{array}\right\} \qquad (17\text{--}31)$$

The formulas for the critical temperatures are as follows:

$$\left.\begin{array}{c} t_{c\overline{n-1}} = t_{cn} - (t_{cn} - t_{cn-1})M_{n-1} \\[1em] t_{c\overline{n-2}} = t_{c\overline{n-1}} - (t_{c\overline{n-1}} - t_{cn-2})M_{n-2} \\[1em] \vdots \qquad \qquad \vdots \\[1em] t_{c\overline{2}} = t_{c\overline{3}} - (t_{c\overline{3}} - t_{c2})M_2 \end{array}\right\} \qquad (17\text{--}32)$$

Likewise, the convergence pressures are given by

$$\left.\begin{array}{c} P_{\overline{n-1}} = P_n - (P_n - P_{n-1})M_{n-1} \\[1em] P_{\overline{n-2}} = P_{\overline{n-1}} - (P_{\overline{n-1}} - P_{n-2})M_{n-2} \\[1em] P_{\overline{2}} = P_{\overline{3}} - (P_{\overline{3}} - P_2)M_2 \end{array}\right\} \qquad (17\text{--}33)$$

By use of the definitions of the M's [Equation (17–31)], it is readily shown that Equations (17–32) and (17–33) reduce to

$$t_{c\overline{2}} = \frac{\displaystyle\sum_{i=2}^{n} m_i t_{ci}}{\displaystyle\sum_{i=2}^{n} m_i} \qquad (17\text{--}34)$$

and

$$P_K = P_{\bar{2}} = \frac{\sum\limits_{i=2}^{n} m_i P_i}{\sum\limits_{i=2}^{n} m_i} \tag{17-35}$$

Of these formulas only Equation (17–34) is used in the correlations that follow. The critical temperature of the pseudoheavy component could be calculated by use of Equation (17–32), but Equation (17–34) is generally more convenient. Again the pseudoheavy component is that component which has a critical temperature $t_{c\bar{2}}$ (based on the specified values of M_2, M_2, ..., M_{n-1}). The equivalent binary, component 1 and component $\bar{2}$, has the same convergence pressure at the system temperature t_s as the multicomponent mixture. Thus the convergence pressure is determined by the specification of t_s and the values for $n - 2$ composition parameters, or

$$P_K = P_K(t_s, M_2, M_3, \ldots, M_{n-1}) \tag{17-36}$$

This development follows that of Hadden (27). Although the convergence pressure could be computed by use of Equation (17–35), the use of an equivalent binary is both easier to apply and also gives more accurate results.

As shown in Figure 17–6, the specification of t_s and $(c - 2)$ values of the M's also determines the isothermal plots of log P versus log K. Specification of the system pressure at $P = P_s$ fixes the system completely. Thus for each component i

$$K_i = K_i(P_s, t_s, M_2, M_3, \ldots, M_{n-1}) \tag{17-37}$$

In the treatment of multicomponent systems the m_i's are commonly specified rather than the M's. For any given set of liquid compositions, the corresponding set of composition parameters may be computed. However, the converse is not true (see Problem 17–4). Fixing the composition parameters leaves m_1 and m_n undetermined. Upon specification of both P_s and t_s and $(c - 2)$ values of the M's, the system is fixed and thus m_1 and m_n are determined.

ANALYSIS OF THE BASIC POSTULATE OF THE METHODS THAT USE CONVERGENCE PRESSURE AS A PARAMETER

This postulate is that the plot of log P versus log K for component i in any multicomponent mixture depends only on the system temperature and the convergence pressure (or $t_{c\bar{2}}$). The assumptions contained in this postulate are best explained by means of the following analysis. First consider a ternary mixture. For such a mixture the specification of M_2 determines $t_{c\overline{2}}$ as shown by Equation (17–27). Also, this value of $t_{c\overline{2}}$ determines the convergence pressure P_K as shown by Figure 17–7. The further specification of t_s determines the log P versus log K_i plots, and fixing the system pressure at $P = P_s$ determines K_i for each component. Thus

$$K_i = K_i(P_s, t_s, M_2) = K_i(P_s, t_s, t_{c\overline{2}}) = K_i(P_s, t_s, P_K) \qquad (17\text{–}38)$$

Observe that for each $t_{c\overline{2}}$ (or P_K one and only one M_2 exists [see Equation (17–27)], and consequently, one and only one log P versus log K_i plot exists for each component. Thus for a ternary mixture, the basic postulate amounts to an alternate statement of Gibbs phase rule and therefore contains no assumptions.

However, this is not the case for multicomponent mixtures that contain more than three components. For a quaternary mixture, Gibbs phase rule gives

$$K_i = K_i(P_s, t_s, M_2, M_3)$$

For this system Equation (17–32) may be written in the form

$$t_{c\overline{2}} = [t_{c4} - (t_{c4} - t_{c3})M_3](1 - M_2) \qquad (17\text{–}39)$$

To replace M_2, M_3 in the expression for K_i by $t_{c\overline{2}}$ without any assumption being involved would require that a one to one correspondence exist between $t_{c\overline{2}}$ and each distinguishable pair of values for M_2 and M_3. However, Equation (17–39) does not satisfy this condition because for each $t_{c\overline{2}}$, infinitely many pairs of values for M_2 and M_3 exist that satisfy Equation (17–39).

In general, for each distinguishable pair of values for M_2 and M_3 a log P versus log K_i plot for any given component exists for each system temperature t_s. If for each pair of values of M_2 and M_3 that give the same value of $t_{c\overline{2}}$ (or P_K), one and only one log P versus log K_i plot is assumed to exist for each component at the system temperature t_s, then the basic postulate is obtained,

$$K_i = K_i(P_s, t_s, t_{c\overline{2}}) = K_i(P_s, t_s, P_K) \qquad (17\text{–}40)$$

The analysis presented for a quaternary mixture is readily generalized for multicomponent mixtures to give the same result, Equation (17–40).

Hanson and Brown (29) were among the first to seek experimental confirmation of Equation (17–40). On the basis of their results and those of other investigators, Equation (17–40) is generally accepted as a good approximation for mixtures of components of the same type. Further support for the validity of Equation (17–40) follows from the good agreement between the K_i's given by correlations based on this relationship and those given by the Kellog charts.

Three of the most recent correlations based on Equation (17–40) are described. The first of these consists of a set of charts recently published by the Natural Gasoline Association of America (NGAA) (57).

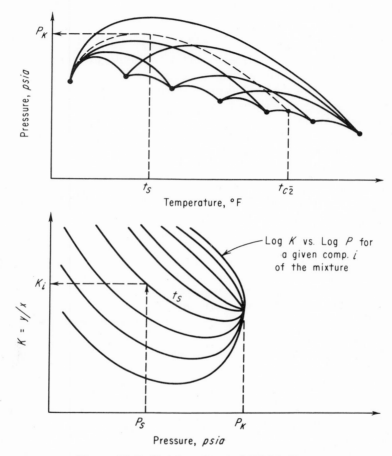

Figure 17–8. Sketches of typical NGAA Charts.

METHOD 1: THE NGAA CHARTS

This method is in essence that described in the previous section in the process of the development of Equation (17–40). Members* and former

* Bryon B. Woertz (chairman), E. A. Gomatsky, K. H. Hachmuth, R. H. Jacoby, H. L. Stone, C. J. Walters, C. E. Webber, E. I. Organick, C. L. DePriester, J. W. Kilmer, H. H. Rachford.

members of the "NGAA Equilibrium Ratio Committee" have prepared charts containing plots of log K versus log P for each of several convergence pressures. There are a total of 135 charts. The convergence pressures range from 600 to 20,000 psia. The components consist of the paraffins and olefins (methane through decane) and nitrogen. Charts are also presented for several binaries whose components are members of different classes of compounds.

In addition to the log K versus log P plots, the set of NGAA charts contains one in which the locus of criticals for each of several binary mixtures is presented. The use of the set of charts is illustrated graphically by Figure 17–8. First, the pseudoheavy component for the mixture is determined by use of Equation (17–34). The intersection of the line $t = t_{c\overline{2}}$ with the locus of criticals determines the critical pressure for component $\overline{2}$. If component $\overline{2}$ does not happen to correspond to a pure component, a symmetrical locus is sketched as shown in Figure 17–8. The intersection of this curve with the line $t = t_s$ determines the convergence pressure P_K. The K-value for any particular component at the system pressure and temperature is then found by use of the appropriate log K versus log P plot as demonstrated in the lower diagram of Figure 17–8.

In the determination of the bubble point temperature corresponding to a specified system pressure and liquid-phase composition, the procedure described might appear to lead to a trial determination of both the system temperature and the convergence pressure. However, because of the relatively small dependence of the K_i's on the convergence pressure, the trial and error procedure is reduced primarily to the finding of the bubble point temperature. This characteristic relationship between the K_i's and P_K permits the use of a single convergence pressure over either the entire column or several plates.

If the system temperature is less than the critical temperature of the lightest component of the mixture, a convergence pressure for the mixture does not exist. However, in order to use the charts, one must be chosen. Following Hadden (27), this pressure is called the "quasi-convergence" pressure. Both Hadden (27) and Winn (86) recommend that for such systems the convergence pressure be taken equal to the critical pressure of the lightest component. Another choice has been recommended by Cajander, Hipkin, and Lenoir (11).

Another problem which sometimes arises is the choice of the light component of the equivalent binary mixture for multicomponent mixtures that are dilute solutions of the relatively light components. Hadden and Grayson (28) recommended that the light component of the equivalent binary be selected as the lightest component of the mixture having a mole fraction (in the liquid phase) equal to or greater than 0.001.

METHOD 2: CORRELATIONS OF WINN, HADDEN, AND GRAYSON

In 1948 Hadden (26) presented nomograms that included the effect of composition on the K-values by use of convergence pressures. Later Winn (86) produced a nomogram that used convergence pressure as the composition parameter. Recently, the work of Winn (86) was extended by Hadden and Grayson (28). Description of the original method of Winn and the recent extensions of Hadden and Grayson follow.

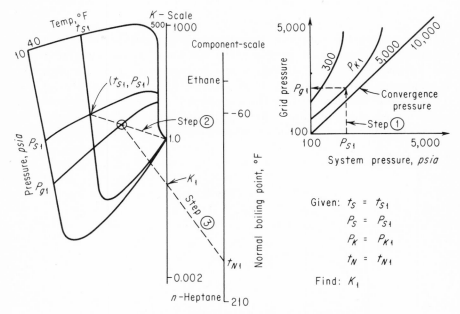

Figure 17–9. Sketch of nomogram of Winn.

A sketch of the basic nomogram and the associated convergence-pressure plot presented by Winn (86) is shown in Figure 17–9. These graphs were employed in the subsequent procedure proposed by Hadden and Grayson. The nomogram constructed by Winn was for a convergence pressure of 5000 psia. However, selecting a suitable grid pressure, P_g, makes possible the use of the single nomogram for all convergence pressures. The appropriate grid pressure, P_g, for a given convergence pressure is found by use of a graph like the one shown in Figure 17–9. (Note that for $P_K = 5000$ psia, $P_g = 5000$ psia).

The broken lines in Figure 17–9 represent the steps required to solve the illustrative example stated there. The general procedure is as follows:

Step (1): On the basis of P_s and P_K, determine P_g graphically as shown.

Step (2): Connect the point (t_s, P_s) on the grid with the point $K = 1$ on the K-scale. Denote the intersection of this line and the pressure isobar $P = P_g$ by a circle as shown.

Step (3): Connect the point of intersection found by Step 2 and the normal boiling point (on the component scale) by a straight line. The intersection of this line with the K-scale gives the desired value of K.

For convergence pressures greater than 5000 psia, K is determined directly by connecting the point (t_s, P_s) and the normal boiling point (on the component-scale) by a straight line. Intersection of this line with the K-scale gives the desired value of K.

A method is given (86) for the extension of the nomogram for components heavier than n-heptane, the heaviest component on the component scale. The procedure consists of calculating the K for ethane (denoted by K_2)

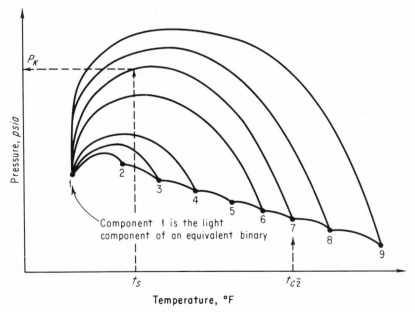

Figure 17–10. Graphic determination of convergence pressure as proposed by Hadden and Grayson.

and the K for n-heptane (denoted by K_7) at the specified conditions for the system. The K for any component i heavier than n-heptane is calculated by use of the formula

$$K_i = \frac{K_7}{(K_2/K_7)^b} \tag{17-41}$$

where b is a constant for any component. An improved and extended set of values for b were recently stated by Hadden and Grayson.

Several other extensions were made by Hadden and Grayson. The original nomogram covered the temperature range of 40 to 800°F. A second nomogram similar to the one depicted in Figure 17–9 was developed for the temperature range of -260 to 100°F. In addition seven charts similar to the sketch shown in Figure 17–10 were provided for the determination of convergence pressures.

Good accuracy for the method was reported by Hadden and Grayson, who found that the average deviation of the calculated values from experimental values of K was 6.8 percent.

A complete set of the 10 working charts is presented in the article by Hadden and Grayson (28).

METHOD 3: NOMOGRAMS OF LENOIR AND CO-WORKERS

In a series of articles (11, 43, 44, 55), Lenoir and co-workers presented a procedure for the determination of K-values. In principle it is like the previous method, but it differs in many details. Like Hadden, Lenoir selected an equivalent binary for the determination of the convergence pressure of the multicomponent mixture. However, the procedure for the selection of this binary differs from the one employed by Hadden (27). Lenoir proposed the following procedure for a mixture composed of n components, numbered in the order of decreasing volatility.

The pseudolight and pseudoheavy components are defined by the methods employed for the determination of their normal boiling points. These methods are summarized by the following formulas.

$$T_{N\overline{1}} = \frac{\sum_{i=1}^{n-1} (x_i F_{Li}) T_{N,i}}{\sum_{i=1}^{n-1} x_i F_{Li}} \tag{17-42}$$

$$T_{N\overline{2}} = \frac{\sum_{i=2}^{n} (x_i F_{Hi}) T_{Ni}}{\sum_{i=2}^{n} x_i F_{Hi}} \tag{17-43}$$

where

> F_{Hi}, F_{Li} = empirically determined weight factors for the mole fractions.
>
> T_{Ni} = normal boiling points (°R) of components 1 through n.
>
> T_{N1}, T_{N2} = normal boiling points (°R) of the pseudolight and pseudoheavy components, respectively.

The values of F_{Hi} and F_{Li} are read directly from experimentally determined curves of log F_{Hi} versus log $(T_{Ni}/T_{N,n})$ and log F_{Li} versus log $(T_{N,1}/T_{Ni})$, respectively. After the normal boiling points of the pseudolight and pseudoheavy components have been computed, the equivalent binary is used to determine the convergence pressure by use of one of a series of graphs of the type depicted by Figure 17–10. Instead of using the identities of the components as parameters as indicated in Figure 17–10, Lenoir and White (44) employed normal boiling points. The graphical procedure for the determination of the convergence pressure is analogous to that described for Method 2. On the basis of the convergence pressure so obtained and the specified temperature, the K-value for a given component is found by use of one of two nomograms which were prepared by Cajander, Hipkin, and Lenoir. These graphs constitute revisions of earlier ones by Myers and Lenoir (55).

The nomograms make use of the "K_{10}-concept," which amounts to the identification of a component by the value of its K at a pressure of 10 psia, a convergence pressure of 5000 psia, and at the system temperature. For paraffin and olefin hydrocarbons, the K-values for two different hydrocarbons were found to be approximately equal provided their respective K_{10}-values and convergence pressures are equal. These values of K are obtained by use of "K_{10}-charts," which consist of plots of K versus temperature for a wide variety of components. A sketch of one of the nomograms is shown in Figure 17–11. One of the nomograms was for system pressures ranging from 10 to 500 psia and the other for pressures ranging from 150 to 1000 psia.

The K-value of a given component in a multicomponent mixture at a specified temperature and pressure is determined by the following procedure.

Step (1): Compute the normal boiling points of the pseudolight and pseudoheavy components by use of Equations (17–42) and (17–43), respectively.

Step (2): On the basis of the equivalent binary found in Step (1), determine the convergence pressure by use of a chart similar to the one illustrated by Figure 17–10.

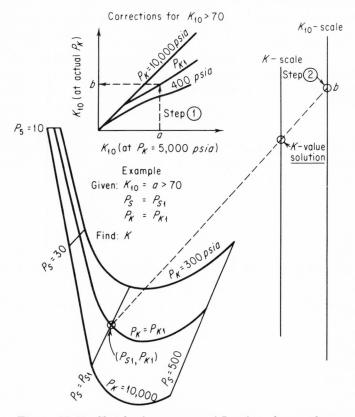

Figure 17–11. Sketch of nomogram of Lenoir and co-workers.

Step (3): For the particular component whose K-value is desired, determine its K_{10}-value at the system temperature by use of the appropriate K_{10}-chart.

Step (4): If $K_{10} < 70$, proceed to Step (5). If $K_{10} > 70$, correct it by use of a graph similar to the one shown in Figure 17–11. This gives a K_{10}-value evaluated at the convergence pressure of the system rather than 5000 psia.

Step (5): Locate the value of K_{10} found by Step (4) on the K_{10}-scale of the nomogram as shown in Figure 17–11. Locate the point (P_K, P_s) on the grid, and connect this point with the one located on the K_{10}-scale by a straight line. The intersection of this line with the K-scale gives the value of K for the given component.

This calculational procedure, which represents the most recent one of Lenoir and co-workers, requires the following set of working charts.

1. Two weight-factor (F_H and F_L) charts; see Lenoir and White (44).
2. Eleven convergence pressure charts; see Lenoir and White (44).
3. Twelve K_{10}-charts; presented by Cajander, Hipkin, and Lenoir (11).
4. Two nomograms; presented by Cajander, Hipkin, and Lenoir (11).
5. A quasi-convergence pressure chart; see Cajander, Hipkin, and Lenoir (11).

The accuracy of the method is good. Cajander, Hipkin, and Lenoir (11) report an average deviation between calculated and experimental values of K of 4.6 percent.

PART III

USE OF ACTIVITY COEFFICIENTS IN THE DETERMINATION OF K-VALUES

When unlike molecules are mixed in the liquid phase, the single composition parameter expressed by convergence pressure does not always adequately describe the effect of composition on the K-values. The variation of K for a given component in a mixture at a fixed temperature and pressure is a function primarily of the composition of the liquid phase. In fact, experimental evidence shows that large variation in the K's results from changes in the liquid compositions at pressures so low that the vapor is not only an ideal solution but also a perfect gas mixture. Thus for many systems Equation (16–69) reduces to

$$K_i = \frac{\gamma_i^L f_i^L}{f_i^v} \cong \frac{\gamma_i^L P_i}{P} \tag{17–44}$$

In spite of the apparent simplicity of this equation, the expressions for the activity coefficients for multicomponent mixtures become almost too cumbersome for practical application. In view of this complication only a few of the various expressions proposed for the correlation of activity coefficients as a function of composition are presented. However, the few that are presented are treated thoroughly. Since the expressions of Van Laar (83, 84), Margules (49), Scatchard and Hamer (74), and one of the equations of Benedict *et al.* (7) represent special cases of a more general equation of Wohl (87), the expression proposed by Wohl will be taken as a starting point. Because of the volumetric functions "q" appearing in this expression, Wohl (87) called it the "q-equation."

THE q-EQUATION OF WOHL

In the original article of Wohl (87) the equation was stated for binary and ternary mixtures. Recently it was restated and extended formally by Hougen, Watson, and Ragatz (34) to include multicomponent mixtures composed of any number of components. For a binary mixture, the four-suffix form of the q-equation is given by

$$\frac{\mathcal{G}^E}{RT(q_1 x_1 + q_2 x_2)} = \sum_{i,j} Z_i Z_j a_{ij} + \sum_{i,j,k} Z_i Z_j Z_k a_{ijk}$$
$$+ \sum_{i,j,k,l} Z_i Z_j Z_k Z_l a_{ijkl} \qquad (17\text{–}45)$$

where

$$a_{ij}, \ldots, a_{ijkl} = \text{constants of the type } a_{ij} = a_{ji}$$
$$q_1, q_2 = \text{constants; they may be regarded as a measure of the molal volumes of components 1 and 2}$$

$$Z_1 = \frac{n_1 q_1}{n_1 q_1 + n_2 q_2}, \quad Z_2 = \frac{n_2 q_2}{n_1 q_1 + n_2 q_2}$$

If the activities are correlated on the basis of the first summation on the right hand side of Equation (17–45) alone, the resulting expression is called a two-suffix (i, j) equation, and it represents the interaction of molecules in groups of two. If both the first and second summations are employed, it is called a three-suffix (i, j, k) equation. The second summation represents the interaction between molecules in groups of three. The three-suffix q-equation is particularly significant because under different conditions, it reduces to each of the well-known relationships proposed for binary mixtures.

The Z's may be called generalized volume fractions since they are of a form analogous to the volume fraction,

$$\frac{n_1 v_1}{n_1 v_1 + n_2 v_2}$$

and since the q's may be considered related to the molal volumes of the pure components (74). However, since the q's may also be regarded as arbitrary constants, the Z's will be called "q-factors" as suggested by Wohl (87).

THE THREE-SUFFIX q-EQUATION FOR BINARY MIXTURES

In the expansion of Equation (17–45) for this case, the number of terms and hence the number of a's occurring in the first summation is given by finding the combinations of 1 and 2 taken two at a time. The result is a_{12} and a_{21}. Similarly, the number of terms occurring in the second summation is equal to the number of combinations of 1 and 2 taken three at a time. Thus

$$\frac{\mathcal{G}^E}{RT(q_1 x_1 + q_2 x_2)} = Z_1 Z_2 a_{12} + Z_2 Z_1 a_{21} + Z_1 Z_2 Z_1 a_{121} + Z_2 Z_1 Z_1 a_{211}$$

$$+ Z_1 Z_1 Z_2 a_{112} + Z_1 Z_2 Z_2 a_{122} + Z_2 Z_1 Z_2 a_{212}$$

$$+ Z_2 Z_2 Z_1 a_{221} \qquad (17\text{–}46)$$

Since the a's containing different combinations of the same numbers are equal by definition, Equation (17–46) reduces to

$$\frac{\mathcal{G}^E}{RT(x_1 q_1 + x_2 q_2)} = 2Z_1 Z_2 a_{12} + 3Z_1^2 Z_2 a_{112} + 3Z_2^2 Z_1 a_{122} \qquad (17\text{–}47)$$

which is readily rearranged to give

$$\frac{\mathcal{G}^E}{RT(x_1 q_1 + x_2 q_2)}$$

$$= Z_1 Z_2 [2a_{12} + 3Z_1 a_{112} + 3Z_2 a_{122}]$$

$$= Z_1 Z_2 [Z_1(2a_{12} + 3a_{112}) + Z_2(2a_{12} + 3a_{122}) - 2(Z_1 + Z_2)a_{12} + 2a_{12}]$$

Since $Z_1 + Z_2 = 1$ for a binary and since $n_T \mathcal{G}^E = G^E$, the last expression may be stated as follows:

$$\frac{G^E}{RT} = \left[n_1 + \left(\frac{q_2}{q_1} \right) n_2 \right] (Z_1 Z_2) \left[Z_1 \left(\frac{q_1}{q_2} \right) B + Z_2 A \right] \qquad (17\text{–}48)$$

where

$$A = q_1(2a_{12} + 3a_{122})$$

$$B = q_2(2a_{12} + 3a_{112})$$

In order to obtain the expressions for $\ln \gamma_1^L$ and $\ln \gamma_2^L$, Equation (17–48) is differentiated with respect to n_1 and n_2 as required by Equation (16–102).

Thus

$$\ln \gamma_1^L = \frac{1}{RT}\left(\frac{\partial G^E}{\partial n_1}\right)_{P,T,n_2} = \left[Z_1^2 Z_2 \frac{q_1}{q_2} B + Z_1 Z_2^2 A\right] + \left(n_1 + \frac{q_2}{q_1} n_2\right)$$

$$\times \left[2Z_1 Z_2 \left(\frac{q_1}{q_2}\right) B \left(\frac{\partial Z_1}{\partial n_1}\right)_{P,T,n_2} + Z_1^2 \left(\frac{q_1}{q_2}\right) B \left(\frac{\partial Z_2}{\partial n_1}\right)_{P,T,n_2}\right.$$

$$\left. + Z_2^2 A \left(\frac{\partial Z_1}{\partial n_1}\right)_{P,T,n_2} + 2Z_1 Z_2 A \left(\frac{\partial Z_2}{\partial n_1}\right)_{P,T,n_2}\right] \qquad (17\text{--}49)$$

From the definitions of Z_1 and Z_2 it is readily shown that

$$\left(\frac{\partial Z_1}{\partial n_1}\right)_{P,T,n_2} = \frac{Z_2}{[n_1 + (q_2/q_1)n_2]}; \quad \left(\frac{\partial Z_2}{\partial n_1}\right)_{P,T,n_2} = \frac{-Z_2}{[n_1 + (q_2/q_1)n_2]}$$

Substitution of these expressions into Equation (17–49) followed by the collection of terms yields the expressions known as the "three-suffix q-equations" for the activity coefficients for a binary mixture.

$$\ln \gamma_1^L = Z_2^2 \left[A + 2\left(\frac{Bq_1}{q_2} - A\right)Z_1\right] \qquad (17\text{--}50)$$

An analogous development gives

$$\ln \gamma_2^L = Z_1^2 \left[B + 2\left(\frac{Aq_2}{q_1} - B\right)Z_2\right] \qquad (17\text{--}51)$$

Observe that the terminal values at infinite dilution are given by taking the following limits.

$$\lim_{Z_1 \to 0} \ln \gamma_1^L = A; \quad \lim_{Z_2 \to 0} \gamma_2^L = B$$

Evaluation of the constants A and B in these and other equations to follow is discussed in a subsequent section. Other well-known equations will now be obtained from Equations (17–50) and (17–51).

THE THREE-SUFFIX EQUATIONS OF MARGULES

If $q_1/q_2 = 1$, Equations (17–50) and (17–51) reduce to the equations of Margules (49). At $q_1/q_2 = 1$, it follows from the definition of Z_1 and Z_2 that $Z_1 = x_1$ and $Z_2 = x_2$. Thus

$$\ln \gamma_1^L = x_2^2[A + 2(B - A)x_1] \qquad (17\text{--}52a)$$

$$\ln \gamma_2^L = x_1^2[B + 2(A - B)x_2] \qquad (17\text{--}53a)$$

Since $x_1 = 1 - x_2$, Equations (17–52a) and (17–53a) may be stated as functions of x_2 and x_1 alone, respectively, as shown by Carlson and Colburn (13).

$$\ln \gamma_1^L = (2B - A)x_2^2 + 2(A - B)x_2^3 \qquad (17\text{–}52\text{b})$$

$$\ln \gamma_2^L = (2A - B)x_1^2 + 2(B - A)x_1^3 \qquad (17\text{–}53\text{b})$$

THE EQUATIONS OF VAN LAAR (TWO-SUFFIX q-EQUATION)

The two-suffix q-equation for a binary mixture consists of the expansion of only the first summation on the right hand side of Equation (17–45). Following the same approach shown for the development of Equation (17–52), the equations of Van Laar (83, 84) follow as a direct result. Alternately, by taking $q_1/q_2 = A/B$, it is readily shown that Equations (17–50) and (17–51) reduce to

$$\ln \gamma_1^L = \frac{Ax_2^2}{[x_2 + (A/B)x_1]^2} = \frac{A}{[1 + (A/B)(x_1/x_2)]^2} \qquad (17\text{–}54)$$

$$\ln \gamma_2^L = \frac{Bx_1^2}{[x_1 + (B/A)x_2]^2} = \frac{B}{[1 + (B/A)(x_2/x_1)]^2} \qquad (17\text{–}55)$$

which are the well-known Van Laar Equations stated in the form suggested by Carlson and Colburn (13).

THE SCATCHARD-HAMER EQUATIONS

If the relationship $q_1/q_2 = v_1/v_2$ is supposed to exist, Equations (17–50) and (17–51) reduce to the equations of Scatchard and Hamer (74), which are as follows:

$$\ln \gamma_1^L = Z_2^2 \left[A + 2 \left(\frac{Bv_1}{v_2} - A \right) Z_1 \right] \qquad (17\text{–}56\text{a})$$

$$\ln \gamma_2^L = Z_1^2 \left[B + 2 \left(\frac{Bv_2}{v_1} - B \right) Z_2 \right] \qquad (17\text{–}57\text{a})$$

where

$$Z_1 = \frac{n_1 v_1}{n_1 v_1 + n_2 v_2}; \quad Z_2 = \frac{n_2 v_2}{n_1 v_1 + n_2 v_2}$$

Alternately, Equations (17–56a) and (17–57a) may be stated in the form

$$\ln \gamma_1^L = A \left(\frac{2Bv_1}{Av_2} - 1\right) Z_2^2 - 2A \left(\frac{Bv_1}{Av_2} - 1\right) Z_2^3 \qquad (17\text{–}56\text{b})$$

$$\ln \gamma_2^L = B \left(\frac{2Av_2}{Bv_1} - 1\right) Z_1^2 - 2B \left(\frac{Av_2}{Bv_1} - 1\right) Z_1^3 \qquad (17\text{–}57\text{b})$$

which was proposed by Carlson and Colburn (13).

COMPARISON OF THE EQUATIONS OF WOHL, MARGULES, VAN LAAR, AND SCATCHARD AND HAMER

On the basis of the existence of a relationship between the q's and the molal volumes of the pure components, the taking of $q_1/q_2 = 1$ amounts to saying that the molal volumes of the pure components are about equal. Thus as Wohl (87) points out, the equations of Margules may be expected to be useful in the treatment of mixtures composed of molecules that are not highly dissimilar. For mixtures of somewhat higher degrees of dissimilarity, the Van Laar equations may be expected to be slightly superior to the Margules equations. In general, the choice of $q_1/q_2 = v_1/v_2$ contained in the Scatchard-Hamer equations can be expected to be superior to the choice of $q_1/q_2 = 1$ upon which the Margules equations are based. The most general form of the three-suffix q-equations is represented by Equations (17–50) and (17–51). These equations are superior to those obtained from them. However, this advantage is achieved through the use of a third constant, q_1/q_2.

Another useful set of equations for the treatment of binary mixtures is presented in a subsequent section. Before consideration of these, the q-equation of Wohl will be applied to a ternary mixture.

APPLICATION OF THE q-EQUATION OF WOHL TO MULTICOMPONENT MIXTURES

Formally, the extension is readily accomplished by replacing the term $(x_1q_1 + x_2q_2)$ in Equation (17–45) by

$$\sum_{h=1}^{c} x_h q_h$$

where c is equal to the total number of components present in the given mixture. Also, the denominator $(q_1 n_1 + q_2 n_2)$ of each Z [as defined below Equation $(17–45)$] is replaced by

$$\sum_{h=1}^{c} n_h q_h$$

Because of the large number of terms involved in three- and four-suffix equations for ternary mixtures, only the expressions for a two-suffix ternary are given. For this case the general form of the q-equation is

$$\frac{\mathcal{G}^E}{RT(x_1 q_1 + x_2 q_2 + x_3 q_3)} = \sum_{i,j} Z_i Z_j a_{ij} \qquad (17–58)$$

which gives upon expansion

$$\frac{\mathcal{G}^E}{RT(x_1 q_1 + x_2 q_2 + x_3 q_3)} = Z_1 Z_2 a_{12} + Z_2 Z_1 a_{21} + Z_1 Z_3 a_{13} + Z_3 Z_1 a_{31}$$

$$+ Z_2 Z_3 a_{23} + Z_3 Z_2 a_{32} = Z_1 Z_2 2 a_{12} + Z_1 Z_3 2 a_{13} + Z_2 Z_3 2 a_{23} \qquad (17–59)$$

If a set of constants, the A's, be defined by

$$2a_{12} q_1 = A_{12} \qquad 2a_{12} q_2 = A_{21}$$

$$2a_{13} q_1 = A_{13} \qquad 2a_{13} q_3 = A_{31}$$

$$2a_{23} q_2 = A_{23} \qquad 2a_{23} q_3 = A_{32}$$

then it follows that

$$q_1/q_2 = A_{12}/A_{21}; \qquad q_1/q_3 = A_{13}/A_{31}; \qquad q_2/q_3 = A_{23}/A_{32};$$

and

$$A_{32}/A_{23} = (A_{31}/A_{13})(A_{12}/A_{21})$$

Introduction of these constants followed by the multiplication of both sides of Equation $(17–59)$ by the total number of moles, n_T, yields

$$\frac{G^E}{RT} = \left(n_1 + n_2 \frac{A_{21}}{A_{12}} + n_3 \frac{A_{31}}{A_{13}} \right) \left[Z_1 Z_2 A_{12} + Z_1 Z_3 A_{13} + Z_2 Z_3 \left(\frac{A_{32} A_{13}}{A_{31}} \right) \right]$$

$$(17–60)$$

As required by Equation $(16–101)$, partial differentiation of Equation $(17–60)$ with respect to n_1 holding all other variables constant yields

$$\ln \gamma_1^L = A_{12} Z_2^2 + A_{13} Z_3^2 + \left(A_{12} + A_{13} - \frac{A_{32} A_{13}}{A_{31}} \right) Z_2 Z_3 \qquad (17–61)$$

In an analogous manner the following expressions for the activity coefficients for components 2 and 3 are obtained.

$$\ln \gamma_2^L = A_{23}Z_3^2 + A_{21}Z_1^2 + \left(A_{23} + A_{21} - \frac{A_{13}A_{21}}{A_{12}}\right)Z_3Z_1 \qquad (17\text{–}62)$$

$$\ln \gamma_3^L = A_{31}Z_1^2 + A_{32}Z_2^2 + \left(A_{31} + A_{32} - \frac{A_{21}A_{32}}{A_{23}}\right)Z_1Z_2 \qquad (17\text{–}63)$$

The terminal values of the activity coefficients given by Equations (17–61), (17–62), and (17–63) are as follows:

$$\lim_{\substack{Z_1 \to 0 \\ Z_2 \to 1}} \ln \gamma_1^L = A_{12}; \quad \lim_{\substack{Z_1 \to 0 \\ Z_3 \to 1}} \ln \gamma_1^L = A_{13}$$

$$\lim_{\substack{Z_2 \to 0 \\ Z_3 \to 1}} \ln \gamma_2^L = A_{23}; \quad \lim_{\substack{Z_2 \to 0 \\ Z_1 \to 1}} \ln \gamma_2^L = A_{21}$$

$$\lim_{\substack{Z_3 \to 0 \\ Z_2 \to 1}} \ln \gamma_3^L = A_{32}; \quad \lim_{\substack{Z_3 \to 0 \\ Z_1 \to 1}} \ln \gamma_3^L = A_{31}$$

When these limits are taken, the particular Z which does not appear in each limit is understood to have the value of zero, for example, if $Z_1 = 0$ and $Z_2 = 1$ then $Z_3 = 0$ since $Z_1 + Z_2 + Z_3 = 1$. The most significant characteristic of these limiting values is that they are the limiting values A and B found previously for binaries. These results may be summarized as follows:

Components Binary Mixture	A	B
1, 2	A_{12}	A_{21}
1, 3	A_{13}	A_{31}
2, 3	A_{23}	A_{32}

If $q_1/q_2 = q_1/q_3 = q_2/q_3 = 1$, then $A_{12} = A_{21}$, $A_{13} = A_{31}$, $A_{23} = A_{32}$ and $Z_1 = x_1$, $Z_2 = x_2$ and $Z_3 = x_3$. For this choice of the q's, Equations (17–61), (17–62), and (17–63) reduce to

$$\ln \gamma_1^L = A_{12}x_2^2 + A_{13}x_3^2 + (A_{12} + A_{13} - A_{23})x_2x_3 \qquad (17\text{–}64)$$

$$\ln \gamma_2^L = A_{23}x_3^2 + A_{12}x_1^2 + (A_{23} + A_{12} - A_{13})x_3x_1 \qquad (17\text{–}65)$$

$$\ln \gamma_3^L = A_{13}x_1^2 + A_{23}x_2^2 + (A_{13} + A_{23} - A_{12})x_1x_2 \qquad (17\text{–}66)$$

By a different approach, Benedict *et al.* (7) obtained this set of equations.

The three-suffix q-equations for ternary mixtures are developed in a manner analogous to that shown for the two-suffix equations. Four-suffix q-equations are presented by Wohl (87) and others obtained therefrom, such as the four-suffix Van Laar, Margules, and Scatchard-Hamer equations.

Of the large number of other equations proposed, among which are (7, 14, 23, 24, 31, 59, 64, 75), only the recent equations of Redlich and Kister are presented. A summary of many of the methods included in this list of references has been presented by Reid and Sherwood (69).

THE EQUATIONS OF REDLICH AND KISTER

Recently Redlich and Kister (66) proposed a set of equations that have the advantage of being both flexible and convenient to use. These equations are similar to those proposed by Gilmont *et al.* (24). In comparison with the Van Laar equations, Redlich *et al.* (67) assert that their equations are much less cumbersome for mixtures that can be represented by only the first one or two terms of the equations and, furthermore, that their equations are always entirely sufficient for mixtures which require three or more terms.

For a binary mixture the Redlich-Kister equation for the excess free energy is

$$\frac{G^E}{RT} = x_1 x_2 [B + C(x_1 - x_2) + D(x_1 - x_2)^2 + \ldots] \qquad (17\text{-}67)$$

where

$$B, C, D, \ldots = \text{constants}.$$

In order to obtain the corresponding expressions for the activity coefficients, both sides of Equation (17-67) are multiplied by n_T (where $n_T = n_1 + n_2$) and

$$\frac{G^E}{RT} = \frac{n_1 n_2}{n_T} \left[B + \frac{C}{n_T}(n_1 - n_2) + \frac{D}{n_T^2}(n_1 - n_2)^2 + \ldots \right] \qquad (17\text{-}68)$$

Then by Equation (16-101)

$$\ln \gamma_1^L = n_2 \left(\frac{\partial (n_1/n_T)}{\partial n_1} \right)_{P,T,n_2} \left[B + \frac{C}{n_T}(n_1 - n_2) + \frac{D}{n_T^2}(n_1 - n_2)^2 + \ldots \right]$$

$$+ \left(\frac{n_1 n_2}{n_T} \right) \left(\frac{\partial [B + (C/n_T)(n_1 - n_2) + (D/n_T^2)(n_1 - n_2)^2 + \ldots]}{\partial n_1} \right)_{P,T,n_2}$$

Application of the rules of partial differentiation yields

$$\left(\frac{\partial n_1/n_T}{\partial n_1} \right)_{P,T,n_2} = -\frac{n_1}{n_T^2} + \frac{1}{n_T} = \frac{n_T - n_1}{n_T^2} = \frac{n_2}{n_T^2}$$

for the first derivative appearing in the expression for $\ln \gamma_1^L$. Continuation of the differentiation as indicated yields

$$\ln \gamma_1^L = \left(\frac{n_2^2}{n_T^2}\right)\left[B + \frac{C}{n_T}(3n_1 - n_2) + \frac{D}{n_T^2}(n_1 - n_2)(5n_1 - n_2)\right.$$

$$\left. + \frac{E}{n_T^3}(n_1 - n_2)^2(7n_1 - n_2) + \ldots\right]$$

When stated in terms of mole fractions, the Redlich-Kister equations for a binary mixture are obtained.

$$\ln \gamma_1^L = x_2^2[B + C(3x_1 - x_2) + D(x_1 - x_2)(5x_1 - x_2)$$

$$+ E(x_1 - x_2)^2(7x_1 - x_2) + \ldots] \qquad (17\text{-}69)$$

$$\ln \gamma_2^L = x_1^2[B + C(x_1 - 3x_2) + D(x_1 - x_2)(x_1 - 5x_2)$$

$$+ E(x_1 - x_2)^2(x_1 - 7x_2) + \ldots] \qquad (17\text{-}70)$$

Another form of these equations used by Redlich and co-workers (66, 67) is obtained by subtraction of Equation (17-70) from (17-69) followed by rearrangement to give

$$\ln \gamma_1^L/\gamma_2^L = B(x_2 - x_1) + C(6x_1x_2 - 1) + D(x_1 - x_2)(8x_1x_2 - 1)$$

$$+ E(x_1 - x_2)^2(10x_1x_2 - 1) + \ldots \qquad (17\text{-}71)$$

Redlich and Kister (66) extended their excess free energy function to include the description of multicomponent mixtures. For the case of mixtures in which the interaction is of the binary type, they proposed the following expression.

$$\frac{\mathcal{G}^E}{RT} = \sum_{i,j} \frac{\mathcal{G}_{ij}}{RT} = \left(\sum_{i,j} x_i x_j\right)[B_{ij} + C_{ij}(x_i - x_j) + \ldots] \qquad (17\text{-}72)$$

where

$\mathcal{G}^E$ = excess free energy of one mole of the mixture.

$\mathcal{G}_{ij}$ = excess free energy of the binary mixture (ij); also since (ij) and (ji) represent the same binary, $\mathcal{G}_{ij} = \mathcal{G}_{ji}$.

Equation (17-72) asserts that the excess free energy for the multicomponent mixture is equal to the sum of the excess free energy functions for each independent binary mixture. For the case of a ternary mixture, Equation (17-72) becomes

$$\frac{\mathcal{G}^E}{RT} = \frac{\mathcal{G}_{12}}{RT} + \frac{\mathcal{G}_{13}}{RT} + \frac{\mathcal{G}_{23}}{RT} \qquad (17\text{-}73)$$

where the expansions for $\mathcal{G}_{13}$ and $\mathcal{G}_{23}$ are analogous to that which follows for $\mathcal{G}_{12}$,

$$\frac{\mathcal{G}_{12}}{RT} = x_1 x_2 [B_{12} + C_{12}(x_1 - x_2) + \ldots] \qquad (17\text{--}74)$$

If, in addition to binary interactions, ternary interactions $(1, 2, 3)$ are involved, Equation $(17\text{--}73)$ is modified to give

$$\frac{\mathcal{G}^E}{RT} = \frac{\mathcal{G}_{12}}{RT} + \frac{\mathcal{G}_{13}}{RT} + \frac{\mathcal{G}_{23}}{RT}$$

$$+ x_1 x_2 x_3 [B_{123} + C_{123}(x_2 - x_3) + C_{131}(x_3 - x_1) + \ldots] \qquad (17\text{--}75)$$

By the scheme of Redlich and Kister, a system of four components may be represented by use of six independent binaries (6 values of $\mathcal{G}_{ij}$), four series for all distinguishable combinations of $x_i x_j x_k$, and one series for $x_i x_j x_k x_l$.

EVALUATION OF THE CONSTANTS IN THE EXPRESSIONS FOR THE ACTIVITY COEFFICIENTS

Suppose vapor-liquid equilibria data are available for a given binary mixture and that the constants in a particular set of expressions must be found for the activity coefficients. On the basis of these data, values for the activity coefficients are calculated directly by use of Equation $(17\text{--}44)$ rearranged to the form

$$\gamma_i^L = K_i f_i^v / f_i^L = f_i^v y_i / f_i^L x_i \qquad (17\text{--}76)$$

The experimental quantities that are generally known are as follows: P, T, P_i, y_i, and x_i. For many mixtures, deviations occur in the liquid phase at pressures low enough so that the vapor behaves like a perfect gas. For such mixtures Equation $(17\text{--}76)$ reduces to

$$\gamma_i^L = P y_i / P_i x_i \qquad (17\text{--}77)$$

If these approximations are not valid, the fugacities of the pure components are computed as discussed under Method I. Note that the definitions of the hypothetical states employed in the calculation of the γ's from the fugacities must be retained when the γ's are used to compute K's by use of Equation $(17\text{--}44)$.

After the γ's have been computed from the data, they may be checked for consistency by making a plot of $\ln \gamma_1^L / \gamma_2^L$ versus x_1 as suggested by Equation $(16\text{--}106)$. If the data are consistent, the area above the line $\gamma_1^L / \gamma_2^L = 1$ should be equal to the area below it. Since this relationship,

Equation (16–106), is based on holding P and T fixed, only one value of x would be possible for a binary mixture. Thus the data may fail this test and yet be consistent because of the variations in either or both P and T.

For the case of an equation with two constants, such as Equations (17–53) and (17–54), only two values of the γ's and the corresponding values of x are required to determine the values of these constants. If several data are available, they may be used to find the best set of values of the constants by use of a curve fitting procedure such as the method of least squares. Since expressions have been given for both γ_1^L and γ_2^L which contain the same constants, two sets of constants may be obtained by use of the same set of experimental data. The selection of the best set of constants could prove difficult unless, because of subsequent considerations, the best curve fit is desired for γ_1^L rather than γ_2^L. If equal weight should be placed on the experimental values for each γ, the equations should be restated in a form containing both γ's such as

$$\ln \gamma_1^L/\gamma_2^L \quad \text{or} \quad \left(\frac{\ln \gamma_1^L}{x_2^2} + \frac{\ln \gamma_2^L}{x_1^2} \right)$$

In the curve-fitting of these data, the particular equation must be stated in linear form. For most of the equations stated, more than one linear form exists. For example, consider Equation (17–52b). This equation is of the following linear form.

$$Y = a_1 X_1 + a_2 X_2 \qquad (17\text{--}78)$$

where

$$a_1 = (2B - A), \quad X_1 = x_2^2$$

$$a_2 = 2(A - B), \quad X_2 = x_2^3$$

$$Y = \ln \gamma_1^L$$

Another linear form is obtained by dividing each member of Equation (17–52b) by x_2^2 to give

$$Y = a_1 + a_2 X_1 \qquad (17\text{--}79)$$

where

$$a_1 = (2B - A); \quad X_1 = x_2^2$$

$$a_2 = 2(A - B); \quad Y = \frac{\ln \gamma_1^L}{x_2^2}$$

Although the dependent variable Y should not generally contain a function of the independent variable, the linearized equation with an intercept may yield better results than the linearized form with an intercept of zero. Note that the best curve fit from the standpoint of application is not necessarily the one which minimizes the error in the dependent variable Y but the one which minimizes the error of a function such as

$$\left| \frac{\gamma_{\text{exp}}^{L} - \gamma_{\text{cal}}^{L}}{\gamma_{\text{exp}}^{L}} \right|$$

or a similar one which will lead to a minimum of error in the final result, K, as given by Equation (17–44). The final correlation may also be checked for thermodynamic consistency by use of Equation (16–106).

When equilibrium data are lacking, activity coefficients may be estimated from the azeotropic compositions and boiling point. Large collections, as well as methods for extending these data, are available (32, 34, 42, 48, 53). Since $y_i = x_i$ at the azeotrope, Equation (17–77) reduces to

$$\gamma_i = P/P_i \qquad\qquad (17\text{–}80)$$

which may be employed to compute γ_1 and γ_2. On the basis of these γ's and the value of x_1 at the azeotrope, two constants (A and B) may be determined for any particular set of equations such as those of either Margules or Van Laar.

APPROXIMATE TREATMENT OF MULTICOMPONENT MIXTURES

Many mixtures are encountered in a refinery in which two distinctive types of components such as aromatics and paraffins are present. With respect to the determination of activity coefficients, McMillin and co-workers (52) have treated such mixtures as pseudobinaries. For relatively narrow boiling mixtures, good results have been obtained. According to this procedure the mole fractions in equations such as Margules are replaced by pseudomole fractions, which are defined as follows:

$$X_1 = \frac{\text{moles of aromatics in liquid}}{\text{moles of aromatics} + \text{moles paraffins in liquid}}$$

$$X_2 = \frac{\text{moles of paraffins in liquid}}{\text{moles of paraffins} + \text{moles of aromatics in liquid}}$$

Then γ_1^L and γ_2^L become the activities for the aromatics and paraffins, respectively.

PART IV

EFFECTS OF TEMPERATURE, PRESSURE, AND COMPOSITION ON ENTHALPY

Of these, the corrections for temperature and pressure are the ones most commonly applied. Attempts have been made both empirically and theoretically to include the effect of composition on enthalpy. Enthalpy correlations are commonly presented in the form of charts. Some of the basic principles upon which these charts are based follow.

EFFECT OF TEMPERATURE ON ENTHALPY

It has become customary to correct the enthalpy for the effect of temperature with the pressure held fixed at zero. The specific heat capacities are commonly stated as functions of temperature at a pressure of zero. Among the numerous collections of heat capacities which have been published are those in the following references (16, 36, 40, 41, 62, 71, 72). From the definition of the heat capacity,

$$(\partial H_i/\partial T)_P = c_{pi} \qquad (17\text{--}81)$$

it follows that the change is enthalpy resulting from a change in temperature at $P = 0$ is given by

$$H_i^v(0, T_2) - H_i^v(0, T_1) = \int_{T_1}^{T_2} c_{pi}^0 \, dT \qquad (17\text{--}82)$$

Observe that the actual substance obeys the perfect gas law $(Pv = RT)$ at $P = 0$. For the case where $T_1 = 0°K$, a large collection of enthalpies have been tabulated (1, 71, 72).

EFFECT OF PRESSURE ON ENTHALPY

For one mole of a pure component integration of Equation (16–10a) gives the following formula for the change in enthalpy with pressure at constant temperature

$$H_i^v(P, T) - H_i^v(0, T) = \int_0^P \left[V - T \left(\frac{\partial V}{\partial T} \right)_P \right] dP \qquad (17\text{--}83)$$

If either the equation of state or P-V-T data are available for a given compound, Equation (17–83) may be used to compute the change in enthalpy with pressure at constant temperature.

Frequently, data are presented in terms of compressibility factors $(Z = Pv/RT)$. For substances having equal compressibility factors at the same sets of reduced temperatures and pressures (the law of corresponding states), the following formula is useful.

$$\frac{H_i^v(P_R, T_R) - H_i^v(0, T_R)}{T_{ci}} = - RT_R^2 \int_0^{P_R} \left(\frac{\partial Z}{\partial T_R}\right)_{P_R} \frac{dP_R}{P_R} \qquad (17\text{–}84)$$

For substances which obey the law of corresponding states, the right-hand side of Equation (17–84) is independent of i, the identity of the component. Therefore, the left hand side is independent of i; and although this ratio is independent of i, the individual members depend on the identity of the component. Numerical values of this enthalpy difference have been tabulated for both liquids and vapors by Hougen, Watson, and Ragatz (34), and charts have also been prepared by Lydersen *et al.* (47). Other useful collections of data are (20, 37).

EFFECT OF COMPOSITION ON ENTHALPY

As shown in Chapter 16, the enthalpy is not affected by composition for the case of an ideal solution; that is, $H_i = \bar{H}_i$. The partial molal enthalpy of a component in a nonideal solution may be calculated by use of the equation of state for the mixture if the equation is available. When the standard state of a component in a mixture is taken to be a perfect gas at 1 atm. and at the temperature of the mixture, the expression [similar to Equation (16–82)] which relates the partial molal enthalpy and the fugacity is derived as follows. Division of each member of Equation (17–12a) by T followed by partial differentiation with respect to T yields,

$$\left(\frac{\partial \bar{G}_i^v/T}{\partial T}\right)_{P,n_i} - \left(\frac{\partial G_i^0/T}{\partial T}\right)_{P,n_i} = R \left(\frac{\partial \ln \bar{f}_i^v}{\partial T}\right)_{P,n_i} \qquad (17\text{–}85)$$

In view of the relationship given by Equation (16–32), the desired expression

$$\frac{H_i^0 - \bar{H}_i^v}{RT^2} = \left(\frac{\partial \ln \bar{f}_i^v}{\partial T}\right)_{P,n_i} \qquad (17\text{–}86)$$

is obtained. For a component in the vapor phase, the expression for $\ln \bar{f}_i^v$ is analogous to the one given by Equation (17–13) for a component in the liquid phase. Partial differentiation of $\ln \bar{f}_i^v$ with respect to T (with the other variables held constant as indicated by Equation (17–86)) leads to the following formula for the partial molal enthalpy as shown by Papadopoulos, Pigford, and Friend (61).

$$
\bar{H}_i - H_i^0 = \left[(B_0 + B_{0i}) RT - 4(A_0 A_{0i})^{1/2} - 8 \frac{(C_0 C_{0i})^{1/2}}{T^2} \right] \rho
$$

$$
+ 3[(b^2 b_i)^{1/3} RT - \tfrac{3}{2}(a^2 a_i)^{1/3}] \rho^2
$$

$$
+ \tfrac{18}{5}(a\alpha)^{2/3}[(a_i\alpha)^{1/3} + (\alpha_i a)^{1/3}] \rho^5
$$

$$
+ 9 \frac{(c_i c^2)^{1/3} \rho^2}{T^2} \left[\frac{1 - \exp(-\gamma\rho^2)}{\gamma\rho^2} - \frac{\exp(-\gamma\rho^2)}{6} \right.
$$

$$
\left. + \frac{\gamma\rho^2 \exp(-\gamma\rho^2)}{3} \right] - \frac{6c\rho^2(\gamma_i/\gamma)^{1/2} I}{T^2 \gamma\rho^2} - \frac{JQ_i}{K} \qquad (17\text{–}87)
$$

where

$$
I = 1 - \left[1 + \gamma\rho^2 + \frac{(\gamma\rho^2)^2}{2} - \frac{(\gamma\rho^2)^3}{3} \right] \exp(-\gamma\rho^2)
$$

$$
J = \left[B_0 RT - 2A_0 - \left(\frac{4C_0}{T^2} \right) \right] \rho + [2bRT - 3a] \rho^2
$$

$$
+ 6\alpha a \rho^5 + \frac{5c\rho^2}{T^2} \left[1 + \gamma\rho^2 - \tfrac{2}{5}(\gamma\rho^2)^2 \right] \exp(-\gamma\rho^2)
$$

$$
K = RT + 2 \left(B_0 RT - A_0 - \frac{C_0}{T^2} \right) \rho + 3(bRT - a) \rho^2
$$

$$
+ 6\alpha a \rho^5 + \frac{3c\rho^2}{T^2} \left[1 + \gamma\rho^2 - \frac{2(\gamma\rho^2)^2}{3} \right] \exp(-\gamma\rho^2)
$$

$$
Q_i = RT + \left[(B_0 + B_{0i}) RT - 2(A_0 A_{0i})^{1/2} - 2 \frac{(C_0 C_{0i})^{1/2}}{T^2} \right] \rho
$$

$$
+ 3[(b^2 b_i)^{1/3} RT - (a^2 a_i)^{1/3}] \rho^2 + 3(a\alpha)^{2/3}[(a\alpha_i)^{1/3} + (\alpha a_i)^{1/3}] \rho^5
$$

$$
+ \frac{3(c^2 c_i)^{1/3} \rho^2}{T^2} (1 + \gamma\rho^2) \exp(-\gamma\rho^2)
$$

$$
- \frac{2c\rho^3}{T^2} (\gamma\rho^2)^{3/2} \gamma_i^{1/2} \exp(-\gamma\rho^2)
$$

CORRELATION OF ENTHALPY DATA

For an ideal solution the enthalpy of the mixture is given by

$$H^v(P, T) = \sum_{i=1}^{c} n_i H_i^v(P, T) \qquad (17\text{--}88)$$

and

$$H^L(P, T) = \sum_{i=1}^{c} n_i H_i^L(P, T) \qquad (17\text{--}89)$$

In theory only the molal enthalpies of the pure components at the temperature and pressure of the mixture are required. Charts for pure components have been prepared by several authors (10, 35, 50, 65, 88). Construction of these charts is based on the relationships given by Equations (17–82) and (17–83) and various experimental data. The results are commonly presented in the form of P (or T) versus enthalpy at parameters of T (or P). The enthalpies read from these charts are based on a datum-value for enthalpy rather than a standard state value. The datum-value differs from the standard state value, as used here, in that both the temperature and pressure are fixed in the definition of the datum. The value commonly assigned for the datum enthalpy is zero. For example, Prengle and Greenhaus (65) assign a value of zero for the enthalpy of the saturated liquid of n-butane at 1 atm. and 31.10°F. As discussed in Chapter 5, a different datum may be employed for each component when the constant-composition method for making enthalpy balances is employed.

In the application of Equations (17–88) and (17–89), two complications arise. For a component in the liquid phase whose critical temperature is below the temperature of the mixture, no liquid phase exists for the pure component. Values of the enthalpy (liquid) of such a component are given by a line labeled "gas in solution" on some charts (51, 68). This line is based on an extrapolation procedure which assumes that a gas in solution at any temperature has the same partial density and enthalpy as the pure component at a pressure given by extrapolation of its vapor pressure curve above the critical point to the temperature of the system (19, 51).

The second difficulty in the use of the charts for pure components arises for those components in the vapor phase that have vapor pressures less than the system pressure at the system temperature. These components do not exist in the vapor phase at the system temperature and pressure. Edmister (19) recommends that the vapor enthalpy of such a component be taken equal to that of the saturated vapor at the system temperature.

Maxwell (51) avoided the second difficulty by making the assumption that the effect of pressure on the enthalpy of a mixture is the same as that for a pure component with the same molecular weight as the mixture. His procedure consists of the evaluation of the enthalpy of the vapor at the system temperature and at low pressure (0 to 1 atm) by use of the pure component charts. On the basis of the enthalpy of the mixture at the system temperature and zero pressure, the enthalpy of the mixture at the temperature and pressure of the mixture is obtained by interpolation with respect to molecular weight.

The last procedure is somewhat similar to the "equivalent component" method proposed by Ragatz *et al.* (68). Such charts may be prepared from the pure component charts by making appropriate cross plots to give enthalpy as a function of temperature, pressure, and molecular weight as described by Edmister (19). Nomograms of this type have been prepared by Scheibel and Jenny (76).

Still a different procedure has been proposed by Peters (63), whose method makes use of the pure component charts. In addition to the pressure parameter, the molal average boiling point appears as a parameter on each chart. This parameter includes to some extent the effect of composition on the enthalpy of a component in the liquid phase.

The partial molal enthalpies, $\bar{H}_i$'s, that include the effect of temperature, pressure, and composition have been determined by use of the results of Benedict and co-workers (3, 4, 5, 6) by Canjar and Edmister (9) and by Papadopoulos *et al.* (61). A graphical procedure was used by Canjar and Edmister while Papadopoulos *et al.* (61) computed the partial molal enthalpies directly by use of Equation (17–87). Based on the same parameters used by Edmister and Ruby (21), Edmister and Canjar (18) prepared nomograms for the partial molal enthalpies.

The partial molal enthalpies are used to make enthalpy balances for a column in the same manner as described previously in Chapter 5 for the molal enthalpies of the pure components. For example, when partial molal enthalpies are employed, Equation (5–9a) becomes

$$L_j = \frac{D[H_D^v - H^v(X_D)_{j+1}] + Q_c}{[H^v(x_j)_{j+1} - H_j^L]} \qquad (17\text{–}90)$$

where

$$H_D^v = \sum_{i=1}^{c} X_{Di}\bar{H}_{Di} \text{ (for a partial condenser)}$$

$$H^v(X_D)_{j+1} = \sum_{i=1}^{c} X_{Di}\bar{H}_{j+1,i}^v$$

$$H^v(x_j)_{j+1} = \sum_{i=1}^{c} x_{ji}\bar{H}_{ji}^v$$

$$H_j^L = \sum_{i=1}^{c} x_{ji}\bar{H}_{ji}^L$$

Except for the evaluation of the partial molal enthalpies, calculations are carried out in the same manner as described in Chapter 5.

NOTATION

(See also Chapter 16)

C_2 = a composition parameter

$\mathcal{G}^E$ = excess free energy per mole of solution

G^E = excess free energy of n_T moles of solution

G_i^0 = free energy of one mole of a perfect gas at any temperature T and at a pressure of 1 atmosphere

H_i^0 = enthalpy of one mole of a perfect gas at any temperature T

m_i = mass fraction of component i in a solution

$M_2, \ldots, M_{n-1}$ = composition parameters based on mass fractions

n = the total number of components; it replaces "c" in equations where c is used to denote a critical property

P_c = critical pressure (absolute)

P_R = reduced pressure; $P_R = P_s/P_c$

P_s = system pressure. The system pressure is also denoted in some cases by P.

P_K = convergence pressure

t_{ci} = critical temperature (°F) of component i

$t_{c\overline{2}}$ = critical temperature (°F) of the pseudoheavy component of the equivalent binary; it is the weight-average of the critical temperatures of components 2 through n

t_s = system temperature (°F); also, the system temperature (°R or °K) is sometimes denoted by T and T_s

T_{ci} = critical temperature (°R or °K) of component i

T_R = reduced temperature; $T_R = T_s/T_c$

T_s = system temperature (°R or °K)

T_M = molal average boiling point. It is computed by Equation (17–15) (or (17–16)) and obtained in °R or °K. Usually it is then converted to °F for plotting purposes as indicated by the graphs shown in this chapter

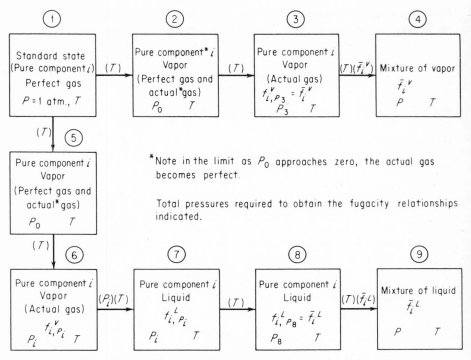

Figure P17-2. Paths for the case where the standard state is a perfect gas at 1 atm and the temperature T.

T_{Ni} = normal boiling point of component i

ρ = molal density

PROBLEMS

17–1   Develop Equations (17–8) and (17–9).

17–2   (a) For the path given in Figure P17–2, show that the difference in free energy between states (1) and (4) is given by

$$\bar{G}_i^v(P, T) - G_i^0(1, T) = \lim_{P_0 \to 0}\left[\int_1^{P_0} \frac{RT}{P}\, dP + \int_{P_0}^{P_3} v_i^v\, dP\right]$$

$$= RT \ln \bar{f}_i^v$$

   (b) Show that the change in free energy between states (1) and (9) is given by Equation (17–12b).

17–3   Develop Equations (17–28), (17–30), (17–34), and (17–35).

17-4   Show that a five component mixture for which M_2, M_3, and M_4 are fixed may be regarded as an equivalent binary composed of component 1 and a pseudoheavy component denoted by $\bar{5}$ whose mole fractions may take on all positive numbers which satisfy the following equations simultaneously

$$m_1 + m_{\bar{5}} = 1$$

$$m_{\bar{5}} = \frac{m_5}{(1 - M_4)(1 - M_3)(1 - M_2)}$$

17-5   Develop Equation (17–50).

17-6   Develop Equation (17–61).

17-7   Develop Equation (17–69).

17-8   Develop Equations (17–83) and (17–84).

17-9   (a) Show that the enthalpy of a perfect gas at unit fugacity (or unit pressure) is equal to the enthalpy of the actual substance at zero pressure and at the same temperature; that is, show that

$$H_i^0(1, T) = H_i^v(0, T)$$

   (b) Show that

$$H_i^0(P, T) = H_i^v(0, T)$$

17-10 Verify the result given by Equation (17–90).

LITERATURE CITED

1. American Petroleum Institute Research Project 44, Chemical Thermodynamic Properties Center, A. and M. College of Texas, College Station, Texas, loose leaf data sheets, 1962.

2. Barr-David, F. H., "Notes on Phase Relations of Binary Mixtures in the Region of the Critical Point," *A.I.Ch.E. Journal*, **2**, 426 (1956).

3. Benedict, M., G. B. Webb, and L. C. Rubin, "An Empirical Equation for Thermodynamic Properties of Light Hydrocarbons and Their Mixtures: Part I—Methane, Ethane, Propane and *n*-Butane," *J. Chem. Phys.*, **8**, 334 (1940).

4. ———, "An Empirical Equation for Thermodynamic Properties of Light Hydrocarbons and Their Mixtures: Part II—Mixtures of Methane, Ethane, Propane and *n*-Butane," *J. Chem. Phys.*, **10**, 747, (1942).

5. ———, "An Empirical Equation for Thermodynamic Properties of Light Hydrocarbons and Their Mixtures: Constants for Twelve Hydrocarbons," *Chemical Engineering Progress*, **47**, No. 8, 419 (1951); "An Empirical Equation for Thermodynamic Properties and Their Mixtures: Fugacities and Liquid-Vapor Equilibria," **47**, No. 9, 449 (1951).

6. Benedict, M., G. B. Webb, L. C. Rubin, and L. Friend, "An Empirical Equation for Thermodynamic Properties of Light Hydrocarbons and Their Mixtures: Reduction of Equation to Charts for Prediction of Liquid-Vapor Equilibria," *Chemical Engineering Progress* **47,** No. 12, 609 (1951).

7. Benedict, M., C. A. Johnson, E. Solomon, and L. C. Rubin, "Separation of Toluene from Paraffins by Azeotropic Distillation with Methanol," *Trans. Am. Inst. Chem. Engrs.,* **41,** 371 (1945).

8. Brown, G. G., "Vapor-Liquid Phase Equilibria in Hydrocarbon Systems," *Petroleum Engineer,* **11,** No. 8, 25 (1940); "Calculations Involved in the Design of Fractionating Columns," **11,** No. 9, 55 (1940).

9. Canjar, L. N. and W. C. Edmister, "Hydrocarbon Partial Enthalpies: Values for Methane, Ethene, Ethane, Propene, Propane, and *n*-Butane," *Chemical Engineering Progress Symposium Series,* **49,** No. 7, 73 (1953).

10. Canjar, L. N., M. Goldman, and H. Marchman, "Thermodynamic Properties of Propylene," *Ind. Eng. Chem.* **43,** 1186 (1951).

11. Cajander, B. C., H. G. Hipkin, and J. M. Lenoir, "Prediction of Equilibrium Ratios from Nomograms of Improved Accuracy," *Journal of Chemical and Engineering Data,* **5,** No. 3, 251 (1960).

12. Carter, R. T., B. H. Sage, and W. N. Lacey, "Phase Behavior in Methane-Propane-*n*-Pentane Systems," *Am. Inst. Mining Met. Engrs. Tech. Pub.,* 1250 (Oct. 1940).

13. Carlson, H. C. and A. P. Colburn, "Vapor-Liquid Equilibria of Non-ideal Solutions," *Ind. Eng. Chem.,* **34,** 581 (1942).

14. Chao, K. C., O. A. Hougen, "Vapour-Liquid Equilibria in the Ternary System: Ethylactate-Benzene Cyclohexane," *Chem. Eng. Sci.,* **7,** 246 (1958).

15. DePriester, C. L., "Light Hydrocarbon Vapor-Liquid Distribution Coefficients," *Chemical Engineering Progress Symposium Series,* **49,** No. 7, 1 (1953).

16. Dreisbach, R. R., *Physical Properties of Chemical Substances,* publication of the Dow Chemical Company, Midland, Michigan (1952).

17. Dodge, B. F., *Chemical Engineering Thermodynamics* (New York: McGraw-Hill Book Company, Inc., 1944).

18. Edmister, W. C. and L. N. Canjar, "Hydrocarbon Partial Enthalpies—Generalized Correlations," *Chemical Engineering Progress Symposium Series,* **49,** No. 7, 85 (1953).

19. Edmister, W. C., "Application of Thermodynamics to Hydrocarbon Processing: Effects of Pressure on Enthalpy," *Petroleum Refiner* **28,** No. 2, 137 (1949); "Application of Thermodynamics to Hydrocarbon Processing: Enthalpy-Entropy Plots for Pure Hydrocarbons," **28,** No. 3, 139 (1949); "Application of Thermodynamics to Hydrocarbon Processing: Entropy Charts for Hydrocarbon Mixtures," **28,** No. 4, 157 (1949).

20. ——, *Applied Hydrocarbon Thermodynamics* (Houston, Texas: Gulf Publishing Co., 1961).

21. Edmister, W. C. and C. L. Ruby, "Activity Coefficients of Hydrocarbons," *Chemical Engineering Progress*, **51**, No. 2, 95–F (1955).

22. Gamson, B. W. and K. M. Watson, "High Pressure Vapor-Liquid Equilibria," *Nat. Petrol. News*, **36**, R623 (Sept. 6, 1944).

23. Gilmont, R., *Thermodynamic Principles* (Englewood Cliffs, N. J.: Prentice-Hall, Inc., 1959), p. 234.

24. Gilmont, R., E. A. Weinman, F. Kramer, E. Miller, F. Hashmall, and D. F. Othmer, "Thermodynamic Correlation of Vapor-Liquid Equilibria: Determination of Activity Coefficients from Relative Volatility," *Ind. Eng. Chem.*, **42**, 120 (1950).

25. Gilliland, E. R. and H. W. Scheeline, "High Pressure Vapor-Liquid Equilibria: Propylene-Isobutane and Propane-Hydrogen Sulfide," *Ind. Eng. Chem.*, **32**, 48 (1940).

26. Hadden, S. T., "Vapor-Liquid Equilibria in Hydrocarbon Systems," *Chemical Engineering Progress*, **44**, 37 (1948); **44**, 135 (1948).

27. ——, "Convergence Pressure in Hydrocarbon Vapor-Liquid Equilibria," *Chemical Engineering Progress Symposium Series*, **49**, No. 7, 53 (1953).

28. Hadden, S. T. and H. C. Grayson, "New Charts for Hydrocarbon Vapor-Liquid Equilibria," *Petroleum Refiner*, **40**, No. 9, 207 (1961).

29. Hanson, G. H. and G. G. Brown, "Vapor-Liquid Equilibria in Mixtures of Volatile Paraffins," *Ind. Eng. Chem.*, **37**, 821 (1945).

30. Hanson, G. H., M. J. Rzaza, and G. G. Brown, "Equilibrium Constants for Methane in Paraffin Mixtures," *Ind. Eng. Chem.*, **37**, 1216 (1945).

31. Hirati, M., "Vapor-Liquid Equilibrium Relations," *Japan Sci. Rev.*, **2**, No. 3, 265 (1952).

32. Horsley, L. H., "Table of Azeotropes and Non-azeotropes," *Ind. Eng. Chem.*, Analytical Ed., **19**, 508 (1947).

33. Hougen, O. A. and K. M. Watson, charts from *Chemical Process Principles* (New York: John Wiley & Sons, Inc., 1946).

34. Hougen, O. A., K. M. Watson, and R. A. Ragatz, *Chemical Process Principles*, 2 ed. (New York: John Wiley & Sons, Inc., 1959).

35. Hurd, C. O., J. L. Valentine, and C. K. Barkelew, "Thermodynamic Properties of Ethane," *Chemical Engineering Progress*, **43**, 25 (1947).

36. *International Critical Tables* (New York: McGraw-Hill Book Company, Inc., 1933).

37. Katz, D. L., D. Cornell, R. Kobayashi, F. H. Poettman, J. A. Vary, J. R. Elenbaas, C. F. Weinang, *Handbook of Natural Gas Engineering* (New York: McGraw-Hill Book Company, Inc., 1959).

38. Katz, D. L. and F. Kurata, "Retrograde Condensation," *Ind. Eng. Chem.*, **32,** 817 (1940).

39. Kay, W. B., "Liquid-Vapor Phase Equilibrium Relations in the Ethane-*n*-heptane System," *Ind. Eng. Chem.*, **30,** 459 (1938).

40. Kelley, K. K. W. S., "High Temperature Heat-Content, Heat Capacity, and Entropy Data for Inorganic Compounds," *Bureau of Mines Bulletin*, 476 (1949).

41. Kobe, K. A. and Associates, *Thermochemistry for the Petroleum Industry* (Houston, Texas: Gulf Publishing Company, 1951).

42. Lecat, M., *Tables azéotropiques*, 2 ed., may be obtained from the author, UCCLE–Bruxelles, 29, rue Auguste Danse, (1949).

43. Lenoir, J. M. and G. A. White, "Vapor Equilibrium Ratios: The General Method Applied to Binary Systems," *Petroleum Refiner* **32,** No. 10, 121 (1953); "Vapor Equilibrium Ratios: Ternary and Multicomponent Systems," **32,** No. 12, 115 (1953).

44. Lenoir, J. M. and G. A. White, "Predicting Convergence Pressure," *Petroleum Refiner*, **37,** No. 3, 173 (1958).

45. Lewis, W. K. and W. C. Kay, "Fugacity of Various Hydrocarbons Above Their Vapor Pressure and Below Their Critical Temperature," *Oil and Gas Journal*, **32,** No. 45, 40 (1934).

46. Lewis, W. K. and C. D. Duke, "Properties of Hydrocarbon Mixtures at High Pressures," *Trans. Am. Soc. Mech. Engrs.*, **54,** 17 (1932).

47. Lydersen, A. L., R. A. Greenkorn, and O. A. Hougen, *Generalized Thermodynamic Properties of Pure Fluids*, University of Wisconsin Engr. Exp. Sta. Report No. 4, October 1955.

48. Mair, B. J., A. R. Glasgow, and F. D. Rossini, "Separation of Hydrocarbons by Azeotropic Distillation," *J. Research National Bureau of Standards*, **27,** 39 (1941).

49. Margules, M., *Sitzber. Akad. Wiss. Wien, Math. naturw. Klasse*, **104,** No. 2, 1243 (1895).

50. Mathews, C. S. and C. O. Hurd, "Thermodynamic Properties of Methane," *Trans. Am. Inst. Chem. Engrs.*, **42,** 55 (1946).

51. Maxwell, J. B., *Data Book on Hydrocarbons*, (New York: D. Van Nostrand Co., Inc., 1951).

52. McMillin, K. K., personal communication, Humble Oil and Refining Co., Baytown, Texas.

53. Meissner, H. P. and S. H. Greenfield, "Composition and Boiling Points of Binary Azeotropes," *Ind. Eng. Chem.*, **40**, 438 (1948).

54. *Liquid-Vapor Equilibrium in Mixture of Light Hydrocarbons, Equilibrium Constants* and *Liquid-Vapor Equilibrium in Mixtures of Light Hydrocarbons*, fugacity charts published by the M. W. Kellog Company, New York (1950).

55. Myers, H. S. and J. M. Lenoir, "Get Your K's by Nonogram," *Petroleum Refiner*, **36**, No. 2, 167 (1957).

56. *Engineering Data Book*, publication of the Natural Gasoline Supply Men's Association, Tulsa, Oklahoma (1951).

57. *Equilibrium Ratio Data Book*, publication of the Natural Gasoline Association of America, 421 Kennedy Building, Tulsa, Oklahoma (1957).

58. Newton, R. H., "Activity Coefficients of Gases," *Ind. Eng. Chem.*, **27**, 302 (1935).

59. Norrish, R. S. and G. H. Twigg, "Simple Constant Linear Equation for Vapor-Liquid Equilibria in Binary Systems," *Ind. Eng. Chem.*, **46**, 201 (1954).

60. Organick, E. I. and G. G. Brown, "Prediction of Hydrocarbon Vapor-Liquid Equilibria," *Chemical Engineering Progress Symposium Series*, **48**, No. 2, 97 (1952).

61. Papadopoulos, A., R. L. Pigford, and L. Friend, "Partial Molal Enthalpies of the Lighter Hydrocarbons in Solution with Other Hydrocarbons," *Chemical Engineering Progress Symposium Series*, **49**, No. 7, 119 (1953).

62. Perry, J. H., ed., *Chemical Engineers Handbook*, 3 ed. (New York: McGraw-Hill Book Company, Inc., 1951).

63. Peters, H. F., "Partial Enthalpies of Light Hydrocarbons," *Petroleum Refiner*, **28**, 109 (1949).

64. Prahl, W., "An Algebraic Representation of Vapor-Liquid Equilibria," *Ind. Eng. Chem.*, **43**, 1767 (1951).

65. Prengle, F. D., L. R. Greenhaus, and R. York, "Thermodynamic Properties of *n*-Butane," *Chemical Engineering Progress*, **44**, 863 (1948).

66. Redlich, O. and A. T. Kister, "Algebraic Representation of Thermodynamic Properties and Classification of Solutions," *Ind. Eng. Chem.*, **40**, 345 (1948).

67. Redlich, O., A. T. Kister, and C. E. Turnquist, "Thermodynamics of Solutions: Analysis of Vapor-Liquid Equilibria," *Chemical Engineering Progress Symposium Series*, **48**, No. 2, 49 (1952).

68. Ragatz, E. G., E. R. McCartney, and R. E. Haylett, "Pressure-Temperature and Low Pressure Total Heat Relationships of Petroleum Fractions," *Ind. Eng. Chem.*, **25,** 975 (1933).

69. Reid, R. C. and T. K. Sherwood, *The Properties of Gases and Liquids* (New York: McGraw-Hill Book Company, Inc., 1958).

70. Robinson, C. S. and E. R. Gilliland, *Elements of Fractional Distillation*, 4 ed. (New York: McGraw-Hill Book Company, Inc., 1950).

71. Rossini, F. D., K. S. Pitzer, R. L. Armett, R. M. Braun, and G. C. Pimentel, *Selected Values of Physical and Thermodynamic Properties of Hydrocarbons and Related Compounds* (Pittsburgh, Penna.: Carnegie Press, Carneigie Institute of Technology, 1953).

72. Rossini, F. D., D. D. Wagman, W. H. Evans, S. Levine, and I. Jaffe, *Selected Values of Chemical Thermodynamic Properties* (Washington, D.C.: U. S. Government Printing Office, 1952).

73. Rzasa, M. J., E. E. Glass, and J. B. Opfell, "Prediction of Critical Properties and Equilibrium Vaporization Constants for Complex Hydrocarbon Systems," *Chemical Engineering Progress Symposium Series*, **48,** No. 2, 28 (1952).

74. Scatchard, G. and W. J. Hamer, "The Application of Equations for the Chemical Potentials to Partly Miscible Solutions," *J. Amer. Chem. Soc.*, **57,** 1805 (1935).

75. Scheibel, E. G. and D. Friedland, "Correlation of Vapor-Liquid Equilibria Data for Nonideal Ternary Systems," *Ind. Eng. Chem.*, **39,** 1329 (1947).

76. Scheibel, E. G. and F. J. Jenny, "Representation of Equilibrium Constant Data," *Ind. Eng. Chem.*, **37,** 80 (1945); and **37,** 990 (1945).

77. Sherwood, T. K. and R. L. Pigford, *Absorption and Extraction*, (New York: McGraw-Hill Book Company, Inc., 1952).

78. Smith, K. A. and R. B. Smith, "Vaporization Equilibrium Constant and Activity Coefficients Charts," *Petroleum Processing*, **4,** Dec. 1949.

79. Smith, J. M. and H. C. Van Ness, *Introduction to Chemical Engineering Thermodynamics* (New York: McGraw-Hill Book Company, Inc., 1959).

80. Smith, K. A. and K. M. Watson, "High Pressure Liquid-Vapor Equilibria: Activity Coefficients for Ideal Systems," *Chemical Engineering Progress*, **45,** 494 (1949).

81. Souders, M., Jr., W. W. Selheimer, and G. G. Brown, "Equilibria Between Liquid and Vapor Solutions of Paraffin Hydrocarbons," *Ind. Eng. Chem.*, **24,** 517 (1932).

82. Taylor, H. S., G. W. Wald, B. H. Sage, and W. N. Lacey, "Behavior of the Methane-*n*-Pentane System," *Oil and Gas Journal*, **38,** No. 1346 (August 10, 1939).

83. Van Laar, J. J., "Über Dampfspannungen von binären Gemischen," *Z. Phys. Chem.*, **72,** 723 (1910).

84. ———, "Zur Theorie der Dampfspannugen von binären Gemischen," *Z. Phys. Chem.*, **83,** 599 (1913).

85. White, R. R. and G. G. Brown, "Phase Equilibria at High Temperatures," *Ind. Eng. Chem.*, **34,** 1162 (1942).

86. Winn, F. W., "Simplified Nomographic Presentation: Hydrocarbon Vapor Liquid Equilibria," *Chemical Engineering Progress Symposium Series*, **48,** No. 2, 121 (1952).

87. Wohl, K., "Thermodynamic Evaluation of Binary and Ternary Liquid Systems," *Trans. Am. Inst. Chem. Engrs.*, **42,** 215 (1946).

88. York, R. and E. F. White, Jr., "Thermodynamic Properties of Ethylene," *Trans. Am. Inst. Chem. Engrs.*, **40,** 227 (1944).

APPENDIX

TABLE A–1 Equilibrium data

$P = 50$ psia.

$(K_i/T)^{1/3} = a_1 + a_2T + a_3T^2 + a_4T^3$, $(T \text{ in } °R)$.

Taken from Reference 3.

Component	$a_1 \times 10$	$a_2 \times 10^3$	$a_3 \times 10^6$	$a_4 \times 10^9$
CH_4	5.097584	0.2407971	−0.5376841	0.2354444
C_2H_6	−7.578061	3.602315	−3.955079	1.456571
C_3H_8	−0.1246870	4.932274	−5.430016	2.036879
$n\text{-}C_4H_{10}$	−6.460362	2.319527	−2.058817	0.6341839
$n\text{-}C_5H_{12}$	−8.381815	2.952740	−2.949674	1.053882
C_6H_{14}	−2.634813	−0.5820756	0.0990418	−0.2293738
C_7H_{16}	−0.4456271	0.2688671	1.065180	−0.5817661
500	9.139924	−3.573887	4.539999	−1.810713

not suitable for
$T < 90°F$!

TABLE A–2 Equilibrium data

$P = 120$ psia. Taken from Reference 5.

K (for i-C_5) $= 0.37088 - 0.55786\ (T/100) + 0.44841\ (T/100)^2 - 0.03704\ (T/100)^3$, ($T$ in °F). $\alpha_i = a_{1i} + a_{2i}\ (T/100) + a_{3i}\ (T/100)^2$, ($T$ in °F).

Component	a_1	a_2	a_3
C_3H_8	11.06095	−5.20067	0.92489
i-C_4	4.69290	−1.82431	0.31755
n-C_4	3.07033	−0.83565	0.12144
i-C_5	1.0000	0.0000	0.00000
n-C_5	0.73827	0.05246	0.00189

TABLE A–3 Equilibrium data

$P = 264.7$ psia. Taken from Reference 4.

K (for i-C_5) $= 0.37088 - 0.55786\ (T/100) + 0.44841\ (T/100)^2 - 0.03704\ (T/100)^3$, ($T$ in °F). $\alpha_i = a_{1i} + a_{2i}\ (T/100) + a_{3i}\ (T/100)^2$ (T in °F).

Component	a_1	a_2	a_3
H_2	436.36196	−257.95576	38.22382
CH_4	63.76528	−29.51969	4.25794
C_2H_6	10.93719	−3.88431	0.55580
C_3H_6	4.03335	−1.14742	0.17389
C_3H_8	3.64797	−1.06605	0.16197
i-C_4	1.46077	−0.18097	0.02721
n-C_4	1.00000	0.00000	0.00000
n-C_5	0.17185	0.22019	−0.02826
n-C_6	0.00541	0.14775	−0.01056
n-C_7	−0.02141	0.07538	0.00061
n-C_8	−0.01184	0.02524	0.00593
360	−0.00145	−0.00053	0.00430
450	0.01431	−0.02071	0.00637

TABLE A–4 Equilibrium data

$P = 300$ psia. Taken from Reference 1.

$(K_i/T)^{1/3} = a_{1i} + a_{2i}T + a_{3i}T^2 + a_{4i}T^3$, ($T$ in °R).

Component	$a_1 \times 10^2$	$a_2 \times 10^5$	$a_3 \times 10^8$	$a_4 \times 10^{12}$
CH_4	32.718139	-9.6951405	6.9229334	-47.361298
C_2H_4	-5.177995	62.124576	-37.562082	8.0145501
C_2H_6	-9.8400210	67.545943	-37.459290	-9.0732459
C_3H_6	-25.098770	102.39287	-75.221710	153.84709
C_3H_8	-14.512474	53.638924	-5.3051604	-173.58329
$i\text{-}C_4H_8$	-10.104481	21.400418	38.564266	-353.65419
$i\text{-}C_4$	-18.967651	61.239667	-17.891649	-90.855512
$n\text{-}C_4$	-14.181715	36.866353	16.521412	-248.23843
$i\text{-}C_5$	-7.5488400	3.2623631	58.507340	-414.92323
$n\text{-}C_5$	-7.5435390	2.0584231	59.138344	-413.12409
$n\text{-}C_6$	1.1506919	-33.885839	97.795401	-542.35941
$n\text{-}C_7$	5.5692758	-50.705967	112.17338	-574.89350
$n\text{-}C_8$	7.1714400	-52.608530	103.72034	-496.46551
400	2.5278960	-17.311330	33.502879	-126.25039
500	3.3123291	-16.652384	24.310911	-64.148982

TABLE A–5 Equilibrium data

$P = 400$ psia. Taken from Reference 3.

$(K_i/T)^{1/3} = a_{1i} + a_{2i}T + a_{3i}T^2 + a_{4i}T^3$, ($T$ in °R).

Component	$a_1 \times 10$	$a_2 \times 10^3$	$a_3 \times 10^6$	$a_4 \times 10^9$
CH_4	-3.2551482	2.3553786	-3.1371170	1.3397973
C_2H_6	-2.7947232	1.4124232	-1.4582948	0.50974162
C_3H_8	-2.7980091	1.1811943	-1.0935041	0.35180421
$i\text{-}C_4$	2.3209137	0.87122379	-0.66100972	0.1667774
$n\text{-}C_4$	-2.3203344	0.83753226	-0.61774360	0.15243376
$i\text{-}C_5$	-0.6981454	0.088862037	0.39689556	-0.29076073
$n\text{-}C_5$	0.37103008	-0.36257004	0.99113800	-0.54441110
500	1.9642644	-0.81121972	1.0586630	-0.39478662

TABLE A–6 Enthalpy data

$P = 120$ psia. Taken from Reference 2.

$h_i = c_{1i} + c_{2i} (T/100) + c_{3i} (T/100)^2$, ($T$ in °F).

$H_i = e_{1i} + e_{2i} (T/100) + e_{3i} (T/100)^2$, ($T$ in °F).

Component	c_1	c_2	c_3	e_1	e_2	e_3
C_3H_8	0.00000	2521.92	175.417	7488.65	1750.51	79.273
$i\text{-}C_4$	0.00000	3345.00	150.000	9592.01	1843.56	221.433
$n\text{-}C_4$	0.00000	2960.00	400.000	8002.89	4382.70	−401.587
$i\text{-}C_5$	0.00000	3681.33	283.334	11645.77	2770.55	156.345
$n\text{-}C_5$	0.00000	3845.00	250.000	12004.88	3168.66	67.456

TABLE A–7 Enthalpy data

$P = 264.7$ psia. Taken from Reference 2.

$h_i = c_{1i} + c_{2i} (T/100) + c_{3i} (T/100)^2$, ($T$ in °F).

$H_i = e_{1i} + e_{2i} (T/100) + e_{3i} (T/100)^2$, ($T$ in °F).

Component	c_1	c_2	c_3	e_1	e_2	e_3
H_2	285.48	151.52	7.377	687.00	99.64	1.9395
CH_4	1840.25	1345.33	−11.110	4864.17	773.26	19.0294
C_2H_6	3147.12	2222.47	10.935	8384.48	1280.67	65.9954
C_3H_6	4213.82	2874.12	40.076	11254.87	1746.81	102.5564
C_3H_8	4425.16	2968.64	48.868	11806.71	1797.38	112.6239
$i\text{-}C_4$	5320.76	3525.03	90.076	13726.02	2261.20	167.3186
$n\text{-}C_4$	5553.24	3641.27	90.076	14851.06	2312.00	155.9965
C_5	6663.21	4161.81	160.848	18757.52	2903.45	233.0578
C_6	7661.12	4658.30	231.661	20445.36	3207.59	287.9913
C_7	8676.69	5066.88	310.574	23038.41	3713.28	328.7941
C_8	9845.04	5353.77	403.497	25539.97	4119.20	405.9716
360	11509.74	6023.85	599.071	30246.89	5121.06	524.2676
450	13897.03	6634.93	880.067	35971.05	6455.20	669.7070

TABLE A-8 Enthalpy data

$P = 300$ psia.

Taken from Reference 2.

$$(h_i)^{1/2} = c_{1i} + c_{2i}T + c_{3i}T^2, \quad (T \text{ in } °R)$$

$$(H_i)^{1/2} = e_{1i} + e_{2i}T + e_{3i}T^2, \quad (T \text{ in } °R)$$

Component	c_1	$c_2 \times 10$	$c_3 \times 10^5$	e_1	$e_2 \times 10^4$	$e_3 \times 10^6$
CH_4	−17.899210	1.7395763	−3.7596114	44.445874	501.04559	7.3207219
C_2H_4	−7.2915000	1.5411962	−1.6088376	56.79638	615.93154	2.4088730
C_2H_6	−8.4857000	1.6286636	−1.9498601	61.334520	588.75430	11.948654
C_3H_6	−12.427900	1.8834652	−2.4839140	71.828480	658.55130	11.299585
C_3H_8	−14.500060	1.9802223	−2.9048837	81.795910	389.81919	36.470900
$i\text{-}C_4H_8$	−16.553450	2.161865	−3.1476209	139.17444	−822.39488	120.39298
$i\text{-}C_4$	−16.5534050	2.1618650	−3.1476209	147.65414	−1185.2942	152.87778
$n\text{-}C_4$	−20.298110	2.3005743	−3.8663417	152.66798	−1153.4842	146.64125
$i\text{-}C_5$	−23.356460	2.5017453	−4.3917897	130.96679	−197.98604	82.549947
$n\text{-}C_5$	−24.371540	2.5636200	−4.6499694	128.90152	−2.0509603	64.501496
C_6	−23.870410	2.6768089	−4.4197793	85.834950	1522.3917	−34.018595
C_7	−25.314530	2.8246389	−4.5418718	94.682620	1479.5387	−19.105299
C_8	−22.235050	2.8478429	−3.8850819	106.32806	1328.3949	1.6230737
400	−6.6369800	2.8400262	−2.7927554	122.35402	1299.6587	17.03455
500	1.9205300	3.0179232	−2.2183809	138.49658	1497.8171	18.641269

LITERATURE CITED

1. Hadden, S. T., "Vapor-Liquid Equilibria in Hydrocarbon Systems," *Chem. Eng. Progr.*, **44,** 37 (1948).

2. Maxwell, J. B., *Data Book on Hydrocarbons*, New York: D. Van Nostrand Company, Inc. (1955).

3. *Equilibrium Ratio Data Book*, published by Natural Gasoline Association of America, 421 Kennedy Bldg., Tulsa, Oklahoma (1957).

4. Robinson, C. S. and E. R. Gilliland, *Elements of Fractional Distillation*, 4 ed. New York: McGraw-Hill Book Company, Inc. (1950) p. 261.

5. Scheibel, G. H. and F. J. Jenny, "Representation of Equilibrium Constant Data," *Ind. Eng. Chem.*, **37,** 80 (1945).

INDEX

Index